THEORY OF SERVOMECHANISMS

THEORY OF

SERVOMECHANISMS

Edited by

HUBERT M. JAMES

PROFESSOR OF PHYSICS
PURDUE UNIVERSITY

NATHANIEL B. NICHOLS

DIRECTOR OF RESEARCH
TAYLOR INSTRUMENT COMPANIES

RALPH S. PHILLIPS

ASSOCIATE PROFESSOR OF MATHEMATICS
UNIVERSITY OF SOUTHERN CALIFORNIA

OFFICE OF SCIENTIFIC RESEARCH AND DEVELOPMENT
NATIONAL DEFENSE RESEARCH COMMITTEE

NEW YORK
DOVER PUBLICATIONS, INC.

Published in Canada by General Publishing Company, Ltd., 30 Lesmill Road, Don Mills, Toronto, Ontario.

Published in the United Kingdom by Constable and Company, Ltd., 10 Orange Street, London W. C. 2.

This Dover edition, first published in 1965, is an unabridged and unaltered republication of the work first published by McGraw-Hill Book Company, Inc., in 1947. It is made available through the kind cooperation of McGraw-Hill Book Company, Inc.

This book was originally published as volume 25 in the Massachusetts Institute of Technology Radiation Laboratory Series.

Library of Congress Catalog Card Number 65-22735

Manufactured in the United States of America

Dover Publications, Inc.
180 Varick Street
New York, N. Y. 10014

EDITORIAL STAFF

Hubert M. James
Nathaniel B. Nichols
Ralph S. Phillips

CONTRIBUTING AUTHORS

C. H. Dowker
Ivan A. Getting
Witold Hurewicz
Hubert M. James
Earl H. Krohn
Warren P. Manger
Carlton W. Miller
Nathaniel B. Nichols
Ralph S. Phillips
Peter R. Weiss

Foreword

THE tremendous research and development effort that went into the development of radar and related techniques during World War II resulted not only in hundreds of radar sets for military (and some for possible peacetime) use but also in a great body of information and new techniques in the electronics and high-frequency fields. Because this basic material may be of great value to science and engineering, it seemed most important to publish it as soon as security permitted.

The Radiation Laboratory of MIT, which operated under the supervision of the National Defense Research Committee, undertook the great task of preparing these volumes. The work described herein, however, is the collective result of work done at many laboratories, Army, Navy, university, and industrial, both in this country and in England, Canada, and other Dominions.

The Radiation Laboratory, once its proposals were approved and finances provided by the Office of Scientific Research and Development, chose Louis N. Ridenour as Editor-in-Chief to lead and direct the entire project. An editorial staff was then selected of those best qualified for this type of task. Finally the authors for the various volumes or chapters or sections were chosen from among those experts who were intimately familiar with the various fields, and who were able and willing to write the summaries of them. This entire staff agreed to remain at work at MIT for six months or more after the work of the Radiation Laboratory was complete. These volumes stand as a monument to this group.

These volumes serve as a memorial to the unnamed hundreds and thousands of other scientists, engineers, and others who actually carried on the research, development, and engineering work the results of which are herein described. There were so many involved in this work and they worked so closely together even though often in widely separated laboratories that it is impossible to name or even to know those who contributed to a particular idea or development. Only certain ones who wrote reports or articles have even been mentioned. But to all those who contributed in any way to this great cooperative development enterprise, both in this country and in England, these volumes are dedicated.

L. A. DuBRIDGE.

Foreword

[illegible]

Preface

THE work on servomechanisms in the Radiation Laboratory grew out of its need for automatic-tracking radar systems. This problem is one of particular difficulty because the signal to be used in tracking may be seriously distorted by interference, fading, and receiver noise. It was therefore necessary to develop the theory of servomechanisms in a new direction, and to consider the servomechanism as a device intended to deal with an input of known statistical character in the presence of interference with known statistical character. The present volume has been prepared largely as an effective method of disclosing this work.

Although the emphasis in this presentation of the theory of servomechanisms has been affected by the special interests of the Radiation Laboratory, it has been our intention to provide a volume which would be, at least in part, of use to every designer of servomechanisms. This book falls into two parts: the first is devoted to the sinusoidal steady-state analysis familiar to engineers in its application to electrical systems; the second to statistical methods of servomechanism design. Each part is provided with an extended mathematical introduction and abundant illustrations.

It should be emphasized that this volume does not, in its entirety, represent an original contribution from the Radiation Laboratory. Reference has been made to published sources whenever this is possible. The information and techniques used in the Radiation Laboratory in designing servomechanisms have been increased by workers in many other laboratories; special acknowledgment should be made of the numerous unidentifiable contributions by Gordon S. Brown and Albert C. Hall, of the MIT Servomechanism Laboratory, and by E. B. Ferrell, of the Bell Telephone Laboratories.

This volume has been prepared under the pressure of a stringent time schedule, at a period when only a part of the attention of the editors and authors could be devoted to it. It could not have been completed without the assistance of many other members of the staff of the Office of Publications. Special acknowledgment is due to Miss Constance D. Boyd, whose contributions as editorial assistant were supplemented by her work as computer and draftsman. Thanks are also due to Mrs. Frances Bourguet and Mrs. Mary Sheats, who served as production assistants, to L. L. Davenport, G. T. Plain, H. A. Straus, C. E. Ingalls, and N. Levinson, who assisted in preparation of material for the book, to Misses Patricia Boland and Elizabeth Campbell, who assisted in the preparation of charts and examples, and to Miss Ethel W. Brown and Miss Patricia M. Davis, who helped in the preparation of Chap. 4.

Primary responsibility for the detailed editing of Chaps. 3 and 4 belongs to N. B. Nichols; responsibility for the rest of the book is shared by H. M. James and R. S. Phillips.

THE AUTHORS.

CAMBRIDGE, MASS.,
July, 1946.

Contents

CHAPTER 1

SERVO SYSTEMS

By I. A. Getting

1·1. Introduction.—It is nearly as hard for practitioners in the servo art to agree on the definition of a servo as it is for a group of theologians to agree on sin. It has become generally accepted, however, that a servo system involves the control of power by some means or other involving a comparison of the output of the controlled power and the actuating device. This comparison is sometimes referred to as feedback. There is a large variety of devices satisfying this description; before attempting a more formal definition of a servo, it will be helpful to consider an example of feedback.

One of the most common feedback systems is the automatic temperature control of homes. In this system, the fuel used in the furnace is the source of power. This power must be controlled if a reasonably even temperature is to be maintained in the house. The simplest way of controlling this source of power would be to turn the furnace on, say, for one hour each morning, afternoon, and evening on autumn and spring days and twice as long during the winter. This would not be a particularly satisfactory system. A tremendous improvement can be had by providing a thermostat feedback that turns the furnace on when the temperature drops below, say, 68° and turns the furnace off when the temperature rises above 72°. This improvement lies in the fact that the output of the power source has been compared with the input (a standard temperature set in the thermostat), and the difference between the two made to control the source of power—the furnace.

A more colloquial name applied to such a system is "a follow-up system." In this example, the operator sets a temperature, and the temperature of the house, in due course, follows the setting.

The term "follow-up system" grew out of the use of servo systems for the amplification of mechanical power. Sometimes the part of the system doing the "following" was remote from the controlling point; such systems were then called "remote control." Remote control can involve tremendous amplification of power; in certain cases remote control may be required by physical conditions, although adequate power is locally available. Let us resort to examples again. On a large naval ship it is necessary to train and elevate 16-in. guns. It is necessary to do this continuously to compensate for the pitch, the roll, and the yaw of the ship. Such a gun and turret may weigh 200 tons. It is obviously impossible to manipulate such a gun manually; power amplification is required. The operator turns a handwheel, and the gun mount is made to rotate so that its position agrees with the position of the handwheel. This is a follow-up system—the gun mount follows the handwheel. In practice, it is possible to place the handwheel either directly on the gun mount or at a remote point, say in the gunnery plotting room below deck. In the latter case the system becomes one of remote control characterized by tremendous amplification. On the other hand, in the same ship a target may be tracked by positioning a telescope attached to the director. There is adequate power available in the director, but the position of the director may need to be repeated in the computer below deck. It is very inconvenient to carry rotating shafts over long distances or through watertight bulkheads; therefore resort is had to a remotely controlled follow-up. The computer input shaft is made to follow the director; but whereas the director had available many horsepower, the input servo in the computer may be only a few watts. Temperature regulators, remote-control units, and power drives are all examples of servo systems.

Definition.—A servo system is a combination of elements for the control of a source of power in which the output of the system or some function of the output is fed back for comparison with the input and the difference between these quantities is used in controlling the power.

1·2. Types of Servo Systems.—Servo systems involving mechanical motion were first used in the control of underwater torpedoes and in the automatic steering of ships. In both cases a gyroscope was used to determine a direction. Power was furnished for propelling the torpedo or the ship. A portion of this power was also available for steering the ship or torpedo through the action of the rudders. Reaction on the rudders required power amplification between the gyroscope element and the rudder. Neither of these systems is simple, because in them two sources of power need to be controlled: (1) power for actuating the rudders and (2) power for actually turning the ship. In systems as complicated as these, the problem of stability is very important. In fact, the most common consideration in the design of any servo system is that of stability.

Consider a ship with rudder hard to port (left). Such a ship will turn to port. If the rudder is kept in this position till the ship arrives at the correct heading and is then restored to straight-ahead position, the ship will continue to turn left because of its angular momentum about its vertical axis. In due course the damping action of the water will stop this rotation, but only after the ship has overshot the correct direction. If the remainder of the servomechanism operates properly, the gyrocompass will immediately indicate an error to the left. If the power amplifier then forces the rudder hard to starboard, the restoring torque of the starboard rudder will limit the overshoot but under the conditions described will also produce a second overshoot, this time to starboard. It is entirely possible that these oscillations from left to right increase with each successive swing and the steering of the ship becomes wild. It is important to note that this instability is closely related to the time lags in the system. The probability of getting into an unstable situation becomes materially reduced as the reaction time of the rudder to small errors in heading becomes extremely short. The stability can also be increased and errors reduced if the rudder displacement is made proportional to the heading error (proportional control). The behavior of the system can be improved even further by anticipation control. Anticipation in this application implies that in the setting of the rudder, use is made of the fact that the gyrocompass error is decreasing or increasing; it may go as far as to take into account the actual rate at which the error is increasing or decreasing. Then, as the ship is approaching the correct heading, anticipation would indicate the necessity of turning the rudder to starboard, even though the error is still to port, in order to overcome the angular momentum of the ship. This deflection of the rudder should be gradually reduced to zero as the correct heading is reached.

The examples given above seem to imply that mechanical servo systems are a product of this century. Actually, human physical motor behavior is largely controlled as a servo system. A person reaches for a saltcellar. He judges the distance between his hand and the saltcellar. This distance is the "error" in the position of his hands. Through his nervous system and subconscious mind this error is used to control muscular motion, the power being derived from the muscular system. As the distance decreases, derivative control (anticipation) is brought into play through subconscious habit, and overshooting of the hand is prevented. A more illustrative example is the process of driving a car. A person who is just learning to drive generally keeps the car on a road by fixing his attention on the edge of the road and comparing the location of this edge of the road with some object on the car, such as the hood cap. If this distance is too small, the learner reacts by turning the steering wheel to the left; if it gets too large, he reacts by turning the steering wheel to the right. It is characteristic of the learner that his driving consists of a continuous series of oscillations about the desired position. The more carefully he drives, that is, the greater his concentration, the higher will be the frequencies of his oscillations and the smaller the amplitude of his errors. As the driver improves, he introduces anticipation, or derivative control. In this condition a driver takes into consideration the rate at which he is approaching his correct distance from the edge of the road, or, what is equivalent, he notices the angle between the direction of car travel and the direction of the road. His control on the steering wheel is then a combination of displacement control and derivative control. His oscillations become long or nonexistent, and his errors smaller.

So long as the road is straight, a driver of this type, acting as a servomechanism, performs tolerably well. However, additional factors come into play as he approaches a bend in the road. Chief among these is the displacement error resulting from the tendency of the operator to go straight. The error due to continuous uniform curvature of the road can be taken out by essentially establishing a new zero position for the steering wheel. A driver performing in this manner exhibits "integral control." Actually, a human being is not a simple mechanism, and he has available in this instance information of other types. His driving is a complicated combination of proportional, derivative, and integral control, mixed with nonlinear elements and knowledge of the direction in which the road is going to turn. This foreknowledge is sometimes referred to as anticipation and is sometimes confused with derivative control. The example serves nevertheless to illustrate the basis of servomechanisms in general. The power to be controlled in this case was derived from the engine of the car. The input to the system was the actual path of the road; the output was the position of the car; and the error mechanism in which the output and input were compared was the human operator.

The human operator is a very common element in many servo systems. Human elements are used in tracking targets for fire control (see Chap. 8) in controlling steam engines, in controlling settings on all sorts of machinery. The human operator is sometimes referred to as a biomechanical link; much can be learned of his response by the application of servo theory.

The term servo system is not commonly used when the system involves a human operator. It is sometimes restricted further to include control only of systems that involve mechanical motion. For example, the automatic volume control of a home radio receiver is a feedback system, in which the output level of the receiver is compared with the desired level (usually a bias voltage) and a difference, or a combination of the differences, sets the gain of the receiver. This closed loop meets all the requirements of a servo system, but it does not involve mechanical motion. We shall apply the term servo system to such devices but shall restrict the term "servomechanism" to servo systems involving mechanical motion. It is, in general, true that the theory of servomechanisms is identical with that of feedback amplifiers as developed in the communications field. There are certain practical differences which at times make this similarity not quite apparent. Servomechanisms may involve the control of power through the use of the electronic amplifier, in which the power is furnished as plate supply for the vacuum tubes; this is very similar to a feedback amplifier. On the other hand, a servomechanism may include only hydraulic devices, a pump furnishing oil at a high pressure being the source of power. The control of this oil flow may be accomplished by hydraulic valves. Mathematically the electronic amplifier and the hydraulic system may be very similar; but in the physical aspects and in the frequencies and power levels involved the two may be (but are not necessarily so) quite different. A hydraulic system may be able to respond to frequencies up to 20 cps; a feedback amplifier may be built to operate up to frequencies as high as thousands of megacycles. Hydraulic systems have been made in power levels up to 200 hp; feedback amplifiers are generally used in ranges of power of a few watts to milliwatts.

In previous examples, reference was made to the use of servo systems as power amplifiers and as a means of remote control. Servo systems perform two other major functions: (1) as transformers of information or data from one type of power to another and (2) as null instruments in computing mechanisms.

It is sometimes desired to change electrical voltage to mechanical motion without introducing errors arising from variations of load or power supply. Such a problem can be solved by the use of a servomechanism. For example, an electric motor is made to rotate a shaft on which is mounted a potentiometer. The voltage on this potentiometer can then be made to vary as any arbitrary function of shaft position. This output voltage is compared with the original electrical voltage, and a difference or some function of it made to control the electric motor. This is a servomechanism.

It should have been clear that in all the preceding examples a comparison was made between output and input and that the source of power was so controlled as to reduce the difference between the output and input to zero. In other words, all servo systems are null devices, sometimes called error-sensitive devices. The advantages of such a system from a standpoint of component design will be indicated in the next section.

A null device can be made to solve mathematical equations such as are involved in the fire-control problem. Figure 1·1 is a schematic for the mechanization of the fire-control problem in one dimension. The future range R depends on the present range r, on the speed of the target in range dr/dt, and on the time T required for a bullet to travel from the gun to the target. The time of flight T of the bullet is some function of the future range R—a function that is generally not available as a simple analytic relation, but only from ballistic tables. The relations between these quantities may be expressed thus:

$$R = r + T\frac{dr}{dt}, \tag{1}$$

$$T = f(R). \tag{2}$$

It is obvious that future range cannot be obtained without knowledge of the time of flight and that time of flight cannot be known without knowing future range. It is necessary to solve these equations simultaneously.

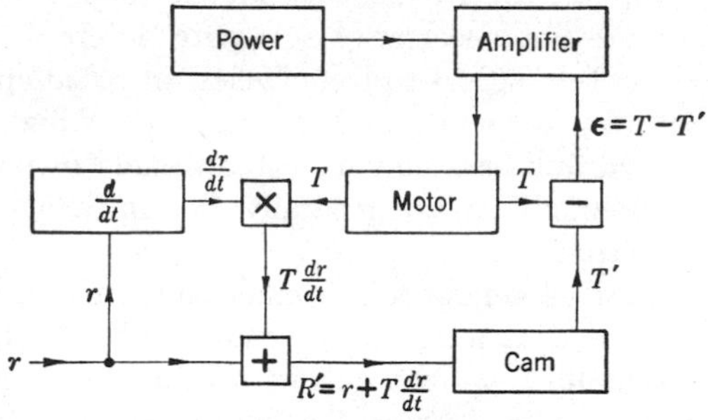

FIG. 1·1.—Servomechanism in a computer.

In Fig. 1·1, range is introduced at the lower left-hand corner. The derivative of range is taken and multiplied by an arbitrary value of time of flight T. The product is added to the observed range, to give a hypothetical future range R'. This hypothetical future range actuates the cam giving the time of flight T' corresponding to this hypothetical future range. If T' were equal to T, the initial assumption of the time of flight would have been correct; this, of course, would be accidental. In general, the assumed value T will differ from T'. The difference $\epsilon = T - T'$ can be fed into an amplifier supplied from an independent source of power, and this amplifier used to drive the motor attached to the T shaft. If now T' is greater than T, the amplifier will apply a voltage to the motor that will drive T to smaller values, tending thus to reduce the difference $T - T'$. When this difference will have reached zero, the future range R and the time of flight T will correspond to the observed range and range rate.

This computation could be done without a servo by having a direct mechanical connection between the output of the cam at T' and the input to the multiplier at T. A little thought will show, however, that practical considerations would limit the usefulness of this arrangement to simple functions and to devices in which the accuracy would not be destroyed by the loads imposed. In the above example, the servo has two important functions: (1) It introduces a flexible link between the cam and the multiplier, and (2) it prevents the feeding of data in a direction opposite to that shown by the arrows.

Equations (1) and (2) can be written in the more general form

$$g(R,T) = 0, \tag{3}$$
$$h(R,T) = 0. \tag{4}$$

In theory, it is always possible to solve such a set of simultaneous equations by eliminating one variable. If, however, g and h are complicated functions or implicitly depend on another independent variable (say time), the solution by analytic methods may become difficult. It is always possible to have recourse to a servo computer of the type illustrated in Fig. 1·1.

Servomechanisms can be classified in a variety of ways. They can be classified (1) as to use, (2) by their motive characteristics, and (3) by their control characteristics. For example, when classified according to use, they can be divided into the following: (1) remote control, (2) power amplification, (3) indicating instruments, (4) converters, (5) computers. Servomechanisms can be classified by their motive characteristics as follows: (1) hydraulic servos, (2) thyratron servos, (3) Ward-Leonard controls, (4) amplidyne controls, (5) two-phase a-c servos, (6) mechanical torque amplifiers, (7) pneumatic servos, and so on. In general, all these systems are mathematically similar. Considerations as to choice of the type of motive power depend on local circumstances and on the particular characteristics of the equipment under consideration. For instance, amplidyne controls are useful in a range above approximately $\frac{1}{2}$ hp. Below the $\frac{1}{2}$-hp range the equipment becomes more bulky than thyratron or two-phase a-c control units. On the other hand, drag-cup two-phase motors are extremely good in the range of a few mechanical watts because of their low inertia but become excessively hot as the horsepower is increased above the $\frac{1}{2}$-hp range. Pneumatic servos are extremely useful in aircraft controls and especially in missile devices of short life where storage batteries are heavy compared with compressed-air tanks. Pneumatic servos are also used in a large number of industrial process control applications.

For the purposes of this book, the most important classification of servomechanisms is that according to their control characteristics. Hazen[1] has classified servos into (1) relay-type servomechanisms, (2) definite-correction servomechanisms, and (3) continuous-control servomechanisms. The relay type of servomechanism is one in which the full power of the motor is applied as soon as the error is large enough to operate a relay. The definite-correction servomechanism is one in which the

[1] H. L. Hazen, "Theory of Servomechanisms," *J. Franklin Inst.*, **218**, 279 (1934).

power on the motor is controlled in finite steps at definite time intervals. The continuous-control servomechanism is one in which the power of the motor is controlled continuously by some function of the error. This book concerns itself with the continuous type of control mechanism. All three types have been used extensively. The relay type is generally the most economical to construct and is useful in applications where crude follow-up is required. It has, however, been successfully applied with high performance output, even for such applications as instruments and power drives for directors. Relays can be made to act very quickly, that is, in times short compared with the time constants of the motor. Under these conditions the relay type of servo can be made to approach continuous control so closely that no sharp line can be drawn. In Chap. 5, an analysis is made of the limitation on continuous-control servomechanisms arising from the use of intermittent data. The second type of servomechanism, the finite step correction, is used principally in instruments.

The continuous-control systems themselves can be further classified according to the manner in which the error signal is used to control the motor: proportional control, integral control, derivative control, antihunt feedback (subsidiary loops), proportional plus derivative control, and so on. The study of these different methods of control is one of the major tasks of this book.

Before continuing the discussion on servomechanisms it is worth while to consider the terminology as it has developed over the past few years. The definition given in the first section requires that a servo system have the following properties: (1) A source of power is controlled and (2) feedback is provided. This definition applies equally well to four fields of applied engineering, which have developed more or less concurrently: (1) feedback amplifiers, (2) automatic controls and regulators, (3) recording instruments, and (4) remote-control and power servomechanisms. As implied by the first sentence of this book, it is difficult to find unique definitions segregating these four fields. It is generally agreed that a servomechanism involves mechanical motion somewhere in the system; there is agreement that the power drives on a gun turret constitute a servomechanism. Temperature regulators are often excluded from the class of servomechanisms and classified as automatic regulators or control instruments, even though such mechanical elements as relays and motors may be used. If there is any rule that seems to apply, then perhaps it is that in a servomechanism the element of greatest time lag should be mechanical and, in general, that the output of the system should be mechanical. For the purposes of this book, the term servo system will include all types of feedback devices and the term servomechanism will be reserved for servo systems involving mechanical output.

1·3. Analysis of Simple Servo Systems.—The purpose of this section is to present simple analyses showing various methods of approach to the mathematical description of servo systems; in subsequent chapters a formal and reasonably complete analysis is given. The mathematical tools used in this first treatment have been derived from the general field of operational calculus and are, therefore, limited to the consideration of linear systems, that is, systems described by linear differential equations

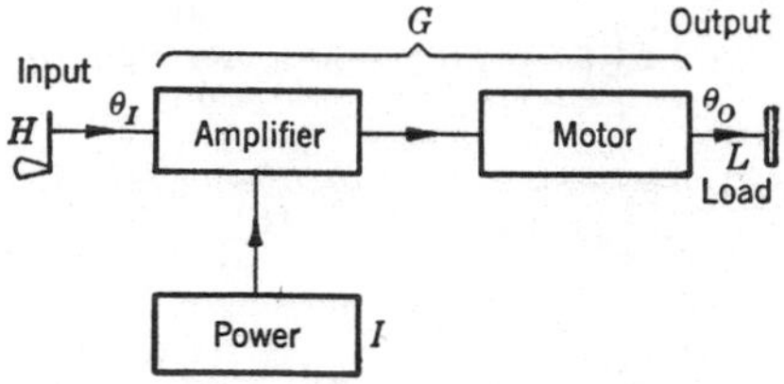

FIG. 1·2.—Open-cycle control system.

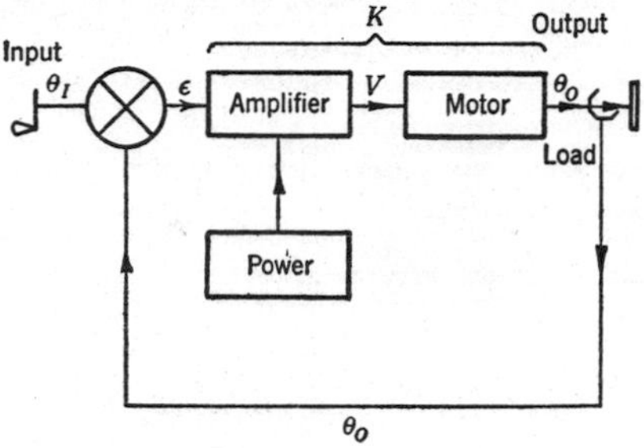

FIG. 1·3.—Simple closed-cycle control system.

with constant coefficients.[1] This limitation restricts only a little the usefulness of the analysis, inasmuch as most practical servomechanisms either are linear or can be approximated sufficiently closely by a linear representation.

The advantages of a servo system in contrast to an open-cycle system are illustrated by even the simplest type of servo system. Figure 1·2 schematically shows an open-cycle control system. If the handwheel H is turned through an angle θ_I, the source of external power is so controlled through the amplifier that the motor rotates the load shaft L through an angle θ_O. In a perfect system, θ_O would at all times be equal to θ_I. This would require, of course, that all the derivatives of θ_O were instantaneously equal to the derivatives of θ_I. Were these conditions to be satisfied, the characteristics of the power supply, the amplifier, and the motor would have to be held constant at all times, or compensation devices would have to be incorporated. The amplifier must be insensitive to power fluctuations; the torque characteristics of the motor must be independent of temperature; the system must be insensitive to load variations; and so on. In general, these requirements cannot be met. The most effective example of the open-cycle system is a vacuum-tube amplifier. It is possible to make a vacuum-tube amplifier in which the output is always proportional to the input within limits of load and power-line fluctuation. This is, however, almost a unique example; it is nearly

[1] M. F. Gardner and J. L. Barnes, *Transients in Linear Systems*, Wiley, New York, 1942; E. A. Guillemin, *Communication Networks*, Vols. 1 and 2, Wiley, New York, 1935; V. Bush, *Operational Circuit Analysis*, Wiley, New York, 1929.

impossible to find a power-control mechanism in which the cycle is not closed mechanically, electrically, or through a human link.

In Fig. 1·3 is shown a schematic of a simple closed-cycle control system. It differs from the open-cycle control system in that the output angle θ_O is subtracted from the input angle θ_I to obtain the error signal ϵ. It is this error signal which is used to control the amplifier. Figure 1·3 represents inverse feedback, or, as it is sometimes called, negative feedback. Let K_1 be the gain of the amplifier. Then the output of the amplifier V is given by

$$V = K_1\epsilon. \tag{5}$$

Assume that the motor has no time lag and a speed at all times proportional to V;

$$\frac{d\theta_O}{dt} = +K_m V. \tag{6}$$

For simple proportional control,

$$\epsilon = \theta_I - \theta_O \tag{7}$$

is used directly as input to the amplifier. Combining Eqs. (5) and (6), we get

$$\frac{V}{K_1} = \theta_I - \theta_O = +\frac{1}{K_1K_m}\frac{d\theta_O}{dt}, \tag{8}$$

or

$$\frac{1}{K}\frac{d\theta_O}{dt} + \theta_O = \theta_I, \tag{9}$$

where $K = K_1K_m$. If we now consider a sinusoidal input θ_I equal to θ_{I0} sin ωt, we get

$$\frac{d\theta_O}{dt} + K\theta_O = K\theta_{I0}\sin\omega t. \tag{10}$$

This equation will be recognized as similar to the equation of an RC-circuit driven by an alternating generator, which is, on writing q for the charge,

$$R\frac{dq}{dt} + \frac{q}{C} = V_0\sin\omega t. \tag{11}$$

The steady-state solution for the RC-circuit can be written

$$q = q_0\sin(\omega t - \phi); \tag{12}$$

where,

$$q_0 = \frac{V_0}{\sqrt{\omega^2R^2 + \frac{1}{C^2}}}, \qquad \tan\phi = +\omega RC \tag{13}$$

and ϕ is the angle by which the charge lags the voltage. Similarly, the solution of Eq. (10) is

$$\theta_0 = \theta_{O0} \sin (\omega t - \phi); \tag{14a}$$

where

$$\theta_{O0} = \frac{\theta_{I0}}{\sqrt{\frac{\omega^2}{K^2} + 1}}; \qquad \tan \phi = + \frac{\omega}{K}. \tag{14b}$$

If K is large compared with ω, this may be expanded by the binomial theorem as

$$\theta_{O0} = \theta_{I0}\left(1 - \frac{1}{2}\frac{\omega^2}{K^2}\right). \tag{15}$$

We see immediately that provided only K is much larger than ω, the output θ_O will be essentially equal to the input θ_I in magnitude and phase; the accuracy of the follow-up requires only making sufficiently high the velocity constant K_m of the motor and the gain K_1 of the amplifier. In contrast to the open-cycle system, it is not necessary to use a compensated amplifier or a motor insensitive to load in such a system. These are the chief and fundamental advantages of inverse feedback.

Equation (15) implies certain limitations on the system shown in Fig. 1·3. In any real amplifier the gain will be high until saturation sets in or up to a definite frequency. Likewise, the motor speed constant will drop off if the speed is increased or torque exceeded. In general, therefore, there will be an upper value to ω beyond which the system will not function. Actually, all motors have time constants, that is, exhibit inertial effects, and it is necessary to consider this time constant in the analysis.

The preceding analysis described the steady state of the servo illustrated in Fig. 1·3 when the input is a sine wave. Let us now consider the transient behavior of the same proportional-control system for transient solution; instead of a sine-wave input let us assume that the input θ_I is zero for all times up to t_0 and then suffers a discontinuous change to a new constant A for all times greater than t_0. In short, a step function is applied as the input to the servo. The differential equation is

$$\frac{d\theta_O}{dt} + K\theta_O = K\theta_I \tag{16}$$

and it is to be solved for

$$\left.\begin{aligned} \theta_I &= 0, & t &< t_0, \\ \theta_I &= A, & t &> t_0; \end{aligned}\right\} \tag{17}$$

the solution is

$$\theta_O = A[1 - e^{-K(t-t_0)}], \qquad t \geqq t_0, \tag{18}$$

as can be shown by substituting in Eq. (16). The step function is shown in Fig. 1·4 as a dotted line, and the response is shown as a full line. It is clear that the output approaches the input as the time beyond t_0 increases without limit. The larger the value of K, that is, the larger the gain of the amplifier and the larger the velocity constant of the motor, the more quickly will the output approach the input. The error at any time t is the difference between the dotted line and the full line. It falls to $1/e$ of its initial value A in a period $1/K$.

It is evident that the transient analysis and the steady-state analysis display the same general features of the system. For example, we see immediately from the transient solution that if the input were a sine

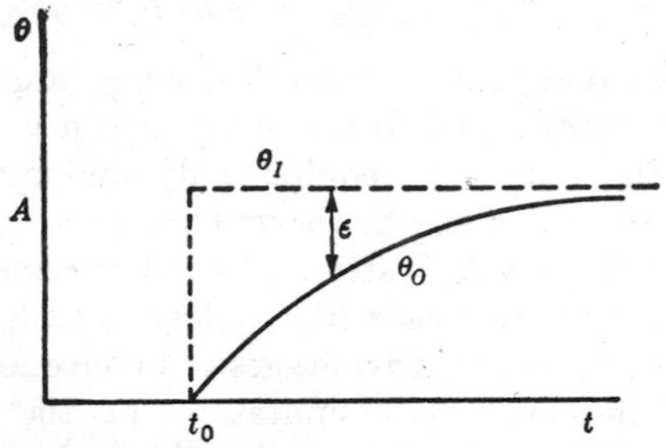

FIG. 1·4.—Response of a simple servo system to a step function.

wave of frequency f, the output would follow it closely only if the period of the sinusoid were greater than $1/K$, that is, f smaller than K.

The solution of Eq. (16) for an arbitrary input can be written in terms of a "weighting function." If θ_I is any input beginning at a finite time, the output will be

$$\theta_O(t) = K \int_0^\infty \theta_I(t - \tau) e^{-K\tau} \, d\tau, \tag{19}$$

as can be verified by substituting into Eq. (16). In the case of the input described by Eq. (17), the output can be computed as

$$\begin{aligned} \theta_O(t) &= \int_0^{t-t_0} AKe^{-K\tau} \, d\tau \\ &= A[1 - e^{-K(t-t_0)}], \end{aligned} \tag{20}$$

as found before. The function

$$W(\tau) = Ke^{-K\tau} \tag{21}$$

is called the weighting function. Physically Eq. (19) means that at any time t the output is equal to a sum of contributions from the input at all past times. Each element of the input appears in the output multiplied by a factor $W(\tau)$ dependent on the time interval τ between the present time t and the time of the input under consideration. $W(\tau)$ thus specifies the weight with which the input at any past moment contributes to the present output. It will be noted that in this example the weighting function is an exponential. When the time interval between input and output is greater than $1/K$, the contributions to the output will be small; the remote past input will have been essentially forgotten.

To summarize, the simple system including proportional control, a linear amplifier, and a motor with no time lag connected as a servo system with negative feedback has been analyzed (1) as a steady-state problem, (2) as a transient problem, and (3) as a problem involving the weighing of the past history of the input. All of these analyses give essentially the same result that the output is equal to the input for frequencies below a critical value equal approximately to K. One should expect that there would be mathematical procedures for going from one type of analysis to another, and such is indeed the case.

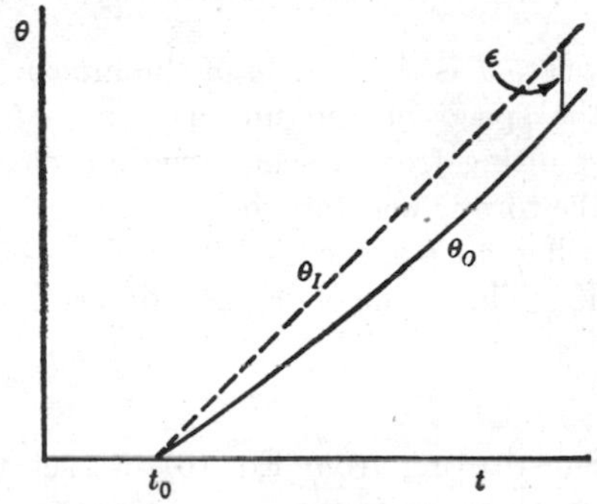

FIG. 1·5.—Response of a simple servo system to sudden change in velocity.

Another interesting type of transient input often used in servo analysis is the discontinuous change in the speed of θ_I. Such as input is shown in Fig. 1·5 by the dotted line. The differential equation now takes the form

$$\frac{1}{K}\frac{d\theta_O}{dt} + \theta_O = B(t - t_0) \qquad \text{for } t > t_0; \tag{22}$$
$$= 0 \qquad \text{for } t < t_0.$$

The output after time t_0 is

$$\theta_O = B\left\{(t - t_0) - \frac{1}{K}[1 - e^{-K(t-t_0)}]\right\}. \tag{23}$$

This is shown as a full line in Fig. 1·5. It is obvious that as time increases, the velocity of the output will eventually equal the velocity of the input; there will, however, be an angular displacement or velocity error between them. The ratio of the velocity to the error approaches the limit K as $t \to \infty$; this is readily seen from the equation

$$\frac{\frac{d\theta_I}{dt}}{\epsilon} = \frac{BK}{B[1 - e^{-K(t-t_0)}]} = \frac{K}{1 - e^{-K(t-t_0)}}. \tag{24}$$

This coefficient K, a product of the gain of the amplifier K_1 and the velocity constant of the motor K_m, is called the velocity-error constant and will hereafter be written K_v. If the loop were opened, it would be the ratio of velocity to displacement at the two open ends. It is obvious that the velocity error in this simple system could be reduced by increasing K. In Chap. 4 we shall see that this error can be made equal to zero by introducing integral control.

As indicated previously, any motor and its load will exhibit inertial effects, and Eq. (6) must be modified by adding a term. The simplest physical motor can be described by a differential equation of the form

$$J \frac{d^2\theta_O}{dt^2} + f_m \frac{d\theta_o}{dt} = K_t V, \tag{25}$$

where J is the inertia of the motor (including that of the load referred to the speed of the motor shaft); f_m is the internal-damping coefficient resulting from viscous friction, electrical loss, and back emf; and K_t is the torque constant of the motor. If there is no acceleration, the motor will go at a speed such that the losses are just compensated by the input V. This value of $d\theta_O/dt$ is determined by the relation

$$f_m \frac{d\theta_O}{dt} = +K_t V. \tag{26}$$

Substituting from Eq. (6), we see that the internal-damping coefficient f_m can be written as

$$f_m = \frac{K_t}{K_m}. \tag{27}$$

Thus the internal-damping coefficient of a motor can be computed by dividing K_t, the stalled-torque constant (say, foot-pounds per volt), by K_m, the velocity constant of the motor (say, radians per second per volt). Equation (25) can be rewritten in the form

$$J \frac{K_m}{K_t} \frac{d^2\theta_O}{dt^2} + \frac{d\theta_O}{dt} = +K_m V = T_m \frac{d^2\theta_O}{dt^2} + \frac{d\theta_O}{dt}, \tag{28}$$

where

$$T_m = J \frac{K_m}{K_t}; \tag{29}$$

the motor inertia appears only in the time constant T_m. In short, the characteristics of the motor can be specified by stating its internal-damping coefficient and its time constant; these can be determined by experimentally measuring stalled torque as a function of voltage, running speed as a function of voltage, and inertia.

If we now use Eq. (28) instead of Eq. (6) as the differential equation representing the behavior of the motor, we can find the output due to an arbitrary input by solving the differential equation

$$\theta_I - \theta_O = \epsilon = \frac{V}{K_1} = \frac{1}{K_1 K_m} \left(T_m \frac{d^2\theta_O}{dt^2} + \frac{d\theta_O}{dt} \right); \tag{30}$$

in simpler form this is

$$T_m \frac{d^2\theta_O}{dt^2} + \frac{d\theta_O}{dt} + K_v\theta_O = K_v\theta_I, \tag{31}$$

where K_v equals K_1K_m. This equation is similar in form to the differential equation of an *LRC* series circuit driven by an external alternating generator.

Just as in the case of Eq. (6), we can write the specific solution of this equation. It will perhaps suffice to get the general solution of the equation that holds when $\theta_I = 0$:

$$T_m \frac{d^2\theta_O}{dt^2} + \frac{d\theta_O}{dt} + K_v\theta_O = 0. \tag{32}$$

Letting

$$p_1 = \alpha + j\omega_0 \qquad \text{and} \qquad p_2 = \alpha - j\omega_0,$$

the solution can be written in the form

$$\theta_O = ae^{p_1t} + be^{p_2t}, \tag{33}$$

where the p's must satisfy

$$p^2 + \frac{p}{T_m} + \frac{K_v}{T_m} = 0. \tag{34}$$

The solution of this is

$$p = -\frac{1}{2T_m} \pm \frac{1}{2}\sqrt{\frac{1}{T_m^2} - \frac{4K_v}{T_m}}. \tag{35}$$

The nature of the solution depends on whether $4K_1K_mT_m$ is less than, equal to, or greater than 1. In the first case the radical is real and the solution consists of overdamped motion (that is, $\alpha < 1/2T_m$). In the second case the output is critically damped, and in the last case the output rings with a Q equal to $\sqrt{K_1K_mT_m}$ (Q as defined in communication practice). The system is always stable, and the output approaches the value of a constant input as $t \to \infty$.

It is characteristic of a second-order linear differential equation of this type that the solutions are always stable; θ_O is always bounded if θ_I is bounded. It is, however, unfortunately true that physical systems are seldom described by equations of lower than the fourth order, especially if the amplifier is frequency sensitive and the feedback involves conversion from one form of signal to another. For example, feedback may be by a synchronous generator with a 60-cycle carrier (see Chap. 4) which will have to be rectified before being added to the input. This rectifier will be essentially a filter described by a differential equation of an order higher than one. The question of stability therefore always plays an important role in discussions of the design of servo systems.

1·4. History of Design Techniques.—Automatic control devices of one kind or another have been used by man for hundreds of years, and descriptions of early servolike devices can be found in literature at least as far back as the time of Leonardo da Vinci. The accumulated knowledge and experience that comprise the present-day science of servo design, however, received a great initial impulse from the work and publications of Nicholas Minorsky[1] in 1922 and H. L. Hazen[1] in 1934. Minorsky's work on the automatic steering of ships and Hazen's on shaft-positioning types of servomechanisms both contained mathematical analyses based on a direct study of the solutions of differential equations similar to those of Sec. 1·3. This approach to the design problem was the only one available for many years, and it was exploited with significant success by intelligent and industrious designers of servomechanisms.

In 1932 Nyquist[2] published a procedure for studying the stability of feedback amplifiers by the use of steady-state techniques. His powerful theorem for studying the stability of feedback amplifiers became known as the Nyquist stability criterion. In Nyquist's analysis the behavior of the servo system with the feedback loop broken is considered. The ratio of a (complex) amplitude of the servo output to the (complex) error amplitude is plotted in the complex plane, with frequency as a variable parameter. If the resulting curve does not encircle the critical point $(-1, 0)$, the system is stable; in fact, the further the locus can be kept away from the critical point the greater is the stability of the system. The theory and application of this criterion are discussed in Chaps. 2 and 4. From the designer's viewpoint, the best advantage of this method is that even in complicated systems time can be saved in analysis and a great insight can be obtained into the detailed physical phenomena involved in the servo loop. Some of the earliest work in this field was done by J. Taplin at Massachusetts Institute of Technology in 1937, and the work was carried further by H. Harris,[3] also of Massachusetts Institute of Technology, who introduced the concept of transfer functions into servo theory. The war created a great demand for high-performance servomechanisms and greatly stimulated the whole subject of servo design. The supposed demands of military security, however, confined the results of this stimulation within fairly small academic and industrial circles, certainly to the over-all detriment of the war effort, and prevented, for example, the early publishing of the fundamental work of G. S. Brown and A. C. Hall.[4] The restricted, but nevertheless fairly

[1] N. Minorsky, "Directional Stability of Automatically Steered Bodies," *J. Am. Soc. Naval Eng.*, **34,** 280 (1922); H. L. Hazen, "Theory of Servomechanisms," *J. Franklin Inst.*, **218,** 279 (1934).

[2] H. Nyquist, "Regeneration Theory," *Bell System Tech. J.*, **XI,** 126 (1932).

[3] H. Harris, "The Analysis and Design of Servomechanisms," OSRD Report 454, January 1942.

[4] G. S. Brown and A. C. Hall, "Dynamic Behavior and Design of Servomechanisms," *Trans., ASME*, **68,** 503 (1946).

widely circulated, publication in 1943 of *The Analysis and Synthesis of Linear Servomechanisms*, by A. C. Hall, gave a comprehensive treatment of one approach to the steady-state analysis of servomechanisms and popularized the name "transfer-locus" method for this approach. Some of the important concepts introduced by steady-state analysis are those of "transmission around a loop" and the use of an over-all system operator.

In 1933 Y. W. Lee published the results of work done by himself and Norbert Wiener, describing certain fundamental relationships between the real and imaginary parts of the transfer functions representative of a large class of physical systems. These basic relationships have been applied in great detail and with great advantage by H. W. Bode[1] to the design of electrical networks and feedback amplifiers. Several groups, working more or less independently, applied and extended Bode's techniques to the servomechanism design problem, and the results have been very fruitful. The resulting techniques of analysis are so rapid, convenient, and illuminating that even for very complicated systems the designer is justified in making a complete analysis of his problem. As is shown in Chap. 4, the complete analysis of a system can be carried through much more rapidly than the usual transfer-locus methods permit, and the analysis of multiple-feedback loop systems is particularly facilitated.

1·5. Performance Specifications.—In designing a servomechanism for a specific application, the designer necessarily has a clear, definite goal in mind; the mechanism is to perform some given task, and it must do so with some minimum desired quality of performance. The designer is, therefore, faced with the problem of translating this essentially physical information into a mathematical definition of the desired performance—one that can then be used as a criterion of success or failure in any attempted pencil-and-paper synthesis of the mechanism.

The most important characteristic of a servo system is the accuracy with which it can perform its normal duties. There are several different ways in which one can specify the accuracy of performance of a servomechanism. The most useful, in many applications, is a statement of the manner in which the output varies in response to some given input signal. The input signal is chosen, of course, to be representative of the type of input signals encountered in the particular application. Many servos are used in gun directors and gun data computers, for instance, to reproduce the motion of the target, a ship or a plane, being followed or tracked by the director. Such motions have certain definite characteristics, because the velocities and accelerations of the targets have finite physical limitations. The performance of such servos is often partially

[1] H. W. Bode, "Feedback Amplifier Design," *Bell System Tech. J.*, **XIX**, 42 (1940).

summarized by a statement of the errors that may exist between the input and output motions under certain peak velocities and accelerations or over certain ranges of velocities and accelerations. Alternatively, one can specify what the errors may be as a function of time as the mechanism reproduces some typical target course.

The performance of a servomechanism can also be specified in terms of its response to a step function. The procedure of experimentally and theoretically studying a servomechanism through its response to a step-function input is extremely useful and is widely used for a number of reasons. The experimental techniques used in such testing are simple and require a minimum of instrumentation. The characteristics of any truly linear system are, of course, completely summarized by its response to a step-function input; that is, if the step-function response is known, the response to any other arbitrary input signal can be determined. It would be expected, therefore, and it is true, that with proper interpretation the step-function response is a powerful and useful criterion of overall system quality.

In some applications the input signals are periodic and can be analyzed into a small number of primary harmonic components. In such cases the performance of the servo system can be specified conveniently by stating the response characteristics of the system to sinusoidal inputs of these particularly important frequencies. With the increased use of sinusoidal steady-state techniques in the analysis and testing of servomechanisms, it has become fairly common to specify the desired frequency response of the system, that is, the magnitude and phase of the ratio of the output θ_O to the input θ_I as a function of frequency—rather than at several discrete frequencies. If the system is linear, its performance is completely described by such a specification, as it is by specification of the response to a step function. Depending upon the particular application and the nature of the input signals, one or the other type of specification may be easier to apply.

In any practical case a servo performance will be required to meet conditions other than that of the accuracy with which it is to follow a given input under standard conditions. The top speed of a servomechanism, such as will arise in slewing a gun or in locking a follow-up mechanism into synchronism, may far exceed the maximum speed during actual follow-up applications. It is sometimes necessary to specify the limits of speed between which it must operate—the maximum speed and minimum desirable speed unaccompanied by jump. For example, a gun-director servo system may be required to have a slewing speed of 60° per second, a top speed during actual following of 20° per second, and a minimum speed of 0.01° per second. The ratio of maximum to minimum following speed is here 2000. This speed ratio constitutes one criterion of goodness of a servo system.

In certain applications (for example, the control of the cutting head of a large planer or boring mill or of the radar antenna aboard a ship) the transient loading on the output member of the servomechanism may be very high. Under these circumstances, a small error in the output should result in the application of nearly the full torque of the motor; indeed, considerations of transient load may require a source of power far in excess of the dynamic load itself. It is generally true in high-performance servomechanisms that almost the entire initial load comes from the armature or rotating element of the motor itself. Better designs of servomotors have tended to increase the ratio of torque to inertia of the motor rotor.

Three other practical factors are important in the design of good servomechanisms and are hence often included in specifications: (1) backlash, (2) static friction, and (3) locking mechanisms. Backlash cannot be analyzed by a consideration of linear systems, because the backlash destroys the exact linearity of a system. Practical experience has shown that the backlash of the mechanical and electrical components limits the static performance of a servo system. Backlash may occur in gear trains, in linkages, or in electrical and magnetic error-sensitive devices. Backlash often has the unfortunate effect of limiting the gain around the loop of a servo system, thereby reducing its over-all effectiveness. Increase in the gain of a servo system invariably results in oscillations of the order of the backlash; the higher the gain the higher the frequency of these oscillations. The increased frequencies of oscillation are accompanied by excessive forces that cause wear and sometimes damage.

Static friction has the same discontinuous character as backlash. If the static friction is high compared with the coulomb friction within the minimum specified speed, extreme jumpiness in the servo performance will result. The error signal will have to build up to a magnitude adequate to overcome the static friction (sometimes called stiction). At this instant the restraining forces are suddenly diminished and the servo tends to overshoot its mark.

Locking mechanisms, such as low-efficiency gears or worm drives, are troublesome in servomechanisms where transient loads are encountered. The effect is that of high static friction, emphasized by the resulting immobility of the device.

It is impossible to construct high-fidelity servomechanisms if mechanical rigidity is not maintained in shafting and gearing. The introduction of mechanical elements with natural frequency comparable to frequencies encountered in the input is equivalent to introducing additional filters into the loop. If such filters are deliberately put in to produce stability, such design may be justified. Unfortunately, it is true that mechanical elements in resonant structures undergo tremendous dynamic forces which may far exceed the stalled-torque loading on the elements. It is generally desirable to specify, as a portion of design criteria, the mechanical resonant frequency of the system.

Another practical consideration in servomechanism design arises from the low power level of the input to the amplifiers. Except under extreme conditions, the error signal is small and the gain of the amplifier may be higher than one million. If, for example, the feedback mechanism consists of electrical elements that may pick up stray voltages or generate harmonics because of nonlinear elements in the circuits, these spurious voltages may exceed the error signal required for the minimum specified servo speed and, unless supressed, may even overload the amplifier.

The application of servomechanisms to the automatic tracking of planes by radar and the application of filter theory to the smoothing of observed data in general for gunnery purposes have brought to light the need for considering the effects of noise in the system; this too must at times be included in the performance specifications. In the case of the automatic tracking of planes by radar (see Chaps. 4, 6, and 7), a radar antenna mount is made to position itself in line with the target. The antenna beam illuminates the target, and the reflections from the target are received by the same antenna mount that transmits the signal. The beam is made to scan in a cone at 30 cps, in such a manner that the signal would come back at a constant signal strength if the target were in the center of the beam. If, on the other hand, the antenna mount points to one side of the target, the reflected signal is modulated at 30 cps. The phase and amplitude of this modulation is the error signal; the phase giving the direction and the amplitude the amount of the error. The phase and amplitude are resolved into errors in elevation and traverse and are used to actuate the servoamplifiers and servomotors on the antenna mount. Were it not for the fact that the reflections from the plane fade in rather haphazard ways, the servo problem would be of the usual type. The presence of the fading in the error-transmission system, however, makes necessary careful design of the system, with due regard for the frequency distribution and magnitude of the fading. For example, if the fading were characterized by a frequency of 5 cps, it would be necessary to design the servo loop in such a way that at 5 cps the response of the system would be either zero or very small. This is, fortunately, a reasonable step, since no plane being tracked will oscillate with such a frequency. If the fading should cover the spectrum from 5 cps to all higher frequencies, then the frequency response of the servo system would have to be equivalent to a low-pass filter with cutoff somewhat below 5 cps. On the other hand, the attenuation of the higher frequencies in the response of the servo system is invariably accompanied by the introduction of acceleration errors; for a fixed amplitude, acceleration goes up as the square of the frequency. Such a system becomes sluggish and may not follow a plane undergoing evasive tactics. A compromise must be made between suppression of the fading and accurate following of the actual motion of the target. Methods by which this can be done are discussed in Chaps. 6 to 8.

There sometimes arises the problem of designing the best possible servo system of a given order of complexity to meet a given need. This is the subject of the second part of the book. The practice before the war in the design of servos was to employ a mechanism *adequate* for the problem. The difficult problems encountered in the war, particularly in the field of fire control, emphasize the necessity of designing the *best possible* servo system consistent with a given kind of mechanism. It is not easy to give a statement of what is the best performance. It has been common practice (though not a desirable one) to specify servo performance in terms of the response, say at two frequencies, and to omit any statement about the stability of the system in the presence of large transients. It is obvious that a system designed to meet these specifications will not necessarily be the best possible servo if the input contains frequencies other than the two specified ones. Indeed, systems designed to a specification of this type have shown such high instability at high frequencies as to be almost useless in the presence of large transients.

If it is desired to design a "best possible servo," it is necessary to define a criterion of goodness. Hall[1] and Phillips[2] have independently applied the criterion that the rms error in the following will be minimized by the "best" servo. For a full statement of the performance of such a servo it is also necessary to describe the input for which the rms error is minimized. In the case of the previous example of automatic radar tracking of an airplane, the problem was to track an airplane on physically realizable courses of the type to be expected in the presence of antiaircraft fire. The input to the servo drives of the antenna mount, except for fading, might be the instantaneous coordinates of the plane flying any one of a large number of paths, approximated as consisting of straight segments; the character of the fading can be observed in a number of trial runs with the radar set to be used. The order of the differential equation describing the servo system was fixed by the characteristics of the amplidyne, the d-c drive motors, and the amplifier. The problem was to determine the proper value of the parameters available for adjustment in the amplifier in such a way that the rms error, averaged over the many straight-line courses of the target, should be a minimum. The use

[1] A. C. Hall, *The Analysis and Synthesis of Linear Servomechanisms*, Technology Press, Massachussetts Institute of Technology, May 1943.

[2] R. S. Phillips, "Servomechanisms," RL Report No. 372, May 11, 1943.

of the rms-error criterion in this problem is justified principally by the fact that it lends itself to mathematical analysis. It is obviously not the best criterion for all types of problems; it gives too great an emphasis to large momentary errors. In the antiaircraft case, large momentary errors might correspond to one or two wild shots. Obviously, it is better to have one or two wild shots, with all the rest close, than to have all shots fall ineffectively with a moderate error. A better working criterion has not yet been developed.

The rms criterion of goodness is particularly useful because it permits one to take into account the presence of noise, provided only that the frequency characteristic or the "autocorrelation function" of the noise is known. The analysis given in the latter part of this book, although difficult for practical designers, is important in industrial applications where transient loading has definite characteristics and where best performance is economically necessary. The loading constitutes in effect a noise and can be treated by the methods there developed.

CHAPTER 2

MATHEMATICAL BACKGROUND

By H. M. James and P. R. Weiss

INTRODUCTION

This chapter will be devoted to a discussion of the mathematical concepts and techniques that are fundamental in the theory of servomechanisms. These ideas will, for the most part, be developed in their relation to filters, of which servomechanisms form a special class. More specifically, the chapter will be concerned with the ways in which the behavior of linear filters in general and servomechanisms in particular can be described and with making clear the relations between the various modes of description.[1]

The input and output of a filter are often related by a *differential equation*, the solution of which gives the output for any given input. This equation provides a complete description of the filter, but one that cannot be conveniently used in design techniques. Other modes of description of the filter are related to the outputs produced by special types of input:

1. The *weighting function* is the filter output produced by an impulse input and is simply related to the output produced by a step input.
2. The *frequency-response function* relates a sinusoidal input to the output that it produces.
3. The *transfer function* is a generalization of the frequency-response function.

These modes of description are simply related, and each offers advantages in different fields of application.

Discussion of these ideas requires the use of mathematical devices such as the Fourier transform and the Laplace transform. For complete discussions of these techniques the reader must be referred to standard texts; for his convenience, however, certain basic ideas are here presented. Although it has not been intended that the analysis of the chapter should be carried through with maximum rigor, the reader will observe that some pains have been taken to provide a logical development of the ideas.

[1] The authors wish to acknowledge helpful discussions with W. Hurewicz in the planning of this chapter.

This development is illustrated by application to lumped-constant filters, in terms of which the relations here discussed are especially easy to understand.

Particular attention has been paid to the discussion of stability of filters, which is of special importance in its application to servomechanisms. The latter part of the chapter is devoted to a discussion of the Nyquist stability criterion and its application to single-loop- and multiloop-feedback systems. Parallel developments in the case of pulsed filters will be found in Chap. 5.

FILTERS

2·1. Lumped-constant Filters.—The most familiar type of filter is the electrical filter consisting of a network of a finite number of lumped resistances, capacitances, and inductances with constant values. Figure 2·1 illustrates a particularly simple filter of this type—an RC-filter consisting of a single resistance R and a single capacitance C.

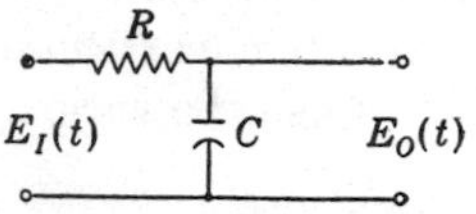

FIG. 2·1.—An RC-filter.

The input to an electrical filter is a voltage $E_I(t)$ supplied by a source that may be taken to have zero internal impedance; the output is an open-circuit voltage $E_O(t)$. Input and output are related by a differential equation. In the case of the RC-filter of Fig. 2·1 this has the easily derived form

$$T \frac{dE_O}{dt} + E_O = E_I, \tag{1}$$

where the quantity $T = RC$ is the time constant of the network. In general, the input and output are related by

$$a_n \frac{d^nE_O}{dt^n} + a_{n-1} \frac{d^{n-1}E_O}{dt^{n-1}} + \cdots + a_0E_O = b_m \frac{d^mE_I}{dt^m} + b_{m-1} \frac{d^{m-1}E_I}{dt^{m-1}} + \cdots + b_0E_I, \tag{2}$$

where the a's and b's are constants and $m, n \leqq 2N$, N being the number of independent loops in the filter network (including one loop through the voltage source but none through the output circuit).

Since this formulation is less common than that in terms of mesh currents, it may be desirable to indicate its derivation. In a N-mesh network of general form, the mesh currents are determined by integro-differential equations which may be written[1] as

[1] See, for instance, E. A. Guillemin, *Communication Networks*, Vol. I, Wiley, New York, 1931, p. 139.

$$\left.\begin{aligned} a_{11}i_1 + a_{12}i_2 + a_{13}i_3 + \cdots + a_{1N}i_N &= E_I, \\ a_{21}i_1 + a_{22}i_2 + a_{23}i_3 + \cdots + a_{2N}i_N &= 0, \\ \cdots\cdots\cdots\cdots\cdots\cdots\cdots & \\ a_{N1}i_1 + a_{N2}i_2 + a_{N3}i_3 + \cdots + a_{NN}i_N &= 0, \end{aligned}\right\} \tag{3}$$

where i_k is the current in the kth mesh and

$$a_{jk}i_k = L_{jk}\frac{di_k}{dt} + R_{jk}i_k + \frac{1}{C_{jk}}\int dt\, i_k. \tag{4}$$

The output voltage is determined by the mesh currents, through an equation of the form

$$a_{N+1,1}\,i_1 + a_{N+1,2}\,i_2 + \cdots + a_{N+1,N}\,i_N = E_O. \tag{5}$$

Equations (3) and (5) may be regarded as $N + 1$ equations in the $3N$ quantities di_k/dt, i_k, $\int dt\, i_k$, $(k = 1, 2, \cdots, N)$. To eliminate such quantities from consideration and to obtain a direct relation between E_O and E_I, one may form the first $2N$ derivatives with respect to time of these $N + 1$ equations. One has then, in all, $(2N + 1)(N + 1)$ equations in the $N(2N + 3)$ quantities

$$\frac{d^{2N+1}i_k}{dt^{2N+1}}, \frac{d^{2N}i_k}{dt^{2N}}, \cdots i_k, \int dt\, i_k, \qquad (k = 1, 2, \cdots, N).$$

These equations involve also E_O, E_I, and their first $2N$ derivatives; between them one can always eliminate the unknown mesh currents and their derivatives, obtaining a linear relation between E_I, E_O, and their first $2N$ derivatives. If some of the quantities L_{jk}, R_{jk}, and C_{jk} are zero, it may not be necessary to take so large a number of derivatives in order to eliminate the unknown current quantities; m and n may then be less than $2N$, as they were found to be in Eq. (1).[1]

When the input voltage $E_I(t)$ is specified, Eq. (2) constitutes a nonhomogeneous linear differential equation that can be solved to determine $E_O(t)$. The general solution of such an equation can be expressed as

[1] If one excludes negative values of L, R, and C from consideration (that is, deals with a passive filter), then no equation will contain a term in di_k/dt, i_k, or $\int dt\, i_k$ unless a similar term occurs in the kth loop equation; this applies, in particular, to the output equation Eq. (5). It follows that when one differentiates Eqs. (3) to obtain new equations with which to eliminate current variables, one obtains at least as many new current variables as new equations. One can increase the number of equations as compared with the number of current variables only by differentiating Eq. (5) and with it a sufficient number of Eqs. (3) to make possible elimination of all the new variables; this may or may not require differentiation of the first of Eqs. (3). The number of derivatives of E_O that must be introduced in order to eliminate all current variables is thus equal to the original excess of variables over equations required for their elimination; the number of derivatives of E_I that must be introduced may be equal to this but need never be larger. Thus in the resultant Eq. (2) one will have $n \geqq m$.

the sum of any solution of the nonhomogeneous equation, plus the general solution of the homogeneous equation obtained by setting equal to zero all terms in E_I:

$$a_n \frac{d^n E_O}{dt^n} + a_{n-1} \frac{d^{n-1} E_O}{dt^{n-1}} + \cdots + a_0 E_O = 0. \tag{6}$$

In the particular case of the *RC*-filter described by Eq. (1) the general solution may be written as

$$E_O(t) = Ae^{-\frac{t}{T}} + \frac{1}{T} \int_0^t d\tau \, E_I(\tau) e^{-\frac{t-\tau}{T}}, \tag{7}$$

where the first term is the general solution of the homogeneous equation

$$T \frac{dE_O}{dt} + E_O = 0 \tag{8}$$

and the second is a particular solution of the nonhomogeneous Eq. (1), as is easily verified by substitution into that equation.

To determine the output voltage $E_O(t)$ it is necessary to know both the input function $E_I(t)$ and the adjustable constants in the general solution of the homogeneous equation. These latter constants are determined by the initial conditions of the problem. One set of initial conditions is especially emphasized in what follows: the condition that the system start from rest when the input is first applied. The resultant output of the filter under this condition will be termed its *normal response* to the specified input. In the case of Eq. (7), the condition that $E_O(t) = 0$ at $t = 0$ implies $A = 0$; the normal response of this filter to an input $E_I(t)$ beginning at $t = 0$ is thus

$$E_O(t) = \frac{1}{T} \int_0^t d\tau \, E_I(\tau) e^{-\frac{t-\tau}{T}}, \tag{9a}$$

or, by a change in the variable of integration,

$$E_O(t) = \frac{1}{T} \int_0^t d\tau \, E_I(t - \tau) e^{-\frac{\tau}{T}}. \tag{9b}$$

2·2. Normal Modes of a Lumped-constant Filter.—The solutions of the homogeneous differential equation [Eq. (6)] are of considerable interest for the discussion of the general behavior of the filter. The filter output during any period in which the input is identically zero is a solution of this homogeneous equation, since during this time Eq. (2) reduces to Eq. (6). The output during any period in which the input E_I is constant can be expressed as the sum of a constant response to this constant input,

$$E_O = \frac{b_0}{a_0} E_I \tag{10}$$

(this being a solution of the nonhomogeneous equation), and a suitable solution of Eq. (6). In this case the solution of the homogeneous equation can be termed the "transient response" of the filter to the earlier history of its input. Transient response can, of course, be defined more generally, whenever the input after a given time t_0 takes on a steady-state form: The *transient response* of the filter is the difference between the actual output of the filter for $t > t_0$ and the asymptotic form that it approaches. This asymptotic form is necessarily a solution of the nonhomogeneous Eq. (2); the transient is a solution of the homogeneous Eq. (6).[1]

The general solution of Eq. (6) is a linear combination of n special solutions, called the normal modes of the filter; these have the form

$$h_i(t) = t^k e^{p_i t}, \tag{11}$$

where k is an integer and p_i is a complex constant. The general form of the solution is then

$$E_O = c_1 h_1(t) + c_2 h_2(t) + \cdots + c_n h_n(t); \tag{12}$$

the values of the constants c_i depend on the initial conditions of the solution or on the past history of the filter.

To determine the normal-mode solutions, let us try e^{pt} as a solution of Eq. (6). On substitution of e^{pt} for E_O, this equation becomes

$$(a_n p^n + a_{n-1} p^{n-1} + \cdots + a_0) e^{pt} = 0. \tag{13a}$$

Thus e^{pt} is a solution of the differential equation if

$$P(p) = a_n p^n + a_{n-1} p^{n-1} + \cdots + a_0 = 0. \tag{13b}$$

This equation has n roots, corresponding to the n normal modes. If all n roots of this equation, $p_1, p_2, p_3, \ldots, p_n$, are distinct, then all normal-mode solutions are of the form $e^{p_i t}$; if p_i is an s-fold root, it can be shown (see, for instance, Sec. 2·19) that the s corresponding normal-mode solutions are

$$e^{p_i t},\ t e^{p_i t},\ t^2 e^{p_i t},\ \cdots,\ t^{s-1} e^{p_i t}.$$

Let us denote the possibly complex value of p_i by

$$p_i = \alpha_i + j\omega_i, \tag{14}$$

where α_i and ω_i are real. If p_i is real, the normal-mode solution is real:

$$h_i(t) = t^k e^{\alpha_i t}. \tag{15}$$

If p_i is complex, its complex conjugate p_i^* will also be a solution of Eq.

[1] It may be emphasized that the normal response of a filter is its *complete* response to an input, under the condition that it start from rest; the normal response may include a transient response as a part.

(13b), since the coefficients a_k are real valued; the normal-mode solutions defined above will be complex but will occur in the transient solution in linear combinations that are real:

$$\frac{1}{2}[h_i(t) + h_i^*(t)] = t^k e^{\alpha_i t} \cos \omega_i t, \tag{16a}$$

$$\frac{1}{2j}[h_i(t) - h_i^*(t)] = t^k e^{\alpha_i t} \sin \omega_i t. \tag{16b}$$

If p_i is purely imaginary there may be purely sinusoidal transients: $\sin \omega_i t$, $\cos \omega_i t$.

It will be noted that the normal-mode solution will approach zero exponentially with increasing t if p_i has a negative real part but will increase indefinitely if the real part of p_i is positive. If all the solutions of Eq. (13b) have negative real parts, the transient response of the filter will always die out exponentially after the input assumes a constant value; the filter is then stable.[1] This may not be so if any p_i has a positive real part; when it is possible for some input to excite a normal mode with positive α_i, then the output of the filter may increase indefinitely with time—the filter is then unstable. It may also happen that the real part of p_i vanishes. If this root is multiple, there will be a normal mode that increases indefinitely with time and will lead to instability of the filter if it can be excited. If the imaginary root p_i is simple, the normal mode is sinusoidal; the system may remain in undamped oscillation after this mode has been excited. It is physically obvious that in such a case a continuing input at the frequency of the undamped oscillation will produce an output that oscillates with indefinitely increasing amplitude. In the precise sense of the word, as defined in Sec. 2·8, such a filter is unstable. In summary, then, we see that a lumped-constant filter consisting of fixed elements is certainly stable if all roots of Eq. (13b) have negative real parts, but may be unstable if any root has a zero or positive real part.

2·3. Linear Filters.—The lumped-constant filters discussed in the preceding sections belong to the more general class of "linear filters." Linear filters are characterized by properties of the normal response—properties that may be observed in the normal response of the RC-filter of Sec. 2·1:

$$E_O(t) = \frac{1}{T}\int_0^t d\tau\, E_I(t - \tau)e^{-\frac{\tau}{T}}. \tag{9b}$$

[1] The words "stable" and "unstable" are used here in a general descriptive sense. We shall later consider the stability of filters in more detail and with greater generality and precision; the ideas here expressed are intended only for the orientation of the reader.

These are

1. The normal response is a linear function of the input, in the mathematical sense. If $y_1(t)$ is the normal response of the filter to the input $x_1(t)$ and $y_2(t)$ is the normal response to the input $x_2(t)$, then the normal response to the input

$$x(t) = c_1x_1(t) + c_2x_2(t) \tag{17}$$

(c_1 and c_2 being arbitrary constants) is

$$y(t) = c_1y_1(t) + c_2y_2(t). \tag{18}$$

2. The normal response at any time depends only on the past values of the input.
3. The normal response is independent of the time origin. That is, if $y(t)$ is the normal response to an input $x(t)$, then $y(t + t_0)$ is the normal response to the input $x(t + t_0)$. This requirement is, essentially, that the circuit elements shall have values independent of time. This constitutes a limitation, though not a serious one, on the types of filters that we shall consider.

It should be pointed out that although few practical filters are strictly linear, most filters have approximately this behavior over a range of values of the input. Consequently, the idealization of a linear system is widely useful and does lead to valuable predictions of the behavior of practical systems.

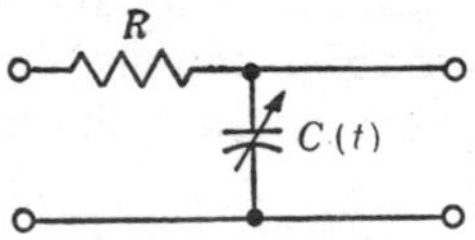

FIG. 2·2.—A filter in which the capacity is a function of time.

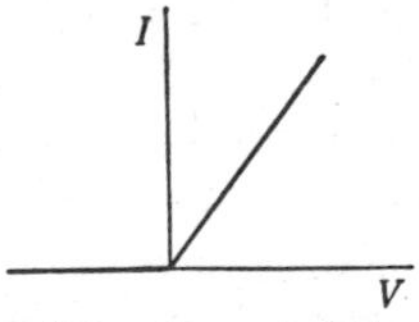

FIG. 2·3.—Current I through a diode rectifier as a function of the potential difference V between anode and cathode.

It should be emphasized that the requirement of linear superposition of responses (Item 1 above) does not suffice to define a linear filter; the circuit elements must also be constant in time. An example of a "nonlinear" filter can be derived from the filter of Fig. 2·1 by making the capacity change in time—as by connecting one of the plates of the condenser through a link to the shaft of a motor (Fig. 2·2). In spite of the fact that the superposition theorem [Eqs. (17) and (18)] applies to this filter, it is not linear, and its normal response cannot be written in an integral form such as Eq. (9*b*).

An example of a filter that is nonlinear in the conventional sense is the familiar diode rectifier. The current through the diode and the output voltage is different from zero only when the potential difference between the anode and cathode is positive (Fig. 2·3). The superposition theorem above does not hold for this system. For example, if $x_1(t) = A$, a constant, and $x_2(t) = A \sin \omega t$, it is easy to see that the combined output to $x_1(t) + x_2(t)$ is not the sum of the outputs due to $x_1(t)$ and $x_2(t)$ separately.

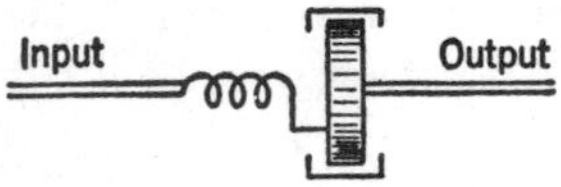

Fig. 2·4.—A mechanical filter.

An example of a mechanical filter is sketched in Fig. 2·4. The input and output shafts are connected through a spring and flywheel; the flywheel is provided with damping that is proportional to its speed of rotation. Such a filter can be made to be linear, at least for small angular displacements of the input and output shafts.

THE WEIGHTING FUNCTION

It will be noted that the relation

$$E_O(t) = \frac{1}{T}\int_0^t d\tau\, E_I(t - \tau)e^{-\frac{\tau}{T}} \tag{9b}$$

expresses the output of a particular linear filter as a weighted mean of all past values of the input; more precisely, the input at a time $t - \tau$ contributes to the output at time t with a relative weight $e^{-\frac{\tau}{T}}$ that is a function of the elapsed time interval τ. (It must be remembered that in this example $E_I(t) = 0$ if $t < 0$.) This method of relating the input and output of a filter by a *weighting function* is generally applicable to linear filters and is of great importance. The weighting function itself is closely related to the normal response of the filter to an impulse input. We shall begin, then, by considering the normal response of linear filters to this particular type of input.

2·4. Normal Response of a Linear Filter to a Unit-impulse Input.—The unit impulse or delta function $\delta(t - t_0)$ is a singular function defined to be zero everywhere except at $t = t_0$, and to be infinite at $t = t_0$ in such a way that it possesses the following integral properties ($t_1 < t_2$):

$$\int_{t_1}^{t_2} dt\, f(t)\delta(t - t_0) = 0 \qquad \text{if } t_1 > t_0 \text{ or } t_2 < t_0, \tag{19a}$$

$$\int_{t_1}^{t_2} dt\, f(t)\delta(t - t_0) = \tfrac{1}{2}f(t_0) \qquad \text{if } t_0 = t_1 \text{ or } t_0 = t_2, \tag{19b}$$

$$\int_{t_1}^{t_2} dt\, f(t)\delta(t - t_0) = f(t_0) \qquad \text{if } t_1 < t_0 < t_2. \tag{19c}$$

The function $\delta(t - t_0)$ may be considered as the limit of a continuous function $\delta_\alpha(t - t_0)$ that is symmetrical in t about the point $t = t_0$ and depends upon a parameter α in such a way that

$$\int_{-\infty}^{+\infty} dt\ \delta_\alpha(t - t_0) \equiv 1, \tag{20a}$$

$$\lim_{\alpha \to 0} \delta_\alpha(t - t_0) = 0 \qquad \text{if } t \neq t_0. \tag{20b}$$

Examples of such functions are

$$\left.\begin{aligned} \delta_\alpha(t - t_0) &= \frac{1}{\alpha\sqrt{\pi}} e^{-\left(\frac{t-t_0}{\alpha}\right)^2}, \\ \delta_\alpha(t - t_0) &= \frac{\alpha}{\pi} \frac{\sin^2\left(\dfrac{t - t_0}{\alpha}\right)}{(t - t_0)^2}; \end{aligned}\right\} \tag{21}$$

as α approaches zero, these functions tend to take on the properties assigned to the unit-impulse function.

The normal response of a linear filter to a unit impulse applied at the time $t = 0$ is denoted by $W(t)$; it will be called the *weighting function*, for reasons to be made evident later. We have, of course,

$$W(t) = 0 \qquad \text{if } t < 0. \tag{22}$$

The weighting function may be discontinuous and may even include terms of the delta-function type for $t_0 \geqq 0$.

The normal response of a linear lumped-constant filter to an impulse input can be determined by consideration of the governing differential equation [Eq. (2)]. After the moment of the impulse, E_I will be zero, and the response $W(t)$ must be a solution of the homogeneous differential equation [Eq. (6)]; that is, it must be a linear combination of the normal modes of the filter. At the moment of the impulse $W(t)$ may be discontinuous; it will even contain a term of the form $c\delta(t)$ when the filter is such that the output contains a term proportional to the input.

In the case of the simple RC-filter described by Eq. (1) there is only one normal mode,

$$h_1 = e^{-\frac{t}{T}}, \tag{23}$$

and the weighting function is of the form

$$\left.\begin{aligned} W(t) &= Ae^{-\frac{t}{T}}, & t > 0, \\ W(t) &= 0, & t < 0. \end{aligned}\right\} \tag{24}$$

One can determine the constant A by integrating Eq. (1) from $-\infty$ to t; with $E_O = W(t)$ and $E_I = \delta(t)$ this becomes

$$TW(t) + \int_{-\infty}^{t} d\tau\ W(\tau) = \int_{-\infty}^{t} d\tau\ \delta(\tau). \tag{25}$$

If $t > 0$, we have, by Eqs. (19c) and (24),

$$TAe^{-\frac{t}{T}} - AT(e^{-\frac{t}{T}} - 1) = 1, \tag{26a}$$

whence

$$A = \frac{1}{T}. \tag{26b}$$

The form of $W(t)$ can be determined by similar methods when there is more than one normal mode. Another method of solution, employing the Laplace transform, will be indicated in Sec. 2·19.

The normal response to a unit impulse can also be determined from an integral formulation of the response to a general input. In the case of our simple RC-filter, one would start with Eq. (9a). The normal response to a unit impulse at time $t_0 > 0$ becomes

$$E_O(t) = \frac{1}{T}\int_0^t \delta(t - t_0)e^{-\frac{t-\tau}{T}}\,d\tau\cdot \tag{27}$$

then, by Eqs. (19),

$$\left.\begin{aligned} E_O(t) &= \frac{1}{T}e^{-\frac{t-t_0}{T}}, & t &> t_0, \\ E_O(t) &= 0, & t &< t_0. \end{aligned}\right\} \tag{28}$$

It follows that for this filter

$$\left.\begin{aligned} W(t) &= \frac{1}{T}e^{-\frac{t}{T}}, & t &> 0, \\ W(t) &= 0, & t &< 0. \end{aligned}\right\} \tag{29}$$

This function is shown as curve a in Fig. 2·5.

The RC-filter shown in Fig. 2·6 has a delta-function term in its weighting function. Its output is determined by the differential equation

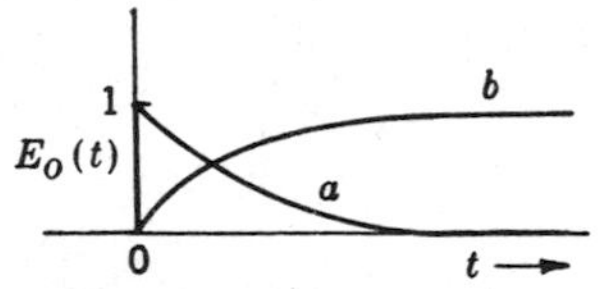

FIG. 2·5.—The normal response of the circuit of Fig. 2·1 with $T = 1$ (a) to a unit-impulse input at $t = 0$ and (b) to a unit-step input starting at $t = 0$.

$$T_1\frac{dE_O}{dt} + E_O = T_1\frac{dE_I}{dt}, \tag{30}$$

where

$$T_1 = RC. \tag{31}$$

The normal-response solution of this equation for an input E_I that begins after time $t = 0$ is

$$E_O(t) = E_I(t) - \frac{1}{T_1}\int_0^t d\tau\, E_I(\tau)e^{-\frac{t-\tau}{T_1}} \tag{32}$$

as can be verified by substitution into Eq. (30). The response of this filter to the impulse input

$$E_I(t) = \delta(t - t_0), \qquad t_0 > 0, \tag{33}$$

is then

$$E_O(t) = \delta(t - t_0) - \frac{1}{T_1} e^{-\frac{t-t_0}{T_1}}; \tag{34}$$

it follows that

$$W(t) = \delta(t) - \frac{1}{T_1} e^{-\frac{t}{T_1}}, \qquad (t \geqq 0). \tag{35}$$

In the discussion that follows we shall consider the weighting function $W(t)$ as a primary characteristic of a filter rather than as a derived quantity to be obtained, say, by solution of a differential equation. Experimentally, it is sometimes practical to obtain the weighting function by recording the response of the filter when a large input is suddenly applied and removed. (It is, of course, essential that this input should not overload the system.) When this is done, the time duration of the input pulse Δt should be short compared with any of the natural periods of the filter; that is, one should have

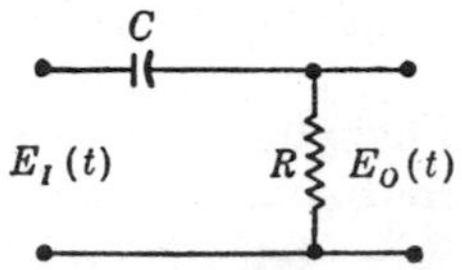

FIG. 2·6.—An RC-filter with a delta-function term in the weighting function.

$$\Delta t \frac{dW(t)}{dt} \ll W(t) \tag{36}$$

for all t. Otherwise, small variations in $W(t)$ may be obscured. An alternative method for the experimental determination of $W(t)$ will be indicated in Sec. 2·7.

2·5. Normal Response of a Linear Filter to an Arbitrary Input.—The normal response of a linear filter to an arbitrary bounded input $E_I(t)$ with at most a finite number of discontinuities can be conveniently expressed in terms of the response to a unit-impulse input. We shall assume that $E_I(t) = 0$ when $t < 0$. This function can be approximated by a set of rectangles as shown in Fig. 2·7. In computing its effect on the filter output, the portion of the input represented by a very narrow rectangle of width Δt_1 and height $E_I(t_1)$, at mean time t_1, can be approximated by the impulse input $E_I(t_1)\,\Delta t_1\,\delta(t - t_1)$; the ability of a filter with a finite response time to distinguish between a true impulse input and a pulse of duration Δt with the same time integral diminishes as Δt approaches zero. One is thus led to approximate the input $E_I(t)$ by a sum of impulses:

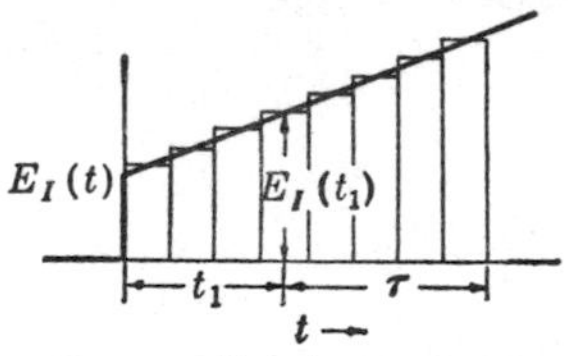

FIG. 2·7.—Approximation of a function $E_I(t)$ by a set of rectangles.

$$E_I(t) \approx \sum_n E_I(t_n)\,\Delta t_n\,\delta(t - t_n). \tag{37}$$

The normal response of a linear filter to a succession of impulse inputs will (by the definition of linearity) be the sum of the responses to each of these inputs. We have now to sum the responses to the incremental inputs of the rectangular decomposition of $E_I(t)$ given by Eq. (37); the resultant sum will approximate the normal response $E_O(t)$ to the input $E_I(t)$.

Let us first split off from the weighting function any delta-function singularities, writing

$$W(t) = W_0(t) + c_0\delta(t) + c_1\delta(t - \tau_1) + c_2\delta(t - \tau_2) + \cdots, + \tag{38}$$

where $0 < \tau_1 < \tau_2 < \ldots$, and $W_0(t)$ is a bounded but not necessarily continuous weighting function. To a unit-impulse input at time $t = 0$ this filter gives a bounded output $W_0(t)$, plus impulse outputs at times $t = 0, \tau_1, \tau_2, \ldots$, with relative magnitudes $c_0, c_1, c_2, \ldots$. These parts of the filter response can be considered separately.

The significance of the delta-function terms in the weighting function is easily appreciated. If there is a term $c_0\,\delta(t)$, the filter gives in response to an impulse input a simultaneous impulse output with magnitude changed by a factor c_0; in response to an arbitrary input $E_I(t)$ it gives an output $c_0E_I(t)$. Similarly, corresponding to the term $c_1\delta(t - \tau_1)$ in the weighting function there is a term $c_1E_I(t - \tau_1)$ in the response to the input $E_I(t)$.

Now let us consider the part of the filter response associated with the bounded function $W_0(t)$. This part of the response to an impulse input $\delta(t - t_1)$ at time t_1 is given by $W_0(t - t_1)$; the response to a differential input $E_I(t_1)\,\delta(t - t_1)\,\Delta t_1$ is thus $E_I(t_1)W_0(t - t_1)\,\Delta t_1$, and the corresponding response of the filter to the approximate input [Eq. (37)] is

$$\sum_n E_I(t_n)W_0(t - t_n)\,\Delta t_n.$$

In the limit as the Δt's approach zero, this becomes

$$\int_0^\infty dt_1\,E_I(t_1)W_0(t - t_1),$$

the exact output due to the bounded part of the weighting function. Since $W_0(t)$ vanishes for negative values of the argument, we may take the upper limit of the integral at $t_1 = t$, and write

$$E_O(t) = c_0E_I(t) + c_1E_I(t - \tau_1) + \cdots + \int_0^t dt_1\,E_I(t_1)W_0(t - t_1). \tag{39}$$

This representation will be valid even when the input contains impulses occurring between the time 0 and t. A more compact and more generally useful form is

$$E_O(t) = \int_0^{t+} dt_1\, E_I(t_1) W(t - t_1). \tag{40}$$

Each delta-function term in the weighting function gives rise to one of the terms appearing before the integral sign in Eq. (39). When the weighting function contains the delta function $c_0\delta(t)$, it is necessary to indicate the upper limit of the integral as $t+$ (that is, t approached from above) in order to include the whole term $c_0E_I(t)$ in the response rather than just half of it. The more compact notation also requires that one write

$$\int_{t_2-\Delta}^{t_2+\Delta} dt_1\, \delta(t_1 - t_2)\, \delta(t - t_1) = \delta(t - t_2) \tag{41}$$

when there are delta functions in both the input and weighting functions.

On introduction of the new variable of integration

$$\tau = t - t_1, \tag{42}$$

we have

$$E_O(t) = \int_{0-}^{t} d\tau\, E_I(t - \tau) W(\tau). \tag{43}$$

This gives the normal response to an arbitrary input as an integral over the past values of the input, each of these values being weighted by the response of the filter to a unit-impulse function.

Equation (9*b*) illustrates this result in a special case in which $W(t)$ is given by Eq. (29); Eq. (9*a*) is similarly a special case of Eq. (40).

2·6. The Weighting Function.—The weighting function provides a complete characterization of the filter. As we have seen, the normal response to any input can be computed by means of the weighting function. In addition, from the weighting function of a lumped-constant filter one can determine the normal modes of the filter, these being the terms of the form $t^k e^{p_i t}$ into which $W(t)$ can be resolved.

The weighting function expresses quite directly what may be called the "memory" of the filter, that is, the extent to which the distant past of the input affects the response at any time. This is evident in the width of the weighting function; the "memory" may be termed long or short according to whether the weighting function is broad or narrow.

The "memory" determines the distortion with which the filter output reproduces the input to the filter; the filter will reproduce well an input that changes but little within the length of the memory of the filter, but it will distort and smooth out changes in the input that take place in a period small compared with the memory. Another aspect of the memory is the *lag* introduced by the filter. If the input is suddenly changed to a new value, the output acquires the corresponding new value only after a period of lag determined by the width of the weighting function.

Examples.—We have already examined the weighting functions of two simple *RC*-filters, as given by Eqs. (29) and (35).

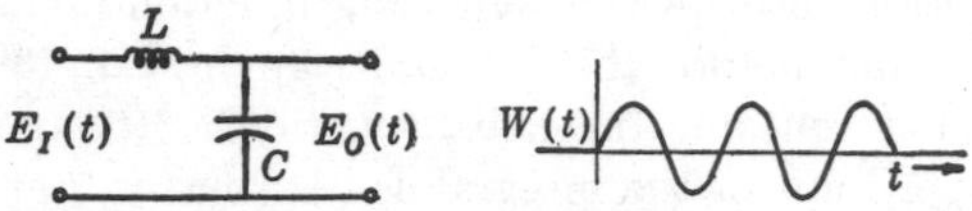

FIG. 2·8.—(*a*) An *LC*-filter; (*b*) the weighting function of the circuit shown in (*a*).

The differential equation for a filter consisting of an inductance L and capacity C, as shown in Fig. 2·8*a*, is

$$\left(\frac{d^2}{dt^2} + \omega_n^2\right) E_O = \omega_n^2 E_I, \qquad \omega_n^2 = \frac{1}{LC}. \tag{44}$$

The weighting function is sinusoidal for $t > 0$, with the angular frequency ω_n:

$$W(t) = \omega_n \sin \omega_n t; \tag{45}$$

this is sketched in Fig. 2·8*b*.

A filter with feedback, such as the servo illustrated in Fig. 1·3, may be governed by the differential equation

$$\left(T\frac{d^2}{dt^2} + \frac{d}{dt} + K\right)\theta_O = K\theta_I, \tag{46}$$

where K is a constant. The weighting function for this filter will be derived by application of Laplace transform methods in Sec. 2·17. The results are as follows. Let

$$\omega_n^2 = \frac{K}{T}, \tag{47a}$$

$$\zeta = \frac{1}{2(KT)^{1/2}}. \tag{47b}$$

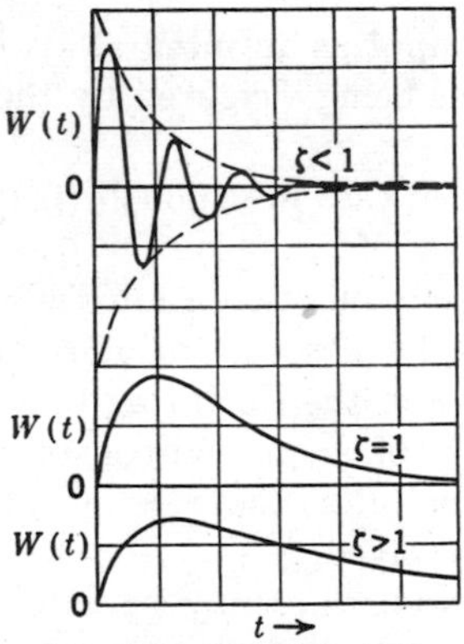

FIG. 2·9.—Weighting function of a simple servomechanism for different relative values of the constants.

The quantities ω_n and ζ are called the undamped natural frequency and the damping ratio, respectively. When $\zeta < 1$, the system is underdamped, and the weighting function is

$$W(t) = \frac{\omega_n}{(1 - \zeta^2)^{1/2}} e^{-\zeta\omega_n t} \sin [(1 - \zeta^2)^{1/2}\omega_n t]. \tag{48}$$

When $\zeta = 1$, the system is critically damped; the weighting function is

$$W(t) = \omega_n^2 te^{-\omega_n t}. \tag{49}$$

When $\zeta > 1$, the system is overdamped, and

$$W(t) = \frac{\omega_n}{2(\zeta^2 - 1)^{1/2}} e^{-\zeta\omega_n t}[e^{(\zeta^2-1)^{1/2}\omega_n t} - e^{-(\zeta^2-1)^{1/2}\omega_n t}]. \tag{50}$$

These three forms of the weighting function are illustrated in Fig. 2·9.

2·7. Normal Response to a Unit-step Input.—The unit-step function $u(t)$ is defined as follows:

$$\left.\begin{aligned} u(t) &= 0 \qquad \text{if } t < 0, \\ u(t) &= 1 \qquad \text{if } t \geqq 0. \end{aligned}\right\} \tag{51}$$

The normal response of a filter to a unit-step input is closely related to its weighting function. In particular, the normal response to a unit step at time $t = 0$ is, by Eq. (43),

$$U(t) = \int_{0-}^{t} d\tau\, W(\tau). \tag{52}$$

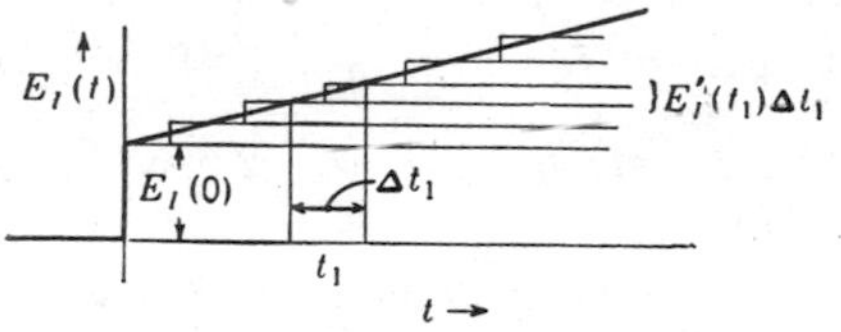

FIG. 2·10.—Approximation of a function $E_I(t)$ by a set of step functions.

Just as the unit-step function is the integral of the unit-impulse function, so the response to a unit-step input is the integral of the response to the unit-impulse input. Conversely, the weighting function of a filter can be determined experimentally as the derivative of the output produced by a unit-step input. The form of the function $U(t)$ for the RC-filter of Fig. 2·1 is illustrated in Fig. 2·5.

Let us assume that both $E_I(t)$ and $W(t)$ are well-behaved functions, with $E_I(t)$ making an abrupt jump from the value 0 to $E_I(0)$ at time $t = 0$. Integrating Eq. (43) by parts, we obtain

$$E_O(t) = E_I(t - \tau)U(\tau)\Big|_{0-}^{t} - \int_{0-}^{t} d\tau \left(\frac{d}{d\tau} E_I(t - \tau)\right)U(\tau), \tag{53a}$$

$$E_O(t) = E_I(0)U(t) + \int_{0-}^{t} d\tau\, E_I'(t - \tau)U(\tau), \tag{53b}$$

$$E_O(t) = E_I(0)U(t) + \int_{0}^{t+} dt_1 E_I'(t_1)U(t - t_1), \tag{53c}$$

where the prime is used to denote the derivative with respect to the indicated argument. The output of the filter is here expressed as the sum of responses to the step functions into which the arbitrary input can be resolved (see Fig. 2·10): an initial step of magnitude $E_I(0)$ at time $t = 0$ and a continuous distribution of infinitesimal steps of aggregate amount $E_I'(t_1)\,\Delta t_1$ in the interval Δt_1 about the time t_1. The corresponding forms of the relation when E_I has other discontinuities or U increases stepwise (W contains delta functions) will need no discussion here.

2·8. Stable and Unstable Filters.—Thus far in the discussion of the weighting function we have made no distinction between *stable* and *unstable* filters. This was possible only because attention was restricted to input functions that differ from zero only after some finite time. To proceed further we must define stable and unstable filters. A *stable* filter is one in which every bounded input produces a bounded output; that is, the normal response of a stable filter never becomes infinitely large unless the input does so. An *unstable* filter will give an indefinitely increasing response to some particular bounded input, though not, in general, to all such inputs.

The weighting function affords a means of determining whether a given filter is stable or unstable, through the following criterion: *A linear filter is stable if and only if the integral of the absolute value of the weighting function,* $\int_{0-}^{\infty} d\tau\, |W(\tau)|$, *is finite.* Thus, the second of the filters mentioned in Sec. 2·6 is unstable, since $\int_{0}^{\infty} d\tau\, |\sin \omega_0\tau|$ does not converge.

To prove that the convergence of this integral assures the stability of the filter we need to show that if $E_I(t)$ is bounded, that is, if there is a constant M such that $|E_I(t)| < M$ for all t, then $E_O(t)$ is also bounded. The filter output may be written

$$E_O(t) = \int_{0-}^{t} d\tau\, E_I(t - \tau)W(\tau), \tag{43}$$

since we restrict our attention to E_I's that are zero for negative values of the argument. As the absolute value of an integral is certainly no greater than the integral of the absolute value of the integrand, we have

$$|E_O(t)| \leqq \int_{0-}^{t} d\tau\, |E_I(t - \tau)||W(\tau)|. \tag{54}$$

The inequality is strengthened by putting in the upper bound for $E_I(t)$ and extending the range of integration:

$$|E_O(t)| \leqq M \int_{0-}^{\infty} d\tau\, |W(\tau)|. \tag{55}$$

Thus, if $\int_{0-}^{\infty} d\tau\, |W(\tau)|$ exists, $E_O(t)$ is bounded.

The proof of the second part of the stability criterion—that the filter is unstable if $\int_{0-}^{\infty} d\tau\, |W(\tau)|$ does not converge—is somewhat longer and will be omitted here. It involves the construction of an input $E_I(t)$ that will make $E_O(t)$ increase without limit, and is essentially the same as the corresponding proof given, in the case of pulsed filters, in Sec. 5·3.

The relation of this result to the earlier discussion (Sec. 2·2) of the stability of linear lumped-constant filters is easily understood. We have noted (Sec. 2·4) that the weighting function of such a filter is a linear combination of its normal-mode functions,

$$W(t) = c_0\,\delta(t) + c_1h_1(t) + c_2h_2(t) + \cdots + c_nh_n(t), \tag{56}$$

the h's being given by Eq. (11). Now the integral $\int_0^\infty |h_i(t)|\,dt$ will not converge for any normal-mode function h_i that has $\alpha_i \geqq 0$, nor can one form any linear combination of these functions for which such an integral converges. Thus the integral $\int_{0-}^\infty |W(t)|\,dt$ will converge if, and only if, the weighting function contains no normal-mode function for which $\alpha_i \geqq 0$. Stability of the filter is thus assured if all the roots of Eq. (13b) have negative real parts, in accord with the ideas of Sec. 2·2. On the other hand, the filter may be stable even when there exist roots with nonnegative real parts if the corresponding undamped normal modes do not appear in the weighting function, that is, if they are not excited by an impulse input. Since any input can be expressed as a sum of impulse inputs, this is sufficient to assure that no undamped modes can be excited by any input whatever. The convergence of $\int_{0-}^\infty |W(\tau)|\,d\tau$ as a criterion of the stability of a filter is thus precise and complete; in effect, it offers a method of determining what normal modes of a filter can be excited—not merely what modes can conceivably exist.

Only when a filter is stable is it possible to speak with full generality of its response to an input that starts indefinitely far in the past. We have seen that for a bounded input $E_I(t)$ which vanishes for $t < 0$, the normal response is

$$E_O(t) = \int_{0-}^{t} E_I(t - \tau)W(\tau)\,d\tau. \tag{43}$$

If E_I has nonzero values when the argument is less than zero, the upper limit of integration must be correspondingly extended; if the input began in the indefinitely remote past, we must write

$$E_O(t) = \int_{0-}^{\infty} E_I(t - \tau)W(\tau)\,d\tau. \tag{57}$$

If the filter is stable—and hence if $\int_{0-}^\infty |W(\tau)|\,d\tau < \infty$—then the integral in Eq. (57) will converge for any bounded input. If, however, this extension of the limit is attempted in the case of an unstable filter, the resulting integral may not converge. This corresponds, of course, to the possibility that an unstable filter subject to an arbitrary input in the indefinitely remote past may give, at any finite time, an infinitely large output.

We shall therefore apply Eq. (57) only in the treatment of stable filters; in dealing with linear filters in general, and unstable ones in particular, it will be necessary to use an equation of the form of Eq. (43) and only inputs that start at a finite time.

THE FREQUENCY-RESPONSE FUNCTION

To this point we have considered the response of a linear filter to two special types of inputs—impulse and step inputs—and the related weighting function by which the filter may be characterized. We now turn our attention to another special type of input—the pure sinusoidal input—and the related frequency-response function, which also serves to characterize any *stable* linear filter.

We shall see that the response of a stable filter to a pure sinusoidal input function is also sinusoidal, with the same frequency but generally different amplitude and phase. The frequency-response function expresses the relative amplitude and phase of input and output as functions of frequency. It is defined only for *stable* filters, since a pure sinusoidal input must start indefinitely far in the past and can thus be considered only in connection with a stable filter. [The input

$$\left.\begin{aligned} E_I(t) &= 0, \qquad & t < 0, \\ E_I(t) &= A \sin \omega_0 t, \qquad & t > 0, \end{aligned}\right\} \tag{58}$$

which might be applied to an unstable filter, is not a pure sinusoid but a superposition of sinusoids with angular frequencies in a band about ω_0.]

The importance of the frequency-response function rests on the fact that any function subject to certain relatively mild restrictions can be written as the sum of sinusoidal oscillations (Sec. 2·11). The response of a linear filter can be expressed as a similar sum of responses to the sinusoidal components of the input by means of the frequency-response function, which relates corresponding components of input and output.

2·9. Response of a Stable Filter to a Sinusoidal Input.—In dealing with sinusoidal inputs and outputs it is convenient to use the complex exponential notation. The general sinusoidal function of angular frequency ω can be represented by a linear combination of the functions $\sin \omega t$ and $\cos \omega t$ or, more compactly, by $a \cos (\omega t + \phi)$, where a is the amplitude and ϕ the phase with respect to some reference time. An even more compact notation is obtained by representing this sinusoid by the complex exponential

$$Ae^{j\omega t} = ae^{j\phi}e^{j\omega t}, \tag{59}$$

of which $a \cos (\omega t + \phi)$ is the real part. Here phase and amplitude are represented together by the complex factor $A = ae^{j\phi}$, of which a is the magnitude and ϕ the phase. A change of amplitude by a factor b, together with a change of phase by $\Delta\phi$, is then represented by multiplication of the complex exponential by the complex number $be^{j\Delta\phi}$; this changes the multiplier of $e^{j\omega t}$ to $abe^{j(\phi+\Delta\phi)}$ and the real part of the whole expression to $ab \cos(\omega t + \phi + \Delta\phi)$.

When a complex function is used to denote a filter input, a complex expression for the output will result. Because of the linear property of the filter, the real part of this complex output is the response of the filter to the real part of the complex input, and similarly for the imaginary parts of input and output. It is thus easy to interpret in real form the results obtained by considering complex inputs.

Use of the complex notation makes it easy to prove that a sinusoidal input to a *stable* filter gives rise to a sinusoidal output. Let

$$E_I(t) = Ae^{j\omega t}. \tag{60}$$

Then, by Eq. (57), we have

$$E_O(t) = A \int_{0-}^{\infty} d\tau\, e^{j\omega(t-\tau)} W(\tau) \tag{60a}$$

$$= Ae^{j\omega t} \int_{0-}^{\infty} d\tau\, e^{-j\omega\tau} W(\tau), \tag{60b}$$

where $W(\tau)$ is the weighting factor of the filter. For reasons that will be evident later we shall denote the convergent integral in Eq. (60*b*) by $Y(j\omega)$:

$$Y(j\omega) = \int_{0-}^{\infty} d\tau\, e^{-j\omega\tau} W(\tau). \tag{61}$$

Then

$$E_O(t) = AY(j\omega)e^{j\omega t}. \tag{62}$$

Thus the filter output is sinusoidal in time; it differs from the input by a constant complex factor $Y(j\omega)$. For unstable filters the integral in Eq. (61) will, in general, not converge.

Considered as a function of the angular frequency, $Y(j\omega)$ is called the *frequency-response function.* This function expresses the amplitude and phase difference between a sinusoidal input at angular frequency ω and the response of the filter. The input amplitude is multiplied by the factor

$$|Y(j\omega)| = [Y(j\omega)Y^*(j\omega)]^{1/2}, \tag{63}$$

and the phase is increased by

$$\phi = \tan^{-1} \frac{1}{j} \left[\frac{Y(j\omega) - Y^*(j\omega)}{Y(j\omega) + Y^*(j\omega)} \right], \tag{64}$$

where the asterisk denotes the complex conjugate.

Experimentally, the frequency-response function of a filter can be determined by comparing the amplitude and phase of sinusoidal inputs at various frequencies with the amplitude and phase of the corresponding outputs. In order to compensate for the fact that any real input starts at a finite time, it is necessary to regard as the response only that part of the output in which the amplitude and phase do not change with time, that is, the so-called "steady-state response."

2·10. Frequency-response Function of a Lumped-constant Filter.—The frequency-response function of a lumped-constant filter is easily determined from the differential equation of the filter. In this equation

$$a_n \frac{d^nE_O}{dt^n} + a_{n-1}\frac{d^{n-1}E_O}{dt^{n-1}} + \cdots + a_0E_O = b_m\frac{d^mE_I}{dt^m} + b_{m-1}\frac{d^{m-1}E_I}{dt^{m-1}} + \cdots + b_0E_I, \quad (2)$$

we may set

$$\left.\begin{aligned} E_I &= e^{j\omega t}, \\ E_O &= Y(j\omega)e^{j\omega t}. \end{aligned}\right\} \quad (65)$$

We have then, on carrying out the differentiations,

$$[a_n(j\omega)^n + a_{n-1}(j\omega)^{n-1} + \cdots + a_0]Y(j\omega)e^{j\omega t} = [b_m(j\omega)^m + b_{m-1}(j\omega)^{m-1} + \cdots + b_0]e^{j\omega t}, \quad (66)$$

whence

$$Y(j\omega) = \frac{b_m(j\omega)^m + b_{m-1}(j\omega)^{m-1} + \cdots + b_0}{a_n(j\omega)^n + a_{n-1}(j\omega)^{n-1} + \cdots + a_0}. \quad (67)$$

The frequency-response function of such a filter is thus a rational function, the ratio of two polynomials in $j\omega$ with coefficients that appear directly in the differential equation.

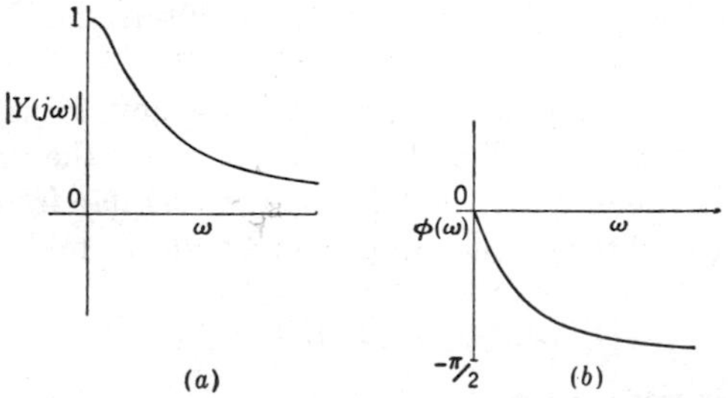

FIG. 2·11.—(a) The amplitude amplification and (b) the phase shift of the circuit of Fig. 2·1.

As examples we may take the two stable filters considered in Sec. 2·6. For the simple RC-filter of Fig. 2·1 we have, on reading the required coefficients from Eq. (1),

$$Y(j\omega) = \frac{1}{j\omega T + 1} \quad (68)$$

The amplitude amplification and phase shift are

$$|Y(j\omega)| = (1 + \omega^2T^2)^{-\frac{1}{2}}, \tag{69a}$$
$$\phi = \tan^{-1}(-\omega T); \tag{69b}$$

these functions are plotted in Fig. 2·11.

The frequency-response function of the simple servomechanism described by Eq. (46) is

$$Y(j\omega) = \frac{K}{(K - T\omega^2) + j\omega} = \frac{\omega_n^2}{(\omega_n^2 - \omega^2) + 2\zeta\omega_n j\omega}. \tag{70}$$

The amplitude amplification and phase shift are

$$|Y(j\omega)| = \left[\left(1 - \frac{\omega^2}{\omega_n^2}\right)^2 + 4\zeta^2\frac{\omega^2}{\omega_n^2}\right]^{-\frac{1}{2}}, \tag{71a}$$

$$\phi = -\tan^{-1}\frac{2\zeta\left(\frac{\omega}{\omega_n}\right)}{1 - \left(\frac{\omega}{\omega_n}\right)^2}; \tag{71b}$$

these quantities are plotted as functions of ω in Fig. 2·12, for $\zeta = \frac{1}{2}$.

2·11. The Fourier Integral.—We have now to consider how an arbitrary input can be expressed as a sum or integral of sinusoidal components.

The representation of a periodic function by a Fourier series[1] will be assumed to be familiar to the reader. Any function $g(t)$ that is periodic in time with period T, is of bounded variation in the interval

$$\frac{-T}{2} < t \leq \frac{T}{2},$$

and is properly defined at points of discontinuity can be expressed as an infinite sum of sinusoidal terms with frequencies that are integral multiples of the fundamental frequency

$$f_1 = \frac{1}{T}. \tag{72}$$

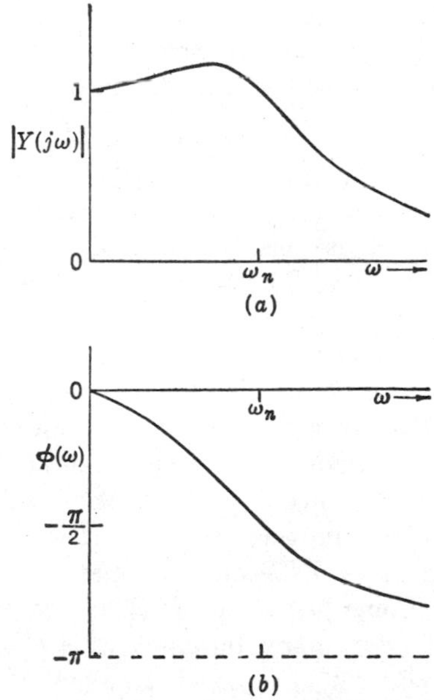

FIG. 2·12.—(*a*) The amplitude amplification and (*b*) the phase shift of a simple servomechanism, as given by Eqs. (71) with $\zeta = \frac{1}{2}$.

[1] A. Zygmund, *Trigonometrical Series*, Zsubwenczi Funduszu Kultury Narodowej, Warsaw-Lwow, 1935; E. T. Whittaker and G. N. Watson, *Modern Analysis*, Macmillan, New York, 1943.

In terms of complex exponentials one can write

$$g(t) = \sum_{n=-\infty}^{+\infty} a_n e^{2\pi i f_1 n t}, \tag{73a}$$

where the coefficients a_n are given by

$$a_n = \frac{1}{T} \int_{-T/2}^{T/2} dt\, g(t) e^{-2\pi i f_1 n t}. \tag{73b}$$

When the function $g(t)$ is not periodic but satisfies other conditions—the convergence of $\int_{-\infty}^{+\infty} dt\, |g(t)|$ is sufficient—it is possible to represent the function, not by a sum of terms with discrete frequencies nf_1, but by a sum of terms with all frequencies f:

$$g(t) = \int_{-\infty}^{+\infty} df\, A(f) e^{2\pi i f t}. \tag{74a}$$

This integral will often converge only in a special sense. The function $A(f)$, which gives the phase and relative amplitude of the component with frequency f, can be computed by means of the formula

$$A(f) = \int_{-\infty}^{+\infty} dt\, g(t) e^{-2\pi i f t}. \tag{74b}$$

Equations (74) provide an extension of Eqs. (73) for the limit as $T \to \infty$. The reader is referred to standard texts[1] for a complete discussion. It will suffice here to show that the extension is plausible. It is obvious that we can construct a function $h(t)$ that is periodic with the period T and is identical with $g(t)$ in the interval $(-T/2 < t \leq T/2)$. Moreover, this can be done however large the (finite) fundamental period T is made. For each value of T, Eqs. (73*a*) and (73*b*) hold, with $h(t)$ in the place of $g(t)$. It is plausible to assume that these equations hold in the limit as $T \to \infty$. If we set $f = n/T$, $df = 1/T$, and $Ta_n = A(f)$, then as T becomes infinite $h(t)$ becomes $g(t)$, and Eqs. (73*a*) and (73*b*) become Eqs. (74*a*) and (74*b*) respectively.

For many purposes it is convenient to express the Fourier integral relations in terms of the angular frequency $\omega = 2\pi f$. With this change of variable, Eq. (74*a*) becomes

$$g(t) = \frac{1}{2\pi} \int_{-\infty}^{+\infty} d\omega\, A\left(\frac{\omega}{2\pi}\right) e^{i\omega t}. \tag{75}$$

[1] E. C. Titchmarsh, *Introduction to the Theory of the Fourier Integrals*, Clarendon Press, Oxford, 1937.

As an alternative form, we shall write

$$g(t) = \frac{1}{2\pi} \int_{-\infty}^{+\infty} d\omega \, G(j\omega) e^{j\omega t}, \tag{76a}$$

where

$$G(j\omega) = \int_{-\infty}^{+\infty} dt \, g(t) e^{-j\omega t}. \tag{76b}$$

Considered as a function of the real angular frequency ω, $G(j\omega)$ will be termed the *Fourier transform* of $g(t)$.

It is clear that $A(f)$ and $G(j\omega)$ are in a sense both Fourier transforms of $g(t)$, since they represent the same function of frequency. They are, however, different functions of their indicated arguments, with

$$A(f) = G(2\pi jf). \tag{77}$$

In this chapter we shall hereafter deal only with the representation $G(j\omega)$, in order to proceed conveniently from the Fourier transform to the Laplace transform.

It should be noted that if $g(t)$ is an even function of t, $g(-t) = g(t)$, then

$$G(j\omega) = 2 \int_0^\infty dt \, g(t) \cos \omega t. \tag{78a}$$

It follows that $G(\omega)$ is an even real-valued function of ω and that $g(t)$ can be written as

$$g(t) = \frac{1}{\pi} \int_0^\infty d\omega \, G(j\omega) \cos \omega t. \tag{78b}$$

If $g(t)$ is an odd function of t, $g(-t) = -g(t)$, then

$$G(j\omega) = 2j \int_0^\infty dt \, g(t) \sin \omega t. \tag{79a}$$

Since $G(j\omega)$ is then an *odd* function of ω, one can write

$$g(t) = \frac{j}{\pi} \int_0^\infty d\omega \, G(j\omega) \sin \omega t. \tag{79b}$$

As an example of the Fourier integral representation, let us consider the function

$$g(t) = e^{-a|t|}, \tag{80a}$$

shown in Fig. 2·13*a*. Then by Eq. (76*b*)

$$\begin{aligned} G(j\omega) &= \int_{-\infty}^{+\infty} dt \, e^{-a|t| - j\omega t} \\ &= \int_{-\infty}^{0} dt \, e^{(-j\omega + a)t} + \int_0^\infty dt \, e^{-(j\omega + a)t} \\ &= \frac{1}{a - j\omega} + \frac{1}{a + j\omega}. \end{aligned} \tag{81}$$

Thus

$$G(j\omega) = \frac{2a}{a^2 + \omega^2}; \tag{80b}$$

this function is plotted in Fig. 2·13*b*. The Fourier integral representation of the given function is, by Eq. (76*a*),

$$e^{-a|t|} = \int_{-\infty}^{+\infty} d\omega \, \frac{a/\pi}{a^2 + \omega^2} \, e^{j\omega t}. \tag{82}$$

The validity of this representation can be proved by evaluating the integral, for instance, by the method of residues.[1] As a brief review of

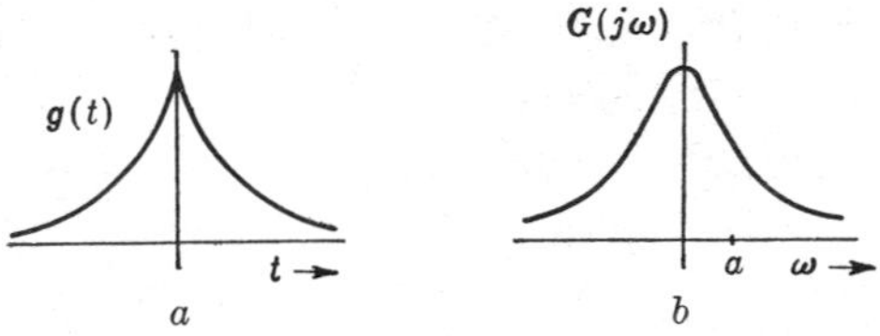

FIG. 2·13.—(*a*) Plot of the function $g(t) = e^{-a|t|}$; (*b*) the Fourier transform of the function $g(t)$.

the method of residues, this evaluation will be carried through in some detail. It is convenient for this purpose to change the variable of integration from ω to $j\omega$ or, more precisely, to introduce the complex variable

$$p = \alpha + j\omega, \tag{83}$$

of which $j\omega$ is the imaginary part, and to replace the integral over real values of ω by an integral over pure imaginary values of p. The integral of Eq. (82) then becomes

$$\int_{-\infty}^{\infty} d\omega \, \frac{a/\pi}{a^2 + \omega^2} \, e^{j\omega t} = \frac{a}{\pi j} \int_{-j\infty}^{j\infty} dp \, \frac{1}{a^2 - p^2} \, e^{pt}, \tag{84}$$

with the path of integration along the imaginary axis in the p-plane, as shown in Fig. 2·14.

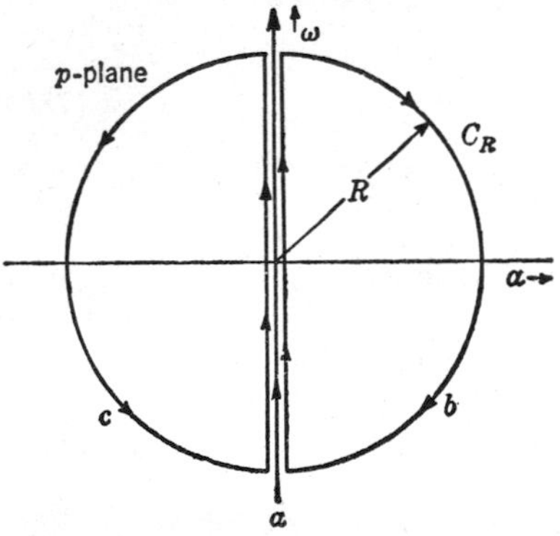

FIG. 2·14.—Paths of integration in the complex p-plane. (*a*) Path of integration $(-j\infty, j\infty)$; (*b*), (*c*) paths of integration for use of method of residues.

By resolving the integrand into partial fractions, the integral in Eq. (84) can be brought into the form

$$\int_{-\infty}^{\infty} d\omega \, \frac{a/\pi}{a^2 + \omega^2} \, e^{j\omega t} = \frac{1}{2\pi j} \int_{-j\infty}^{j\infty} dp \left(\frac{1}{p + a} - \frac{1}{p - a} \right) e^{pt}. \tag{85}$$

[1] See E. C. Titchmarsh, *The Theory of Functions*, Oxford, New York, 1932.

It remains, therefore, to evaluate expressions of the form

$$I = \frac{1}{2\pi j} \int_{-j\infty}^{j\infty} dp \frac{1}{p - a} e^{pt}. \tag{86}$$

We now apply the method of residues. If $t < 0$, the integrand approaches zero as $|p| \to \infty$ in the right half of the p-plane; in fact, it can be shown that the line integral along the semicircle C_R of radius R in the right half plane approaches zero as R becomes infinite. Let us then consider the line integral of this integrand around the closed contour (b) of Fig. 2·14. This consists of two parts: the integral along the imaginary axis from $-jR$ to $+jR$ and the integral around the semicircle C_R:

$$I(R) = \frac{1}{2\pi j} \oint dp \frac{1}{p - a} e^{pt} = \frac{1}{2\pi j} \left(\int_{-jR}^{+jR} + \int_{C_R} \right) dp \frac{1}{p - a} e^{pt}. \tag{87a}$$

As $R \to \infty$, the second integral tends to zero, and the first approaches the integral I of Eq. (86). Thus

$$I = \lim_{R\to\infty} I(R) = \lim_{R\to\infty} \frac{1}{2\pi j} \oint dp \frac{1}{p - a} e^{pt}; \tag{87b}$$

the desired line integral can be evaluated as the limit of a contour integral. Now the integral around the closed contour is equal to $2\pi j$ times the sum of the residues of the integrand at all poles enclosed by the contour, taken with a minus sign because the integration is in the clockwise sense. As $R \to \infty$, the contour (b) of Fig. 2·14 will come to enclose all poles in the right half plane. If a has a positive real part the integrand has a pole in the right half plane, and

$$I = -\frac{1}{2\pi j} 2\pi j e^{at} = -e^{at} \qquad [t < 0,\ Re(a) > 0].^{1} \tag{88a}$$

If a has a negative real part, there is no such pole, and

$$I = 0, \qquad [t < 0,\ Re(a) < 0]. \tag{88b}$$

Since the a of Eq. (85) is a positive real quantity, the first term contributes nothing to the integral, and

$$\int_{-\infty}^{+\infty} d\omega \frac{a/\pi}{a^2 + \omega^2} e^{j\omega t} = e^{at} = e^{-a|t|}, \qquad (t < 0). \tag{89}$$

If $t > 0$, the integrand of Eq. (86) approaches zero as $|p| \to \infty$ in the left half plane. By arguments similar to those above, the desired integral is equal to the integral around the contour (c) of Fig. 2·14, in the limit as $R \to \infty$. This is in turn equal to $2\pi j$ times the sum of the

[1] The symbol $Re(a)$ denotes the real part of a.

residues in the left half plane, taken with a plus sign because the integration is in the counter clockwise sense. Thus

$$I = 0, \qquad [t > 0, Re(a) > 0], \tag{90a}$$
$$I = e^{at}, \qquad [t > 0, Re(a) < 0]. \tag{90b}$$

In Eq. (85) the second term contributes nothing to the integral, and

$$\int_{-\infty}^{+\infty} d\omega \frac{a/\pi}{a^2 + \omega^2} e^{j\omega t} = e^{-at} = e^{-a|t|}, \qquad (t > 0). \tag{91}$$

On combining these results, one verifies the truth of Eq. (82).

2·12. Response of a Stable Filter to an Arbitrary Input.—Let us consider the response of a stable linear filter to an input $g_I(t)$ with Fourier transform $G_I(j\omega)$. Then

$$g_I(t) = \frac{1}{2\pi} \int_{-\infty}^{+\infty} d\omega\, G_I(j\omega) e^{j\omega t}. \tag{92}$$

Since the response of the filter to an input $e^{j\omega t}$ is the output $Y(j\omega)e^{j\omega t}$, it follows from the linear property of the filter that its response to the input $g_I(t)$ is the output

$$g_O(t) = \frac{1}{2\pi} \int_{-\infty}^{+\infty} d\omega\, G_I(j\omega) Y(j\omega) e^{j\omega t}. \tag{93}$$

It is evident that the Fourier transform of the filter output is

$$G_O(j\omega) = Y(j\omega) G_I(j\omega). \tag{94}$$

That is, *the Fourier transform of the filter output is equal to the Fourier transform of the input multiplied by the frequency-response function of the filter.*

2·13. Relation between the Weighting Function and the Frequency-response Function.—The relation between the frequency-response function of a stable filter and the weighting function has been stated in Sec. 2·9:

$$Y(j\omega) = \int_{0-}^{\infty} d\tau\, e^{-j\omega\tau} W(\tau). \tag{61}$$

Since $W(\tau)$ vanishes for $\tau < 0$, we may write

$$Y(j\omega) = \int_{-\infty}^{+\infty} d\tau\, e^{-j\omega\tau} W(\tau). \tag{95}$$

The frequency-response function of a stable filter is the Fourier transform of the weighting function. It is important to note that this theorem is restricted to stable filters. For unstable filters the integral in Eq. (95) will, in general, not exist. The inverse of this relation is, of course,

$$W(t) = \frac{1}{2\pi} \int_{-\infty}^{+\infty} d\omega\, Y(j\omega) e^{j\omega t}. \tag{96}$$

The significance of this relation and the importance of the restriction to stable filters may be illustrated by a consideration of lumped-constant filters, for which the frequency-response function is

$$Y(j\omega) = \frac{b_m(j\omega)^m + b_{m-1}(j\omega)^{m-1} + \cdots + b_0}{a_n(j\omega)^n + a_{n-1}(j\omega)^{n-1} + \cdots + a_0}, \qquad (m \leqq n). \tag{67}$$

For simplicity, let us assume that the complex constants

$$p_i = \alpha_i + j\omega_i, \tag{14}$$

which are the roots of the equation

$$P(p) = a_n p^n + a_{n-1}p^{n-1} + \cdots + a_0, \tag{13b}$$

are all distinct. Then $Y(j\omega)$ can be expressed as a sum of partial fractions,

$$Y(j\omega) = C_0 + \frac{C_1}{j\omega - p_1} + \frac{C_2}{j\omega - p_2} + \cdots + \frac{C_n}{j\omega - p_n}, \tag{97}$$

where the constants C_i depend on the b's as well as on the a's. The constant C_0 will vanish unless $m = n$.

First, let us assume that all the p's have negative real parts—all normal modes of the filter are damped. Let us further assume that $m < n$. Then the filter is stable, and we should be able to compute $W(t)$ as

$$W(t) = \frac{1}{2\pi}\int_{-\infty}^{+\infty} d\omega \left(\frac{C_1}{j\omega - p_1} + \cdots + \frac{C_n}{j\omega - p_n}\right) e^{j\omega t}. \tag{98}$$

To evaluate this integral it is again convenient to introduce the complex variable

$$p = \alpha + j\omega, \tag{99}$$

of which $j\omega$ is the imaginary part. The integral of Eq. (98) then becomes

$$W(t) = \frac{1}{2\pi j}\int_{-j\infty}^{+j\infty} dp \left(\frac{C_1}{p - p_1} + \cdots + \frac{C_n}{p - p_n}\right) e^{pt}, \tag{100}$$

with the path of integration along the imaginary axis in the p-plane, as shown in (*a*) of Fig. 2·14. This integral can then be evaluated by the method of residues.

Following the procedure outlined in Sec. 2·11, if $t < 0$ we integrate around the contour (*b*) in Fig. 2·14. Since for the stable filter none of the poles of the integrand lie in the right half plane, it follows that

$$W(t) = 0, \qquad t < 0. \tag{101a}$$

If $t > 0$, we integrate around the contour (*c*) in Fig. 2·14. Each term $C_i/(p - p_i)$ contributes to the integral in this case, and we obtain

$$W(t) = C_1e^{p_1t} + C_2e^{p_2t} + \cdots + C_ne^{p_nt}, \qquad t > 0. \tag{101b}$$

Thus we have found that the weighting function is a sum of normal modes; in addition, we have a means of determining the constants C_n by resolution of the frequency response $Y(j\omega)$ into partial fractions.

These results for a stable filter are in accord with our earlier ideas about the weighting function. Now let us consider an unstable filter. We shall see that for such a filter the frequency response is *not* the Fourier transform of the weighting function; the assumption that it is will lead us to false results. We assume, then, that some of the p's have positive real part and that these p's appear in the resolution of $Y(j\omega)$ into partial fractions. Let us attempt to compute $W(t)$ by means of Eqs. (98) and (100). For $t < 0$ we no longer obtain $W(t) = 0$ but

$$W(t) = -\sum_{\substack{i \\ (\alpha_i > 0)}} C_i e^{p_i t}, \qquad (t < 0), \tag{102a}$$

a sum including a term for each p_i with positive real part. On the other hand, when $t > 0$, the contour of integration surrounds only poles with negative real part, and we obtain

$$W(t) = \sum_{\substack{i \\ (\alpha_i < 0)}} C_i e^{p_i t}, \qquad (t > 0). \tag{102b}$$

Both these results are erroneous: the weighting function must be zero for $t < 0$ and must include a normal mode with positive real part when $t > 0$.

2·14. Limitations of the Fourier Transform Analysis.—The Fourier transform techniques considered above are useful in the discussion of filters, but their applicability is limited by the fact that the Fourier transform is not defined for many quantities with which one may need to deal. We have just seen that the weighting function of an unstable filter does not have a Fourier transform. The same is true of many important types of filter input: the unit-step function, the pure sinusoid, the "constant-velocity function" $[x(t) = vt]$, the increasing exponential; for none of these functions does the integral of the absolute magnitude converge.

In some cases it is possible to extend the discussion by the introduction of convergence factors, which modify the functions sufficiently to cause the Fourier transform to exist but not so much as to hinder the interpretation of the results. This device is sometimes useful but may involve mathematical difficulties in the use of double-limiting processes.

A more generally satisfactory procedure is to make use of the Laplace transform. This is defined for functions that differ from zero only when $t > 0$ (that is, after some definite instant); it is defined for all practical filter inputs, for the normal responses to these inputs, and for the weighting functions of stable and unstable filters. The treatment of filters by Laplace transform methods is closely parallel to the discussion in terms of Fourier transforms, but its relative freedom from restrictions makes it decidedly the more powerful method.

THE LAPLACE TRANSFORM

The following discussion of the Laplace transform and its applications is necessarily limited in scope and detail. No attempt has been made to state theorems in their maximum generality. For a more extended treatment the reader must be referred elsewhere.[1]

2·15. Definition of the Laplace Transform.—Let $g(t)$ be a function defined for $t \geqq 0$, and let

$$|g(t)| \leqq Ke^{at} \tag{103}$$

for some positive constant a. Then the integral

$$F(p) = \int_0^\infty dt\, g(t)e^{-pt} \tag{104}$$

is absolutely convergent for all complex values of p such that the real part of p is greater than a. Considered as a function of the complex variable p, $F(p)$ is termed the Laplace transform of $g(t)$; it may be denoted also by

$$\mathfrak{L}[g(t)] = \int_0^\infty dt\, g(t)e^{-pt}, \tag{105}$$

the argument p being understood. If a is the greatest lower bound of real constants for which $g(t)$ satisfies an inequality of the form of Eq. (103), the Laplace transform of $g(t)$ converges absolutely in the half plane to the right of $p = a$; a is called the *abscissa of absolute convergence*. The region of definition of $\mathfrak{L}[g(t)]$ can usually be extended by analytic continuation to include the entire p-plane, except for the points at which $F(p)$ is singular. In what follows, this extension of the domain of definition will be assumed.

The Laplace transformation can be defined for certain types of functions that do not satisfy Eq. (103). In what follows we shall consider only functions that contain a finite number of delta-function singularities, in addition to a part satisfying Eq. (103). When one of these delta functions occurs at $t = 0$, we shall define the Laplace transform as

$$\mathfrak{L}[g(t)] = \int_{0-}^\infty dt\, g(t)e^{-pt}. \tag{106}$$

[1] G. Doetsch, *Theorie und Anwendung der Laplace Transformation*, Springer, Berlin, 1937; H. S. Carslaw and J. C. Jaeger, *Operational Methods in Applied Mathematics*, Oxford, New York, 1941; D. V. Widder, *The Laplace Transform*, Princeton University Press, Princeton, N. J., 1941.

This extension of the definition of the Laplace transform is necessary, in view of the two-sided character of the delta function, to assure that

$$\lim_{t_0 \to 0} \mathfrak{L}[g(t - |t_0|)] = \mathfrak{L}[g(t)]. \tag{107}$$

For pure imaginary values of p, $p = j\omega$, the Laplace transform of a function $g(t)$ that is identically zero for $t < 0$ becomes its Fourier transform—if this exists. Thus the Laplace transform is, in a sense, a generalization of the Fourier transform [Eq. (76b)] applicable when $g(t)$ vanishes for $t < 0$.

The inverse of the Laplace transformation [Eq. (104)] is

$$g(t) = \frac{1}{2\pi j} \int_{b-j\infty}^{b+j\infty} dp\, F(p) e^{pt}, \tag{108}$$

where the path of integration in the complex plane runs from $b - j\infty$ to $b + j\infty$, to the right of the abscissa of absolute convergence.

Examples.—It will be worth while to give a number of examples of the Laplace transform for future reference. They can be verified by direct integration.

EXAMPLE 1.—The unit-step function $u(t)$:

$$\left.\begin{aligned} u(t) &= 0, \qquad t < 0, \\ u(t) &= 1, \qquad t \geqq 0. \end{aligned}\right\} \tag{109a}$$

$$\begin{aligned} \mathfrak{L}[u(t - t_0)] &= \int_0^\infty dt\, u(t - t_0) e^{-pt} \\ &= \int_{t_0}^\infty dt\, e^{-pt} = \frac{e^{-pt_0}}{p}, \qquad (t_0 \geqq 0). \end{aligned} \tag{109b}$$

In particular, we note that

$$\mathfrak{L}[u(t)] = \frac{1}{p}. \tag{109c}$$

EXAMPLE 2:

$$g(t) = \begin{cases} 0, & (t < 0), \\ \sin \omega t, & (t \geqq 0); \end{cases} \tag{110a}$$

$$\mathfrak{L}(g) = \frac{\omega}{p^2 + \omega^2}. \tag{110b}$$

EXAMPLE 3:

$$g(t) = \begin{cases} 0, & (t < 0), \\ t^n, & (t \geqq 0); \end{cases} \tag{111a}$$

$$\mathfrak{L}(g) = \frac{n!}{p^{n+1}}. \tag{111b}$$

In particular, we note that for the "unit-ramp function,"

$$g(t) = \begin{cases} 0, & (t < 0), \\ t, & (t \geqq 0); \end{cases} \tag{112a}$$

$$\mathfrak{L}(g) = \frac{1}{p^2}. \tag{112b}$$

EXAMPLE 4:

$$g(t) = \begin{cases} 0, & (t < 0), \\ t^n e^{at}, & (t \geqq 0); \end{cases} \tag{113a}$$

$$\mathfrak{L}(g) = \frac{n!}{(p - a)^{n+1}}. \tag{113b}$$

EXAMPLE 5.—The unit-impulse function $\delta(t - t_0)$:

$$\mathfrak{L}[\delta(t - t_0)] = \int_{0-}^{\infty} dt\, \delta(t - t_0)e^{-pt} = e^{-pt_0}, \qquad (t_0 \geqq 0). \tag{114}$$

In particular,

$$\mathfrak{L}[\delta(t)] = 1. \tag{115}$$

2·16. Properties of the Laplace Transform.—We here note some properties of the Laplace transform that are useful in determining the transform of a function or the inverse of a given transform. All functions considered will be of the restricted class defined in Sec. 2·15.

Linearity.—If $g_1(t)$ and $g_2(t)$ have the transforms $\mathfrak{L}(g_1)$ and $\mathfrak{L}(g_2)$, then

$$\mathfrak{L}(c_1 g_1 + c_2 g_2) = c_1\mathfrak{L}(g_1) + c_2\mathfrak{L}(g_2), \tag{116}$$

where c_1 and c_2 are arbitrary constants.

Laplace Transform of a Derivative:

$$\mathfrak{L}\left(\frac{dg}{dt}\right) = p\mathfrak{L}(g). \tag{117}$$

The proof is simple:

$$\mathfrak{L}\left(\frac{dg}{dt}\right) = \int_{0-}^{\infty} dt\, \frac{dg}{dt}\, e^{-pt} = g(t)e^{-pt}\Big|_{0-}^{\infty} + p\int_{0-}^{\infty} dt\, g(t)e^{-pt}$$
$$= g(0-) + p\mathfrak{L}(g), \tag{118}$$

from which Eq. (117) follows, since for all functions under discussion $g(0-)$ vanishes.

Thus we see that multiplication of the Laplace transform of a function by p corresponds to taking the derivative of the function with respect to t. An example of this relation is provided by the unit-step function $u(t)$ and its derivative, the unit-impulse function $\delta(t)$. By Eq. (117) we must have

$$\mathfrak{L}[\delta(t)] = p\mathfrak{L}[u(t)]; \tag{119}$$

by the results of the preceding section this is

$$1 = p\frac{1}{p}. \tag{120}$$

Laplace Transform of an Integral:

$$\mathcal{L}\left[\int_{0-}^{t} dt\, g(t)\right] = \frac{1}{p}\,\mathcal{L}[g(t)]. \tag{121}$$

This is essentially the same as Eq. (117), with $g(t)$ here playing the role of dg/dt in that equation.

Division of a Laplace transform by p thus corresponds to integration of the function with respect to t, with appropriate choice of the lower limit of the integral. Since n-fold application of the operator $\int_{0-}^{t} dt$ to the unit-step function gives

$$\left(\int_{0-}^{t} dt\right)^{n} u(t) = \frac{t^n}{n!}, \qquad (t > 0), \tag{122}$$

it follows that

$$\mathcal{L}\left(\frac{t^n}{n!}\right) = \left(\frac{1}{p}\right)^{n}\frac{1}{p}; \tag{123}$$

the result of Example 3 of the preceding section then follows from the linearity of the Laplace transform.

Laplace Transform of $e^{-at}\, g(t)$.—If $g(t)$ has the Laplace transform $F(p)$, then

$$\mathcal{L}[e^{-at}g(t)] = F(p + a). \tag{124}$$

For example, $\mathcal{L}[t^n e^{at}u(t)]$ is obtained by replacing p by $p - a$ in

$$\mathcal{L}[t^n u(t)] = \frac{n!}{p^{n+1}}.$$

This is the result stated in Eq. (113*b*).

Laplace Transform of the Convolution of Two Functions.—Let $g_1(t)$ and $g_2(t)$ be two functions of t that vanish for $t < 0$. The convolution of these two functions is

$$h(t) = \int_{0-}^{\infty} d\tau\, g_1(\tau)g_2(t - \tau) = \int_{0-}^{\infty} d\tau\, g_1(t - \tau)g_2(\tau). \tag{125}$$

If $g_1(t)$, $g_2(t)$, and $h(t)$ all possess Laplace transforms, then

$$\mathcal{L}(h) = \mathcal{L}(g_1)\mathcal{L}(g_2). \tag{126}$$

For

$$\begin{aligned} \mathcal{L}(h) &= \int_{0-}^{\infty} dt\, e^{-pt} \int_{0-}^{\infty} d\tau\, g_1(\tau)g_2(t - r) \\ &= \int_{0-}^{\infty} d\tau\, g_1(\tau)e^{-p\tau} \int_{0-}^{\infty} dt\, g_2(t - \tau)e^{-p(t-\tau)}. \end{aligned} \tag{127}$$

Changing the variable of integration in the second integral to $s = t - \tau$, and remembering that $g_2(s) = 0$ if $s < 0$, we have

$$\mathcal{L}(h) = \int_{0-}^{\infty} d\tau\, g_1(\tau)e^{-p\tau} \int_{0-}^{\infty} ds\, g_2(s)e^{-ps}, \tag{128}$$

which is a restatement of Eq. (126).

The multiplication of two Laplace transforms thus corresponds to formation of the convolution of their inverse functions. This is often a convenient way to determine the inverse of a given Laplace transform when it can be factored into two Laplace transforms with recognizable inverses.

Limiting Values of the Laplace Transform.—Let $F(p)$ be the Laplace transform of $g(t)$. When the indicated limits exist, then the following theorems are valid.

$$\lim_{p\to 0} pF(p) = \lim_{t\to\infty} g(t). \tag{129}$$

If $g(t)$ contains no delta-function term at $t = 0$,

$$\lim_{p\to\infty} pF(p) = g(0+). \tag{130}$$

If $g(t)$ contains a term $K\,\delta(t)$, then

$$\lim_{p\to\infty} F(p) = K, \tag{131}$$

and

$$\lim_{p\to\infty} p[F(p) - K] = g(0+). \tag{132}$$

The proof of these relations can be carried out along the following lines when $g(t)$ contains no delta functions. We note that

$$pF(p) = \int_{0-}^{\infty} dt\, g(t)pe^{-pt} = -\int_{0-}^{\infty} dt\, g(t)\frac{d}{dt}(e^{-pt}). \tag{133}$$

Integrating by parts, we have

$$\left.\begin{aligned} pF(p) &= -g(t)e^{-pt}\Big|_{0-}^{\infty} + \int_{0-}^{\infty} dt\,\frac{dg}{dt}\,e^{-pt} \\ &= \int_{0-}^{\infty} dt\,\frac{dg}{dt}\,e^{-pt}, \end{aligned}\right\} \tag{134}$$

where dg/dt may contain delta functions corresponding to discontinuities in g, including a term $g(0+)\,\delta(t)$ corresponding to a discontinuity at $t = 0$. In the limit as $p \to \infty$, only this last delta function will contribute to the integral on the left; one has

$$\lim_{p\to\infty} pF(p) = \int_{0-}^{0+} dt\,\frac{dg}{dt} = g(0+). \tag{135}$$

Similarly, replacing e^{-pt} in the integrand by its limit as $p \to 0$, one obtains

$$\lim_{p\to 0} pF(p) = \int_{0-}^{\infty} dt \frac{dg}{dt} = g(\infty). \tag{136}$$

2·17. Use of the Laplace Transform in Solution of Linear Differential Equations.—The Laplace transform theory offers a convenient method for the solution of linear differential equations, such as the filter equation

$$a_n \frac{d^nE_O}{dt} + a_{n-1}\frac{d^{n-1}E_O}{dt^{n-1}} + \cdots + a_0E_O = b_m\frac{d^mE_I}{dt^m} + b_{m-1}\frac{d^{m-1}E_I}{dt^{m-1}} + \cdots + b_0E_I. \tag{2}$$

The formulation of this method is particularly simple when the initial conditions on the solution E_O correspond to starting of the system from rest under an input E_I that begins at a definite time, say $t = 0$; that is, when it is required to find the *normal response* of the system to such an input. Under such conditions, both sides of Eq. (2) represent functions that begin to differ from zero only at $t = 0$. Equating the Laplace transforms of the two sides of this equation and making use of the properties of the transforms as discussed in the preceding section, we have

$$(a_np^n + a_{n-1}p^{n-1} + \cdots + a_0)\mathfrak{L}[E_O(t)] = (b_mp^m + b_{m-1}p^{m-1} + \cdots + b_0)\mathfrak{L}[E_I(t)]. \tag{137}$$

Writing

$$Y(p) = \frac{b_mp^m + b_{m-1}p^{m-1} + \cdots + b_0}{a_np^n + a_{n-1}p^{n-1} + \cdots + a_0}, \tag{138}$$

as in Eq. (67), we have

$$\mathfrak{L}[E_O(t)] = Y(p)\mathfrak{L}[E_I(t)]. \tag{139}$$

Thus it is easy to obtain the Laplace transform of the filter output by multiplying the Laplace transform of the input by a rational function in p with coefficients read from the differential equation. The output itself can then be determined by application of the inverse Laplace transformation [Eq. (108)] or by resolving the Laplace transform of the output into parts with recognizable inverses.

As an example, let us determine the weighting function of the RC-filter of Fig. 2·6. This can be obtained by solving Eq. (30) with $E_I(t) = \delta(t)$. We have then, by Eq. (115),

$$\mathfrak{L}[E_I(t)] = 1. \tag{140}$$

In this case Eq. (139) becomes

$$\mathfrak{L}[E_O(t)] = \frac{T_1p}{T_1p + 1}\mathfrak{L}[E_I(t)]. \tag{141}$$

Thus, for the delta-function input, the Laplace transform of the output is

$$\mathfrak{L}[W(t)] = \frac{T_1 p}{T_1 p + 1} = 1 - \frac{1}{T_1} \frac{1}{p + \frac{1}{T_1}}. \tag{142}$$

The inverse of 1 is, of course, $\delta(t)$; the inverse of the second term follows from Eqs. (113), with $n = 1$. We thus find

$$\left.\begin{aligned} W(t) &= 0, && (t < 0), \\ W(t) &= \delta(t) - \frac{1}{T_1} e^{-\frac{t}{T}}, && (t \geqq 0), \end{aligned}\right\} \tag{143}$$

in agreement with Eq. (35).

As a second example, we may derive the weighting functions given in Eqs. (48) to (50). These are solutions of Eq. (46), which can be rewritten, by use of Eqs. (47), as

$$\frac{d^2\theta_O}{dt^2} + 2\zeta\omega_n \frac{d\theta_O}{dt} + \omega_n^2\theta_O = \omega_n^2\theta_I. \tag{144}$$

Thus

$$\mathfrak{L}(\theta_O) = \frac{\omega_n^2}{p^2 + 2\zeta\omega_n p + \omega_n^2} \mathfrak{L}(\theta_I). \tag{145}$$

For a delta-function input, $\mathfrak{L}(\theta_O)$ becomes

$$\mathfrak{L}[W(t)] = \frac{\omega_n^2}{p^2 + 2\zeta\omega_n p + \omega_n^2} = Y(p). \tag{146}$$

The denominator factors into

$$\{p + \omega_n[\zeta + (\zeta^2 - 1)^{1/2}]\}\ \{p + \omega_n[\zeta - (\zeta^2 - 1)^{1/2}]\};$$

resolving the term on the right into partial fractions, we obtain

$$\mathfrak{L}[W(t)] = \frac{\omega_n}{2(\zeta^2 - 1)^{1/2}} \left[\frac{1}{p + \omega_n\zeta - \omega_n(\zeta^2 - 1)^{1/2}} - \frac{1}{p + \omega_n\zeta + \omega_n(\zeta^2 - 1)^{1/2}}\right]. \tag{147}$$

Double application of Eqs. (113) then gives

$$\left.\begin{aligned} W(t) &= 0, \qquad (t < 0), \\ W(t) &= \frac{\omega_n}{2(\zeta^2 - 1)^{1/2}} [e^{-\omega_n\zeta t + \omega_n(\zeta^2-1)^{1/2}t} - e^{-\omega_n\zeta t - \omega_n(\zeta^2-1)^{1/2}t}], \qquad (t \geqq 0). \end{aligned}\right\} \tag{148}$$

This general result takes the forms of Eqs. (48) to (50) for $\zeta < 1$, $\zeta \to 1$, and $\zeta > 1$, respectively.

THE TRANSFER FUNCTION

2·18. Definition of the Transfer Function.—The *transfer function* of a filter is defined to be the Laplace transform of its weighting function. In this volume, transfer functions will usually be denoted by $Y(p)$, with distinguishing subscripts as required. We have, then,

$$Y(p) = \mathfrak{L}[W(t)] = \int_{0-}^{\infty} dt\, W(t)e^{-pt}. \tag{149}$$

The normal response of a linear filter (stable or unstable) to an input $E_I(t)$ that is zero for $t < 0$ can be written as

$$E_O(t) = \int_{0-}^{\infty} d\tau\, E_I(t - \tau)W(\tau). \tag{57}$$

It will be noted that this is the convolution of the input and the weighting function, as defined in Eq. (125). It follows, by Eq. (126), that when the Laplace transforms exist,

$$\mathfrak{L}[E_O(t)] = Y(p)\mathfrak{L}[E_I(t)]: \tag{139}$$

The transfer function of a filter is the ratio of the Laplace transforms of any normal response and the input that produces it. The use of the symbol $Y(p)$ in Eq. (139) and throughout the whole of the preceding development is thus consistent with the notation for the transfer function here introduced. Instead of defining the transfer function for the lumped-constant filter directly by Eq. (138), we have chosen to define it as the Laplace transform of the weighting function, which has been taken to be the more primitive concept in this chapter.

The transfer function may be regarded as a generalization of the frequency-response function. Unlike the frequency-response function, it is defined for unstable filters as well as stable filters. It is defined for general complex values of the argument p, and not just for pure imaginary values of $j\omega$ (ω is real valued). When the frequency-response function exists, it can be obtained from the transfer function by replacing the argument p by $j\omega$ [compare Eqs. (61) and (149)]; the values of the frequency-response function are the values of the transfer function along the imaginary axis in the p-plane.

In the preceding section we have seen how, for a lumped-constant filter, Eq. (139) can be derived from the differential equation of the filter and how it can be used, instead of the differential equation, in determining the normal response of the filter to a given input. In solving many problems it is possible to deal exclusively with the Laplace transforms of input and output and with transfer functions, except perhaps in the final interpretation of the transforms in terms of functions of time. It is then useful to abbreviate the notation of Eq. (139) and to write simply

$$E_O(p) = Y(p)E_I(p), \tag{150}$$

the indication of the argument p giving sufficient warning that it is a Laplace transform which is involved.

Filters consisting of many parts can be described by differential equations that govern the several parts or by a single differential equation derived from these by elimination of intermediate variables. In the same way one can describe the components of a filter by equations of the form of Eq. (150) and can eliminate variables between these equations, by purely algebraic manipulation, to obtain a similar equation governing the over-all characteristics of the filter. This calculus of Laplace transforms provides a formally simpler description of the systems than that in terms of differential equations and will be much used in this book.

A very simple example is provided by a filter that consists of two filters in series. The first filter, with transfer function $Y_1(p)$, receives an input E_I and yields an output E_M; E_M then serves as input to a second filter, with transfer function $Y_2(p)$, which gives the final output E_O. In terms of Laplace transforms we have

$$E_M(p) = Y_1(p)E_I(p), \tag{151a}$$
$$E_O(p) = Y_2(p)E_M(p). \tag{151b}$$

Eliminating $E_M(p)$, we obtain

$$E_O(p) = Y_1(p)Y_2(p)E_I(p). \tag{152}$$

We seen then, that the over-all transfer function of the complete filter is

$$Y(p) = Y_1(p)Y_2(p): \tag{153}$$

The transfer function of two filters in series is the product of their individual transfer functions. By Eqs. (125) and (126) one can infer that the weighting function of two filters in series is the convolution of their separate weighting functions:

$$W(t) = \int_{0-}^{\infty} d\tau\, W_1(\tau)W_2(t - \tau). \tag{154}$$

This result can also be derived from the relations

$$E_M(t) = \int_{0-}^{t} d\tau\, E_I(t - \tau)W_1(\tau), \tag{155a}$$
$$E_O(t) = \int_{0-}^{t} d\tau\, E_M(t - \tau)W_2(\tau), \tag{155b}$$

which correspond to Eqs. (151a) and (151b), respectively.

2·19. Transfer Function of a Lumped-constant Filter.—The transfer function is more generally useful in the discussion of filters than is the frequency-response function, in part because it is defined for a wider class of filters. For an illustration of its use we shall return to the consideration of lumped-constant filters, for which the transfer functions are rational functions of p, with coefficients that can be read from the governing differential equation:

$$Y(p) = \frac{b_m p^m + b_{m-1}p^{m-1} + \cdots + b_0}{a_n p^n + a_{n-1}b^{n-1} + \cdots + a_0}. \tag{138}$$

If $m > n$, the resolution of Eq. (138) into partial fractions contains terms of the form $A_{m-n}p^{m-n}, A_{m-n-1}p^{m-n-1}, \ldots, A_1 p$. The filter output then contains terms proportional to the first and up to the $(m - n - 1)$th derivative of the input. In particular, $W(t)$ contains these derivatives of the delta-function input. Then $\int_{0-}^{\infty} dt\, |W(t)|$ does not converge, as can be seen by considering the functions approximating to the delta function; the filter is unstable. We have already noted that with a passive lumped-constant filter one cannot have $m > n$.

If $m \leqq n$ and the root p_i of

$$P(p) = a_n p^n + a_{n-1}p^{n-1} + \cdots + a_0 = 0 \tag{13b}$$

is s_i-fold, the general resolution of Eq. (138) into partial fractions is of the form

$$\begin{aligned} Y(p) = C_0 &+ \frac{C_{11}}{p - p_1} + \frac{C_{12}}{(p - p_1)^2} + \cdots + \frac{C_{1,s_1}}{(p - p_1)^{s_1}} \\ &+ \frac{C_{21}}{p - p_2} + \frac{C_{22}}{(p - p_2)^2} + \cdots + \frac{C_{2,s_2}}{(p - p_2)^{s_2}} \\ &+ \cdots. \end{aligned} \tag{156}$$

The inverse of this is, by Eqs. (111) and (113),

$$\left.\begin{aligned} &W(t) = 0, \qquad (t < 0), \\ W(t) &= C_0\delta(t) \\ &+ \left[C_{11} + \frac{C_{12}}{1!}t + \frac{C_{13}t^2}{2!} + \cdots + \frac{C_{1,s_1}t^{(s_1-1)}}{(s_1 - 1)!}\right]e^{p_1 t} \\ &+ \left[C_{21} + \frac{C_{22}}{1!}t + \frac{C_{23}t^2}{2!} + \cdots + \frac{C_{2,s_2}t^{(s_2-1)}}{(s_2 - 1)!}\right]e^{p_2 t} \\ &+ \cdots. \qquad\qquad (t \geqq 0) \end{aligned}\right\} \tag{157}$$

The delta-function term appears in the weighting function only if $m = n$; it represents a term in the general output that is proportional to the input. The other terms in $W(t)$ represent the transient response of the filter to the impulse input, expressed as a sum of normal-mode functions.

It is evident that the weighting function will contain an undamped normal mode and the filter will be unstable if and only if the resolution of

$Y(p)$ into partial fractions contains a p_i with nonnegative real part. This is not the same as saying that the filter is stable if and only if Eq. (13*b*) has no such roots; it may have such roots and still be stable if the corresponding factor $(p - p_i)^{s_i}$ in the denominator in Eq. (138) is canceled out by a similar factor in the numerator. When this happens, one may say that the network has an undamped natural mode but that the input terminals are so connected to the filter that no input can excite this type of response. This may be a very precarious type of stability, since a small change in the filter constants—in the b's—may make this cancellation inexact and the filter unstable.

2·20. The Stability Criterion in Terms of the Transfer Function.—It will be noted that p's with nonnegative real parts will be absent from Eq. (156) and the lumped-constant filter will be stable if and only if $Y(p)$ has no poles in the right half of the p-plane or on the imaginary axis. This is a special case of a more general stability criterion: If the transfer function $Y(p)$ is analytic in the right half plane and is well behaved on the imaginary axis—for instance, if the absolute value squared of dY/dp is integrable—then the filter is stable. If at least one singular point of $Y(p)$ lies in the right half plane, or if at least one pole lies on the imaginary axis, then the filter is unstable.

It will be noticed that the preceding theorem does not cover all possible situations; in particular, it does not settle the case where there are singularities other than poles on the imaginary axis. It is certainly adequate, however, for most practical problems; for all filters with lumped elements the transfer function is a rational function analytic except for poles.

The proof of this general stability criterion will be indicated briefly If the absolute value squared of dY/dp is integrable along the imaginary axis, then, by the Parseval theorem,[1] $|tW(t)|^2$ and $(1 + t^2)|W(t)|^2$ are integrable. It follows, by Schwartz's inequality for integrals, that

$$\int_{0-}^{\infty} dt\,|W(t)| = \int_{0-}^{\infty} dt\,(1 + t^2)^{1/2}|W(t)|\,\frac{1}{(1 + t^2)^{1/2}}$$
$$\leq \sqrt{\int_{0-}^{\infty} dt\,(1 + t^2)|W(t)|^2}\,\sqrt{\int_{0-}^{\infty} dt\,\frac{1}{1 + t^2}}; \quad (158)$$

$\int_{0-}^{\infty} dt\,|W(t)|$ is bounded and the filter must be stable. On the other hand, it is evident that for a stable filter the Laplace transform of the weighting function is analytic and uniformly bounded in the right half plane. The transform function can therefore have no singularities inside the right half plane. Furthermore it could have no pole on the imaginary

[1] See, for instance, E. C. Titchmarsh, *Introduction to the Theory of Fourier Integrals*, Clarendon Press, Oxford, 1937, pp. 50–51.

axis and still remain uniformly bounded in the right half plane. This concludes the proof of the second part of the theorem.

SYSTEMS WITH FEEDBACK

2·21. Characterization of Feedback Systems.—A mechanical or electrical system with feedback is one in which the output of some part of the system is used as an input to the system at a point where this can affect its own value. A servo system is a feedback system in which the actual output is compared with the input, which is the *desired* output, and the driving element is activated by the difference of these quantities.

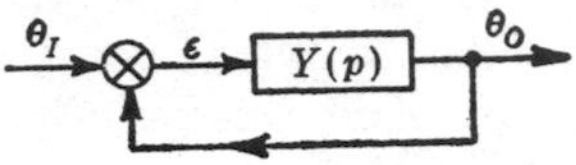

FIG. 2·15.—Servo schematic.

Figure 2·15 is a block diagram showing the essential connections of a servo system. The output θ_O is fed into a mixer or comparator (in mechanical systems, a differential) where it is subtracted from the input θ_I to produce the error signal

$$\epsilon(t) = \theta_I(t) - \theta_O(t). \tag{159}$$

This signal controls the output through a system of amplifiers, motors, and other devices, here shown as a box. To complete the formal description of the system it is necessary only to specify the relation established between ϵ and θ_O by the contents of this box. If the system is linear, this can be specified as a transfer function $Y(p)$; in terms of the Laplace transforms we can write simply

$$\theta_O(p) = Y(p)\epsilon(p). \tag{160}$$

The transfer function $Y(p)$ will be called the *feedback transfer function.* It is the transfer function around the entire feedback loop, from the output of the differential (ϵ) back to the input to the differential (θ_O).

The over-all performance of the servo can be described by another transfer function $Y_0(p)$, which relates the input and output of the system:

$$\theta_O(p) = Y_0(p)\theta_I(p). \tag{161}$$

This may be called the *over-all transfer function*, or the *transfer function of the system.* This transfer function must be carefully distinguished from the feedback transfer function, to which it is simply related. Equation (159) implies that

$$\epsilon(p) = \theta_I(p) - \theta_O(p); \tag{162}$$

elimination of $\epsilon(p)$ from Eqs. (160) and (162) yields the very important relation

$$Y_0(p) = \frac{Y(p)}{1 + Y(p)}. \tag{163}$$

Since Eqs. (159) and (161) are defining equations for ϵ and Y_0, Eq. (163) is valid for any feedback system for which Eq. (160) is valid. In certain types of systems Eq. (160) will not be valid if $Y(p)$ is interpreted as the transfer function around the entire loop. This occurs when the servo output is not combined directly with the input but is further filtered in the feedback loop; the driving elements of the system are then activated by the difference between the input and this function of the output. For example, a modification of the servo system of Fig. 2·15 is shown in Fig.

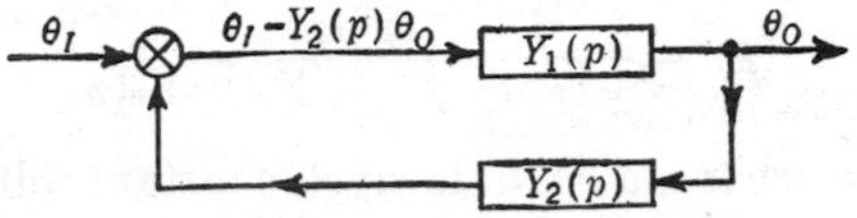

FIG. 2·16.—Servo with added filter in feedback loop.

2·16. A filter has been inserted in the feedback loop to provide an input to the differential that is not $\theta_O(p)$ but $Y_2(p)\theta_O(p)$. In such a system

$$Y_1(p)[\theta_I(p) - Y_2(p)\theta_O(p)] = \theta_O(p). \tag{164}$$

The over-all transfer function is thus

$$Y_0(p) = \frac{\theta_O(p)}{\theta_I(p)} = \frac{Y_1(p)}{1 + Y_1(p)Y_2(p)}. \tag{165}$$

On the other hand, the transfer function around the loop is

$$Y_l(p = Y_1(p)Y_2(p); \tag{166}$$

$Y_0(p)$ and $Y_l(p)$ are not related by Eq. (163). It will be noted that Eq. (165) expresses the transfer function of the system as a fraction in which the denominator is 1 plus the transfer function around the loop. This can always be done.

Such servo systems as that shown in Fig. 2·16 are not, in general, satisfactory. If the system is to have a zero static error, it is clear that the feedback filter must always give the same asymptotic response to a step function; that is, $\lim_{p\to 0} pY_2(p)(1/p) = Y_2(0) = 1$ [see Eq. (129)]. Since changes in the parameters of the filter may change the value of $Y_2(0)$, it is not customary to filter the output before comparing it with the input; on the other hand, such a filtering action may be inadvertently introduced by elasticity in the gear trains and by other factors.

A servo system may contain more than one feedback loop. Figure 2·17, for instance, show a feedback system with two loops. The inner loop serves to modify the characteristics of the driving elements; the whole of the contents of the dashed box of Fig. 2·17 corresponds to the box of Fig. 2·15. In this system we have

$$\mu = \epsilon - Y_2(p)\theta_O(p), \tag{167a}$$

$$\theta_O(p) = Y_1(p)\mu. \tag{167b}$$

Eliminating μ from these equations, we obtain

$$\theta_O(p) = \frac{Y_1(p)}{1 + Y_1(p)Y_2(p)}\,\epsilon(p) = Y(p)\epsilon(p). \tag{168}$$

Thus

$$Y(p) = \frac{Y_1(p)}{1 + Y_1(p)Y_2(p)}. \tag{169}$$

The transfer function of the system is given by Eq. (163) or, more explicitly, by

$$Y_0(p) = \frac{Y_1(p)}{1 + Y_1(p) + Y_1(p)Y_2(p)}. \tag{170}$$

Since a servomechanism is a lumped-constant filter with transfer function $Y_0(p)$, its stability can be discussed by application of the general theory of filter stability: A servomechanism will be stable if and only if $Y_0(p)$ has no poles in the right half of the p-plane or on the imaginary axis. From Eq. (163) it is evident that $Y_0(p)$ will have a pole only where $1 + Y(p)$ has a zero. [A pole of $Y(p)$ is merely a point where $Y_0(p)$ equals 1.] Thus *a servomechanism will be stable if and only if* $1 + Y(p)$ *has no zeros in the right half of the p-plane or on the imaginary axis.* Such a statement will be universally valid only if $Y(p)$ is defined by Eq. (160). One can replace $Y(p)$ in this statement by the loop transfer function $Y_l(p)$ only if $Y_0(p)$ and $Y_l(p)$ are related by Eq. (163); in other cases one must reexamine the relation between these quantities. Such cases will not be considered further in this chapter.

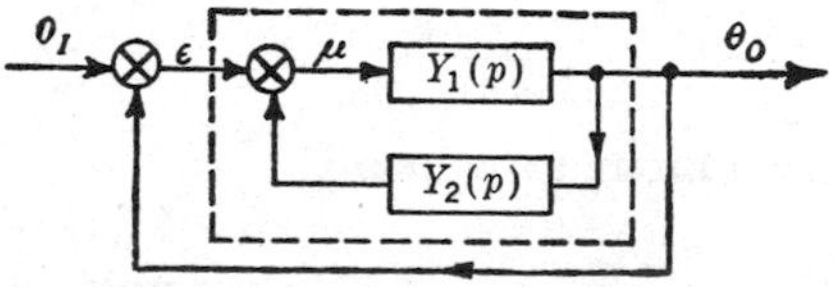

FIG. 2·17.—Servo with two feedback loops.

The feedback transfer function is of basic importance in the theory of servomechanisms—for the discussion of stability, for the evaluation of errors in servo performance, and in general throughout the design procedure. We shall therefore turn to a discussion of its properties.

2·22. Feedback Transfer Function of Lumped-constant Servos.—The feedback transfer function of a lumped-constant servo can be written as

$$Y(p) = \frac{K_s}{p^s}\frac{Q_m(p)}{P_n(p)}, \qquad m \leqq n, \tag{171}$$

where s is an integer, K_s is a constant, and $Q_m(p)$ and $P_n(p)$ are polynomials of degree m and n respectively, the coefficients of the zero power of p being taken as unity. The constant K_s in this expression will be called the *gain;* in general it is defined as

$$K_s = \lim_{p\to 0} p^s Y(p), \tag{172}$$

the exponent s being so chosen as to make the limit finite and different from zero.

The value of s has an important bearing on the properties of the system. Eliminating θ_O between Eqs. (161) and (162), one can express the error in terms of the input,

$$\epsilon(p) = \frac{1}{1 + Y(p)} \theta_I(p). \tag{173}$$

Given the form of $\theta_I(p)$ and the limiting form of $Y(p)$ as $p \to 0$ (that is, K_s/p^s) one can determine, by application of Eq. (129), the limiting value approached by the servo error as $t \to \infty$. For example, let us consider a step-function input with the Laplace transform [Eq. (109c)]

$$\theta_I(p) = \frac{1}{p}. \tag{174}$$

The limiting value of the error as t becomes infinite is

$$\begin{aligned} \epsilon(\infty) &= \lim_{p \to 0} p \frac{1}{1 + Y(p)} \frac{1}{p} \\ &= \lim_{p \to 0} \frac{1}{1 + \frac{K_s}{p^s} \frac{Q_m}{P_n}} = \lim_{p \to 0} \frac{1}{1 + \frac{K_s}{p^s}}. \end{aligned} \tag{175}$$

The continued action of the servo will eventually reduce the error to zero only if $s \geqq 1$. If $s = 0$, then the limiting value of the error is

$$\epsilon(\infty) = \frac{1}{1 + K_O}. \tag{176}$$

Now let us assume that $s = 1$, so that the static error of the system is zero, and find the steady-state error arising when the input changes at a uniform rate. We consider then the constant velocity input with Laplace transform $\theta_I = 1/p^2$ [Eq. (111b)]. The error with which this input is followed will approach

$$\begin{aligned} \epsilon(\infty) &= \lim_{p \to 0} p \frac{1}{1 + Y(p)} \frac{1}{p^2} \\ &= \lim_{p \to 0} \frac{1}{p + K_1 \frac{Q_m}{P_n}} \\ &= \frac{1}{K_1}. \end{aligned} \tag{177}$$

Thus, if the feedback transfer function has a simple pole at the origin ($s = 1$), the system will follow a unit constant-velocity input with an error (lag) that is the reciprocal of the gain. This gain K_1 is called the *velocity-error constant.*

If the system is to have zero error for a constant-velocity input, the condition to be satisfied is $s \geqq 2$; that is, the feedback transfer function must have a second-order pole at the origin. If $s = 2$, the system will show an error for a constant acceleration input ($\theta_I = 2/p^3$);

$$\epsilon(\infty) = \lim_{p \to 0} \frac{2}{p^2 + K_2 \dfrac{Q_m}{P_n}}.$$

$$= \frac{2}{K_2}. \tag{178}$$

The quantity $(K_2/2)$ is then called the *acceleration-error constant.*

2·23. The Feedback Transfer Locus.—The feedback transfer function furnishes one with a complete description of the servomechanism. It is a complex-valued analytic function of the complex variable p; as such it is completely determined by its values along a curve. The imaginary axis has special significance in this connection because $Y(j\omega)e^{j\omega}$ is the steady-state response of the feedback loop to the pure sinusoidal input $e^{j\omega}$; $Y(j\omega)$ can therefore be measured directly by experiment. The plot of $Y(j\omega)$ in the complex Y-plane for all real values of ω is called the *feedback transfer locus;* it is also referred to as the Nyquist diagram of the transfer function. As we shall see, this locus furnishes us with a very convenient way of determining the stability and the performance characteristics of the servomechanism.

Since the networks and devices with which we are concerned can be represented by differential equations with real coefficients, we have

$$Y^*(j\omega) = Y(-j\omega). \tag{179}$$

It follows that the real part of $Y(j\omega)$ is an even function and the imaginary part an odd function of ω. Consequently the transfer locus is symmetric about the real axis in the Y-plane; in plotting this locus it is necessary to draw only the graph for positive values of ω—the remainder of the locus is then obtained by reflection in the real axis.

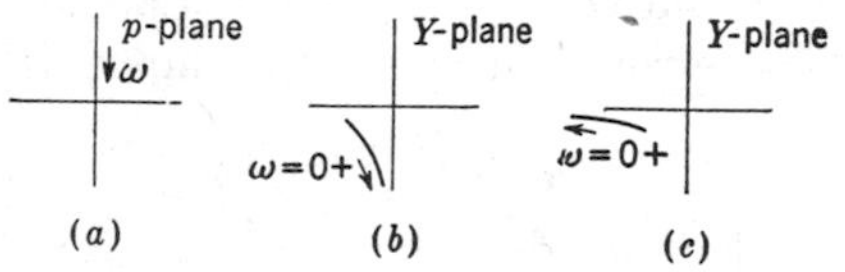

FIG. 2·18.—The approach of $Y(j\omega)$ to infinity for a first-order pole (b) and a second-order pole (c) as $\omega \to 0+$ (a).

The properties of the feedback transfer function discussed in Sec. 2·22 are readily recognized in the transfer locus. If the static error for the system is zero, then the feedback transfer function must have a pole at $p = 0$. If the pole is of the first order, then, as shown in (b) of Fig. 2·18, $Y(j\omega)$ becomes infinite along the negative imaginary axis as $\omega \to 0+$ (the + indicates that ω approaches the origin from positive values as in Fig. 2·18a). For a second-order pole at the origin (a zero steady-state error for a constant-velocity input), $Y(j\omega)$ becomes infinite along the negative real axis as shown in Fig. 2·18c. In general, if the feedback transfer function has a pole of order s at the origin, $Y(j\omega)$ approaches infinity along the direction that makes an angle of $(-\pi/2)s$ with the positive real axis.

The limiting form of the transfer locus as $\omega \to \infty$ can also be easily obtained. Let b_m and a_n respectively be the coefficients of p^m in $Q_m(p)$ and p^n in $P_n(p)$ [Eq. (171)]; then as $\omega \to +\infty$,

$$Y(p) \to \frac{K_s}{p^{s+n-m}} \frac{b_m}{a_n}. \tag{180}$$

In general, $s + n - m > 0$; and $Y(j\omega)$ approaches zero from a direction that makes an angle of $(-\pi/2)(s + n - m)$ with the positive real axis. For example, if Q_m/P_n is a constant divided by a polynomial of first degree in p, $Y(j\omega)$ approaches zero along the negative real axis for $s = 1$ and along the positive imaginary axis for $s = 2$.

2·24. Relation between the Form of the Transfer Locus and the Positions of the Zeros and Poles.—In the preceding section the feedback transfer locus was defined as a mapping in the Y-plane of the imaginary axis in the p-plane. It is now necessary to define this locus more carefully. Usually the feedback transfer function will have a pole at the origin, and it may have other poles along the imaginary axis. As p passes through these poles, there are discontinuities in the transfer locus; this locus then falls into segments corresponding to the part of the imaginary axis between $+\infty$ and the first such pole reached with decreasing $j\omega$, the part between the first and second poles, and so on. In order to define the connection between these segments we shall now modify the previous definition of the transfer locus.

Let us consider a path in the p-plane that lies along the imaginary axis, except that it shall include a small semicircular detour in the right half plane about the singular points on the imaginary axis, and a large semicircular path in the right half plane, from very large negative imaginary values to very large positive imaginary values (see Fig. 2·19). For sufficiently small detours about the poles on the imaginary axis and for a sufficiently large semicircular connecting path, this closed path will enclose all of the poles and zeros of any rational function $Y(p)$ inside the right half plane. We shall call the closed curve that results from mapping any such contour onto the Y-plane the transfer locus of $Y(p)$.

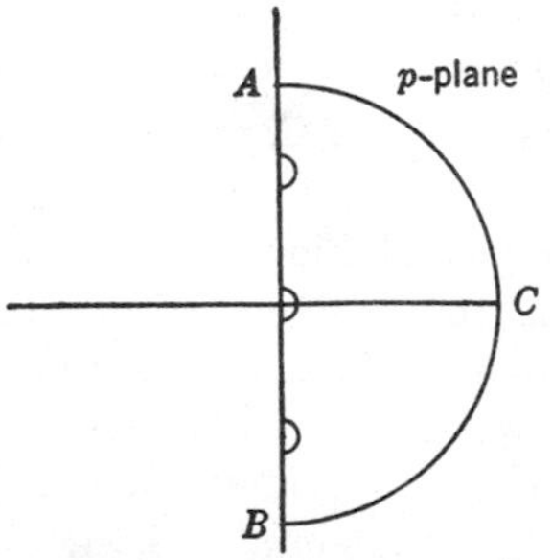

FIG. 2·19.—Closed path in the p-plane.

The so-defined transfer locus can be determined experimentally. It is evident that the locus for nonsingular frequencies can be obtained as the steady-state response to sinusoidal inputs at these frequencies. The mapping of the semicircles in the p-plane onto the Y-plane can be determined as follows. Near the singular frequencies the system will, in general, overload. One can, however, determine from such tests the order of the pole, which as we shall see is sufficient to define the transfer locus about the detours. The same is true for the large semicircle (about the point at infinity).

If the pole at p_1 is of order s, then in traversing the semicircle from $p_1 + j\rho$ to $p_1 - j\rho$ (for sufficiently small but positive ρ), the curve traced in the Y-plane by $Y(p)$ will be essentially an arc of a circle traversed in the counterclockwise direction through an angle of about $s\pi$. This follows immediately from the fact that in the neighborhood of p_1 the transfer function is approximately of the form

$$Y(p) = \frac{A}{(p - p_1)^s} \tag{181a}$$

or

$$Y(p_1 + \rho e^{j\phi}) \approx A\rho^{-s}e^{-js\phi}, \tag{181b}$$

where A is a complex-valued constant.

Similarly, for very large values of $|p|$ (the outer semicircle in the p-plane) we have

$$Y(p) \approx \frac{K_s b_m}{a_n}\frac{1}{p^{s+n-m}} = \frac{K_s b_m}{a_n}\frac{e^{-j(s+n-m)\phi}}{R^{s+m-n}}. \tag{180}$$

As the large semicircle is traversed by the point $p = Re^{j\phi}$, from $\phi = -\pi/2$ to $\phi = +\pi/2$, $Y(p)$ traverses a circular arc of small radius (approaching zero with $1/R^{s+m-n}$) through an angle $-(s + n - m)\pi$.

We have now seen how the feedback transfer function maps the closed curve of Fig. 2·19 into a closed curve Γ in the Y-plane. The right half of the p-plane is thus mapped by $Y(p)$ into the interior of Γ. Consequently if $Y(p)$ is equal to -1, for instance, for some point in the right half plane, then the contour Γ will encircle the point $(-1,0)$ in the Y-plane. Since the servomechanism will be stable if and only if $Y(p)$ does not equal -1 for any point in the right half of the p-plane, or on the imaginary axis, it is clear that the transfer locus furnishes us with another means of determining the stability of the servo. How this can be done will be discussed in the following sections.

2·25. A Mapping Theorem.—We shall now prove a theorem of analysis that is useful in the discussion of the stability of servomechanisms.

Let $G(p)$ be a rational function of p. If the point p in the p-plane describes a closed contour C in the positive[1] sense, the point $G(p)$ in the G-plane describes a closed contour Γ (Fig. 2·20). *If the contour C encircles in a positive sense Z zeros and P poles (this takes into account the multiplicity of zeros and poles), the corresponding contour Γ in the G-plane encircles the origin*

$$N = Z - P \tag{182}$$

times in a positive sense.

We here assume that none of the zeros or poles lies on the contour in the p-plane; a slight modification of the contour will always allow it to satisfy this condition, since the zeros and poles of $G(p)$ are isolated. The term "encircle" is defined as follows: Consider a radial line drawn from the point p_1 to a representative point P on the closed contour C. As the point P describes the contour C in some sense, the radial line sweeps out an angle that will be some multiple of 2π. If this angle is $2\pi n$, then the contour encircles the point p_1, n times. The sign of n will depend upon the sense in which P describes C.

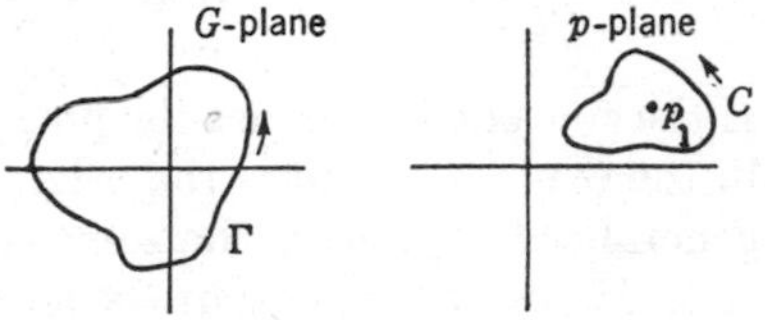

FIG. 2·20.—Mapping of a closed contour in the p-plane onto the G-plane.

We shall prove the theorem in stages. Suppose first that the function has a single root at $p = p_1$:

$$G(p) = A(p - p_1), \tag{183}$$

where A is a constant. In polar form this becomes

$$G(p) = A\rho e^{j\phi}. \tag{184}$$

It is clear that as the point p describes a contour C in the positive sense, the corresponding point in the G-plane describes a contour Γ in a positive sense. The number of times that Γ encircles the origin is precisely the total change in $\phi/2\pi$ which occurs when p traces C once. Thus Γ encircles the origin once if C contains p_1 in its interior but otherwise does not encircle the origin.

If the function has two distinct roots p_1 and p_2, then

$$G(p) = A(p - p_1)(p - p_2). \tag{185}$$

When written in polar form, this is

$$G(p) = A\rho_1\rho_2 e^{j(\phi_1+\phi_2)}, \tag{186}$$

where $p - p_1 = \rho_1 e^{j\phi_1}$ and $p - p_2 = \rho_2 e^{j\phi_2}$. If the contour C encircles no roots, the total change in $(\phi_1 + \phi_2)$ is zero and Γ does not encircle the origin. If the contour C encircles one or both the roots, the total change

[1] The interior of the contour is always on the left as the point describes the contour.

in $(\phi_1 + \phi_2)$ is 2π or 4π and Γ encircles the origin in a positive sense once or twice, respectively.

If the two roots are equal, any contour enclosing one will, of course, enclose the other, and the corresponding contour in the G-plane will encircle the origin twice. In general, if the contour C encircles a root of mth order, or m distinct zeros, the contour Γ encircles the origin m times in a positive sense.

Now let us consider a function with a pole of first order at $p = p_1$,

$$G(p) = \frac{A}{p - p_1} = \frac{A}{\rho} e^{-i\phi}. \tag{187}$$

If the contour C encircles the pole $p = p_1$ in a *positive* sense, the contour Γ in the G-plane encircles the origin once in a *negative* sense. This can be generalized in exactly the same fashion as was done above with respect to the zeros; if the contour C encircles n poles in a positive sense, then the contour Γ in the G-plane encircles the origin n times in a negative sense.

We can combine these types of function to form one that has both zeros and poles. Suppose $G(p)$ is a rational fraction

$$G(p) = \frac{Q_m(p)}{P_n(p)}, \qquad m \leqq n, \tag{188}$$

where $Q_m(p)$ and $P_n(p)$ are polynomials of degree m and n respectively. This can be written in factored form as

$$G(p) = A\,\frac{(p - p_1)(p - p_2)\,\cdots\,(p - p_m)}{(p - P_1)(p - P_2)\,\cdots\,(p - P_n)}, \tag{189}$$

where some of the roots $p_1, p_2, \ldots, p_m$ and some of the poles $P_1, P_2, \ldots, P_n$ may be repeated. As p describes in a positive sense a closed contour that encircles Z zeros and P poles, the phase angle of G changes by $+2\pi$ for each of the enclosed zeros and by -2π for each of the enclosed poles. The total number of times that the corresponding contour in the G-plane encircles the origin is exactly $Z - P$. This establishes the validity of the mapping theorem.

2·26. The Nyquist Criterion.—Now let us apply the theorem of the preceding section to the function

$$G(p) = 1 + Y(p) \tag{190}$$

and to the closed contour in the p-plane illustrated in Fig. 2·19. The map of a contour in the p-plane onto the Y-plane can be obtained by shifting the corresponding map on the G-plane to the left by one unit. It follows that the contour C in the p-plane, described in a positive sense, will map into a contour Γ in the Y-plane that encircles the point $(-1,0)$ in a positive sense $N = Z - P$ times. The transfer locus—a curve of this type for which C encloses all zeros and poles of $1 + Y(p)$ that lie inside the right half of the p-plane—will thus encircle the point $(-1,0)$ a number of times that is the difference between the total number of zeros and the total number of poles of $1 + Y(p)$ inside the right half of the p-plane. This result, together with the fact that the system will be stable only if the number of zeros is zero, can be used in the discussion of the stability of servomechanisms.

There is a well-known theorem due to Nyquist[1] that applies to feedback systems in which the feedback transfer function is that of a passive network. The feedback transfer function of even a single-loop servo is not usually of this form; the very presence of a motor introduces a pole at the origin. It remains true, however, that single-loop servos of a large and important class have feedback transfer functions with no poles *inside* the right half of the p-plane. *To these single-loop servos* the following theorem applies: *The servo will be stable if and only if the locus of the feedback transfer function does not pass through or encircle the point* $(-1,0)$ *in the Y-plane.*

This can be proved as follows. First of all, let us assume that the over-all transfer function

$$Y_0(p) = \frac{Y(p)}{1 + Y(p)} \tag{163}$$

has a pole on the imaginary axis. Then $1 + Y(p)$ has a zero for some point p on the imaginary axis, and $Y(p) = -1$; the feedback transfer locus passes through the point $(-1,0)$. We know that in this case the servo is unstable (Sec. 2·20), in agreement with the statement of the Nyquist criterion.

Now let us assume that there is no pole of $Y_0(p)$ on the imaginary axis. Then the servo will be stable if and only if $1 + Y(p)$ has no zeros in the right half of the p-plane. Now single-loop servo systems of the class that we are considering have no poles of $Y(p)$ in the right half of the p-plane; that is, $P = 0$. The contour C does not pass through any poles or zeros of $1 + Y(p)$, since the poles are bypassed by detours and we are now considering only the case where there are no poles of $Y_0(p)$ [i.e. no zeros of $1 + Y(p)$] on the imaginary axis. It follows that the feedback transfer locus will encircle the point $(-1,0)$ a number of times that is exactly equal to the number of zeros of $1 + Y(p)$ in the right half plane. The servo will thus be stable if and only if the number of encirclements is zero. This concludes the proof of the criterion.

Examples.—As an application of the Nyquist criterion we shall now consider the type of servo described by Eq. (46). The feedback transfer function for this system is

$$Y(p) = \frac{K}{p(T_m p + 1)}, \tag{191}$$

[1] H. Nyquist, "Regeneration Theory," *Bell System Tech. Jour.*, **11**, 126 (1932).

where K is the gain and T_m the motor time constant. A rough sketch of the locus of the feedback transfer function is shown in Fig. 2·21. The full line shows the portion of the locus obtained for positive values of ω; the dotted line that obtained for negative values of ω. The semicircle about the origin corresponds to the indentation made to exclude the origin. The arrows indicate the direction in which the locus is traced as ω goes from $+\infty$ to $-\infty$. Actually what is drawn is the locus of $Y(p)/K$; the critical point is then $(-1/K,0)$ instead of $(-1,0)$. (The reason for drawing the locus in this way is that it is much easier to change the position of the critical point than to redraw the locus for different values of the gain.) According to the Nyquist criterion this servo system is stable, since the feedback transfer function locus does not encircle the point $[-(1/K), 0]$.

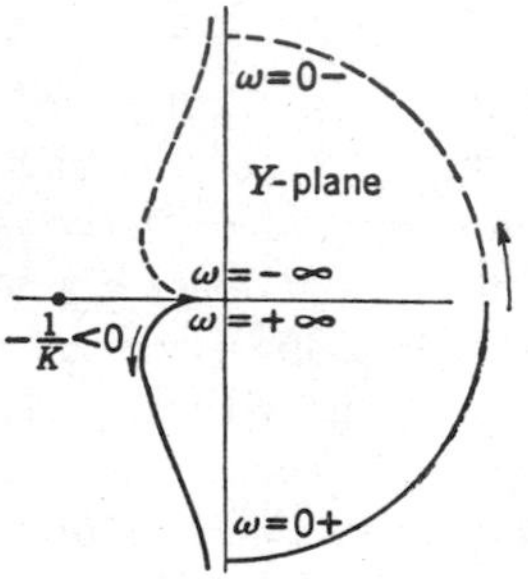

FIG. 2·21.—Locus of the feedback transfer function $Y(p) = K/[p(T_mp + 1)]$.

Theoretically, the system will be stable however large the gain. This is not actually the case, because the feedback transfer function in Eq. (191) only approximates that of the physical servomechanism. A closer approximation includes the time constant T_a of the amplifier; then

$$\frac{Y(p)}{K} = \frac{1}{p(T_mp + 1)(T_ap + 1)}. \tag{192}$$

The locus of this feedback transfer function is shown in Fig. 2·22. For small values of the gain K, the critical point $[-(1/K), 0]$ is not enclosed by the locus and the system is stable; for large values of the gain, the point $[-(1/K), 0]$ is encircled twice by the locus, and the system is unstable. It is easy to obtain the limiting value of K for which the system becomes unstable. The value of ω for which the locus crosses the negative real axis is easily found to be $\omega_0 = 1/\sqrt{T_mT_a}$. Since T_m is much larger than T_a, the magnitude of Y at this point is

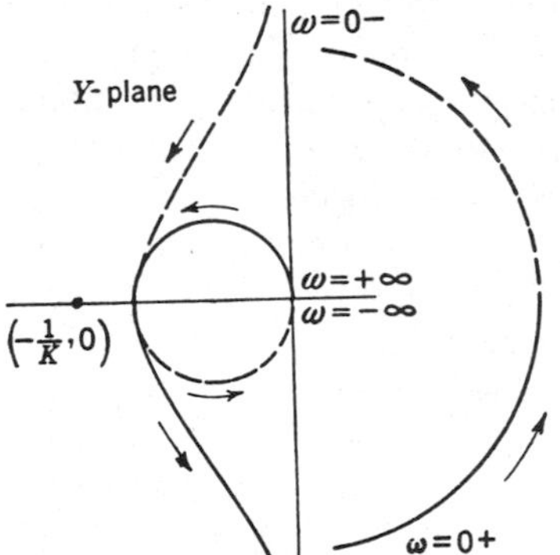

FIG. 2·22.—Locus of the feedback transfer function $[Y(p)/K] = 1/[p(T_mp + 1)(T_ap + 1)]$.

$$|Y|_0 \approx KT_a. \tag{193}$$

For stability, then, KT_a must be less than unity; that is,

$$K < \frac{1}{T_a}. \tag{194}$$

2·27. Multiloop Servo Systems.—In single-loop servo systems the feedback transfer function has no poles inside the right half of the p-plane. As a consequence the stability criterion has the simple form given in the previous section. For multiloop servo systems, however, the feedback transfer function may contain poles in the interior of the right half plane; this can occur when one of the inner loops is unstable. When this is the case, the more general form of the theorem in Sec. 2·24 must be applied. It remains true that the system is stable if and only if there are no zeros of $1 + Y(p)$ in the right half plane, but the number of times that the feedback transfer locus encircles the point $(-1,0)$ is equal to the number of zeros *minus the number of poles*. An independent determination of the number of poles inside the right half of the p-plane must be made, after which the number of zeros can be obtained by reference to the transfer locus and use of Eq. (182).

In general, because of the form of the feedback transfer function for a multiloop system, it is not very difficult to determine the number of these poles. As stated in Sec. 2·21, the feedback transfer function for multiloop systems will often be of the form

$$Y(p) = \frac{Y_1(p)}{1 + Y_1(p)Y_2(p)}. \tag{169}$$

If there are three independent loops in the system, $Y_1(p)$ may itself be of the form

$$Y_1(p) = \frac{Y_3(p)}{1 + Y_3(p)Y_4(p)}. \tag{195}$$

A procedure for determining the stability of the multiloop servo system will be made clear by considering such a three-loop system. The poles of $Y_3(p)Y_4(p)$ can be obtained by inspection, since this, in all likelihood, will be a relatively simple function. The locus of $Y_3(p)Y_4(p)$ is then sketched to determine the number of times that it encircles the point $(-1,0)$. From this number N and the number of poles of

$$Y_3(p)Y_4(p)$$

in the right half of the p-plane, the number of zeros of $1 + Y_3(p)Y_4(p)$ in this region can be obtained; this is the number of poles of $Y_1(p)$ inside the right half of the p-plane. The number of poles of $Y_2(p)$ in the right half of the p-plane can be determined by inspection; the number of poles of $Y_1(p)Y_2(p)$ is the sum of these numbers. The locus of $Y_1(p)Y_2(p)$ is then drawn, and the number of poles of $Y(p)$ in this region is determined as before. Finally the locus of $Y(p)$ is drawn, and from this locus is deduced the number of zeros of $1 + Y(p)$ in the right half of the p-plane. Thus by use of a succession of Nyquist diagrams it can be determined whether or not the system is stable.

Examples of Multiloop Systems.—We shall first discuss a two-loop system of the type sketched in Fig. 2·17. Let us suppose that the inner loop consists of a tachometer plus a simple *RC*-filter of the type shown in Fig. 2·6. The tachometer output is a voltage proportional to the derivative of the servo output. The transfer function for the combination is therefore

$$Y_2(p) = K_1 p \frac{T_0 p}{T_0 p + 1}, \tag{196}$$

where K_1 is the factor of proportionality. We shall suppose that the amplifier-plus-motor has the transfer function

$$Y_1(p) = \frac{K_2}{p(T_m p + 1)(T_a p + 1)}. \tag{197}$$

The feedback transfer function is

$$Y(p) = \frac{Y_1(p)}{1 + Y_1(p)Y_2(p)}. \tag{169}$$

To determine whether or not $Y(p)$ has any poles in the right half of the p-plane it is necessary to examine

$$Y_1(p)Y_2(p) = \frac{K_1 K_2 T_0 p}{(T_m p + 1)(T_a p + 1)(T_0 p + 1)}. \tag{198}$$

The transfer locus for $Y_1(p)Y_2(p)$ is shown in Fig. 2·23. Since

$$Y_1(p)Y_2(p)$$

has no poles in the right half of the p-plane, the Nyquist criterion can be applied to determine whether $1 + Y_1Y_2$ has any zeros in the right half of the p-plane. It is evident from Fig. 2·23 that the locus does not encircle the point $(-1,0)$ for $K_1K_2 \geqq 0$; consequently $1 + Y_1Y_2$ has no zeros in the right half plane, and $Y(p)$ has no poles in this region. It follows that the simple Nyquist criterion can be applied in this case.

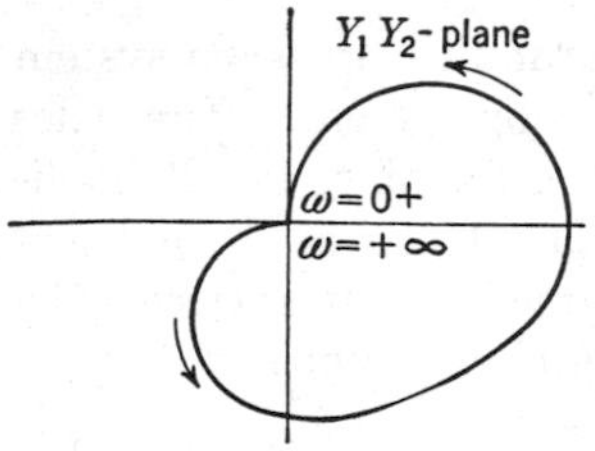

FIG. 2·23.—Transfer locus of $Y_1(p)Y_2(p) = (K_1K_2T_0P)/[(T_mp + 1)(T_ap + 1)(T_0p + 1)]$.

As a second example we shall consider a servo for which the simple Nyquist criterion is not valid. We shall again consider the system shown in Fig. 2·17 and shall suppose that the tachometer and filter combination has the transfer function

$$Y_2(p) = K_1 p \left(\frac{T_0 p}{T_0 p + 1}\right)^3 \tag{199}$$

and that the amplifier plus motor can be described by

$$Y_1(p) = \frac{K_2}{p(T_m p + 1)}. \tag{200}$$

We shall further assume that $T_0 > T_m$. As above, the feedback transfer function is

$$Y(p) = \frac{Y_1(p)}{1 + Y_1(p)Y_2(p)}, \tag{169}$$

where now

$$Y_1(p)Y_2(p) = \frac{K_1K_2}{(T_mp + 1)} \left(\frac{T_0p}{T_0p + 1}\right)^3 \tag{201}$$

The locus of Y_1Y_2 is sketched in Fig. 2·24 for positive values of ω only This locus intersects the negative real axis at about the frequency

$$\omega_0 \approx \frac{1}{\sqrt{3}} \frac{1}{T_0}. \tag{202}$$

The magnitude of Y_1Y_2 at this frequency is

$$|Y_1Y_2(\omega_0)| \approx \tfrac{1}{8}K_1K_2. \tag{203}$$

Thus the inner loop is stable if $\frac{1}{8}K_1K_2 < 1$. If $\frac{1}{8}K_1K_2 > 1$, the inner loop is unstable and, indeed, an application of the theorem of Sec. 2·25 shows that in this case there are two zeros of the function $1 + Y_1Y_2$ in the right half of the p-plane.

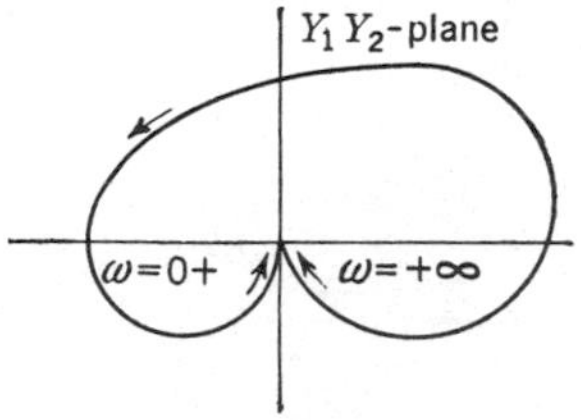

FIG. 2·24.—Transfer locus of $Y_1(p)Y_2(p) = [K_1K_2/(T_mp + 1)] [T_0p/(T_0p + 1)]^3$.

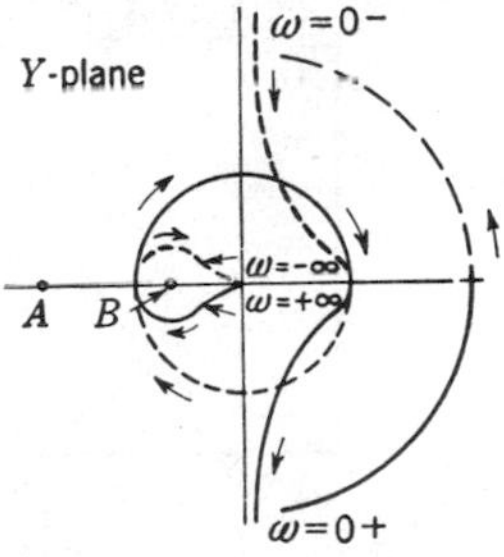

FIG. 2·25.—Feedback transfer locus.

We shall now assume that the gain is set so that the inner loop is unstable. A sketch of the feedback transfer locus is shown in Fig. 2·25; the origin of the p-plane has been excluded from the right half of the p-plane by the usual detour. If the gain K_1 is such as to make the point $(-1,0)$ be at A, then $N = 0$. Since $Y(p)$ has two poles in the right half of the p-plane, $0 = Z - 2$, or $Z = 2$; the system is unstable. If the simple Nyquist criterion were applied to this system, it would lead to the false conclusion that the system is stable. If the gain K_1 is such as to make the point $(-1,0)$ fall at B, then $N = -2$. In this case $-2 = Z - 2$ and $Z = 0$; the system is stable. In applying the simple Nyquist criterion one would have obtained a double encirclement of the critical point in a negative direction; the result would then have been ambiguous.

CHAPTER 3

SERVO ELEMENTS

BY C. W. MILLER

3·1. Introduction.—In this chapter there will be presented some examples of the physical devices that are common components in electronic servo loops. Its purpose is to describe a few actual circuits and mechanisms that may assist in the physical understanding of the problems discussed in following chapters—the design and mathematical consideration of the entire servo loop. This chapter can, however, serve only as a cursory introduction to the field of servo components.

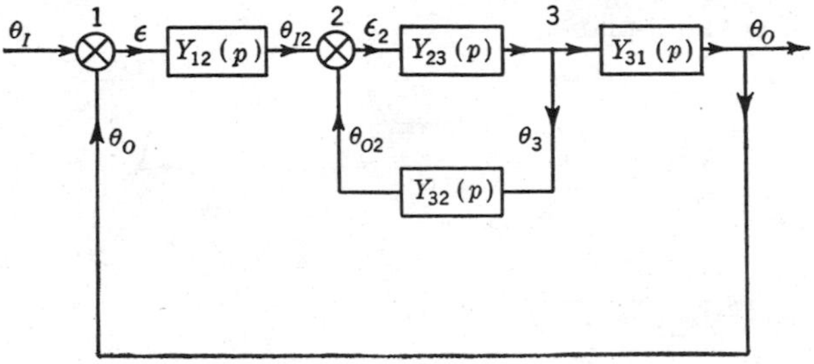

FIG. 3·1.—Simple servo loop.

Since the types of devices commonly utilized in the more complex servo loops are the same as in relatively simple servo loops, it is sufficiently informative to consider the possible elements in such a simple loop as that presented in Fig. 3·1. In this figure the common mechanical differential symbol has been employed to indicate any device that has an output proportional to the difference of two inputs. Thus,

$$\epsilon = \theta_I - \theta_O. \tag{1}$$

The various "boxes" employed in the loop have transfer characteristics defined by

$$Y_{mn}(p) = \frac{\theta_n(p)}{\theta_m(p)}. \tag{2}$$

In general, attention will be focused on the frequency dependence of these transfer characteristics rather than on amplification or gain. Because of this, no space will be devoted, for example, to the quite involved problem of the design of vacuum-tube amplifiers. Special attention will be paid, however, to error-measuring systems and their inaccuracies. This emphasis is based on the fact that such elements are not included in the servo loop and therefore no amount of care in the design of the loop will decrease the error resulting from their inadequacies.

The equation relating the input quantity θ_I and the output quantity θ_O in Fig. 3·1 is

$$\frac{\theta_O}{\theta_I} = \frac{Y_{12}(p)Y_{23}(p)Y_{31}(p)}{1 + Y_{12}(p)Y_{23}(p)Y_{31}(p) + Y_{23}(p)Y_{32}(p)}. \tag{3}$$

The relation between error ϵ and the output quantity is

$$\frac{\theta_O}{\epsilon} = \frac{Y_{12}(p)Y_{23}(p)Y_{31}(p)}{1 + Y_{23}(p)Y_{32}(p)}. \tag{4}$$

It is to be noted that the loop in the example involves two devices of the differential type. Differential 1 of Fig. 3·1 is an error-measuring system; such systems will receive extended discussion in this chapter. Amplifiers may be employed in either or both of the boxes $Y_{12}(p)$ and $Y_{23}(p)$. In one of these boxes there may be also a device for changing the nature of the signal carrier; such elements will be mentioned in this chapter. Also, special transfer characteristics may be desired for operating on the error ϵ; suitable networks for this will be presented. Equalizing or stabilizing feedback is employed by the path through $Y_{32}(p)$, and a section of this chapter will present examples of the devices commonly used to obtain a desired transfer characteristic $Y_{32}(p)$. The remaining box, the transfer characteristic of which is given as $Y_{31}(p)$, is often a gear train and as such has (if it is properly designed) no interesting frequency dependence. Some discussion, however, will be included on the problem of gear trains.

There is, of course, no clear-cut rule for separating the components of a servo loop. Indeed, even with the same servo loop it is sometimes helpful to make different separations that depend upon the particular interest at the time. In this chapter, the attempt will be made to separate transfer functions according to physical pieces of equipment. To maintain consistency with Fig. 3·1, primes will be used if additional equipment is involved.

3·2. Error-measuring Systems.—Necessary components of any closed-loop system are those devices which measure the deviation between the actual output and the desired output.

It is important that this difference, or error, be presented in the form most suitable for the other components in the control system. Thus the location of equipment, as well as the choice of the physical type of error signal and its transmission, is important. For example, a mechanical differential is rarely used as a device to obtain the difference between the actual output and the desired output, because it is often impractical to realize these two quantities as physically adjacent shaft rotations. Also, one may or may not desire the error as a shaft rotation, the choice depending upon the amplifying system to be used and its required placement.

Certainly one must also choose an error-measuring system that has an inherent accuracy greater than that required of the over-all loop. Often both static accuracy and dynamic accuracy of the system must be examined. Many error-measuring devices produce "noise" of such a nature that the component frequencies are proportional to the rate of change of the input and output quantities. The response of the loop to this noise must be considered.

In addition to such noise, error-measuring systems utilizing a-c carrier voltages commonly have in the final output not only a voltage proportional to the error, with a fixed phase shift from the excitation voltage, but also a voltage that is not a function of error and is 90° out of phase with the so-called error voltage. Harmonics of both voltages are usually also present. The phase shift of the error voltage, if reasonably constant for the class of device, is not a serious problem but must be considered in the design of the other components. The quadrature voltage and the harmonic voltages are often very troublesome because they tend to overload amplifiers and to increase the heating of motors. Special design, nevertheless, can eliminate this problem (see Sec. 3·12).

Finally, the components of the error-measuring system must be mechanically and electrically suitable for the application; that is, the error-measuring system must fulfill its function for a sufficient length of time under velocities and accelerations of the variables being transmitted and with the exposure, impacts, temperatures, etc., encountered in the anticipated use of the equipment.

Because of the ease of transmission of signals and the resulting freedom in placement of equipment, electrical devices have had wide applications as error-measuring devices. A few types will be discussed in the following sections.

3·3. Synchros.—This discussion, elementary in nature, will be restricted to a type of synchro that is in common use in Army, Navy, and some nonmilitary equipment.

If the axis of a coil carrying an alternating current makes an angle θ with the axis of a second concentric coil, the induced emf in the second coil will be $K \cos \theta$, where K is a constant dependent upon the frequency and the magnitude of the current in the primary coil, the structure of the coils, and the characteristics of the magnetic circuit. If two additional secondary coils are added with their axes 120° and 240° from the axis of the first secondary coil (see Fig. 3·2), the emf's will be

$$\left.\begin{aligned} E_{OS2} &= K \cos \theta, \\ E_{OS1} &= K \cos (\theta - 120°), \\ E_{OS3} &= K \cos (\theta - 240°), \end{aligned}\right\} \tag{5}$$

where the subscripts indicate the points between which the voltage is measured and their order gives the sense of the measurement. The terminal voltages will be

$$\left.\begin{aligned} E_{S1S2} &= K \sqrt{3} \cos (\theta + 30°), \\ E_{S2S3} &= K \sqrt{3} \cos (\theta + 150°), \\ E_{S3S1} &= K \sqrt{3} \cos (\theta + 270°). \end{aligned}\right\} \tag{6}$$

In Fig. 3·2 the labeling is that for Navy synchros, and the circuit as drawn is physically equivalent to a Navy synchro viewed at the end of the synchro from which the rotor shaft extends. It is standard practice in the Navy, however, to consider counterclockwise rotation positive rather than clockwise, as in Fig. 3·2.

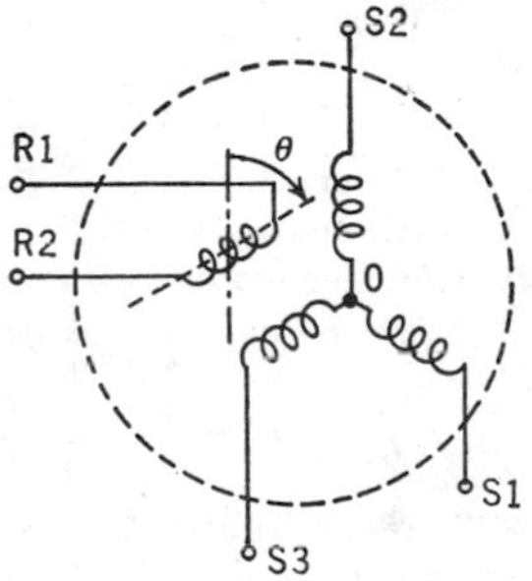

FIG. 3·2.—Schematic diagram of a synchro.

Various modifications of the construction of a synchro exist to suit different functional uses. In this section, only synchro transmitters, synchro repeaters, and synchro control transformers will be mentioned. In these units, the three stator coils are located on a laminated magnetic frame that surrounds and supports the rotor. Synchro transmitters and repeaters have a salient pole or "dumbbell" type rotor, but a control transformer has a cylindrical rotor. A mechanical damper is built into synchro repeaters to decrease oscillatory response. For a more detailed discussion of these types of synchros (and for discussion of other types), one or more of the various references should be consulted.[1]

Table 3·1 gives a brief summary of some of the characteristics of a few of the Army and Navy synchros.

3·4. Data System of Synchro Transmitter and Repeater.—Such a device as that described in Sec. 3·3, so constructed that the angle θ can be changed at will by turning the rotor (the primary), is known as a

[1] "Synchros and Their Application," Bell Telephone Laboratories, Systems Development Department, Report No. X-63646, Issue 2, New York, Mar. 19, 1945; "Specifications for Synchro Transmission Units and Systems," O.S. No. 671, Rev. D, Bureau of Ordnance, Navy Department, Washington, Feb. 12, 1944; "Specifications for Units, A. C. Synchronous for Data Transmission," FXS-348 (Rev. 7) Tentative Specification, Frankford Arsenal, Mar. 9, 1943; "United States Navy Synchros, Description and Operation," Ordnance Pamphlet No. 1303, A Joint Bureau of Ordnance and Bureau of Ships Publication, Navy Department, Washington, Dec. 15, 1944.

synchro transmitter (or generator) when it is used in transmitting electrically the value of the angle θ. By use of a synchro repeater (or motor), the angle θ may be reproduced at a remote position as a shaft rotation. A synchro repeater is similar in structure to a synchro transmitter, except for the addition of the damper previously mentioned. Because of the difference in use, the rotor of the repeater is free to rotate with little friction and low-inertia loads, whereas the transmitter rotor is mechanically constrained to the value of θ that is to be transmitted. A repeater is connected to a transmitter as indicated in Fig. 3·3.

TABLE 3·1.—SYNCHRO UNITS FOR 115-VOLT, 60-CYCLE OPERATION

Synchro	Weight, lb	Stator, volts	Rotor, volts	Excitation current, amp	Unit torque, gradient, oz-in./degree	Unit static accuracy, degrees		Rotor inertia, lb in.^{2}
						Avg	Max	
5G Navy generator..	5	90	115	0.6	0.4	0.2	0.6	0.31
6G Navy generator..	8	90	115	1.3	1.2	0.2	0.6	0.94
7G Navy generator..	18	90	115	3.0	3.4	0.2	0.6	2.4
1F Navy motor.....	2	90	115	0.3	0.06	0.5	1.5	0.026
5F Navy motor.....	5	90	115	0.6	0.4	0.2	0.6	0.31
1CT Navy control transformer.......	2	90	55	0.045	....	0.2	0.6	0.026
3CT Navy control transformer.......	3	90	55	.....	....	0.1	0.3	.....
5CT Navy control transformer.......	5	90	55	0.045	....	0.1	0.3	0.31
IV Army transmitter	4.8	105	115	0.55	0.48	0.25	0.5	.....
I-4 Army transmitter	11.8	105	115	1.0	1.0	0.25	0.5	.....
X Army repeater....	1.3	105	115	0.12	0.020–0.025	1.0	2.0	.....
V Army repeater....	4.8	105	115	0.55	0.48	0.25	0.5	.....
II-6 Army repeater..	10.3	105	115	0.55	0.53	0.25	0.5	.....
XXV Army transformer..........	1.3	104	60	.....	....	....	0.9	.....
XV Army transformer..........	4.8	104	58	.....	....	....	0.9	.....

If the rotor of the repeater has the same angular relationship to its stator coils as the rotor of the transmitter has to its stator coils, no current will flow in the stator leads. This is a minimal-energy position. If the angles are different, currents flow in the stator leads and equal torques are exerted upon both the transmitter and the repeater rotors in such a sense as to reduce the misalignment and thus to approach a minimal-energy position. Since the transmitter rotor is constrained, the repeater rotor turns until it assumes an angular position θ, to within the errors caused by construction difficulties and friction. It will be shown

(Sec. 3·6) that the restoring torque when a synchro unit is connected to a similar unit acting as a transmitter is very nearly $57.3T_u \sin (\theta' - \theta)$, where T_u is the unit torque given in Table 3·1. There is a position of zero torque at 180° misalignment, but it is unstable.

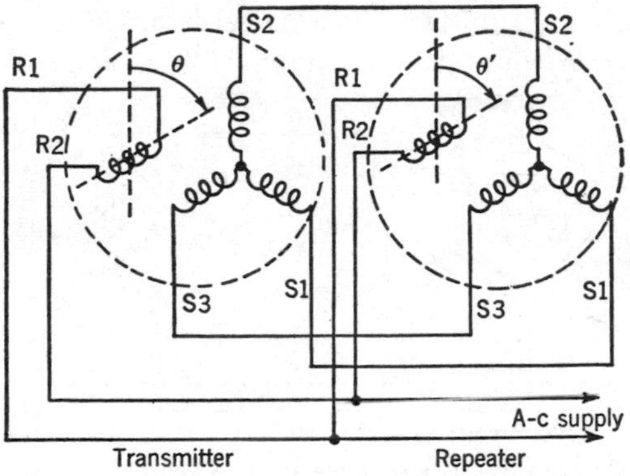

FIG. 3·3.—Synchro transmitter connected to synchro repeater.

In some cases where it is necessary to reproduce a variable quantity remotely as a rotation, the primary system can easily stand any torque that might be reflected upon it. It might seem that a simple transmitter-repeater system would have wide use in such cases. As is seen, however, from Table 3·1, small loading would cause very appreciable errors even for the larger synchros. If the error ever exceeds 180°, the synchro repeater will seek a null 360° from the proper angle. In fact, the synchro repeater may lock to a zero torque position after any number of multiples of 360° measured at its own shaft. This makes it difficult to obtain greater torques by gearing down to the load, though some schemes have been devised.

As a further disadvantage, the transfer characteristic of a transmitter-repeater system exhibits a high resonant peak (an amplification of 2 to 8, depending on the manufacturer) at a frequency between 4 and 8 cps. Any increase in the inertia at the synchro shaft results in a still poorer transfer characteristic.

For these reasons, simple transmitter-repeater data systems are generally used to drive only light dials. In such a use, a coarse dial (so-called "low-speed" dial) is driven by one transmitter-repeater combination in which shaft values are such that the 360° ambiguity is of no consequence or such that the ambiguity will be avoided by limits on the variable. A fine dial (so-called "high-speed" dial) for accurate interpolation between graduations on the low-speed dial is driven by a second transmitter-repeater combination. Since it is used only for interpolation, the 360° ambiguity causes no concern.

By adding torque-amplifying equipment that is activated by the rotation of the synchro-repeater shaft, many types of servos can be devised. They range from simple types in which the rotor activates a switch that directly controls an electric motor, to more complex systems in which, for instance, the synchro repeater controls a valve in a hydraulic amplifier.

3·5. Synchro Transmitter with Control Transformer as Error-measuring System.—Without torque amplification, a synchro-transmitter-

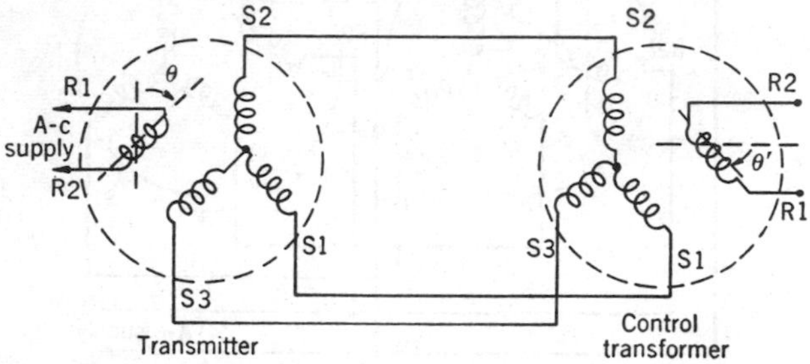

FIG. 3·4.—Synchro transmitter connected to a synchro control transformer.

repeater combination is not, in general, satisfactory as a follow-up because of the low torque and poor response characteristic. As a result of the extensive development of the science of electronics and of design advances in electric motors and generators, torque amplification is often obtained by electrical means. For this, the natural input is a voltage rather than a shaft rotation. To meet this need, synchro control transformers have been developed. Figure 3·4 shows how a control transformer is connected to a transmitter.

With neglect of source impedance, the voltages given in Eq. (6) will be impressed across corresponding stator leads of the control transformer. These voltages will produce proportional fluxes, which will add vectorially to give a resultant flux having the same angular position in respect to the control-transformer stator coils as the transmitter rotor has to its stator coils. If the rotor of the control transformer is set at right angles to this flux, no voltage is observed across terminals R1-R2. If the angle of rotation θ' of the control-transformer rotor is less than θ, an a-c voltage appears across R1-R2 with a slight phase lead (about 10°) with respect to the line voltage. If θ' is greater than θ, an a-c voltage is again observed across R1-R2, but with an additional 180° phase shift. In fact, the voltage appearing across R1-R2 may be expressed as $E_{R1R2} = E_{max} \sin (\theta - \theta')$. Since E_{max} is usually about 57 volts, there is, for small errors, about a volt per degree of error measured at the synchro shaft. In addition, a quadrature voltage (with harmonics), usually less than 0.2 volt in magnitude, is present even at $\theta' = \theta$. Note that there is a "false zero" 180° from the proper zero.

By use of a phase-sensitive combination of amplifier and motor, a torque can be obtained that can be used to make θ' just equal to θ. This is accomplished by connecting the input of the amplifier to terminals R1-R2 of the control transformer and controlling a motor, geared to the control-transformer rotor, with the output of the amplifier. If the equipment to be positioned is also geared to the motor, a simple servomechanism is thus obtained. Examination of the phase of the voltage for angles very near the "false zero" mentioned above shows that it is an unstable position. The servo will quickly synchronize to the proper zero.

It is to be noted that here, as for the synchro-transmitter-repeater data system, the error in following must not exceed 180° at the synchro shaft, or this servo system will seek a null 360° or a multiple of 360° (measured at the synchro shaft) from the proper angle. Therefore, the same requirements on shaft values must be imposed here as were mentioned for the single synchro-transmitter-repeater combination.

Difficulties in fabrication introduce inaccuracies in synchros as shown in Table 3·1. These inaccuracies are a serious limitation on the use of the previously described system using a single transmitter and control transformer. Such an error-measuring system is often called a "single-speed" synchro data system.

The effect of inaccuracies of synchros on the precision of transmission of a quantity can be greatly decreased by operating the synchro at a smaller range of the variable per revolution of the synchro. For example, if the servo problem is to reproduce accurately the train angle of a director, a "1-speed" synchro system will be needed. For this there are needed a synchro transmitter geared one-to-one to the director and, of course, a synchro control transformer geared one-to-one to the remote equipment that is to follow the director. Since 360° rotation of the director rotates the synchro through 360°, a 0.5° inaccuracy of the synchro system would give 0.5° inaccuracy in reproduction of the angle. This 1-speed synchro has no stable ambiguous zeros. It can now be paralleled with a "high-speed" synchro system, so geared, for example, that 10° of director rotation turns this second transmitter 360°. A similarly geared control transformer is added to the remote equipment. The synchros are now aligned or electrically zeroed (see previous references in Sec. 3·3 for technique) by so clamping their frames that when the error between director position and the position of the remote equipment is zero, both synchro systems produce zero-error voltage. With such a pair of high-speed synchros the inherent inaccuracy in reproducing the train angle has been reduced by a factor of 36; for example, it is 0.013° if an inaccuracy of 0.5° exists at the synchro shaft. Unfortunately, the high-speed (which can in this case be called 36-speed) system has 35 false zeros, or lock-in points.

The 1-speed system gives approximate information of the total train angle; the 36-speed system gives very accurate indication of the angle, but only if it is synchronized at the proper zero.

A switching system is needed to put the 1-speed system in control until the reproduced train angle is approximately correct and then throw the control to the 36-speed synchro system. Such a circuit is often called a "synchronizing" circuit. An example of a type of such a circuit is shown in Fig. 3·5.

The action of the circuit is quite simple. The first tube $V1$ acts as an amplifier. The second tube is biased below cutoff. As the 1-speed error

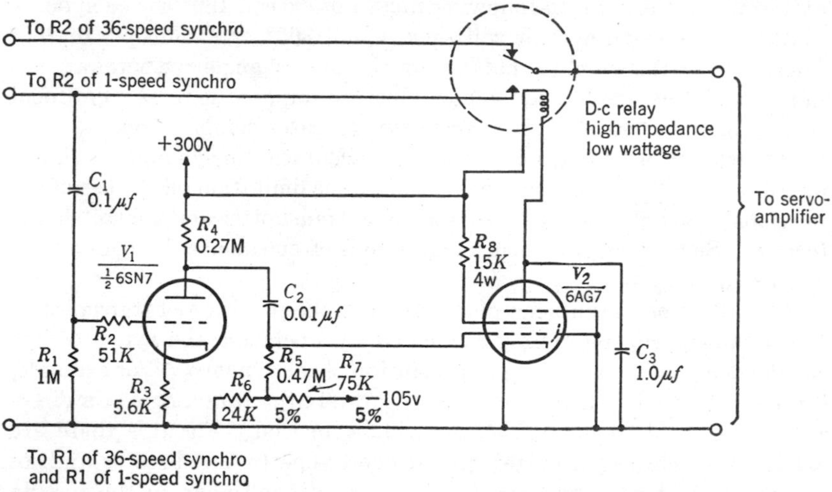

FIG. 3·5.—Synchronizing circuit for dual-speed synchro system.

voltage increases, there is no effect on the plate current of $V2$ until the error has reached a critical value related to the bias on $V2$, at which point the average plate current of $V2$ increases rapidly. This critical value of error is chosen either by changing the gain of the first stage or by changing the bias on $V2$ so that the 1-speed system assumes control before there is any danger of locking-in on one of the adjacent false zeros of the 36-speed system.

Since the error should be low while the servo follows motions of the director, this circuit will not need to function except when the follow-up system is first turned on or when there is a severe transient in the motion of the director.

There are some considerations that tend to limit the extent to which the shaft value of the high-speed synchro control transformer is decreased in an effort to improve the accuracy of a servo and, incidentally, also to increase the gain of the transmission system in volts per unit of error. One limitation is that the high-speed synchros should not be driven at too high a rate at the maximum velocity of the transmitted variable. For example, Navy units listed in Table 3·1 should not be driven faster than 300 rpm, though there are special units, similar in other respects, that can be driven up to 1200 rpm. Inertia considerations should not be overlooked. Often the synchros, even if at 36-speed, reflect to the motor shaft inertia that is not negligible, especially for small motors. Synchronizing difficulties may arise at low shaft values of the high-speed synchro. Because the region of high-speed control is extremely narrow, a comparatively short time is required for the servo to pass completely through this region. A large number of overshoots or even sustained oscillation may result. Finally, little is gained by lowering the shaft value of the high-speed synchro if backlash in the synchro gearing is causing more error than that inherent in the synchros or, in general, if the other components in the loop do not merit increased accuracy from the data transmission.

The above director follow-up system will serve to illustrate a problem encountered in dual-speed synchro systems. If the follow-up mechanism is turned off and the director is rotated through an angle that is close to an integral multiple of 180°, the 36-speed system will be at or near a stable zero (see Fig. 3·6*a*). Furthermore, the system is at or near the false zero of the 1-speed synchros, and there will be insufficient signal to activate the relay of the synchronizing circuit. Thus the follow-up, if turned on, would remain 180° from the proper angle until some condition arose that caused sufficient error to throw the relay. Such an ambiguous zero exists in any dual-speed data system at those values of the transmitted variable which require an even number of rotations of the high-speed synchro and an integral number of half revolutions of the low-speed synchro.

The problem of this ambiguous zero can be solved by putting in series with the error voltage from the 1-speed synchro control transformer a voltage E_{SO} that has a magnitude in the range

$$S_{HS} - \epsilon_C > 2\,\frac{57}{E_{max}}\,E_{SO} > \epsilon_C, \qquad (7)$$

where ϵ_C is the critical error angle that will throw the synchronizing relay, S_{HS} is the shaft value of the high-speed synchro system, and E_{max} is the maximum error voltage that the synchro can deliver. The voltage E_{SO} is often called an "antistick-off" voltage.

The purpose of this voltage E_{SO} is to displace the false zero of the 1-speed system so that there is enough voltage from the 1-speed system to throw the synchronizing relay at what was the ambiguous zero. Of course, the 1-speed false zero must not be displaced so much that it approaches the next stable null of the high-speed system.

The displacement of the false zero can better be understood if one follows through the procedure of adding the voltage step by step. Figure 3·6*a* is a plot of the magnitude of the voltages observed from both the 1- and the 36-speed synchro systems as the director is rotated through 360° of train angle with the follow-up turned off. In this figure, when the

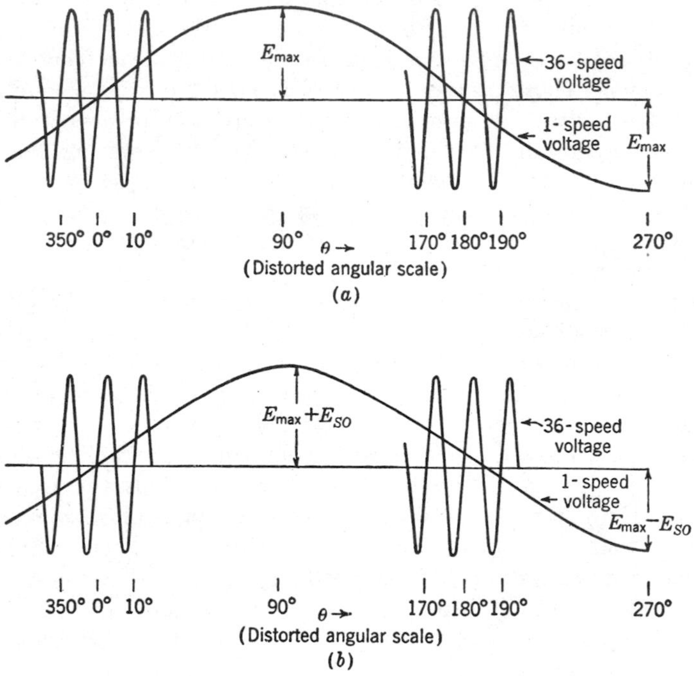

FIG. 3·6.—Adding stick-off voltage to dual-speed synchro system.

plot of the magnitude of the a-c error voltage passes below the baseline, it indicates a phase shift of 180°. For clarity, only the voltages in the region of 0° (the angle at which the remote equipment has been left) and in the region of 180° (the region of the ambiguous zero that we wish to eliminate) are plotted. This is merely a partial plot of

$$E_L = E_{max} \sin \theta, \tag{8a}$$

and

$$E_H = E_{max} \sin (36\theta), \tag{8b}$$

where E_L is the error voltage from the 1-speed system, E_H is the error voltage from the 36-speed system, and θ is the angle through which the director has been turned.

If a voltage E_{SO} from the same a-c source that is used to excite the synchro generators is added to the 1-speed error voltage, the voltages become

$$E'_L = E_{max} \sin \theta + E_{SO}, \tag{9a}$$
$$E_H = E_{max} \sin (36\theta). \tag{9b}$$

This will displace upward the curve in Fig. 3·6*a* labeled "1-speed error voltage."

Now it is still necessary that when the director is at the same angle as the remote equipment, the error voltage from the 1- and 36-speed systems be zero and of the same phase for small errors. Therefore, we realign the low-speed control transformer to obtain these conditions, and the result is shown in Fig. 3·6*b*. The equations for the voltages are now

$$E''_L = E_{max} \sin (\theta - \phi) + E_{SO}, \tag{10a}$$
$$E_H = E_{max} \sin (36\theta). \tag{10b}$$

Since at $\theta = 0$, $E''_L = 0$, we have

$$E_{SO} = E_{max} \sin \phi. \tag{11}$$

The new position of the false zero θ_f of the 1-speed system is given by the solution of

$$\left.\begin{aligned} 0 &= E_{max} \sin (\theta_f - \phi) + E_{max} \sin \phi, \\ \text{or} \qquad \theta_f &= 180 + 2\phi. \end{aligned}\right\} \tag{12}$$

Thus the false zero has been shifted through an angle 2ϕ. It is desired that the false zero be shifted by an amount greater than ϵ_C, the critical error angle associated with the throwing of the synchronizing relay. Then the follow-up will be unable to settle in the stable zero at 180° of the 36-speed system because the synchronizing relay will be energized. Also, the false zero must be shifted by an amount that differs by ϵ_C from an integral multiple of the shaft value S_{HS} of the high-speed synchro. For practical reasons, it is well to limit the shift to an amount less than the shaft value of the high-speed synchro. Therefore,

$$S_{HS} - \epsilon_C > 2\phi > \epsilon_C. \tag{13}$$

Since ϕ is fairly small, we may write

$$S_{HS} - \epsilon_C > 2 \frac{57}{E_{max}} E_{SO} > \epsilon_C \qquad \text{(values in degrees)}. \tag{14}$$

For a 1- and 36-speed system, such as our example, $S_{HS} = 10°$ and ϵ_C is usually about 2°. Thus a reasonable choice of E_{SO} is about 3 volts, because $E_{max} \approx 57$ volts.

We may generalize the above formula to include systems in which the low-speed synchro is not at 1-speed and obtain

$$S_{HS} - \epsilon_C > \frac{S_{LS}}{\pi} \frac{E_{SO}}{E_{max}} > \epsilon_C, \tag{15}$$

in which S_{LS} is the shaft value of the low-speed synchro and S_{HS}, S_{LS}, and ϵ_C are all expressed in the same units of the variable.

3·6. Coercion in Parallel Synchro Systems.—So far in this discussion there has been no mention of the effects of the internal impedance of synchro units. As more follow-up systems composed of synchro repeaters or combinations of synchro repeaters and transformers are added in

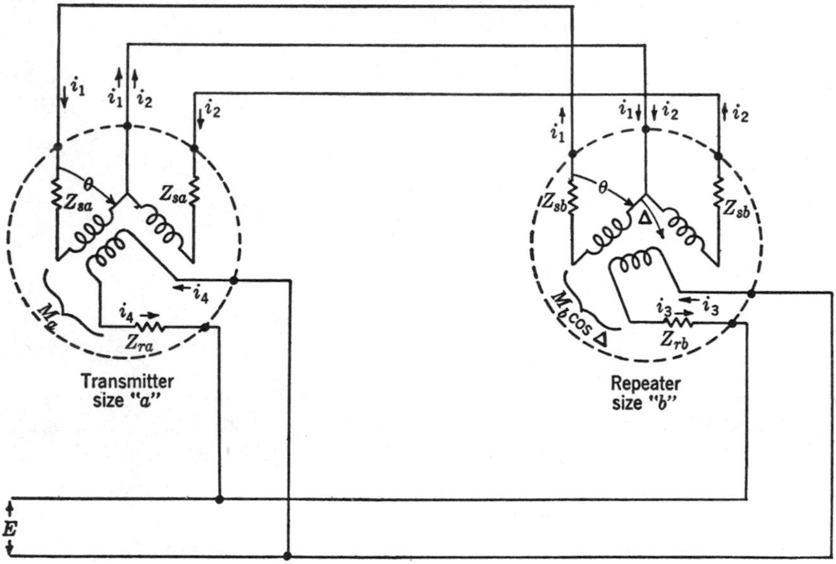

FIG. 3·7.—Simplified synchro circuit for torque calculations.

parallel to a single synchro transmitter, impedance effects become more pronounced.

Simple relationships, predicting these effects with satisfactory accuracy for small angular errors between transmitter and follow-up, can be obtained from elementary reasoning. These relationships are supported both by experiment and by precise analysis.[1]

We are interested in a synchro system that is transmitting a fixed angle θ. For generality, a transmitter of size a and a repeater of size b (such as, for instance, a Navy 7G driving a Navy 5F) are chosen. The Y-connected stator system is replaced by a stator system composed of

[1] T. M. Linville and J. S. Woodward, "Selsyn Instruments for Position Systems," *Elec. Eng.*, New York, **53**, 953 (1934).

one coil with its axis at an angle θ (thus parallel to the transmitter rotor) and a second coil with its axis at an angle $\theta + 90°$. This is an equivalent circuit for computing torque, provided appropriate circuit values are used. By applying a small torque to the rotor of the repeater, a small angular error Δ is introduced into the system. The configuration is drawn in Fig. 3·7.

Examination of Fig. 3·7 shows that the current i_1 will be, to lowest-order terms, proportional to $1 - \cos\Delta \approx \Delta^2/2$. Thus both i_1 and its derivative in respect to Δ are negligibly small, and the torque will arise predominately from the currents i_2 and i_3. If one ignores loop 1, the equations for i_2 and i_3 are

$$i_2 = \frac{j\omega ME \sin\Delta}{Z_{rb}(Z_{sa} + Z_{sb}) + \omega^2 M^2 \sin^2\Delta}, \tag{16a}$$

$$i_3 = \frac{E}{Z_{rb} + \dfrac{\omega^2 M^2 \sin^2\Delta}{Z_{sa} + Z_{sb}}}, \tag{16b}$$

where M is the mutual inductance, at $\Delta = 90°$, between the repeater rotor and the repeater stator coil carrying the current i_2.

The energy of the simplified circuit is

$$U = \tfrac{1}{2}(L_a + L_b)i_2 i_2 + M \sin\Delta i_2 i_3 + \tfrac{1}{2}L_{rb} i_3 i_3, \tag{17}$$

where L_a and L_b are the inductive coefficients of the stator windings of the synchros size a and b respectively and L_{rb} is the inductive coefficient of the rotor of the size b synchro.

The torque is proportional to the rate of change of this energy with the angle Δ. If it is assumed that $M = \sqrt{L_b L_{rb}}$ and that the resistance of the windings is small compared with the reactance, one obtains

$$T = K \frac{E_s^2 \sin\Delta}{\omega^2(L_a + L_b)}, \tag{18}$$

in which E_s is the secondary voltage for $\Delta = 90°$ with no loading and K is constant.

We note that the torque obtained when a synchro unit is used with a similar unit is, for units size a and b,

$$\left.\begin{aligned} T_a &= K \frac{E_s^2 \sin\Delta}{2\omega^2 L_a} = (T_u)_a \sin\Delta, \\ T_b &= K \frac{E_s^2 \sin\Delta}{2\omega^2 L_b} = (T_u)_b \sin\Delta. \end{aligned}\right\} \tag{19}$$

The symbol T_u is unit torque in ounce-inch per radian and is $180/\pi$ times the value listed in Table 3·1. With substitution of these expressions, Eq. (18) becomes

$$T = 2\frac{(T_u)_b \sin\Delta}{1 + R}, \tag{20a}$$

where

$$R \equiv \frac{(T_u)_b}{(T_u)_a}. \tag{20b}$$

If, now, we drive n repeaters of size b, each following with the same error (as they well may, because of similar friction loading), the term L_b in Eq. (18) is reduced by a factor $1/n$. The torque is equally distributed at the n shafts, so that at each repeater shaft the torque is

$$T = 2\,\frac{(T_u)_b \sin \Delta}{n + R}. \tag{21}$$

With similar reasoning, the torque at each repeater shaft can be computed when different sizes of repeaters are connected to a single transmitter. The decrease in the torque gradient as more repeaters are connected to a transmitter will result in greater error, because the friction load at each repeater remains constant. For conservative estimates, one may assume that three-quarters of the error for a given repeater arises from friction and proceed on that assumption to compute the increased error as loading decreases the torque gradient.

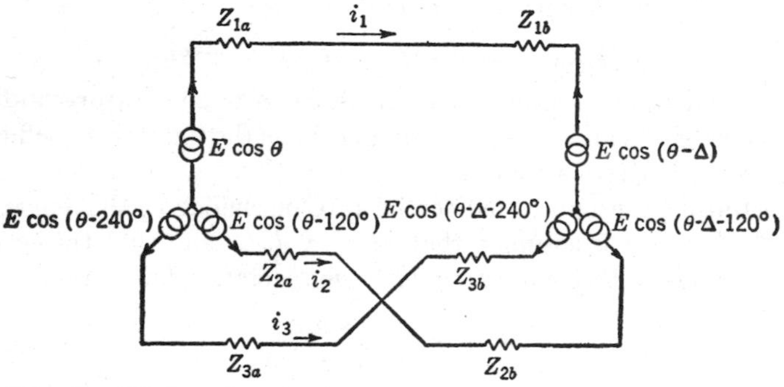

FIG. 3·8.—Simplified synchro circuit for terminal-voltage calculations.

$$Z_{1a} = Z_a + \frac{\omega^2 M_a^2}{Z_{ra}} \cos^2 \theta, \qquad Z_{1b} = Z_b + \frac{\omega^2 M_b^2}{Z_{rb}} \cos^2 (\theta - \Delta),$$

$$Z_{2a} = Z_a + \frac{\omega^2 M_a^2}{Z_{ra}} \cos^2 (\theta - 120°), \qquad Z_{2b} = Z_b + \frac{\omega^2 M_b^2 \cos^2 (\theta - \Delta - 120°)}{Z_{rb}}$$

$$Z_{3a} = Z_a + \frac{\omega^2 M_a^2}{Z_{ra}} \cos^2 (\theta - 240°), \qquad Z_{3b} = Z_b + \frac{\omega^2 M_b^2}{Z_{rb}} \cos^2 (\theta - \Delta - 240°).$$

It is often desired to connect a control transformer to a transmitter that is already carrying a load of one or more repeaters. Therefore it is worth investigating the accuracy of such a system. This involves obtaining expressions for the stator voltage of a transmitter under load. We shall again use only simple approximations. Figure 3·8 is the circuit of a transmitter (size a) connected to a motor (size b) from which, by Thévenin's theorem, the rotor circuits have been removed. The mesh equations are

$$\left.\begin{aligned}
&E\sqrt{3}[\cos(\theta+30°) - \cos(\theta-\Delta+30°)] \\
&\qquad = i_1(Z_{1a}+Z_{1b}) - i_2(Z_{2a}+Z_{2b}), \\
&E\sqrt{3}[\cos(\theta+150°) - \cos(\theta-\Delta+150°)] \\
&\qquad = i_1(Z_{1a}+Z_{1b}) - i_3(Z_{3a}+Z_{3b}), \\
&E\sqrt{3}[\cos(\theta+270°) - \cos(\theta-\Delta+270°)] \\
&\qquad = i_2(Z_{2a}+Z_{2b}) - i_3(Z_{3a}+Z_{3b}).
\end{aligned}\right\} \tag{22}$$

The meaning of the impedance terms is indicated in Fig. 3·8.

In manipulation of Eqs. (22), we will need to examine the general factor

$$\frac{Z_{na}}{Z_{na}+Z_{nb}} = \frac{1}{1+\dfrac{Z_b\left[1+\dfrac{\omega^2M_b^2\cos^2(\phi-\Delta)}{Z_{rb}^2}\left(\dfrac{Z_{rb}}{Z_b}\right)\right]}{Z_a[1+(\omega^2M_a^2\cos^2\phi/Z_{ra}^2)(Z_{ra}/Z_a)]}} \approx \frac{1}{1+\dfrac{Z_b}{Z_a}} \equiv C. \tag{23}$$

The factor C is a constant for a given configuration of synchros because $Z_{rb}/Z_b \approx Z_{ra}/Z_a$, and because $(\omega^2M_a^2\cos^2\phi)/Z_{ra}^2 = -E_{s\phi}^2/E_r^2$, where $E_{s\phi}$ is appropriate stator voltage for the general angle ϕ and E_r is the rotor voltage. Multiplying each side of Eqs. (22) by Eq. (23) and recalling that Δ is a small angle, we obtain

$$\left.\begin{aligned}
CE\sqrt{3}\,\Delta\cos(\theta+120°) &= i_1Z_{1a} - i_2Z_{2a}, \\
CE\sqrt{3}\,\Delta\cos(\theta+60°) &= i_1Z_{1a} - i_3Z_{3a}, \\
CE\sqrt{3}\,\Delta\cos\theta &= i_2Z_{2a} - i_3Z_{3a}.
\end{aligned}\right\} \tag{24}$$

These expressions are the internal voltage drops in the transmitter. Therefore, the apparent stator voltages are

$$\left.\begin{aligned}
&E\sqrt{3}[\cos(\theta+30°) - \Delta C\cos(\theta+120°)] \\
&\qquad = E\sqrt{3}\cos(\theta+30°-C\Delta), \\
&E\sqrt{3}[\cos(\theta+150°) - \Delta C\cos(\theta+60°)] \\
&\qquad = E\sqrt{3}\cos(\theta+150°-C\Delta), \\
&E\sqrt{3}[\cos(\theta+270°) - \Delta C\cos\theta] \\
&\qquad = E\sqrt{3}\cos(\theta+270°-C\Delta).
\end{aligned}\right\} \tag{25}$$

Comparing these apparent voltages with Eq. (6), we note that because of loading, the stator voltages for the system that should be transmitting the angle θ are voltages which would be associated with the angle $\theta - C\Delta$. Therefore, any servo employing control transformers in this system will have an additional error of $-C\Delta°$. With reasoning identical with that presented in obtaining Eq. (20), it can be shown that

$$C = \frac{1}{1+\dfrac{(T_u)_b}{(T_u)_a}}. \tag{26}$$

It should be emphasized that in a complex system of synchros fed from a single generator, there are both "steady-state" errors due to loading and interaction errors during any transitory response. Since synchro repeaters are fairly unstable devices, the transmitter that is chosen must be so large that the repeater oscillations are not excessively reflected in the control-transformer signal.

3·7. Rotatable Transformers.—A rotatable transformer resembles a synchro in that it has a wound armature that can be rotated relative to a stator system. The stator system, however, is composed of a single winding rather than three distributed in space. The device is, in fact, a simple two-winding transformer so constructed that one winding can be rotated in respect to the other winding. As an element for simple transmission of data, it has rather restricted use. It possesses only one major advantage over a three-stator winding synchro—it requires one less lead. Occasionally, for instance in transmitting data from a gyro supported in a gimbal system, the reduction of leads is important. If, for some such reason, it is decided to use a follow-up system employing rotatable transformers, one transformer is appropriately mounted on, say, the gimbal system of the gyro so that the angular rotation of the rotor with respect to the stator is the desired datum. This datum could well be the true elevation angle.

For thermal reasons, it is preferable to excite the stator winding of such a transformer rather than its rotor. The voltage E_s from the secondary (rotor) winding at no load will be, to a close approximation,

$$E_s = -\frac{j\omega M E_p \cos\theta}{Z_p}, \tag{27}$$

where the subscript p refers to the primary, s to the secondary, and θ is the angle between the axis of the two coils. In terms of the angular variable β to be transmitted, the expression for the secondary voltage is

$$E_s = -\frac{j\omega M E_p \cos(\beta + K)}{Z_p}, \tag{28}$$

where K is an alignment parameter.

An identical rotatable transformer is mounted on the remote equipment that is to reproduce the angle β. It is so aligned that its voltage is identical with that expressed in Eq. (28). The units are then connected as suggested by the equivalent circuit presented in Fig. 3·9. The series connection of the primaries will be mentioned later.

The error voltage is given by

$$\begin{aligned} V &= (E_s)_{\max}[\cos(\beta + K) - \cos(\beta + K + \Delta)] \\ &\approx (E_s)_{\max}\,\Delta \sin(\beta + K), \end{aligned} \tag{29}$$

with the assumption of a small value of Δ.

It is evident that the gain (volts per degree error) is not constant for this error-measuring system but varies with the transmitted variable as $\sin(\beta + K)$. Therefore, it can be used only in transmitting a variable that is limited to some range such that β has a variation of less than 180°.

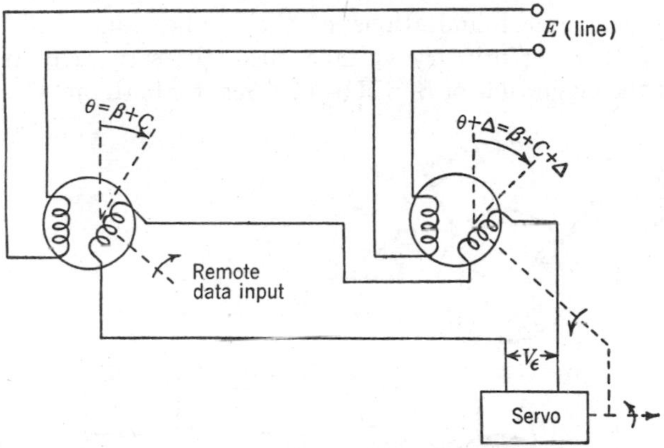

FIG. 3·9.—Error system using rotatable transformers.

Furthermore, it is important to adjust K to minimize the gain variation.[1] This establishes the appropriate value of K as

$$K = 90° - \frac{\beta_L + \beta_U}{2}, \tag{30}$$

where β_u and β_L are the upper and lower limits of β. The associated percentage change of gain is

$$\Delta G = \left(1 - \cos\frac{\beta_U - \beta_L}{2}\right) 100. \tag{31}$$

The permissible change of gain for a servo will not be discussed in this section. The analysis for investigation of the effects of change of gain is usually not difficult; a greater problem is often that of locating and determining all of the possible gain variations. A gain change of more than 20 per cent in the error-measuring system is often undesirable. This would limit the range of β to about 75° in the above equation.

A practical difficulty is indicated by Eq. (29). If the a-c voltages from the secondaries differ in time phase by α degrees, the subtraction is imperfect; a quadrature voltage, with a small phase difference α and a small amplitude $\alpha \frac{(E_s)_{\max}}{57} \sin\left(\beta - \frac{\beta_L - \beta_U}{2}\right)$ volts, is present in addition to the true error voltage. For example, if $(E_s)_{\max}$ is 20 volts and α is

[1] In some cases it may be preferred to choose a value of K influenced by an important region of β as well as the total range of the value of β.

2°, the quadrature voltage is about 0.4 volt at the extreme of β suggested above; this is a voltage of greater magnitude than the error voltage for an error of 1°. This quadrature voltage can be diminished by exciting the primaries in series, as has been done in Fig. 3·9. Often this is a good solution. The fact that frequently the units are necessarily small in size because of mechanical limitations of the application, tends to set a requirement of lower primary voltage; also, the series circuit helps to assure that the magnitude of E_s will be identical for both units.

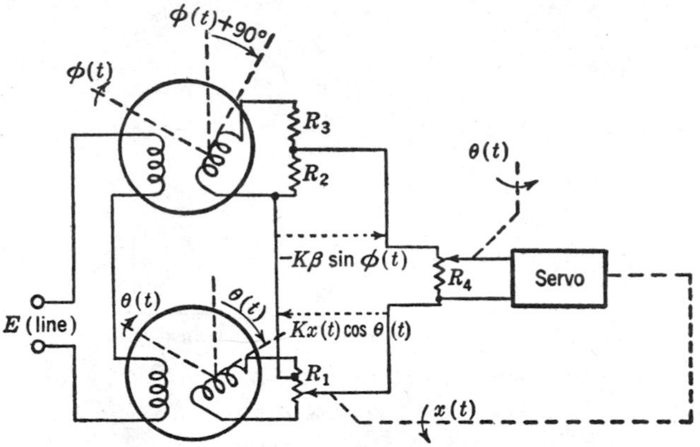

FIG. 3·10.—Computational error-transmission system.

Often a rotatable transformer is present in an error-measuring system as a computational device. As a simple example, suppose that it is desired to solve continuously with the aid of a servo the following explicit equation for $x(t)$:

$$x(t) = \gamma \frac{\sin \phi(t)}{\cos \theta(t)}, \tag{32a}$$

where γ is a constant, $\phi(t)$ is without limit, and $\theta(t)$ has limits that restrict $x(t)$ to finite values. For ease of solution, the equation can be rearranged as

$$\cos \theta(t) x(t) - \gamma \sin \phi(t) = 0. \tag{32b}$$

The sine and cosine terms can be obtained from rotatable transformers. The circuit is that of Fig. 3·10.

The error voltage across R_4 is

$$V_\epsilon = K \cos \theta(t) \, \Delta x, \tag{33}$$

where K is a dimensional design parameter and Δx is the error in x. The gain is $K \cos \theta(t)$. The limits of $\theta(t)$ determine whether or not it may be necessary to remove this gain variation. One simple way is indicated in Fig. 3·10, in which the resistor R_4 is a potentiometer or attenuator in series with a fixed resistor. The potentiometer is so wound that the resistance measured from the arm to the lower data line is

$$R_4 \frac{\sec \{N\alpha(t) + [\theta(t)]_{\min}\}}{\sec \{N[\alpha(t)]_{\max} + [\theta(t)]_{\min}\}}.$$

In this expression $[\alpha(t)]_{\max}$ is the total useful rotation of the potentiometer and N indicates the proper gearing, defined by

$$[\theta(t)]_{\max} - [\theta(t)]_{\min} = N[\alpha(t)]_{\max}. \tag{34}$$

The resistor from the lower terminal of the potentiometer to the data line should have a value $R_4 \frac{\sec [\theta(t)]_{\min}}{\sec [\theta(t)]_{\max}}$.

3·8. Potentiometer Error-measuring Systems.—In some special applications it is desirable to use a d-c signal carrier. The inputs may exist "naturally" as direct current, as in the problem of controlling or recording the output of a d-c generator, or an input may have been brought

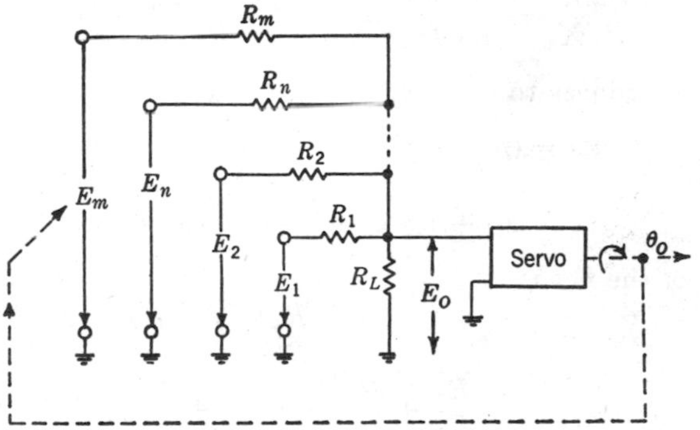

FIG. 3·11.—Data system for multiple additive inputs.

deliberately to a d-c level, so that smoothing of the data can be accomplished with greater facility. In some such cases, it may be advantageous to utilize potentiometers as elements in the data system; since accuracy and life are of prime importance, these are invariably of the wire-wound type. If a slide-wire type is used, the data are continuous, but it is difficult to obtain reasonable values of over-all resistance. For this reason the more common type of potentiometer in which a contact arm makes turn-to-turn contact is in wide use.

An error-measuring system utilizing potentiometers might be of the form of Fig. 3·11, which has been generalized to indicate the possibility of more than one input quantity. It will be assumed that the inputs are to have equal weighting. Some or all the input voltages might well be obtained from potentiometers.

The output of the net, with the servo off, is

$$E_O = \frac{1}{1 + \frac{R_L}{R_1} + \frac{R_L}{R_2} + \cdots + \frac{R_L}{R_n} + \frac{R_L}{R_m}} \left(\frac{R_L}{R_1} E_1 + \frac{R_L}{R_2} E_2 + \cdots \frac{R_L}{R_n} E_n + \frac{R_L}{R_m} E_m \right) \quad (35)$$

The following relations may be obtained by design:

$$\left. \begin{aligned} E_1 &= K_1 \theta_{I1} \\ E_2 &= K_2 \theta_{I2} \\ &\cdot \quad \cdot \quad \cdot \quad \cdot \\ E_n &= K_n \theta_{In} \\ E_m &= -K_m \theta_O. \end{aligned} \right\} \quad (36)$$

The output voltage of the net E_O is, of course, the error voltage and is expressible as $G\epsilon$, where G is the voltage gain of the net. If

$$\frac{R_m}{R_1}\frac{K_1}{K_m} = \frac{R_m}{R_2}\frac{K_2}{K_m} = \cdots = \frac{R_m}{R_n}\frac{K_n}{K_m} = 1, \quad (37)$$

then Eq. (35) reduces to

$$E_O = G\epsilon, \quad (38a)$$

where

$$\epsilon = \theta_{I1} + \theta_{I2} + \cdots + \theta_{In} - \theta_O. \quad (38b)$$

The gain G of the net is

$$G = K_m \frac{\frac{R_L}{R_m}}{1 + \frac{R_L}{R_1} + \frac{R_L}{R_2} + \cdots + \frac{R_L}{R_n} + \frac{R_L}{R_m}}. \quad (39)$$

The net shown in Fig. 3·11 is only a simple example of what may be used. Multiplication and division of functions of variables can also be achieved; in fact, nets can be designed that, by the aid of a servo, obtain continuous solutions to quite complex equations.

Adding networks of the form presented above is often useful in accomplishing the function of Differential 2 of Fig. 3·1. In such a case, the feedback quantity from the output of Box 32 is one input quantity to the network, the output of Box 12 is the second input quantity, and the output of the network feeds into Box 23.

In the type of potentiometer in which the contact arm makes turn-to-turn contact, the data are discontinuous. The nature and position of these discontinuities are of interest both in accuracy considerations and in understanding the "noise" that such a potentiometer system adds to the true data. Such discontinuities are of the order of E_S/T, where E_S is the voltage across the potentiometer and T is the total number of turns on the potentiometer card. Thus they are small, but the development of accurate servo-controlled potentiometer winding machines has advanced to the stage where it is of value to examine even such small errors.

We shall examine these discontinuities for a potentiometer that has been wound perfectly with T identical turns. A physically equivalent circuit is presented in Fig. 3·12. The effective width of the contact arm is $Kd - b + d/c$, where d is the distance between centers of the wires along the contact surface, b is the width of the effective contact surface

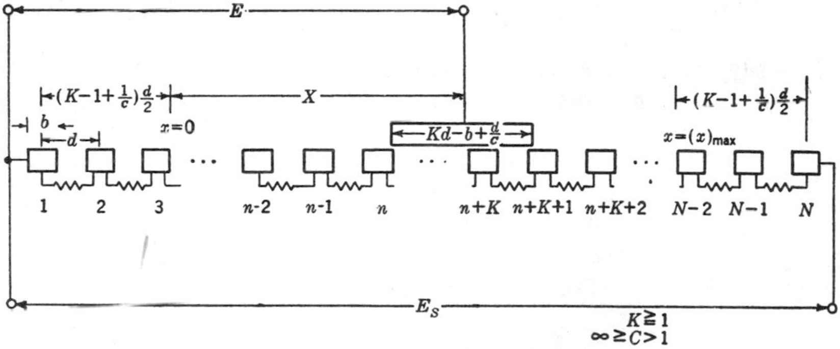

FIG. 3·12.—Equivalent circuit for a potentiometer.

of a single wire, K is an integer equal to or greater than 1, and c is a number greater than 1. For a contact-arm motion of d/c, K turns will be short-circuited; for a contact-arm motion of $[1 - (1/c)]d$, $K - 1$ turns will be short-circuited. In each of these regions, the voltage observed at the contact arm will remain constant. Actually, since this cycle may be used to determine K, d, and $1/c$, the following derivation is valid for any shape of contact arm or wire surface. If we consider such a cycle in the region of the nth contact surface, we have

$$\left.\begin{aligned} x_1 &= \left(n - \frac{1}{2} - \frac{1}{c}\right)d, \\ x_2 = x_3 &= \left(n - \frac{1}{2}\right)d, \\ x_4 &= \left(n + \frac{1}{2} - \frac{1}{c}\right)d, \end{aligned}\right\} \tag{40}$$

where x_1 and x_2 are the extreme values of x for which the K turns between the nth and the $n + K$ contact surfaces are short-circuited and x_3 and x_4 are the extreme values of x for which the $K - 1$ turns between the $n + 1$ and the $n + K$ contact surfaces are short-circuited. As seen from Fig.

3·12, the assumption has been made that the potentiometer is

$$\left[(K-1)+\left(\frac{1}{c}\right)\right]d$$

shorter than its actual physical length, and half of this correction is subtracted from each end. This correction is needed to minimize the errors. Intuitively, one realizes that it arises from the short-circuiting action of the contact arm.

The inherent potentiometer error due to resolution will be defined as

$$\epsilon = \left(\frac{E}{E_s}\right)_{\text{actual}} - \left(\frac{E}{E_s}\right)_{\text{perfect}} \tag{41a}$$

Obviously, the extreme errors occur at x_1, x_2, x_3, and/or x_4. At the extremes of the region of short-circuiting K turns, Eq. (41*a*) becomes

$$\epsilon_{(1,2)} = \frac{n-1}{T-K} - \frac{x_{(1,2)}}{T-K+1-\frac{1}{c}}. \tag{41b}$$

At the extremes of the regions of short-circuiting $K-1$ turns, Eq. (41*a*) becomes

$$\epsilon_{(3,4)} = \frac{n}{T-K+1} = \frac{x_{(3,4)}}{T-K+1-\frac{1}{c}}. \tag{41c}$$

If we ignore terms that are always of the order of T^{-2} and assume $T \gg K$ and $1/c$, we obtain from Eqs. (41*b*) and (41*c*):

$$\left.\begin{aligned}
\epsilon_1 &= \frac{1}{2T}\left[\frac{n\left(2-\frac{2}{c}\right)}{T}+\frac{2}{c}-1\right],\\
\epsilon_2 &= \frac{1}{2T}\left[\frac{n\left(2-\frac{2}{c}\right)}{T}\right]-1,\\
\epsilon_3 &= \frac{1}{2T}\left(1-\frac{2n}{cT}\right),\\
\epsilon_4 &= \frac{1}{2T}\left(\frac{2}{c}-1-\frac{2n}{cT}\right).
\end{aligned}\right\} \tag{42}$$

Examination of Eqs. (42) shows that

$$\left.\begin{aligned}
(\epsilon_1)_{N-n} &= -(\epsilon_2)_n,\\
(\epsilon_2)_{N-n} &= -(\epsilon_1)_n,\\
(\epsilon_3)_{N-n} &= -(\epsilon_4)_n,\\
(\epsilon_4)_{N-n} &= -(\epsilon_3)_n.
\end{aligned}\right\} \tag{43}$$

If we define Δ as equal to $(1/c - \frac{1}{2})$, it is also true that

$$\left.\begin{aligned}(\epsilon_1)_{+\Delta} &= -(\epsilon_4)_{-\Delta}\\(\epsilon_2)_{+\Delta} &= -(\epsilon_3)_{-\Delta}\end{aligned}\right\}. \tag{44}$$

Because of Eqs. (43) and (44), it is of interest to examine the errors for only $0 < n < N/2$ and $1 < c \leqq 2$. Figure 3·13 shows the errors given by Eqs. (42) for some values of n and $1/c$. It is to be noted that the potentiometer, if perfectly aligned, has apparent resolution of at least

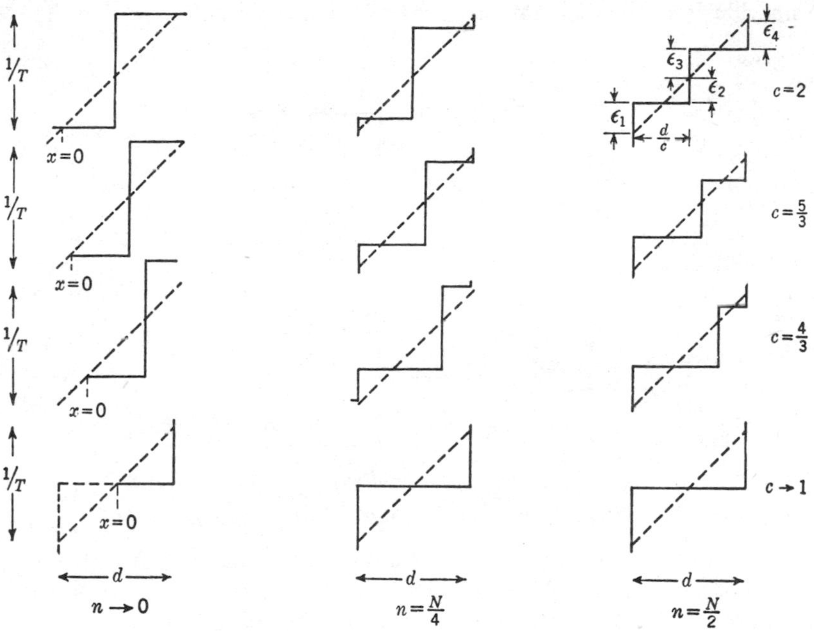

FIG. 3·13.—Potentiometer resolution and errors.

$1/2T$ and, for $c = 2$, consistent resolution at the center of the potentiometer of $1/4T$.

Often it is impractical to avoid using the potentiometer in the region of $x = 0$. This is especially true when a function capable of positive and negative values is being converted into an electrical voltage by means of a tapped potentiometer. There is a region of zero voltage at the tap that is $[Kd + (d/c)]$ units wide. This represents a separation of

$$(K - 1)d + \left(\frac{d}{c}\right)$$

between the intercept on the x-axis of the best voltage slope for negative x

and the intercept on the x-axis of the best voltage slope for positive x. This, if the error is split, makes the voltage always too low on either side of the tap, and an additional constant error of magnitude

$$\left[\frac{K - 1 + (1/c)}{2T}\right]$$

is present. Obviously, in such tapped potentiometers K must be kept small.

The broad zero-voltage region may be avoided by "floating" the potentiometer, that is, not grounding the zero potential point. This,

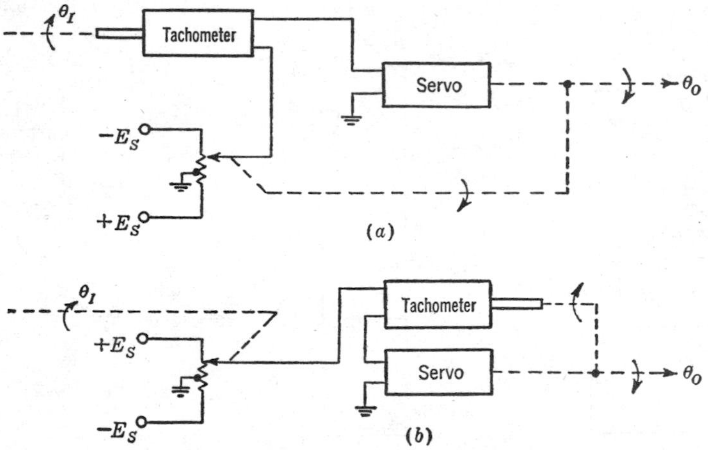

FIG. 3·14.—Differentiation and integration by error-measuring elements.

however, permits the coordinate of the zero potential to drift if, because of loading, $+E_s$ is not identical with $-E_s$ or if thermal differences cause nonuniform changes of the resistance in the potentiometer.

It can be seen that the noise arising from the finite resolution of the potentiometer will have a fundamental frequency dependent upon spacing of the wires, the portion of the potentiometer in use, the contact arm parameter c, and the velocity of the contact arm. The amplitude of the noise will be dependent on the first three of these parameters. Because of this noise, it is generally unwise to attempt to utilize error-derivative nets in high-gain servos using such error-measuring systems, for the amplifier or motor may overload or overheat as the result of the high gain for such noise.

Since only discrete voltages may be obtained from such potentiometers, high-gain servos may display a tendency to chatter with a very small amplitude in seeking a voltage value that is not obtainable. With a higher degree of stability in the loop, the tendency usually disappears.

Computational error-measuring elements are not restricted to those which perform the algebraic manipulations of multiplication, division, addition, and subtraction. There are also elements that can be used to perform the operations of integration and differentiation. To accomplish these operations, any device can be used that has an output proportional to the time rate of change of the input. Such a device will be called here a "tachometer." If the input exists as a shaft rotation, a simple tachometer is a small d-c generator. Usually such a tachometer has a permanent-magnet field, but there is no reason why the field cannot be supplied by an external electrical source; the output voltage will then be the product of some function and the speed of the shaft of the tachometer. Indeed, one might thus obtain the second derivative of the motion of a shaft, although accuracy greater than a few per cent would be difficult to obtain.

Simple examples of circuits using electrical tachometers and potentiometers are presented in Fig. 3·14. In Fig. 3·14*a*, the error voltage is

$$V_\epsilon = K_T p \theta_I - E_s \frac{\theta_O}{(\theta_O)_{\max}}, \tag{45a}$$

and, for the steady state,

$$\theta_O = \left[\frac{K_T}{E_s} (\theta_O)_{\max} \right] p\theta_I \equiv C_1 p \theta_I. \tag{45b}$$

In Fig. 3·14*b*, the error voltage is

$$V_\epsilon = E_s \frac{\theta_I}{(\theta_I)_{\max}} - K_T p \theta_O, \tag{46a}$$

whence

$$\theta_O = \left[\frac{E_s}{(\theta_I)_{\max}} \frac{1}{K_T} \right] \frac{\theta_I}{p} \equiv C_2 \frac{\theta_I}{p}. \tag{46b}$$

In the above equations, K_T is, of course, the voltage-speed constant of the tachometer. For a certain permanent-magnet tachometer,[1] which has been used in many equipments, $K_T = 35.50/1800$ volts per rpm ± 10 per cent, with ± 0.5 volt depending on direction of rotation. The linearity of this tachometer is 0.5 per cent. The tachometer has a large number of commutator segments (18) to reduce noise.

3·9. Null Devices.—There exist error-measuring systems that, although often not employing elements materially different from those described above, are unique in their application and do deserve separate classification. They will be called null devices, because they contribute no error that is a function of the magnitude of the transmitted variable.

An example will serve as a definition. Here the problem is to position a shaft with high torque to the same angle as a shaft on which only

[1] Type B44, Electric Indicator Co., Stamford, Conn.

a slight load may be imposed. If the shafts can be so placed as to have a common axis, the low-torque shaft can carry the rotor of a rotatable transformer and the high-torque shaft the stator. If the unit is properly aligned, there will be zero output voltage at zero error; and if error exists, the phase of the output voltage will indicate the sense of the error. Since the null position is used, no error will be contributed by the rotatable transformer. It is important that the error-voltage output be fairly linear with error, but this is a problem of servo-loop gain and not of positional accuracy.

It is apparent that many types of null device are possible. One shaft may, for instance, carry one set of the plates of a condenser, and the other shaft the other set of plates for the condenser. If, then, this condenser is one arm of a bridge circuit excited by alternating current, proper error signals can be obtained from the output of the bridge. On the other hand, coupling between the two shafts may be by a narrow light beam. The low-torque shaft may carry a light source or a mirror to reflect a beam of light from a source on the follow-up shaft. The follow-up shaft then carries a prism which splits the received light beam and sends it to two photoelectric tubes. Zero error, of course, should exist when the outputs of the two photoelectric tubes are equal. Both of the examples in this paragraph, however, are subject to possible errors arising from variations in several elements; for example, variations in the other arms of the bridge in the first case or differences in the characteristics in photoelectric tubes in the second. On the other hand, such systems impose truly negligible loads on the low-torque shaft. The designer must weigh such considerations for each particular application.

In some problems, the displacement to be followed exists as a linear motion. Many of the devices used in following rotational displacement are then applicable with obvious modifications.

One device, a so-called "*E*-transformer," has been widely utilized, especially in following linear motions. A sketch is presented in Fig. 3·15*a*. The *E* section is carried by the follow-up, while the bar section is carried by the displacement to be followed. Motions are in the plane of the paper and across the figure as indicated by x_O and x_I. Terminals 1 to 2 are excited from the appropriate a-c source. There is one position of the bar for which zero voltage (ideally) is observed across terminals 3 to 4. This is the position in which the bar gives such coupling that equal and opposite emf's are induced in the secondary. Practically, there will be harmonic and quadrature voltages left at the null position. For a displacement of the bar to the left of that zero position, a voltage of phase ϕ appears across the secondary terminals 3 to 4; and for a displacement to the right, a voltage of phase $\phi + 180°$ appears across the secondary. This voltage, then, may be used as an error voltage, and it is not difficult to obtain at least approximate proportionality between error and voltage for small errors. One must be certain, however, that variations in coupling arising from causes other than the difference between x_I and x_O, such as mechanical looseness, do not occur, because such variations impair the accuracy of the device.

There is an important extension of the idea of an E-transformer that is useful in following an object that moves in two coordinates. Such a problem is encountered when a radar director is to be stabilized by reference to a gyro axis that is kept pointed at the target. The device consists of two single-coordinate E-transformers at right angles to each other, with a common center, or primary pole. This assembly is moved

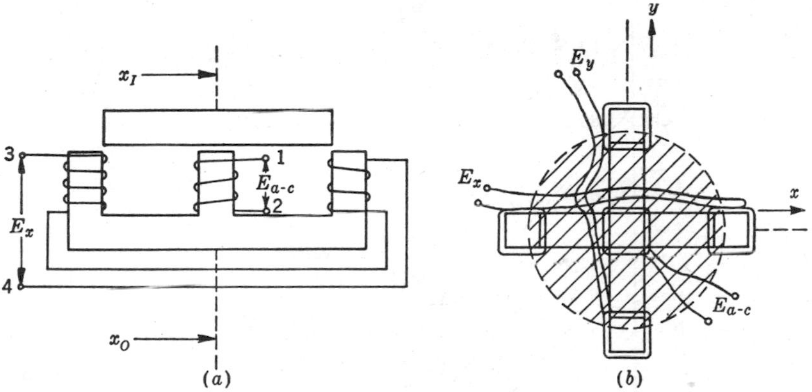

FIG. 3·15.—E-transformers.

by the follow-up. The input motion, from a gyro in our example, moves a dome, shown dotted in the plan view of Fig. 3·15b. The separate error voltages for the two servo systems involved, train and elevation, are available from the two secondary systems.

3·10. Motors and Power Amplifiers.—Most d-c servo motors, used with controlled armature voltage and fixed-field excitation, have torque-speed characteristics that, to a very good approximation, may be defined by either of the sets of conventional coefficients. If one starts with the assumption that the torque M is linear with the armature current and that the current is a function of motor speed Ω_m and applied voltage E_m, one has

$$M = \frac{dM}{di_m} i_m = \frac{dM}{di_m} \frac{E_m}{\left(\dfrac{\partial E_m}{\partial i_m}\right)_{\Omega_m}} + \frac{dM}{di_m}\left(\frac{\partial i_m}{\partial \Omega_m}\right)_{E_m} \Omega_m$$

$$= K_t \frac{E_m}{Z_m} - K_t \frac{K_e}{Z_m} \Omega_m, \quad (47)$$

or one may directly assume $M = f(\Omega_m, E_m)$, and then

$$M = -\left(\frac{\partial M}{\partial \Omega_m}\right)_{E_m}\left(\frac{\partial \Omega_m}{\partial E_m}\right)_M E_m + \left(\frac{\partial M}{\partial \Omega_m}\right)_{E_m} \Omega_m = f_m K_m E_m - f_m \Omega_m. \quad (48)$$

In the above equations E_m and i_m are the voltage applied to the motor armature and the current flowing through the armature. The coefficients defined by Eqs. (47) and (48) have descriptive names: K_t is the torque-current constant; K_e is the back-emf constant; K_m is the speed-voltage constant; and f_m is the internal-damping coefficient. It is seen that $K_m = K_e^{-1}$. Strictly, Eq. (48) assumes that there is no time lag between

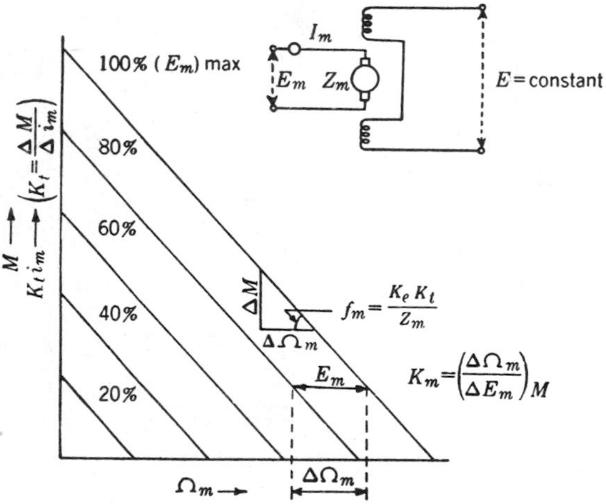

FIG. 3·16.—D-c motor characteristics.

i_m and E_m. Figure 3·16 illustrates the constants for a hypothetical d-c servo motor. Except at high values of i_m where saturation effects may appear, existing d-c servo motors have characteristics that are, for practical purposes, similarly linear.

Two-phase low-inertia motors have been developed that are very convenient for low-wattage control applications. For many of these a-c motors the conventional coefficients are far from constant over the whole range of excitation and speed. More accurate analysis of the motors, however, does not yield a simple relation for $M = f(\Omega_m, E_m)$. For this reason it is common practice to use the coefficients defined in Eqs. (47) and (48). Fortunately, they are often fairly constant for low speeds and voltages. Figure 3·17 shows how the coefficients vary for one two-phase motor. For this same motor K_t/Z_m is reasonably constant over a wide range of E and Ω_m. It is seen that for speeds less than one-fourth of maximum speed, f_m and K_m are fairly constant. Thus, for applications where accurate performance is not required at the higher speeds, one may analyze the loop using low-speed evaluations of the constants. It is advisable, however, to investigate the stability of the loop at intermediate and high speeds, because different values of the motor time constant and the loop gain will be encountered.

In many cases it is possible to employ gain devices or amplifiers that are nearly independent of the frequency over the region of frequencies

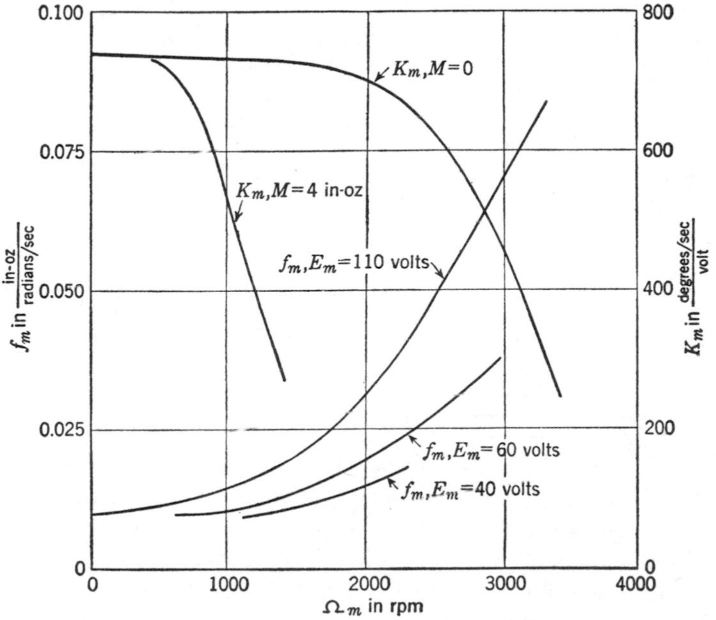

FIG. 3·17.—Characteristics of two-phase a-c motor, Diehl FPE49-2. Sixty cycle, 110 volts on fixed phase, 11-watt maximum output rating.

that is of interest in the closed servo loop. For example, most vacuum-tube amplifiers can be represented as having a transfer characteristic

$$Y_{12}(p) = \frac{G_{12}}{Tp + 1} \tag{49}$$

to a satisfactory degree of exactness. Since the attainment of an appropriate value of G_{12} is the primary concern in amplifier design, the equivalent time constant T is often somewhat accidental. Fortunately, it is usually small. The wise designer, however, will experimentally determine $Y_{12}(p)$ to reassure himself concerning the small magnitude of T and to obtain its value. Similar statements hold for any vacuum-tube amplification that might exist in Box 23 or Box 32.

The final, or power, stage of amplifying equipment may employ any of several elements depending upon the magnitude of power required and the designer's preferences. For applications utilizing very small motors (less than $\frac{1}{10}$ hp) saturable reactors or electronic tubes, either the gaseous or vacuum type, are in common use. Power vibrators, thyratrons, or rotary magnetic amplifiers are often employed for controlling larger motors.

Since the rotary magnetic amplifier (amplidyne) has received wide application as a power stage driving a d-c motor, it may be of value to

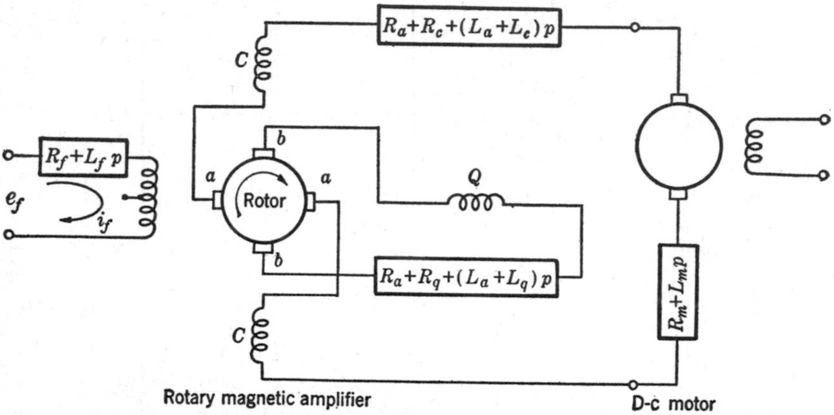

FIG. 3·18.—Rotary magnetic amplifier and d-c motor.

obtain an expression for the transfer characteristic of such a combination. The equivalent circuit is shown in Fig. 3·18. The axis of the rotary amplifier established by the direction of the flux from the excitation current i_f is commonly called the direct axis. Quantities associated with this axis will be characterized by the subscript d, and those associated with the axis at right angles to this direction (the quadrature axis) will have a subscript q. In this primary direct-axis field, ϕ_d is a wound rotor driven by an auxiliary motor at a speed S. It is apparent that

$$\phi_d = K_1 i_f = \frac{K_1}{R_f}\frac{e_f}{T_f p + 1}, \qquad T_f \equiv \frac{L_f}{R_f}, \tag{50}$$

in which K_1 is a constant describing the magnetic circuit. Because of the rotation of the rotor, an emf is developed between the brushes b with a magnitude

$$e_q = SK_2\phi_d = (R_a + R_q)(T_q p + 1)i_q, \qquad T_q \equiv \frac{L_a + L_q}{R_a + R_q}. \tag{51}$$

The constant K_2 is determined by the material and structure of the machine. The quadrature-axis current i_q creates a quadrature-axis field ϕ_q that may be augmented by the coil Q of impedance $R_q + L_q p$.

The quadrature field causes an emf to be developed between brushes *a*. An expression for this emf can be derived from Eqs. (50) and (51),

$$\left.\begin{aligned} e_d = SK_3 i_q &= \frac{G_a e_f}{(1 + T_f p)(1 + T_q p)}, \\ G_a &\equiv \frac{S^2 K_1 K_2 K_3}{R_f(R_a + R_q)}. \end{aligned}\right\} \tag{52}$$

The load current in the armature circuit would produce a direct-axis flux that would oppose the exciting flux. Thus the machine would have very poor regulation. To eliminate this difficulty, compensating coils C are present to cancel out the flux in the direct axis due to load current.

Since the emf e_d is applied to the motor-armature circuit, the relation may be written

$$e_d = i_m R(T_a p + 1) + K_e \Omega_m, \tag{53a}$$

in which

$$R \equiv R_a + R_c + R_m = \text{total armature circuit resistance}, \tag{53b}$$

$$T_a \equiv \frac{L_a + L_c + L_m}{R_a + R_c + R_m}. \tag{53c}$$

The torque resulting from the motor-armature current i_m will be consumed in accelerating the inertia J_m of the motor rotor, the inertia J_g of the gear train which is reflected to the motor, and the inertia of the load J_l reduced to motor speed; it also will be dissipated in overcoming any viscous friction $f_g \Omega_m$ in the gearing and bearings. Thus the torque equation is

$$\left(J_m + J_g + \frac{J_l}{N^2}\right) p\Omega_m + f_g \Omega_m = \frac{K_t}{R} \frac{(e_d - K_e \Omega_m)}{T_a p + 1}, \tag{54}$$

in which N is the gearing ratio to the load. With J' as the total effective inertia at the motor shaft, Eq. (54) may be rewritten as

$$\frac{K_T}{R}(e_d - K_e \Omega_m) = f_g\left(\frac{J'}{f_g} p + 1\right)(T_a p + 1)\Omega_m. \tag{55a}$$

Since $J'/f_g \gg T_a$, this equation is usually approximated as

$$\left.\begin{aligned} \frac{K_T}{R} e_d &= \left(f_g + \frac{K_e K_t}{R}\right)(T_{ma} p + 1)\Omega_m, \\ T_{ma} &= \frac{J'}{f_g + \dfrac{K_e K_t}{R}}. \end{aligned}\right\} \tag{55b}$$

Usually $f_g \ll (K_e K_t)/R$; then, using Eq. (51), the final transfer function for the power stage and motor is, since $\Omega_m = p\theta_O$,

$$\frac{\theta_O}{e_f} = \frac{K_m G_a}{p(T_{ma}p + 1)(T_q p + 1)(T_f p + 1)}. \tag{56}$$

Suppose that a simple servo is constructed using an electronic amplifier (with gain G_1 and lag T) in Box 12, a motor-amplidyne combination in Box 23, and no equalizing-feedback path. If an error-measuring system is employed with a voltage gain of G_ϵ volts per unit of error and Box 31 is a simple gear train of reduction N, Eq. (2) becomes

$$\left.\begin{aligned} \frac{\theta_O}{\epsilon} &= \frac{K_v}{p(T_{ma}p + 1)(T_f p + 1)(T_q p + 1)(Tp + 1)}, \\ K_v &\equiv \frac{G_\epsilon G_1 G_a K_m}{N}. \end{aligned}\right\} \tag{57}$$

3·11. Modulators.—It is sometimes desirable to convert a d-c signal to an a-c signal that has a determinate phase relative to an existing a-c voltage. For example, this is desired when a two-phase a-c servomotor is used in a loop that has an error-measuring system utilizing d-c voltages. Because of the difficulties of d-c amplification, it is often preferred to make this transition before any d-c amplification and to postpone amplification until the signal is in a-c form. Thus it is common that little or no extraneous noise or false error signal can be tolerated. This often rules out various schemes of modulation employing vacuum tubes in favor of mechanical modulation, such as is obtained with a vibrator.

One form of a synchronous vibrator employs a flat reed, or leaf, fixed at one end and with the other end free and carrying an iron slug. Encircling this free end is a fixed coil, excited from the alternating current to which the vibrator is to be synchronized. The coil creates an oscillating magnetic field with its vector lying along the length of the reed; as a result the face of the slug at the tip of the reed has an alternating magnetic polarity. Just above this end of the reed are the poles of a permanent magnet, so placed that the face of the slug is subjected to a fixed field perpendicular to the flat of the reed. Thus the reed is subjected to an alternating force and will oscillate with a fundamental frequency equal to the fundamental frequency of the current flowing in the exciting coil. If the reed is mechanically resonant at a frequency near the exciting frequency, large amplitude is obtained with little expenditure of exciting power. This resonance frequency, however, must not be too near the exciting frequency or a small change of exciting frequency will produce a large change in the phase of the oscillation of the reed. One commercial design[1] has made the compromise that a vibrator for 60-cycle use employs

[1] Synchronous Converter No. 75829-1, Brown Instrument Co., Philadelphia, Pa.

a reed resonant at about 80 cps. This gives about a 12° lag between the reed motion and the exciting voltage; the latter may, of course, be shifted in phase by a fixed amount if so desired. In servos using two-phase motors, it is often convenient to obtain the required phase shift for the controlled phase in this fashion. The same vibrator, to be excited from 6.3 volts, has a coil impedance of about 120 ohms, almost purely resistive. Because of the harmonic content in the exciting voltage, it is preferable to

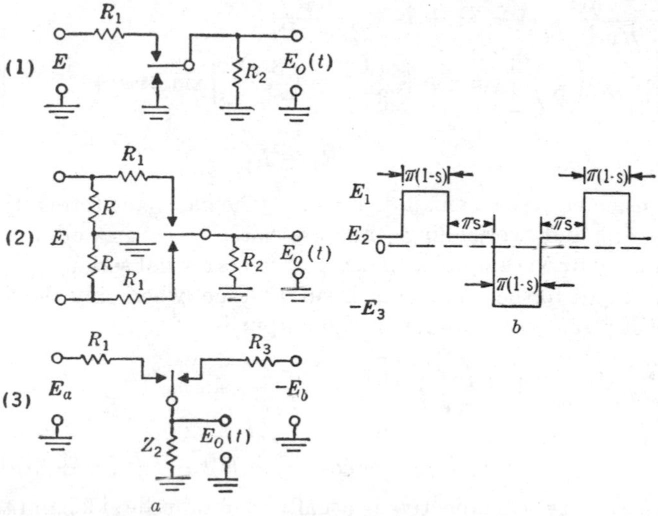

FIG. 3·19.—Vibrators as modulators. (a) Three possible circuits; (b) generalized output.

obtain the phase shift by a series inductance rather than by using a series capacitance.

The reed carries electrical contacts and acts as the pole of a double-throw single-pole switch with a noise level less than 2 μv. For a certain fraction of the cycle, the pole may short-circuit both fixed contacts.

Figure 3·19*a* presents three possible circuits employing synchronous vibrators as modulators. A generalized output, for which it is assumed that the input voltages do not vary significantly during a modulation period, is given in Fig. 3·19*b*. It may be expressed as

$$f(t) = \left(\frac{E_1 - E_3}{2}\right)(1 - s) + sE_2 + \frac{2}{\pi}(E_1 + E_3)\sum_{m=1}^{\infty}\frac{1}{2m-1}\cos\left[s\frac{\pi}{2}(2m-1)\right]\sin\left[\omega_0(2m-1)t\right] + \frac{2}{\pi}(2E_2 - E_1 + E_3)\sum_{n=1}^{\infty}\frac{1}{2n}\sin(s\pi n)\cos(2\omega_0 nt), \tag{58}$$

where the driving voltage has been assumed to be $V \sin(\omega_0 t + \beta)$, β is equal to the lag observed in the vibrator reed, and s is the fraction of the cycle for which the pole and the two contacts are shunted to each other.

For Circuit 1 in Fig. 3·19a, $E_2 = E_3 = 0$, and the output can be expressed, from Eq. (58), as

$$f(t) = \frac{E}{2}\frac{R_2}{R_1 + R_2}(1 - s) + E\frac{2}{\pi}\frac{R_2}{R_1 + R_2}\left\{\left[1 - \left(\frac{s\pi}{2}\right)^2\right]\sin\omega_0 t + \frac{1}{3}\left[1 - \left(\frac{3s\pi}{2}\right)^2\right]\sin 3\omega_0 t + \cdots\right\}$$
$$- E\frac{2}{\pi}\frac{R_2}{R_1 + R_2}(s\pi\cos 2\omega_0 t + \cdots) \qquad (59)$$

if s is considered to be a small quantity. The harmonic terms will cause some heating and overloading; they are small, however, and are usually so attenuated by the amplifier that these effects are not serious.

If the input to the vibrator is $E \sin mt$, then, when only the first two terms of Eq. (59) are considered, the output is

$$f(t) = \frac{E}{\pi}\frac{R_2}{R_I + R_2}\left[1 - \left(\frac{s\pi}{2}\right)^2\right]\left[\frac{\pi}{2}\frac{(1 - s)}{1 - \left(\frac{s\pi}{2}\right)^2}\sin mt\right.$$
$$\left. + \cos(\omega_0 - m)t - \cos(\omega_0 + m)t\right]. \qquad (60)$$

In such a case the sole objective is usually to obtain the sideband terms of frequency $\omega_0 - m$ and $\omega_0 + m$. In many cases the presence of the additional ($\sin mt$)-term in the output causes no apparent difficulty. In feedback loops, however, it has been observed that a circuit similar to Circuit 2 in Fig. 3·19 permits higher gain. Such a circuit has only the ($\sin n\omega_0 t$)-terms in its output, so that no term similar to the first in Eq. (60) is produced.

Circuit 3 is of interest because it combines the operations of obtaining the difference of two voltages and of modulating that difference. Often Z_2 is so chosen that it is very large compared with R_1 and R_3. If Z_2 is complex, care must be taken to maintain the gain at the carrier frequency.

The output of Circuit 3 may be expressed in terms of servo error. If $R_1 = R_3$, $Z_3 = \infty$, $E_a = K\theta_I$, and $-E_b = K\theta_O$, its output reduces to

$$f(t) = K\left[\theta_I\left(\frac{3}{2}s + \frac{1}{2}\right) + \theta_O\left(\frac{3}{2}s + \frac{1}{2}\right)\right]$$
$$+ \epsilon\frac{2K}{\pi}\left[1 - \left(\frac{s\pi}{2}\right)^2\right]\sin\omega_0 t \cdots. \qquad (61)$$

When modulation is performed at a low signal level, care has been taken to avoid coupling by stray capacitance to a-c voltage leads. For example, in Circuit 1 there is stray capacitance C_n between a voltage source $E_n \sin(\omega_0 t + \phi)$ and the leaf contact and ungrounded contact. Since this stray capacitance will be quite small, for usual circuits the contribution to $E_O(t)$ from this coupling is

$$\omega_0 \left[\frac{(R_1 R_2)}{(R_1 + R_2)} \right] C_n E_n \cos(\omega_0 t + \phi)$$

for the half of the modulation cycle that E_O is not zero. For simplicity, assume that s is zero and that the voltage driving the reed is $\sin(\omega_0 t + \beta)$, where, as before, β is the phase lag of the reed. Then the effect on E_O of the stray coupling is, in fundamental frequency components,

$$E_O(t) = \left(\frac{2}{\pi} \frac{R_2}{R_1 + R_2} E - \frac{1}{2} \omega_0 \frac{R_1 R_2}{R_1 + R_2} C_n E_n \sin \phi \right) \sin \omega_0 t + \frac{1}{2} \omega_0 \frac{R_1 R_2}{R_1 + R_2} C_n E_n \cos \phi \cos \omega_0 t. \quad (62)$$

It is seen that, in general, both an in-phase component and a quadrature component have been added by the stray coupling. If the voltage driving the reed has been shifted approximately 90° to obtain phase shift for a two-phase servomotor, the stray coupling causes little or no servo error from "standoff" in the voltage E. A quadrature component, however, will exist. If the voltage driving the reed has not been materially shifted in phase, the quadrature component is small but there is a "standoff" error equal to that which would cause a change in E of amount

$$\Delta E = \frac{\pi}{4} \omega_0 R_1 C_n E_n. \quad (63)$$

For example, if $C_n = 2 \times 10^{-6}$ μf, $R_1 = 1$ megohm, $\omega_0 = 377$, $E_n = 6.3$ volts, then ΔE is about 6 mv.

3·12. Phase-sensitive Detectors.—It is often necessary to change from an a-c error voltage to a d-c error voltage. For instance, if a synchro error-measuring system is used with a servo loop in which the power-output stage is an amplidyne, it is clearly desirable to have a circuit that will have a d-c output with the sign depending on the phase of the a-c error voltage and with the magnitude proportional to the magnitude of the a-c error voltage. Such a device is called a phase-sensitive detector. There are many variations in design; one possible circuit is presented in Fig. 3·20.

In Fig. 3·20, it is seen that the voltage applied to the full-wave rectifying diode D_1 is $V_1 = V_r + V_\epsilon - V_{01}$ and the voltage applied to the other diode D_2 is $V_2 = V_r - V_\epsilon - V_{02}$. The voltage V_r is often called the "reference voltage." If it is assumed that

$$V_\epsilon = V_\epsilon \cos(\omega t + \theta), \tag{64a}$$
$$V_r = V_r \cos \omega t, \tag{64b}$$

then

$$V_1 = \sqrt{(V_r + V_\epsilon \cos\theta)^2 + (V_\epsilon \sin\theta)^2}\cos(\omega t + \phi_1) - V_{01}, \tag{65a}$$
$$V_2 = \sqrt{(V_r - V_\epsilon \cos\theta)^2 + (V_\epsilon \sin\theta)^2}\cos(\omega t - \phi_2) - V_{02}, \tag{65b}$$
$$\phi_1 \equiv \tan^{-1}\left(\frac{V_\epsilon \sin\theta}{V_r + V_\epsilon \cos\theta}\right), \qquad \phi_2 \equiv \tan^{-1}\left(\frac{V_\epsilon \sin\theta}{V_r - V_\epsilon \cos\theta}\right). \tag{65c}$$

If θ is small, Eqs. (65) reduce to

$$V_1 = (V_r + V_\epsilon \cos\theta)\cos\omega t - V_{01}, \tag{66a}$$
$$V_2 = (V_r - V_\epsilon \cos\theta)\cos\omega t - V_{02}. \tag{66b}$$

It will be noted that the gain is not very sensitive to the phase angle θ.

For frequencies of the order of ω, the load impedances across which V_{01} and V_{02} are developed are kept large compared with the internal

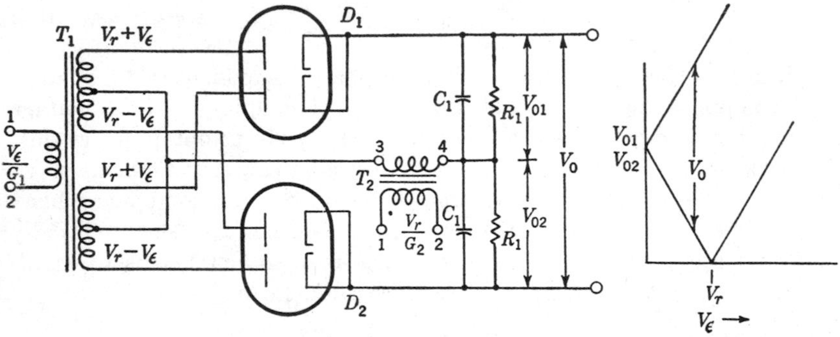

FIG. 3·20.—Phase-sensitive detector.

impedance of the diodes and transformers. This avoids the effects of nonsimilarity in these internal impedances and in the loads themselves and helps to realize the full voltage gain G_1 of transformer T_1. A high load impedance requires a high value of R_1 and a low value of C_1. To decrease time delay, the product R_1C_1 is kept small, and poor filtering results (10 per cent ripple is usually tolerated). Fortunately, if θ is small, the ripple due to the reference voltage tends to cancel in the circuit given here; relatively little ripple is present in that output when the error is small. In connection with ripple it is worth noting that noise similar to ripple can be caused by small differences in the voltage gain of the secondary sections of T_1. Again this will be proportional to error voltage.

In the steady state, V_1 and $V_2 \to 0$, and the output voltages are approximately d-c, with values

$$\left.\begin{aligned} V_{01} &= V_r + V_\epsilon, \\ V_{02} &= V_r - V_\epsilon, \qquad (V_\epsilon \leqq V_r); \end{aligned}\right\} \tag{67}$$

therefore

$$V_0 = 2V_\epsilon \qquad \text{if } V_\epsilon \leqq V_r.$$

Thus V_0 is linear with the magnitude of the error. If an error of the opposite sense is assumed, the phase of V_ϵ shifts 180°, and the sign of the output voltage is negative.

If $V_\epsilon > V_r$, $V_{02} = V_\epsilon - V_r$ and $V_0 = 2V_r$. This limiting action is sometimes desirable if circuits of integral type follow the rectifier, because it establishes the maximum output that will be "integrated."

If θ approaches $\pi/2$, Eqs. (65) can be written

$$V_1 = \sqrt{V_r^2 + V_\epsilon^2}\cos(\omega t + \phi') - V_{01}, \tag{68a}$$

$$V_2 = \sqrt{V_r^2 + V_\epsilon^2}\cos(\omega t - \phi') - V_{02}, \tag{68b}$$

$$\phi' \equiv \tan^{-1}\frac{V_\epsilon}{V_r}. \tag{68c}$$

It is seen that no net direct current results from the circuit, provided that either the voltage gains of the secondary sections of T_1 are identical or that the differences average in such a way as to produce zero net effect. In the output, however, there is increased ripple due to the difference in phase between $V_r + V_\epsilon$ and $V_r - V_\epsilon$, because the ripple does not cancel.

This insensitiveness to a quadrature component in the error signal is very advantageous, not only in eliminating a quadrature component that has arisen from some sort of unfortunate characteristic of the error-measuring circuit but also in separating for a particular servo the appropriate error signal from a total error signal that contains data for two servos. For instance, in radar tracking the total error voltage may be

$$E_\epsilon = G(\epsilon_E \sin \omega t + \epsilon_T \cos \omega t), \tag{69}$$

where ϵ_E and ϵ_T are the errors in elevation and traverse respectively. By applying this error voltage to two phase-sensitive-detector systems in parallel, one of which is supplied with a reference voltage $V_r = V_r \sin \omega t$ and the other with a reference voltage $V_r' = V_r' \cos \omega t$, the error data for the traverse and elevation servos are separated into two isolated voltages. When it is desirable to eliminate a quadrature component but to obtain the final error signal as an a-c voltage, a phase-sensitive detector may be used and followed by a modulator, such as the vibrator discussed in Sec. 3·11.

In some variations of the phase-sensitive-detector circuit, the reference voltage is introduced separately into the two diode-rectifier sections in such a way that a nonuniformity of transformer secondaries may produce a small d-c output of the circuit with zero error. If a zero-error d-c output exists, regardless of cause, the servo will "stand off" from its proper zero. Indeed, such "standoff" may exist in a servo because of any extraneous error data that appear in the forward channel, such as the pickup mentioned in Sec. 3·11 in connection with the synchronous vibrator. Its magnitude can be easily established if limits can be set on the magnitude of the false data. If at the point of origin of the extraneous data (of magnitude Δ) one unit of error produces G units of datum quantity (volts in the above case), the standoff is Δ/G units of error. Thus the later in the loop the extraneous data appear the less is the resulting inaccuracy. Amplidynes, for instance, often have an appreciable output at zero input due to hysteresis; but because they are used in the final power stage, little inaccuracy results.

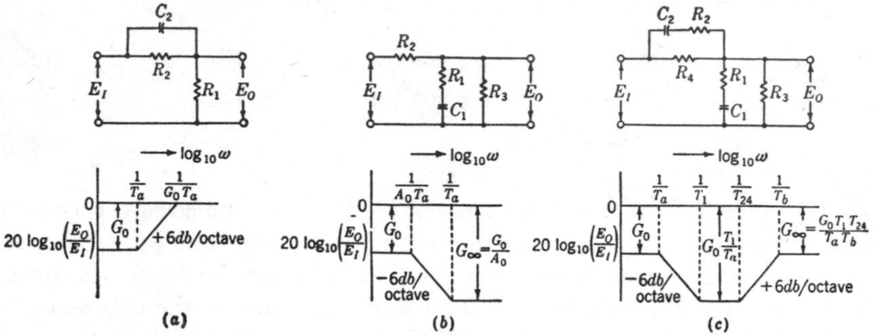

FIG. 3·21.—Equalizing networks for operating on d-c error voltage.
(a) $E_O/E_I = (T_ap + 1)/(G_0T_ap + 1)$; (b) $E_O/E_I = G_0[(T_ap + 1)/(A_0T_ap + 1)]$;
(c) $E_O/E_I = G_0[(T_1p + 1)(T_{24}p + 1)]/[(T_ap + 1)(T_bp + 1)]$.

3·13. Networks for Operating on D-c Error Voltage.—A simple servo transfer characteristic, such as was presented in Sec. 3·10, is of the form

$$\frac{\theta_O}{\epsilon} = \frac{1}{p}\frac{K_v}{(T_1p + 1)(T_2p + 1)(T_3p + 1)\cdots}. \tag{70}$$

As the gain is increased in an effort to reduce the error in following, the servo often becomes unstable before the gain is high enough for satisfactory performance. By insertion of circuits having proper transfer characteristics in Box 12 (Fig. 3·1), it is often possible to increase the gain to the desired value and yet maintain satisfactory stability. Examples of such networks, useful if the error is at a d-c voltage level, are shown in Fig. 3·21. The transfer characteristics are plotted asymptotically. This type of plot and its departures from the actual curve will be discussed in Sec. 4·10.

The network given in Fig. 3·21a has the transfer characteristic

$$Y_1 = \frac{E_O}{E_I} = G_0\frac{T_ap + 1}{G_0T_ap + 1}\begin{cases} G_0 \equiv \dfrac{R_1}{R_1 + R_2}. \\ T_a \equiv R_2C_2 \end{cases} \tag{71}$$

Such a network is often called a "derivative-plus-proportional net," because it has the same characteristics as an "ideal" derivative-plus-proportional device $[Y = G(Tp + 1)]$ for frequencies less than $1/(G_0T_a)$. It is not difficult to obtain any reasonable values for the frequencies $1/T_a$ and $1/(G_0T_a)$.

The network given in Fig. 3·21*b* has the transfer characteristic

$$Y_1 = \frac{E_O}{E_1} = G_0 \frac{T_a p + 1}{T_b p + 1}, \tag{72a}$$

where

$$T_a \equiv R_1 C_1, \tag{72b}$$
$$T_b \equiv [R_1 + R_3(1 - G_0)]C_1, \tag{72c}$$
$$G_0 \equiv \frac{R_3}{R_2 + R_3}. \tag{72d}$$

The resistance R_3 is usually determined by requirements of the following stage. Because this net has the same characteristic as an ideal integral-plus-proportional device $\{Y = G[(1/Tp) + 1]\}$ for frequencies greater than $1/T_b$, it is sometimes called an integral-plus-proportional network. Again, T_a and T_b can be established independently.

In servo design, cases often arise in which it is desired to have a transfer characteristic combining the properties of both of the above networks. In order to reduce the number of d-c stages, the networks are usually combined directly. Such a composite network is shown in Fig. 3·21*c*. The transfer characteristic is

$$\frac{E_O}{E_1} = \frac{(T_1 p + 1)(T_{24} p + 1)}{\left(T_1 T_{24} + \frac{R_4}{R_3} T_{13} T_2\right) p^2 + \left[T_1 + T_{24} + \frac{R_4}{R_3}(T_{13} + T_2)\right] p + 1 + \frac{R_4}{R_3}}, \tag{73a}$$

where $T_1 \equiv R_1 C_1$; $T_{24} \equiv (R_2 + R_4)C_2$; $T_{13} \equiv (R_1 + R_3)C_1$; $T_2 \equiv R_2 C_2$. We may write Eq. (73*a*) in the form

$$\frac{E_O}{E_1} = G_0 \frac{(T_1 p + 1)(T_{24} p + 1)}{(T_a p + 1)(T_b p + 1)}, \qquad G_0 \equiv \frac{R_3}{R_4 + R_3}. \tag{73b}$$

The design of the servo loop involves adjusting the magnitudes of T_1, T_{24}, T_a, T_b, and G_0. The gain at very high frequencies G_∞ is

$$G_\infty = G_0 \frac{T_1 T_{24}}{T_a T_b} \tag{74a}$$

and is also of interest because of the presence of noise in the error signal. Since it is obviously defined if T_1, T_{24}, T_a, T_b, and G_0 are fixed, choice of these quantities should be influenced by considerations of an acceptable G_∞.

If R_3 is determined by grid-circuit requirements or other impedance requirements of the following stage, there are precisely the requisite number of parameters to establish the four time constants and the low-frequency gain G_0. It is to be noted that the inequality

$$G_\infty = \frac{G_0 T_1 T_{24}}{T_a T_b} \leqq 1 \tag{74b}$$

cannot be violated; the upper limit occurs at $R_2 = 0$.

Comparison of Eqs. (73*a*) and (73*b*) yields, in terms of C_1 and C_2, and the quantities that it is desired to fix,

$$T_a T_b = G_0 T_1 T_{24} + (1 - G_0)(T_1 + R_3 C_1)\left[T_{24} - \left(\frac{1 - G_0}{G_0}\right) R_3 C_2\right], \tag{75a}$$

$$T_a + T_b = T_1 + T_{24} + R_3(1 - G_0)\left[C_1 - \left(\frac{1 - G_0}{G_0}\right) C_2\right]. \tag{75b}$$

Solution of Eqs. (75*a*) and (75*b*) for C_2 gives

$$C_2 = \frac{G_0}{2R_3(1 - G_0)^2}\left\{T_1 G_0 + T_{24}(2 - G_0) - T_a - T_b \pm \sqrt{(T_a + T_b - G_0 T_1 - G_0 T_{24})^2 - 4G_0\left[T_a T_b\left(\frac{1 - G_0}{G_0}\right) - T_1 T_{24}(1 - G_0)\right]}\right\}. \tag{76a}$$

Commonly the first term under the square-root sign is much greater than the second, and so we may obtain the approximation

$$C_2 \approx \frac{G_0}{R_3(1 - G_0)}\left[T_{24} - \frac{T_a T_b - T_1 T_{24} G_0}{T_a + T_b - G_0(T_1 + T_{24})}\right]. \tag{76b}$$

With this value of C_2, C_1 is obtained from Eq. (75*b*):

$$C_1 = \frac{T_a + T_b - T_1 - T_{24}}{R_3(1 - G_0)} + \frac{1 - G_0}{G_0} C_2. \tag{77}$$

Then

$$\left.\begin{aligned} R_1 &= \frac{T_1}{C_1}, \\ R_4 &= R_3 \frac{1 - G_0}{G_0}, \\ R_2 &= \frac{T_{24}}{C_2} - R_3\left(\frac{1 - G_0}{G_0}\right). \end{aligned}\right\} \tag{78}$$

A common difficulty is that the total capacity $C_1 + C_2$ becomes very large, especially if a very large time constant in the denominator is desired. The expression for the total capacity becomes, with use of the approximation of Eq. (76*b*),

$$C_1 + C_2 = \frac{1}{R_3(1 - G_0)}\left[T_a + T_b - T_1 - \frac{T_a T_b - T_1 T_{24} G_0}{T_a + T_b - G_0(T_1 + T_{24})}\right]. \tag{79a}$$

Apparently T_1 should be chosen greater than T_{24}, although the economy is not usually impressive. It is seen that the total capacity required decreases if R_3 can be increased. For usual design requirements on the time constants, the total capacity also decreases as lower values of G_0 are accepted and approaches the lower limit

$$(C_1 + C_2)_{\text{lim}} = \frac{1}{R_3}\left(T_a + T_b - T_1 - \frac{T_aT_b}{T_a + T_b}\right). \tag{79b}$$

Since the components of the network are often determined empirically, an analytical examination of the resulting loop characteristic is desirable. The values of G_0, T_1, and T_{24} are easily obtained, but the values of T_a and T_b are not so obvious. If T_a is assumed to be the larger of the two time constants, then

$$T_a = \frac{\beta + \beta\sqrt{1 - \dfrac{4\alpha}{\beta^2}}}{2}, \tag{80a}$$

and

$$T_b = \frac{\beta - \beta\sqrt{1 - \dfrac{4\alpha}{\beta^2}}}{2}, \tag{80b}$$

where

$$\beta \equiv G_0\left[T_1 + T_{24} + \frac{R_4}{R_3}(T_{13} + T_2)\right], \tag{80c}$$

$$\alpha \equiv G_0\left[T_1T_{24} + \frac{R_4}{R_3}T_{13}T_2\right]. \tag{80d}$$

Frequently $4\alpha < \beta^2$, and then, approximately,

$$T_b \approx \frac{\alpha}{\beta} = \frac{T_1T_{24} + \dfrac{R_4}{R_3}T_{13}T_2}{T_1 + T_{24} + \dfrac{R_4}{R_3}(T_{13} + T_2)}, \tag{80e}$$

$$T_a \approx \beta - \frac{\alpha}{\beta} = G_0\left[T_1 + T_{24} + \frac{R_4}{R_3}(T_{13} + T_2)\right] - T_b. \tag{80f}$$

3·14. Networks for Operating on A-c Error Signal.—It can be demonstrated that if a voltage $V = M(t)\cos\omega_0 t$, in which ω_0 is the fixed carrier frequency, is impressed on a network the transfer characteristic of which is

$$Y(j\omega) = G[1 + jT_d(\omega - \omega_0)], \tag{81}$$

the output is

$$V_0 = G\left[M(t) + T_d\frac{dM(t)}{dt}\right]\cos\omega_0 t. \tag{82}$$

Thus such a network has precisely the characteristics associated with a true proportional-derivative device and as such would be useful in equalization of servo loops employing a-c error data.

Many networks have been utilized to approximate the transfer characteristic expressed in Eq. (81). The network that will be discussed first is the parallel "T" net,[1] as given in Fig. 3·22a.

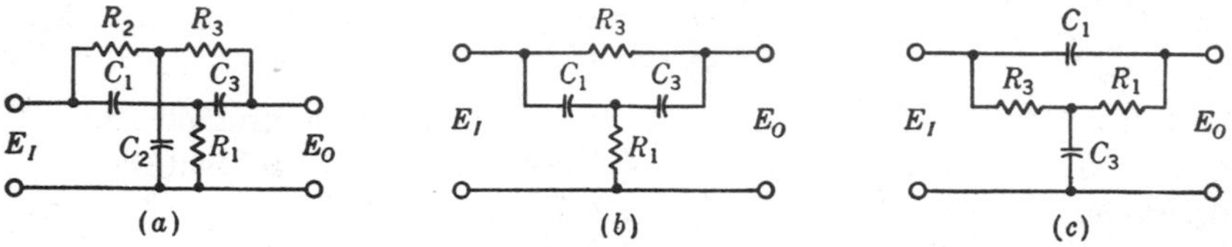

FIG. 3·22.—Parallel-T and bridge-T networks.

It is to be noted that a load resistor and a source impedance have not been included in Fig. 3·22. If $Y(p)$ is the transfer characteristic of one of the networks of Fig. 3·22, Z_I the input impedance with the output open-circuited, Z_I the impedance looking back into the output with the input short-circuited, then

$$\frac{E_0}{E_I} = \frac{Y(p)}{\left(1 + \frac{Z}{Z_I}\right)\left(1 + \frac{Z_{22}}{Z_L}\right) - \frac{Z_I}{Z_L}[Y(p)]^2} = Y'(p), \tag{83}$$

where Z is the source impedance to the voltage E_0, Z_L is the load impedance, and $Z_{22} = Z_I + Z_I[Y(p)]^2$. The deviations of $Y'(p)$ from $Y(p)$ have been investigated, both by mathematical analysis and by actual use of the nets in servos, and have been found, in general, to be small when the values of Z and Z_L employed are those associated, for example, with a synchro or a low-impedance phase-shifting net as a source and a vacuum tube as a load. In the following discussion the source impedance and load impedance are neglected, with the approximation that they are zero and infinite, respectively.

The general expression for the transfer characteristic of the parallel T of Fig. 3·22a is

$$\frac{E_O}{E_I} = \frac{[T_1T_2T_3p^3 + T_1(S_2 + T_3)p^2 + (T_1 + S_1)p + 1]}{[T_1T_2T_3p^3 + T_1(S_2 + T_3)p^2 + T_2(T_1 + S_1 + T_3)p^2 + (T_1 + S_1 + T_2 + S_2 + T_3)p + 1]} \tag{84}$$

where $T_1 = R_1C_1$, $T_2 = R_2C_2$, $T_3 = R_3C_3$, $S_1 = R_1C_3$, and $S_2 = R_2C_3$. This expression may be made to assume the form

[1] A. Sobczyk, "Parallel 'T' Stabilizing Networks for A-c Servos," RL Report No. 811, Mar. 7, 1946.

$$\frac{E_O}{E_I} = \frac{\left(\frac{u}{\omega_0} p + 1\right)\left(\frac{1}{\omega_0^2} p^2 + \frac{2}{\omega_0^2 T_d} p + 1\right)}{\left(\frac{u}{\omega_0} p + 1\right)\left(\frac{1}{\omega_0^2} p^2 + \frac{2}{\omega_0^2 l} p + 1\right)} = \frac{l}{T_d} \frac{1 + jT_d \frac{\omega + \omega_0}{2\omega} (\omega - \omega_0)}{1 + jl \frac{\omega + \omega_0}{2\omega} (\omega - \omega_0)}, \tag{85}$$

if the following relations are satisfied:

$$\left.\begin{aligned} T_1 &= \frac{l}{T_d} \frac{(\omega_0 T_d u^2 + 2u + \omega_0 T_d)}{2\omega_0 \left(1 - \frac{l}{T_d}\right)}, \\ T_2 &= \frac{u^2}{T_1 \omega_0}, \\ T_3 &= \frac{1}{u\omega_0}, \\ S_1 &= \frac{2}{\omega_0^2 T_d} + \frac{u}{\omega_0} - T_1, \\ S_2 &= \frac{2}{\omega_0^2 l} - \frac{2}{\omega_0^2 T_d} - \frac{1}{\omega_0 u} - T_2. \end{aligned}\right\} \tag{86}$$

If the modulation of the input voltage does not create sidebands lying far from ω_0, Eq. (85) approximates the ideal characteristics of Eq. (81), except for the presence of the time lag l.

The physical requirement that S_1 and S_2 be positive imposes on u the simultaneous restrictions

$$\frac{1}{l\omega_0} - \frac{2}{T_d\omega_0} - \frac{1}{l\omega_0}\sqrt{1 - l^2\omega_0^2} < u < \frac{1}{l\omega_0} - \frac{2}{T_d\omega_0} + \frac{1}{l\omega_0}\sqrt{1 - l^2\omega_0^2} \tag{87}$$

and

$$\frac{2l\omega_0 - \omega_0 T_d \left(1 + \sqrt{1 - l^2\omega_0^2}\right)}{4 - \frac{4l}{T_d} - lT_d\omega_0^2} < u < \frac{2l\omega_0 - \omega_0 T_d \left(1 - \sqrt{1 - l^2\omega_0^2}\right)}{4 - \frac{4l}{T_d} - lT_d\omega_0^2}. \tag{88}$$

It is to be noted that, for realizability, $l \leqq 1/\omega_0$.

A design procedure is apparent. It is assumed that theoretical or experimental considerations have determined acceptable values of T_d and l. The carrier frequency ω_0 is, of course, known. The restrictions on u are established by Eqs. (87) and (88). The time constants T_1, T_2, T_3, S_1, and S_2 are computed, with a value of u not too near the end points for a reason discussed later. Then if one component, C_3, for example, is specified, the other components are determined, because

$$R_1 = \frac{S_1}{C_3}, \qquad R_2 = \frac{S_2}{C_3}, \qquad R_3 = \frac{T_3}{C_3}, \qquad C_1 = \frac{T_1}{R_1}, \qquad C_2 = \frac{T_2}{R_2}. \tag{89}$$

The choice of u and of the one component should be influenced by impedance considerations. The input impedance, with the output open-circuited, Z_I, and the output impedance with the input short-circuited, Z_O, can be expressed as functions of u and C_3:

$$Z_1\left(C_3, \frac{u}{\omega_0}\right) = \frac{1}{C_3} \frac{\left(\frac{u}{\omega_0} p + 1\right)\left(\frac{1}{\omega_0^2} p^2 + \frac{2}{l\omega_0^2} p + 1\right)}{\left[\left(\frac{1}{S_1} + \frac{1}{S_2}\right)\frac{1}{\omega_0^2} + \frac{u}{\omega_0}\right]\frac{u}{\omega_0} p^3 + \left(\frac{2}{l\omega_0^2} - \frac{2}{T_d\omega_0^2}\right)\left(\frac{T_1}{S_1} + \frac{u}{\omega_0 S_2}\right) p^2 + \left(\frac{T_1}{S_1} + \frac{T_2}{S_2} + 1\right) p}, \tag{90a}$$

$$Z_O\left(C_3, \frac{u}{\omega_0}\right) = \frac{T_2\left(\frac{2}{\omega_0^2 T_d} + \frac{u}{\omega_0}\right) p^2 + \left[\left(\frac{2}{\omega_0^2 T_d} + \frac{u}{\omega_0}\right)(1 + S_2 u\omega_0) + T_2\right] p + (1 + S_2 u\omega_0)}{C_3 u\omega_0 \left(\frac{u}{\omega_0} p + 1\right)\left(\frac{1}{\omega_0^2} p^2 + \frac{2}{l\omega_0^2} p + 1\right)}. \tag{90b}$$

It is evident that as u approaches an end point of one of the critical regions, so that S_1 or S_2 approaches zero, Z_I approaches zero. Also, to avoid low input impedance, the gain $G = l/T_d$ should not be chosen too near the upper bound of $1/(T_d\omega_0)$.

Since odd sizes of condensers are difficult to obtain, it is useful to present a design procedure that may be applied when values of C_1, C_2, and C_3 are known and values for R_1, R_2, and R_3 are desired for a given T_d. The relations are

$$R_1 = \frac{1}{\omega_0} \frac{\left(\frac{2}{\omega_0 T_d} + u\right)}{C_1 + C_3}, \tag{91a}$$

$$R_2 = \frac{C_1 + C_3}{C_1\omega_0} \frac{u^2}{\left(\frac{2}{\omega_0 T_d} + u\right) C_2}, \tag{91b}$$

$$R_3 = \frac{1}{u\omega_0 C_3}, \tag{91c}$$

in which u must be a solution of

$$\frac{C_1 + C_3}{C_1} u^3 - \frac{2}{\omega_0 T_d} \frac{C_2(C_1 + C_3)}{C_3 C_1} u^2 - \frac{C_2}{C_1} u + \frac{2}{\omega_0 T_d} \frac{C_2}{C_3} = 0. \tag{91d}$$

For $C_1 = C_2 = C_3$, the positive solutions for u are $u = 1/\sqrt{2}$ and $u = 2/(T_d\omega_0)$. The gain $G = l/T_d$ can be obtained from the expression

$$\frac{2}{G} = \frac{C_1 + C_3}{C_1} \left(\frac{\omega_0 T_d}{\dfrac{2}{\omega_0 T_d} + u} + \omega_0 T_d u \right) + 2. \tag{92}$$

Table 3·2 presents circuit constants for the case of three equal condensers ($u = 1/\sqrt{2}$).

TABLE 3·2.—PARALLEL T WITH EQUAL CONDENSERS
$R_3 = 0.003751$ megohms, $C_1 = C_2 = C_3 = 1.000$ μf, $f_0 = 60$ cps

$T_d\omega_0$	Notch interval, cps	$R_1 \times 10^3$, megohms	$R_2 \times 10^3$, megohms	Forward gain	Reverse gain	Input impedance $Z_1 \times 10^3$, megohms	Output impedance $Z_0 \times 10^3$, megohms	Reverse phase shift at ω_0, degrees
2.5	±24.0	1.9980	1.760	0.225900	0.174190	1.324–1.545j	1.798–1.768j	−5.00
5.0	±12.0	1.4680	2.395	0.110500	0.094550	1.303–1.573j	1.565–1.768j	−1.84
7.5	± 9.0	1.2910	2.723	0.076900	0.064670	1.303–1.620j	1.469–1.768j	−0.95
10.0	± 6.0	1.2030	2.934	0.052370	0.048070	1.289–1.640j	1.418–1.768j	−0.57
15.0	± 4.0	1.1140	3.155	0.033950	0.032000	1.280–1.675j	1.364–1.768j	−0.27
20.0	± 3.0	1.0700	3.286	0.025050	0.023940	1.274–1.695j	1.337–1.768j	−0.16
30.0	± 2.0	1.0260	3.427	0.016400	0.015900	1.267–1.717j	1.306–1.768j	−0.06
40.0	± 1.5	1.0040	3.503	0.012180	0.012020	1.264–1.729j	1.293–1.768j	−0.04
50.0	± 1.2	0.9907	3.550	0.009682	0.009500	1.261–1.737j	1.285–1.768j	−0.02
60.0	± 1.0	0.9818	3.582	0.008034	0.007910	1.260–1.742j	1.279–1.768j	−0.01
∞	Resonant	0.9378	3.751	0	0	1.250–1.768j	1.250–1.768j	0

The "notch interval" as recorded in Table 3·2 is defined as the frequency interval between the points for which the output of an ideal proportional-derivative net would be $\sqrt{2}$ times the minimum output.

In Table 3·2, the resistors are in megohms and the capacitors in microfarads. A parallel T differing only in impedance level may be obtained by multiplying the resistors by a constant and dividing the capacitors by the same constant. For certain classes of parallel-T networks, a proportional-derivative characteristic still exists if input and output are interchanged; Table 3·2 also gives some of the reverse characteristics of the T described there.

It is worth mentioning one method of using a parallel T that is sometimes useful in experimental work in which it is desired to obtain a value of T_d empirically. If $T_d\omega_0$ is taken to be infinite in the preceding formulas, a resonant parallel T is obtained, with a transfer characteristic

$$\frac{jl \dfrac{\omega + \omega_0}{2\omega} (\omega - \omega_0)}{1 + jl \dfrac{\omega + \omega_0}{2\omega} (\omega - \omega_0)}.$$

If this resonant T is then connected as shown in Fig. 3·23 to a potentiometer of impedance low compared with the input impedance of the T, the output can be written as

$$\frac{E_O}{E_I} = \frac{R_2}{R_1 + R_2} \frac{1 + jT_d \dfrac{\omega + \omega_0}{2\omega} (\omega - \omega_0)}{1 + jl \dfrac{\omega + \omega_0}{2\omega} (\omega - \omega_0)}, \tag{93}$$

in which $T_d = [1 + (R_1/R_2)x]l$ and can thus be adjusted within the limits $l < T_d < [1 + (R_1/R_2]l$.

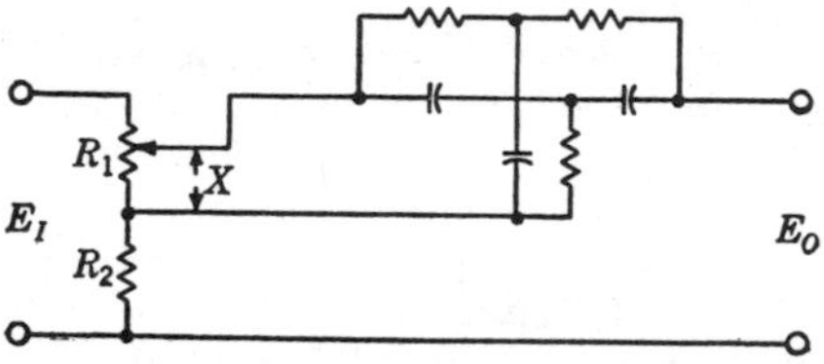

FIG. 3·23.—Circuit for variable T_d.

As interesting simplification of the parallel T follows if, in Fig. 3·22*a*, either $R_2 = 0$ or $C_1 = \infty$. Then circuits of the form shown in (*b*) and (*c*) of Fig. 3·22 are obtained. Such networks are commonly called bridge-T networks. In an effort to discuss the circuits simultaneously, the parts have been renumbered.

The transfer characteristic is

$$\frac{E_O}{E_I} = \frac{T_1T_3p^2 + (T_1 + S_1)p + 1}{T_1T_3p^2 + (T_1 + S_1 + T_3)p + 1}, \tag{94}$$

where $T_1 = R_1C_1$, $T_3 = R_3C_3$, and $S_1 = R_1C_3$ in Circuit *b* and $S_1 = R_3C_1$ in Circuit *c*. To obtain the approximate derivative characteristic of the form

$$\frac{E_O}{E_I} = \frac{l}{T_d} \frac{1 + jT_d \dfrac{\omega + \omega_0}{2\omega} (\omega - \omega_0)}{1 + jl \dfrac{\omega + \omega_0}{2\omega} (\omega - \omega_0)}, \tag{95}$$

the time constants must be defined by the following relations:

$$\left.\begin{aligned} T_3 &= \frac{2}{\omega_0^2}\left(\frac{1}{l} - \frac{1}{T_d}\right), \\ T_1 &= \left(\frac{1}{2\dfrac{1}{l} - \dfrac{1}{T_d}}\right), \\ S_1 &= \frac{2}{T_d\omega_0^2} - \frac{1}{2\left(\dfrac{1}{l} - \dfrac{1}{T_d}\right)}. \end{aligned}\right\} \tag{96}$$

For positive S_1, the gain $G = l/T_d$ must satisfy the inequality,

$$G < \frac{4}{4 + T_d^2\omega_0^2}. \tag{97}$$

Since for the parallel T the upper bound of gain is $1/(T_d\omega_0)$, it is observed that for a given T_d, less gain can be obtained from a bridge T. Because of noise in the signal, the smaller time lag l for a given T_d in a bridge T is a disadvantage when compared with a parallel T.

TABLE 3·3.—CONSTANTS FOR SYMMETRICAL BRIDGE T, CIRCUIT b
$C_1 = C_2 = 1.000$ μf

$T_d\omega_0$	Notch interval, cps	$R_1 \times 10^3$, megohms	$R_3 \times 10^3$, megohms	Gain	Input impedance $Z_1 \times 10^3$, megohms	Output impedance $Z_0 \times 10^3$, megohms
2.5	±24.0	1.06100	6.63	0.2424200	1.70790–2.135j	1.60750–2.009j
5.0	±12.0	0.53050	13.26	0.0740700	0.98780–2.470j	0.98240–2.456j
7.5	± 9.0	0.35360	19.89	0.0343300	0.68380–2.564j	0.68300–2.561j
10.0	± 6.0	0.26530	26.53	0.0196100	0.52030–2.602j	0.52010–2.601j
15.0	± 4.0	0.17680	39.79	0.0088110	0.35050–2.629j	0.35060–2.629j
20.0	± 3.0	0.13260	53.05	0.0049750	0.26390–2.639j	0.26390–2.639j
30.0	± 2.0	0.08841	79.58	0.0022170	0.17640–2.647j	0.17640–2.647j
40.0	± 1.5	0.06631	106.10	0.0012480	0.13250–2.649j	0.13250–2.649j
50.0	± 1.2	0.05305	132.60	0.0007994	0.10600–2.650j	0.10600–2.650j
60.0	± 1.0	0.04420	159.20	0.0005552	0.08836–2.651j	0.08836–2.651j
100.0	± 0.6	0.02653	265.30	0.0002000	0.05304–2.652j	0.05304–2.652j

For Circuit b, in terms of arbitrary condensers,

$$\left.\begin{aligned} R_1 &= \frac{2}{T_d\omega_0^2(C_1 + C_3)}, \\ R_3 &= \frac{T_d}{2}\left(\frac{1}{C_1} + \frac{1}{C_3}\right), \\ G &= \frac{4}{T_d^2\omega_0^2\left(1 + \dfrac{C_3}{C_1}\right) + 4}. \end{aligned}\right\} \tag{98}$$

Similar formulas for Circuit c, in terms of arbitrary resistors, are obtained for C_1, C_3, and G if in Eq. (98) R_1 is interchanged with C_1 and R_3 is interchanged with C_3.

For Circuit b

$$\left.\begin{aligned} Z_I &= R_1 + \frac{T_3p + 1}{C_1T_3p^2 + (C_1 + C_3)p}, \\ Z_O &= \frac{R_3[(S_1 + T_1)p + 1]}{T_1T_3p^2 + (T_1 + S_1 + T_3)p + 1}, \end{aligned}\right\} \tag{99}$$

and for Circuit *c*

$$\left.\begin{aligned} Z_I &= \frac{1}{C_3p} + \frac{R_3(T_1p + 1)}{(T_1 + S_1)p + 1}, \\ Z_O &= \frac{R_1T_3p + R_1 + R_3}{T_1T_3p^2 + (S_1 + T_1 + T_3)p + 1}, \end{aligned}\right\} \tag{100}$$

in which Z_I and Z_O have the meaning established above for the parallel T.

Table 3·3 gives some circuit constants for the bridge T for Circuit *b*; for Circuit *c*, R_1 is merely interchanged with C_1 and R_3 with C_3.

Tolerance requirements have been fully investigated[1] for the T networks given in this section. The expressions, however, are quite lengthy and will not be presented. In general, it may be said that to hold the ω_0 of the T to within 5 per cent, the notch width to within 2 per cent of ω_0, and the phase shift to zero $\pm 10°$, for a parallel T with a $T_d\omega_0$ of 15 each component must be held to about 0.5 per cent.

3·15. Operation on θ_O—Feedback Filters.—In the design of servos that are to employ an internal feedback loop, it is necessary to obtain a signal, usually a voltage, from a point in the loop as near the output as possible. This is commonly obtained from a tachometer driven directly from the motor shaft. Thus there results a voltage that is proportional to the speed of this shaft and that may be modified by one of the nets, discussed in this section, before being subtracted from the error.

If it is impractical to employ a tachometer, a simple bridge circuit with d-c motors may be used to obtain a voltage proportional to speed. The motor current may be expressed to a reasonable approximation as

$$i_m = \frac{e_d - K_e\Omega_m}{R_m + R_c + R_a}, \tag{101}$$

in which the terms have the same definition as those used in Sec. 3·10. With this relationship and the torque equation

$$K_t i_m = Jp\Omega_m + f_g\Omega_m,$$

it can be shown that the output voltage E_O from the bridge circuit as shown in Fig. 3·24, is

$$\left.\begin{aligned} E_O &= \frac{R_1}{R_1 + R_2} K_e(T_{m0}p + 1)\Omega_m, \\ T_{m0} &= \left(\frac{1 - \dfrac{R_2}{R_1}\dfrac{R_c}{R_m}}{1 + \dfrac{R_c}{R_m}}\right) T_{ma}, \end{aligned}\right\} \tag{102}$$

if it is assumed that $f_m \gg f_g$.

[1] Sobczyk, *op. cit.*

Often R_c includes the resistance o the compensating coil in the motor required for proper commutation. The positive limit of T_{m0} (at $R_2 = 0$) may be increased, if desired, by shunting this coil with a resistive divider and obtaining E_O between a point on the divider and Terminal 2 of the motor. When the bridge is balanced, $T_{m0} = 0$, and a voltage directly proportional to speed is obtained. Negative values of T_{m0} are obtained when $R_2/R_1 > R_mR_c$. The possible infinite negative value of T_{m0} suggested by Eq. (102) is a fallacy resulting from the fact that the viscous damping of the gear train was considered negligible compared with internal damping of the motor. Actually, the negative values of T_{m0} are of little interest; usually the bridge is either balanced to obtain the speed voltage or designed to obtain a positive T_{m0}. The presence of the positive T_{m0} introduces a derivative term in the feedback loop and thus can be used to increase phase margin, permitting higher feedback gain.

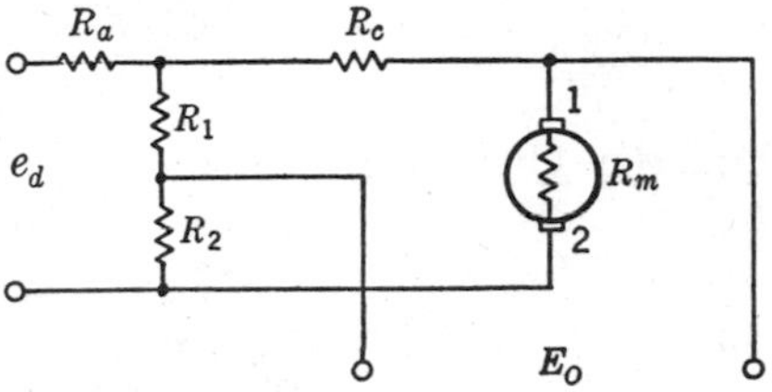

FIG. 3·24.—Bridge circuit for obtaining feedback voltage.

In a simple servo loop, if a voltage proportional $d\theta_O/dt$ is subtracted from the error voltage, the effect is identical with that which would be obtained by increasing the viscous damping, say, in the gear train. This, of course, has stabilizing action but also results in greater error in following constant-velocity inputs. Thus, in servos using such an internal feedback loop at d-c level for equalization, it is desirable to use a high-pass network between the source of d-c voltage and the mixing stage in which the modified d-c voltage is subtracted from the error signal. Single-, double-, and triple-section RC-filters are commonly used. Networks employing inductors have also been used, but the usefulness of such networks is limited, owing to the nonlinear properties of the large inductances required (about 1000 to 10,000 henrys).

The single-section high-pass RC-network shown in Fig. 3·25a is characterized by a single time constant $T = RC$, and the transfer function may be written as

$$\frac{E_O}{E} = \frac{Tp}{Tp + 1},$$
$$T \equiv RC, \tag{103}$$

which, asymptotically, is represented by a rising 6-db/octave section to $\omega = 1/T$ and a constant 0-db gain for high frequencies. Asymptotic plots and the departure from the actual curve are discussed in Sec. 4·10. The phase angle is $+90°$ for low frequencies, decreasing toward zero at high frequencies. At $\omega = 1/T$ the phase shift is $\pm 45°$.

The two-section high-pass RC-network is shown in Fig. 3·25b. Its transfer characteristic is

$$\frac{E_O}{E} = \frac{T_1T_2p^2}{T_1T_2p^2 + \left(1 + \frac{R_1}{R_2} + \frac{T_1}{R_2}\right)T_2p + 1}, \tag{104a}$$

where

$$T_1 \equiv R_1C_1, \tag{104b}$$
$$T_2 \equiv R_2C_2. \tag{104c}$$

Equation (104a) can also be written in two other ways:

$$\frac{E_O}{E} = \frac{T_aT_bp^2}{(T_ap + 1)(T_bp + 1)}, \tag{104d}$$
$$\frac{E_O}{E} = \frac{(Tp)^2}{(Tp)^2 + 2\zeta Tp + 1}, \tag{104e}$$

where T_a = longer effective time constant,
T_b = smaller effective time constant,
ζ = damping ratio ($\zeta > 1$),
$T = \sqrt{T_aT_b} = \sqrt{T_1T_2}$ = mean time constant.

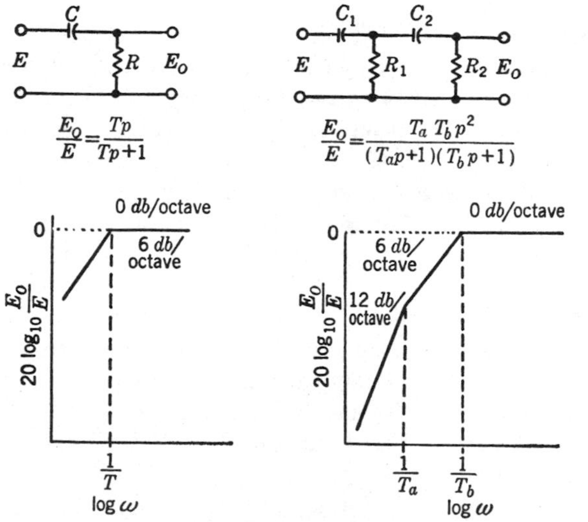

a *b*

FIG. 3·25.—High-pass filters for d-c feedback. (a) Single-section high-pass filter, $E_O/E = T_p/(T_p + 1)$; (b) two-section high-pass RC-network,

$$E_O/E = (T_aT_bp^2)[(T_ap + 1)(T_bp + 1)].$$

When the asymptotic transfer function is written in the form of Eq. (104d), it becomes apparent that it rises at 12 db/octave to $\omega = 1/T_a$, then at 6 db/octave to $\omega = 1/T_b$, and is then constant at 0 db for higher frequencies (see Sec. 4·10). The 12-db/octave portion if extended to the 0-db axis would cross it at

$$\omega = \frac{1}{\sqrt{T_aT_b}} = \frac{1}{T}. \tag{105}$$

It is also apparent from Eq. (104d) that there are only two primary parameters, T_a and T_b; the form in which these primary parameters will be used here is T_a/T_b and $\sqrt{T_aT_b} = T$.

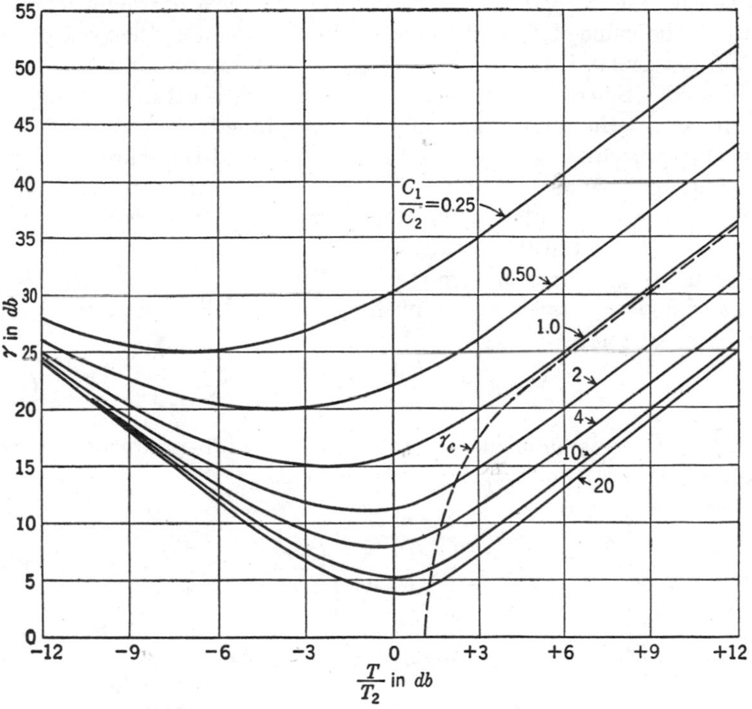

FIG. 3·26.—Graph for designing two-section high-pass RC-filter.

The following relations hold between the variables:

$$\zeta = \frac{1}{2}\,\frac{1 + \left(\frac{T}{T_2}\right)^2\left(1 + \frac{C_2}{C_1}\right)}{\frac{T}{T_2}}, \tag{106a}$$

$$\frac{T_a}{T_b} = \gamma = 2\zeta^2 - 1 + 2\zeta\sqrt{\zeta^2 - 1} = f\left(\frac{T}{T_2}, \frac{C_1}{C_2}\right). \tag{106b}$$

The relationship indicated in Eq. (106b) is plotted for several values of C_1/C_2 in Fig. 3·26.

In the usual circuits, the output resistor R_2 is required to be less than some critical value due to grid-return requirements or other impedance-level considerations. With this fact in mind, a possible design procedure becomes apparent. Experimental or theoretical work has determined T_a, T_b, and R_2. Thus γ, T, and R_2 are fixed. By the use of

$$\gamma = f\left(\frac{T}{T_2}, \frac{C_1}{C_2}\right)$$

as given by Fig. 3·26, T/T_2 can be determined for a particular choice of C_1/C_2. The value of T_2 and thus the value of C_2 can be then established. By the particular value of C_1/C_2 employed in determining T/T_2, C_1 is established. Since $T_1 = T^2/T_2$, T_1 is known, R_1 is established, and the components of the filter are completely determined.

Such a procedure, however, ignores the fact that there are four circuit elements, but it is desired to establish only three parameters. It seems desirable to use the other parameter to minimize the total capacitance $C_0 \equiv C_1 + C_2$ used in the circuit.

Fortunately, γ increases monotonically with ζ. Thus establishing γ, T, and R_2 is equivalent to establishing ζ, T, and R_2. Equation (106a) may be rewritten as

$$\zeta = \frac{1}{2}\frac{R_2C_2 - R_1C_0}{T}. \tag{106c}$$

Solving for C_0 and minimizing C_0 for fixed ζ, T, and R_2 produce a new relationship between ζ and the circuit components:

$$\zeta_C = \frac{1}{2}\sqrt{\frac{R_2C_2}{R_1C_1}}\,\frac{2\dfrac{C_1}{C_2} - 1}{\dfrac{C_1}{C_2} - 1}. \tag{106d}$$

Comparison of this with Eq. (106a) gives

$$\left(\frac{T_1}{T_2}\right)_C = \frac{\left(\dfrac{C_1}{C_2}\right)^2}{\left(\dfrac{C_1}{C_2}\right)^2 - 1} \tag{106e}$$

as the necessary condition for the minimization, which makes it possible to write

$$\zeta_C = \frac{1}{2}\left[\frac{T_2}{T} + \frac{T}{T_2} + \sqrt{\left(\frac{T}{T_2}\right)^2 - 1}\right]; \tag{106f}$$

use of this in Eq. (106b) yields $\gamma_C = f(T/T_2)$, a plot of which has been included in Fig. 3·26.

Thus, for economy in total capacitance, the design procedure suggested above is modified in that the choice of the value of C_1/C_2 should be determined by the intersection of the desired value of γ with the γ_C-curve.

General equations relating the tolerance on the components of the filter with the variation of T_a, T_b, T, and γ may be derived in the usual manner.

$$\frac{\partial T_a}{T_a} = \left(\frac{1}{2} + AD\right)\frac{\partial R_1}{R_1} + \left(\frac{1}{2} - AD\right)\frac{\partial R_2}{R_2} + \left(\frac{1}{2} + BD\right)\frac{\partial C_1}{C_1} + \left(\frac{1}{2} - BD\right)\frac{\partial C_2}{C_2}, \qquad (107a)$$

$$\frac{\partial T_b}{T_b} = \left(\frac{1}{2} - AD\right)\frac{\partial R_1}{R_1} + \left(\frac{1}{2} + AD\right)\frac{\partial R_2}{R_2} + \left(\frac{1}{2} - BD\right)\frac{\partial C_1}{C_1} + \left(\frac{1}{2} + BD\right)\frac{\partial C_2}{C_2}, \qquad (107b)$$

$$\frac{\partial T}{T} = \frac{1}{2}\frac{\partial R_1}{R_1} + \frac{1}{2}\frac{\partial R_2}{R_2} + \frac{1}{2}\frac{\partial C_1}{C_1} + \frac{1}{2}\frac{\partial C_2}{C_2}, \qquad (107c)$$

$$\frac{\partial \gamma}{\gamma} = AD\frac{\partial R_1}{R_1} - AD\frac{\partial R_2}{R_2} + BD\frac{\partial C_1}{C_1} - BD\frac{\partial C_2}{C_2}, \qquad (107d)$$

in which

$$A \equiv \frac{1}{2}\,\frac{\dfrac{T_1}{T_2}\left(\dfrac{C_1}{C_2} + 1\right) - \dfrac{C_1}{C_2}}{\dfrac{T_1}{T_2}\left(\dfrac{C_1}{C_2} + 1\right) + \dfrac{C_1}{C_2}},$$

$$B \equiv \frac{1}{2}\,\frac{\dfrac{T_1}{T_2}\left(\dfrac{C_1}{C_2} - 1\right) - \dfrac{C_1}{C_2}}{\dfrac{T_1}{T_2}\left(\dfrac{C_1}{C_2} + 1\right) + \dfrac{C_1}{C_2}},$$

$$D \equiv \frac{2\zeta}{(\zeta^2 - 1)^{1/2}}.$$

TABLE 3·4.—TOLERANCE COEFFICIENTS FOR MINIMUM CAPACITANCE CASES

$\frac{C_1}{C_2}$	$\frac{T_1}{T_2}$	AD	BD	$\frac{1}{2} + AD$	$\frac{1}{2} - AD$	$\frac{1}{2} + BD$	$\frac{1}{2} - BD$
2	1.333	0.522	−0.174	1.022	−0.022	0.326	0.674
4	1.067	0.307	−0.184	0.807	−0.193	0.316	0.684
6	1.029	0.235	−0.168	0.735	−0.265	0.332	0.668
8	1.016	0.196	−0.153	0.696	−0.304	0.347	0.653

Table 3·4 gives the tolerance coefficients for two of the minimum capacitance cases. It will be observed that the main contribution to the errors comes from the square-root relation between T and T_1T_2 and that the change in the ratio of the effective time constants is of a smaller order. This means that a given percentage error in one of the components will produce about one-half of that percentage error in the two effective time constants.

3·16. Gear Trains.—For use in control, a gear train must meet certain requirements of efficiency, reversibility, rigidity, backlash, strength, and inertia. Unfortunately, theoretical work has not progressed to the stage where all of these standards can be expressed mathematically.

In regard to efficiency, usual engineering reasoning applies, since this will directly affect the size of the motor that must be employed. Furthermore, it is to be noted that high starting friction produces rough following of the input at low speeds. High viscous friction decreases the effective velocity-error constant. Also, since it cannot be treated as a constant from gear train to gear train or as a function of time, its stabilizing action can be a source of serious design error.

At present there is no satisfactorily complete analysis of the problems encountered when servo control is employed with an irreversible gear train, such as certain worm reductions. Bitter experience, indicates however, that except possibly where the load inertia and load torques are small, irreversible gear trains should be avoided. It is felt that the difficulty is caused by the locking that takes place in many irreversible gear trains when subject to load torques.

The rigidity should be such that with the expected load inertia, there will be no natural frequencies that are less than, as a rough estimate, five to ten times the highest resonant frequency of the rest of the control loop. Naturally the rigidity of any portion of the gear train not enclosed in the loop must be such that errors arising from deflections under load are tolerable.

Backlash in gear trains, if enclosed in the loop, often produces instabilities of either very high or very low frequency. Usually the amplitude is of the order of magnitude of the backlash. A rule based only on experience is that the backlash must be less than one-half of the acceptable following error. If the backlash is not enclosed in the loop, the resulting error can, of course, be equal to the backlash.

Obviously, the gear train should be sturdy enough to withstand the maximum torque load that it will experience. An estimate of the maximum load can be obtained. The torque exerted on the motor rotor M_m and the torque exerted on the load M_l are related by

$$M_l = \frac{J_l N}{J_l + J_m N^2} M_m, \tag{108}$$

where J_l is the inertia of the load and J_m is the inertia of the motor armature and first gear and the inertia of the rest of the gear train, of reduction N, is ignored.

Usually it is only in control problems employing fair-sized motors that concern exists about the strength of the gear train. Thus the motor is usually direct current, and the relation $M = K_T i_m$ holds over a wide range of i_m. Under severe conditions, however, saturation effects may occur.

The greatest torque load will be experienced in one of two cases:

CASE I: If the load is blocked and a maximum voltage E_m, is applied to the motor, then from Eq. (108)

$$M_l = N(M_m)_{i_m}, \tag{109}$$

since in such a case $J_l = \infty$. The quantity $(M_m)_{i_m}$ is the torque associated with a current $i_m = E_m/R_m$ and may be less than $K_t i_m$ due to saturation.

CASE II: If the maximum voltage E_m is suddenly reversed after the motor has attained full speed, then

$$M_l = \frac{J_l N}{J_l + J_m N^2} (M_m)_{2i_m} \tag{110}$$

if the motor is assumed to run with a back emf equal to the applied emf for constant speeds. This is approximately correct with high-efficiency gear trains and no torque load on the output of the gear train. The quantity $(M_m)_{2i_m}$ is the torque produced by a current $i_m = 2E_m/R_m$.

A comparison of Eqs. (109) and (110) shows that if

$$\frac{(M_m)_{i_m}}{(M_m)_{2i_m}} < \frac{1}{1 + \dfrac{J_m}{J_l} N^2}, \tag{111}$$

Case II gives the greater torque but, if

$$\frac{(M_m)_{i_m}}{(M_m)_{2i_m}} > \frac{1}{1 + \dfrac{J_m N^2}{J_l}}, \tag{112}$$

Case I gives the greater torque.

In applications involving servomotors of a few mechanical watts output, the inertia of the gear train, especially the first mesh or two, is far from negligible compared with the inertia of the motor armature. If the inertia[1] of the gearing past the fourth gear (Fig. 3·27) is considered negligible, the following equation may be written for the total inertia J'_m observed at the motor shaft, N' being the total gear reduction to the inertia load J_l:

$$J'_m = J_m + J_g + \frac{J_l}{N'^2}, \tag{113a}$$

[1] The following treatment is from an unpublished paper by N. B. Nichols.

If it is assumed that the gears (of diameter D, width W) are all solid and of a material with a density ρ,

$$J_g = \frac{\pi\rho}{32}\left[W_1D_1^4 + \left(\frac{D_1}{D_2}\right)^2 W_2D_2^4 + \left(\frac{D_1}{D_2}\right)^2 W_3D_3^4 + \left(\frac{D_1}{D_2}\right)^2\left(\frac{D_3}{D_4}\right)^2 W_4D_4^4\right]. \qquad (113b)$$

In Eq. (110b), the small inertia of the idler shafts has been ignored or, if desired, absorbed by change of pinion width W. With the use of $N_{12} \equiv D_2/D_1$ and $N \equiv (D_2/D_1)(D_4/D_3)$, Eq. (113$b$) may be written as

$$J_g = J_0\left[\frac{W_1}{W_2} + N_{12}^2 + \frac{1}{N_{12}^2}\frac{W_3}{W_2}\left(\frac{D_3}{D_1}\right)^4 + \frac{N^2}{N_{12}'}\frac{W_4}{W_2}\left(\frac{D_3}{D_1}\right)^4\right], \qquad (113c)$$

where J_0 is the moment of inertia of a motor pinion of the same width as the second gear.

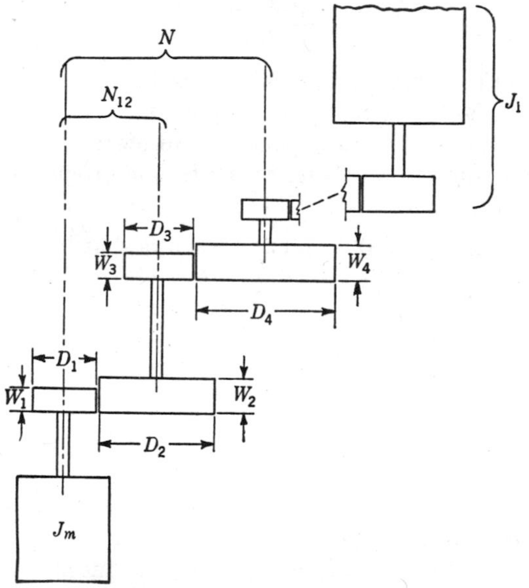

FIG. 3·27.—Spur gear train.

The interest now lies in the value of N_{12} that will minimize J_g for fixed values of W_1/W_2, W_3/W_2, W_4/W_2, N, and D_3/D_1. Such a value will be a solution of the equation

$$N_{12}^6 - \frac{W_3}{W_2}\left(\frac{D_3}{D_1}\right)^4 N_{12}^2 - 2N^2\frac{W_4}{W_2}\left(\frac{D_3}{D_1}\right)^4 = 0, \qquad (114a)$$

which can be written as

$$x^3 + 2 = 3Kx \qquad (114b)$$

if

$$x \equiv N_{12}^2 N^{-2/3} \left(\frac{W_4}{W_2}\right)^{-1/3} \left(\frac{D_3}{D_1}\right)^{-4/3},$$

$$3K = \left(\frac{W_3}{W_2}\right)\left(\frac{W_4}{W_2}\right)^{-2/3} \left(\frac{D_3}{D_1}\right)^{4/3} N^{-4/3}.$$

In general, K will be small. To a zero-order approximation

$$x_0 = -2^{1/3}, \tag{115}$$

and to a first-order approximation

$$x_1 = -2^{1/3}(1 - \tfrac{3}{2}Kx_0)^{1/3} \approx -2^{1/3}(1 + 2^{-2/3}K). \tag{116}$$

Usually the zero-order approximation is sufficient. For instance, if $W_3/W_2 = W_4/W_2 = D_3/D_1 = 1$, $N = 8$, the first-order correction contributes only about 1 per cent to the value of x_0. When this correction is neglected, $N_{12} = 2.25$ and $J_g = 8.6J_0$. It has often been the practice to make the first reduction as large as possible in a mistaken effort to minimize inertia. It is worth noting in the above case that if the reduction of 8 had been taken in a single mesh, the inertia of the gearing at the motor shaft J_g would have been $65J_0$.

The following table compares the inertia of the gear train for the minimal case with that inertia resulting from an equivalent single reduction. Again, the assumption has been made that

$$\frac{W_3}{W_2} = \frac{W_4}{W_2} = \frac{D_3}{D_1} = 1.$$

TABLE 3·5.—INERTIA OF VARIOUS GEAR TRAINS

N_{12}	N_{34}	N	$\frac{J_g}{J_0}$	(a), in.² oz	(b), in.² oz
8.00	....	8	65.0	0.0074	0.372
2.25	3.56	8	8.6	0.0010	0.049
12.00	....	12	145.0	0.0165	0.832
2.57	4.67	12	11.1	0.0013	0.064
18.00	....	18	325.0	0.0369	1.870
2.94	6.12	18	14.0	0.0016	0.080
27.00	....	27	730.0	0.0828	4.180
3.36	8.03	27	18.1	0.0020	0.103

Table 3·5 gives in Column (a) the resulting inertia if J_0 is from a 9T, 48P, $\frac{3}{16}$-in.-wide brass pinion and Column (b) is from a 24T, 48P, $\frac{3}{16}$-in.-wide brass pinion. These inertias may be compared with a motor-armature inertia of 0.077 in.² oz for a Diehl two-phase 2-watt motor (FPE25) and 0.66 in.² oz for Diehl 11- and 22-watt motors (FPE49-2 and FPF49-7).

CHAPTER 4

GENERAL DESIGN PRINCIPLES FOR SERVOMECHANISMS

BY N. B. NICHOLS, W. P. MANGER, AND E. H. KROHN[1]

The systematic treatment of multiple-loop servomechanisms is quite complex and will not be attempted in this chapter. Systems with only one independent input variable will first be treated: the discussion can be readily extended to systems with more than one independent input variable by the usual superposition theorem which applies to all linear systems.

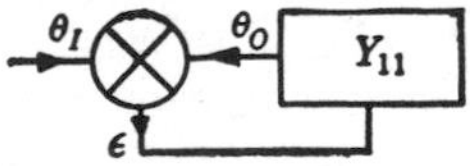

FIG. 4·1.—Single-differential servo system.

4·1. Basic Equations.—The simplest single-input servomechanism has only one error-measuring element (the differential in the usual symbolic diagram) and one transfer element. A simple example of this type has been discussed in Chap. 1; its symbolic diagram is shown in Fig. 4·1. Its equations may be written

$$\epsilon = \theta_I - \theta_O, \tag{1}$$

$$\frac{\theta_O}{\epsilon} = Y_{11}, \tag{2}$$

$$\frac{\theta_O}{\theta_I} = \frac{Y_{11}}{1 + Y_{11}}, \tag{3}$$

$$\frac{\epsilon}{\theta_I} = \frac{1}{1 + Y_{11}}, \tag{4}$$

where Y_{11}, θ_O, θ_I, and ϵ are functions of p or $j\omega$, depending on the type of solution desired. The function Y_{11} is called the loop transfer function or the feedback function and is usually composed of a number of products that are the transfer functions of the individual elements of the servo loop. The Nyquist stability test discussed in Chap. 2 can now be applied to the loop transfer function Y_{11}, to determine whether or not the expressions in Eqs. (3) or (4) correspond to a stable system. The interpretation of the test is simplified if, as is usually the case, $Y_{11}(p)$ has no zeros or poles in the right half plane when p is regarded as a complex variable.

For the simple servo considered in Chap. 1 we have

$$Y_{11}(p) = \frac{K_v}{p(T_m p + 1)}, \tag{5}$$

[1] N. B. Nichols is the author of Secs. 4·1 and 4·14 to 4·19 inclusive; W. P. Manger of Secs. 4·2 to 4·9, and 4·12 to 4·13; E. H. Krohn of Secs. 4·10 and 4·11.

where K_v = velocity-error constant,

T_m = motor time constant.

Adding an equalizing lead network, we obtain

$$Y_{11}(p) = \frac{K_v(T_1p + 1)}{p(T_mp + 1)(T_2p + 1)}, \tag{6}$$

where T_1 = lead-network time constant, sometimes called the derivative time constant,

T_2 = lead-network lag (less than T_1).

Proceeding in this manner, we can build up more complex functions for a single-loop or single-differential system.

In a two-differential single-input system there are two possible configurations, as illustrated in Fig. 4·2. These systems include another

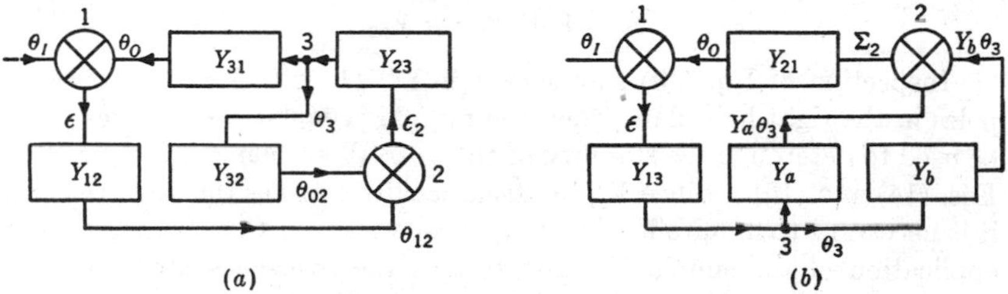

FIG. 4·2*a* and *b*.—Two-differential servo systems.

type of junction, which may be called a *branch point*. A branch point has one incoming function and two outgoing functions which are identically equal to the incoming one. The differential junction has two incoming functions and one outgoing function which is equal to the algebraic difference of the two incoming ones. The symbolic diagram or the associated equations must, of course, indicate which of the incoming functions retains its sign on traversing the junction and which changes its sign.

The equations for Fig. 4·2*a* may be written

$$\epsilon + \theta_O = \epsilon + Y_{31}\theta_3 = \theta_I, \tag{7}$$

$$\epsilon_2 + \theta_{O2} - \theta_{I2} = \epsilon_2 + Y_{32}\theta_3 - Y_{12}\epsilon = 0, \tag{8}$$

$$\theta_3 - Y_{23}\epsilon_2 = 0. \tag{9}$$

Using Eqs. (8) and (9) and eliminating ϵ_2, we find

$$\frac{\theta_3}{Y_{12}\epsilon} = \frac{1}{Y_{32}} \frac{Y_{23}Y_{32}}{1 + Y_{23}Y_{32}}, \tag{10}$$

where the expression on the right may be looked upon as the effective transfer function between the output of Y_{12} and the input to Y_{31}. The expression on the right may be rewritten to obtain

$$\frac{\theta_3}{Y_{12}\epsilon} = \frac{1}{Y_{32}} \frac{Y_{22}}{1 + Y_{22}}, \tag{11}$$

where Y_{22} is the loop transfer function for the subsidiary loop associated with differential 2 in Fig. 4·2*a*. Using Eq. (7), one obtains

$$\frac{\theta_O}{\epsilon} = \frac{Y_{12}Y_{31}}{Y_{32}} \frac{Y_{22}}{1 + Y_{22}} \tag{12}$$

or

$$\frac{\theta_O}{\epsilon} = \frac{Y_{12}Y_{23}Y_{31}}{1 + Y_{23}Y_{32}} = \frac{Y_{11}^0}{1 + Y_{22}}, \tag{13}$$

where Y_{11}^0 is the loop transfer function associated with differential 1 when $Y_{32} = 0$. We also have

$$\frac{\theta_O}{\theta_1} = \frac{Y_{11}^0}{1 + Y_{11}^0 + Y_{22}}, \tag{14}$$

$$\frac{\epsilon}{\theta_I} = \frac{1 + Y_{22}}{1 + Y_{11}^0 + Y_{22}}. \tag{15}$$

Inspection of Eq. (13) shows that if $Y_{11}^0/(1 + Y_{22})$ has no zeros or poles in the right half plane, then the normal Nyquist stability test may be used to determine the stability of the over-all system characterized by Eqs. (14) and (15). Since Y_{11}^0 by itself usually satisfies this requirement, it is necessary to inquire if $1/(1 + Y_{22})$ separately does. It follows that application of the simple Nyquist test to the over-all system requires that the subsidiary loop represented by Eq. (11) be stable. The two-loop transfer functions enter Eqs. (13) to (15) in a rather simple manner that permits an easy derivation of the system equations. Combining Eqs. (12) and (7), one obtains

$$\frac{\theta_O}{\theta_I} = \frac{\dfrac{Y_{12}Y_{31}}{Y_{32}} \dfrac{Y_{22}}{1 + Y_{22}}}{1 + \dfrac{Y_{12}Y_{31}}{Y_{32}} \dfrac{Y_{22}}{1 + Y_{22}}} = \frac{Y_{11}}{1 + Y_{11}}. \tag{16a}$$

Equation (16*a*) emphasizes the reason for calling this a two-loop system: Y_{22} appears in Y_{11} in the same manner that

$$Y_{11} = \frac{Y_{12}Y_{31}}{Y_{32}} \frac{Y_{22}}{1 + Y_{22}} \tag{16b}$$

appears in the complete expression for θ_O/θ_I.

In Fig. 4·2*b* there are two single-element paths for data to leave junction 3 and enter junction 2. The equations associated with Fig. 4·2*b* are easily shown to be

$$\frac{\theta_O}{\epsilon} = Y_{13}(Y_a + Y_b)Y_{21}, \tag{17}$$

$$\frac{\theta_O}{\theta_I} = \frac{Y_{13}(Y_a + Y_b)Y_{21}}{1 + Y_{13}(Y_a + Y_b)Y_{21}}, \tag{18}$$

where differential 2 has been assumed to have the equation

$$\Sigma_2 = Y_a\theta_3 + Y_b\theta_3.$$

One observes that Y_a and Y_b enter Eqs. (17) and (18) in a different manner from that in which Y_{32} and Y_{23} enter the previous equations. The transfer function between junctions 2 and 3 is really only the sum $Y_a + Y_b$; there is no loop equation associated with differential 2. In other words, Fig. 4·2b is in reality only a single-loop system with a loop transfer function $Y_{13}(Y_a + Y_b)Y_{21} = Y_{11}$.

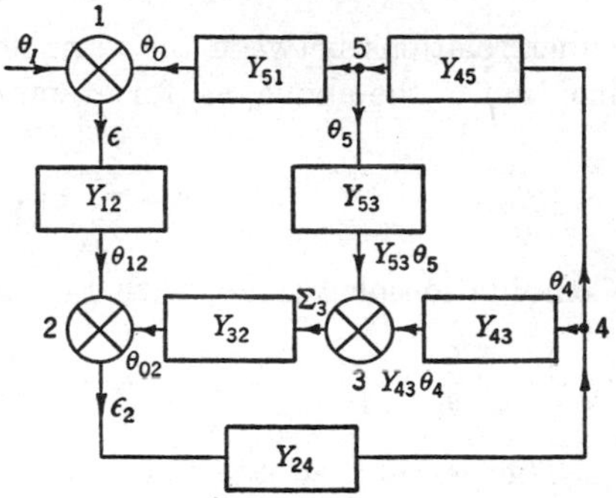

FIG. 4·3.—A three-differential servo system.

There are many three-differential systems, and no exhaustive treatment is contemplated here. The schematic shown in Fig. 4·3 has been used in amplidyne servos employing quadrature series and armature voltage or tachometer feedback for equalization, together with an error-signal equalizer. The equations for Fig. 4·3 may be written as

$$\epsilon + \theta_O = \epsilon + Y_{51}\theta_5 = \theta_I, \tag{19}$$
$$\epsilon_2 - Y_{12}\epsilon + Y_{32}\Sigma_3 = 0, \tag{20}$$
$$\Sigma_3 - Y_{43}\theta_4 - Y_{53}\theta_5 = 0, \tag{21}$$
$$\theta_4 - Y_{24}\epsilon_2 = 0, \tag{22}$$
$$\theta_5 - Y_{45}\theta_4 = 0, \tag{23}$$

where Y_{12} = error-equalizer transfer function,
Y_{24} = power-amplifier and amplidyne transfer function (open circuit),
Y_{43} = quadrature-series field transfer function,
Y_{45} = motor-amplidyne transfer function,
Y_{53} = tachometer transfer function,
Y_{32} = feedback-equalizer transfer function,
Y_{51} = gear-train transfer function.

Solving the five simultaneous equations for a number of the variables, we obtain

$$\frac{\theta_O}{\theta_I} = \frac{Y_{12}Y_{24}Y_{45}Y_{51}}{1 + Y_{12}Y_{24}Y_{45}Y_{51} + Y_{24}Y_{43}Y_{32} + Y_{24}Y_{45}Y_{53}Y_{32}}, \tag{24}$$
$$\frac{\epsilon}{\theta_I} = \frac{1 + Y_{24}Y_{43}Y_{32} + Y_{24}Y_{45}Y_{53}Y_{32}}{1 + Y_{12}Y_{24}Y_{45}Y_{41} + Y_{24}Y_{43}Y_{32} + Y_{24}Y_{45}Y_{53}Y_{32}}, \tag{25}$$

$$\frac{\theta_O}{\epsilon} = \frac{Y_{12}Y_{24}Y_{45}Y_{51}}{1 + Y_{24}Y_{43}Y_{32} + Y_{24}Y_{45}Y_{53}Y_{32}}, \tag{26}$$

$$\frac{\theta_{O2}}{\theta_{12}} = \frac{Y_{24}Y_{43}Y_{32} + Y_{24}Y_{45}Y_{53}Y_{32}}{1 + Y_{24}Y_{43}Y_{32} + Y_{24}Y_{45}Y_{53}Y_{32}}, \tag{27}$$

$$\frac{\theta_{O2}}{\epsilon_2} = Y_{24}Y_{43}Y_{32} + Y_{24}Y_{45}Y_{53}Y_{32}. \tag{28}$$

Other relations between the variables may be obtained by simple combination of the above, as, for example,

$$\frac{\theta_4}{\theta_O} = \frac{1}{Y_{45}Y_{51}}. \tag{29}$$

Combination of Eq. (29) with Eq. (24) gives

$$\frac{\theta_4}{\theta_I} = \frac{Y_{12}Y_{24}}{1 + Y_{12}Y_{24}Y_{45}Y_{51} + Y_{24}Y_{43}Y_{32} + Y_{24}Y_{45}Y_{53}Y_{32}}. \tag{30}$$

The previous equations are in proper form for a Nyquist test of successive loops in order to determine the stability of the system. Inspection of Eq. (24) shows that the equation for this circuit is the same as that of a two-loop system [see Eq. (14)] with an inner-loop transfer function of $Y_{24}Y_{43}Y_{32} + Y_{24}Y_{45}Y_{53}Y_{32}$ and an outer-loop transfer function given by Eq. (26). This means that one can first study the loop characterized by Eq. (28). The difference between the number of zeros and poles in the right half plane of the function

$$1 + Y_{24}Y_{43}Y_{32} + Y_{24}Y_{45}Y_{53}Y_{32}$$

can be found by means of the Nyquist test. In the usual case there will be no poles or zeros (the inner-loop equalization networks being designed to give no zeros), and the system will be stable when the outer loop is opened by making Y_{12} zero (reducing preamplifier gain to zero). Having applied the Nyquist test to the inner loop, one may draw the Nyquist diagram for the complete system by the use of Eq. (26) and determine the difference between the number of zeros and poles of $1 + \theta_O/\epsilon$. In order that the system be stable, $1 + \theta_O/\epsilon$ can have no zeros in the right half plane. If the inner loop is stable and, as is usual, $Y_{12}Y_{24}Y_{45}Y_{51}$ has no poles in the right half plane, then $1 + \theta_O/\epsilon$ will have no poles and the simple Nyquist criterion will apply.

4·2. Responses to Representative Inputs.—A general discussion of the nature of typical servomechanism responses to representative inputs requires a general definition of the functions that characterize servomechanisms. All the mathematical knowledge available from an inspection of the structure of a servomechanism can be given by a statement of the loop transfer functions for each closed loop in the system. The following discussion will apply to a two-loop system. The analysis can readily be extended to include multiple-loop systems if desired. The transfer function of the principal, or error, loop, when the other loop is open, will be denoted by $Y_{11}^0(p)$; it will be of the form

$$Y_{11}^0(p) = K_1 p^{\alpha_1} \frac{f_1(p)}{g_1(p)}. \tag{31}$$

The loop gain of the inner loop may be written as

$$Y_{22}^0(p) = K_2 p^{\alpha_2} \frac{f_2(p)}{g_2(p)}, \tag{32}$$

where f and g are polynomials in p of the general form

$$\begin{aligned} f(p) &= 1 + a_1 p + a_2 p^2 + \cdots + a_r p^r, \\ g(p) &= 1 + b_1 p + b_2 p^2 + \cdots + b_s p^s, \end{aligned} \tag{33}$$

and the α's are integers.

The transfer function relating the output θ_O to the input θ_I can be written

$$\frac{\theta_O}{\theta_I}(p) = \frac{Y_{11}^0(p)}{1 + Y_{11}^0(p) + Y_{22}^0(p)} = \frac{Y_{11}(p)}{1 + Y_{11}(p)}. \tag{34}$$

We now proceed to establish certain limitations imposed on the loop transfer functions $Y(p)$. Suppose that a unit-step function input is applied to the servomechanism with transfer function given by Eq. (34). Then

$$\theta_O(p) = \frac{Y_{11}^0(p)}{p} \frac{1}{1 + Y_{11}^0(p) + Y_{22}^0(p)}. \tag{35}$$

The asymptotic behavior of $\theta_O(t)$ for large values of t is given by (see Chap. 2)

$$\lim_{t \to \infty} \theta_O(t) = \lim_{p \to 0} p\theta_O(p)$$

or

$$\lim_{t \to \infty} \theta_O(t) = \lim_{p \to 0} \left(\frac{K_1 p^{\alpha_1}}{1 + K_1 p^{\alpha_1} + K_2 p^{\alpha_2}} \right). \tag{36}$$

If the servomechanism is to have zero static error, $\theta_O(t)$ must approach 1 for large values of t. Evidently α_1 must be negative for this to be true. Equation (36) may be written

$$\lim_{t \to \infty} \theta_O(t) = \lim_{p \to 0} \left(\frac{K_1}{p^{-\alpha_1} + K_1 + K_2 p^{\alpha_2 - \alpha_1}} \right). \tag{37}$$

It is seen that α_1 must be less than 0 and α_2 must be greater than α_1 in order that the servomechanism have zero static error.

The condition on α_1 can easily be derived from physical reasoning. We consider $Y_{11}(p)$ as the loop gain and imagine the loop to be opened as shown in Fig. 4·4. If a steady signal ϵ is applied as shown, then the output θ_O should move continuously in an attempt to balance out this error signal. This will be the case only if the exponent α_1 is equal to or less than -1. We call any feedback loop having a transfer function of the form of Eq. (31) or (32) a "zero-static-error loop" if $\alpha_1 \leqq -1$.

The restrictions on α_2 are somewhat more complicated. When $\alpha_1 = -1$, we have the condition $\alpha_2 \geqq 0$. Thus the subsidiary loop cannot be of the zero-static-error type if the over-all loop is to be of the zero-static-error type. In a system with $\alpha_1 \leqq -2$ (we will see later that such a servomechanism is characterized by zero final error when following a constant-velocity input) it is necessary that $\alpha_2 \geqq -1$. Such a servomechanism may then have a subsidiary loop of the zero-static-error type. It will be seen subsequently, however, that in the presence of such a subsidiary loop the over-all loop will *not* be characterized by zero velocity error.

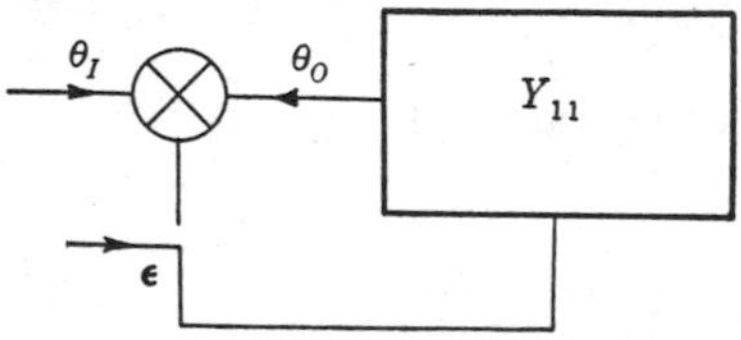

FIG. 4·4.—Simple servo with feedback loop opened.

A further restriction is placed on the loop transfer functions of Eqs. (31) and (32), in that they must approach zero at infinite frequency. In practice this is assured by the presence of parasitic elements in the loops. In terms of Eq. (33), we must have $r + \alpha < s$. It is sometimes convenient to ignore this restriction when investigating only the low-frequency characteristics of a system. One must, however, always be careful not to draw unwarranted conclusions when this condition is neglected.

It can be shown that the over-all transfer function $\theta_O(p)/\theta_I(p)$ has the same general form as the transfer function of a low-pass filter; such servomechanisms can be considered as a special class of low-pass filter. The frequency response of the two-loop system is given by Eq. (34), with $j\omega$ substituted for p. Making use of the least severe restriction on α_2, $\alpha_2 = \alpha_1 + 1$, Eq. (34) becomes

$$\frac{\theta_O}{\theta_I}(j\omega) = K_1 \frac{f_1(j\omega)}{g_1(j\omega)} \frac{1}{(j\omega)^{-\alpha_1} + K_1 \dfrac{f_1(j\omega)}{g_1(j\omega)} + K_2 j\omega \dfrac{f_2(j\omega)}{g_2(j\omega)}}. \tag{38}$$

For zero frequency this reduces (for α_1 negative) to

$$\left[\frac{\theta_O}{\theta_I}(j\omega)\right]_{\omega=0} = \frac{K_1}{K_1} = 1. \tag{39}$$

For very large frequencies θ_O/θ_I approaches zero at least as fast as $1/\omega$, and we see that a servomechanism does indeed behave like a low-pass filter. An ideal servomechanism, able to reproduce an input signal exactly, would of course have a transfer function of unity, that is, would be an ideal low-pass filter with a very high cutoff frequency. (This description of an ideal servomechanism is reasonable only in the absence of noise, since only then is it desirable to reproduce the input signal

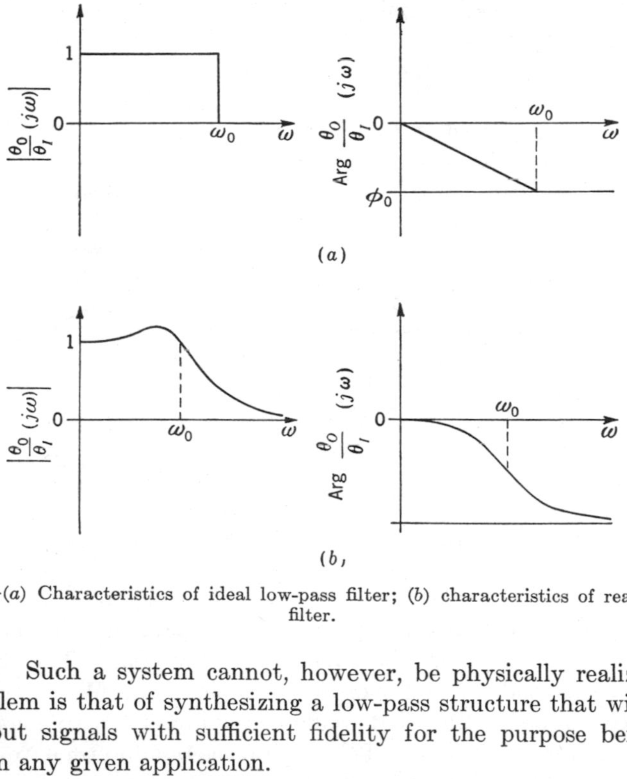

FIG. 4·5.—(a) Characteristics of ideal low-pass filter; (b) characteristics of real low-pass filter.

exactly.) Such a system cannot, however, be physically realized, and our problem is that of synthesizing a low-pass structure that will reproduce input signals with sufficient fidelity for the purpose being considered in any given application.

Communications engineers have defined an ideal low-pass filter to be one having a transfer function with magnitude and phase such as are shown in Fig. 4·5*a*. This filter has a gain of unity in a finite pass band from $\omega = 0$ to ω equal to some frequency ω_0. The gain outside this band is identically zero. The phase of the transfer function is zero for $\omega = 0$ and varies linearly with ω in the pass band. The phase can be left undefined outside the pass band. It should be pointed out that it is not physically possible to construct a filter with such a rapid cutoff, and we might thus expect some nonphysical behavior of the filter. This particular transfer function is chosen, however, since it enables one to obtain some rather simple relationships between the frequency and transient behavior of filters. If we suppose that a unit step function is applied to this filter, we can compute the output by means of the inverse Fourier transform. The result is[1]

$$\theta_O(t) = \frac{1}{2} + \frac{1}{\pi}\,\mathrm{Si}\left[\omega_0\left(t - \frac{\phi_0}{\omega_0}\right)\right], \tag{40}$$

where $\mathrm{Si}(x)$ is the sine integral of x, given by

$$\mathrm{Si}(x) = \int_0^x \frac{\sin y}{y}\,dy. \tag{41}$$

Equation (40) is plotted in Fig. 4·6a. Examination of Eq. (40) shows that the response is small but not zero for negative time—one of the nonphysical characteristics introduced by the arbitrary choice of the

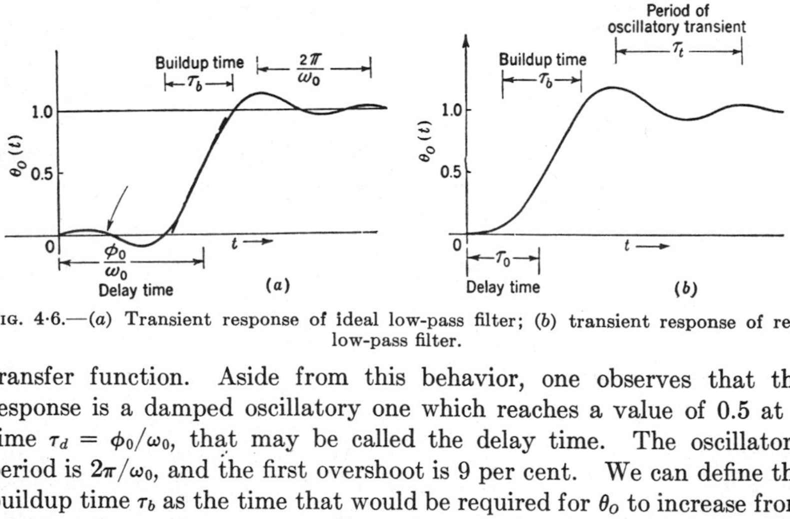

FIG. 4·6.—(a) Transient response of ideal low-pass filter; (b) transient response of real low-pass filter.

transfer function. Aside from this behavior, one observes that the response is a damped oscillatory one which reaches a value of 0.5 at a time $\tau_d = \phi_0/\omega_0$, that may be called the delay time. The oscillatory period is $2\pi/\omega_0$, and the first overshoot is 9 per cent. We can define the buildup time τ_b as the time that would be required for θ_O to increase from 0 to 1 at the maximum rate. To evaluate the buildup time we calculate the slope of the response curve at $t = \phi_0/\omega_0$:

$$\left(\frac{d\theta_O}{dt}\right)_{t=\phi_0/\omega_0} = \frac{1}{\pi}\frac{d}{dt}\,\mathrm{Si}\left[\omega_0\left(t - \frac{\phi_0}{\omega_0}\right)\right]_{t=\phi_0/\omega_0} = \frac{\omega_0}{\pi}. \tag{42}$$

Thus $\tau_b\omega_0 = \pi$, or, with $\omega_0 = 2\pi f_0$,

$$\tau_b f_0 = \tfrac{1}{2}. \tag{43}$$

This expression, together with the expressions for the delay time and oscil-

[1] E. A. Guillemin, *Communication Networks*, Vol. II, Wiley, New York, 1931, p. 477.

latory period, gives the salient relationships between the frequency-response behavior and the transient response of an "ideal" low-pass filter.

The forms of the attenuation and phase characteristics of a physical low-pass filter are shown in Fig. 4·5*b*. This real filter differs from the ideal one in that there is some transmission outside the nominal pass band and there are some frequencies in the pass band that are transmitted with gain greater than unity. The phase characteristic is also not a

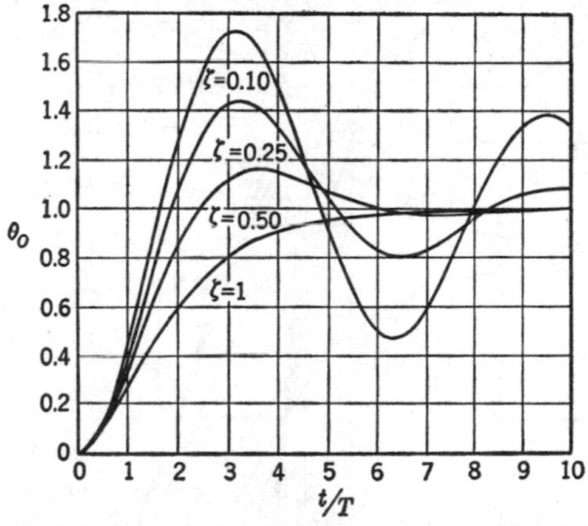

FIG. 4·7.—Transient response for the transfer function $(T^2p^2 + 2\zeta Tp + 1)^{-1}$.

linear function of frequency. We shall define ω_0 for such a filter as the value of ω at which $|\theta_O/\theta_I|$ is -3 db. In the case of filters having a peaked or resonance response it is sometimes convenient to define ω_0 as that value of ω at which the response becomes unity after the peak. The step-function response of such a filter is sketched in Fig. 4.6*b*; it is of the same form as the response of the ideal low-pass filter. The response is, of course, zero for negative time.

A low-pass filter characteristic that occurs frequently is given by

$$\frac{\theta_O}{\theta_I}(p) = \frac{1}{T^2p^2 + 2\zeta Tp + 1}. \qquad (44)$$

The responses of this filter to unit-step functions, for different values of ζ, are plotted in Fig. 4·7, and the frequency response characteristics for similar values of ζ are plotted in Fig. 4·8. The correlation exhibited between the peak height [maximum value of $|\theta_O(\omega)/\theta_I(\omega)|$ in the complete frequency range] and the magnitude of the overshoot of the transient response is representative of most servomechanism performances. The magnitude of the first overshoot of the step-function response, the frequency-response peak height, and the frequency at which the peak occurs (or the frequency at which the gain has dropped to unity) are often used as figures of merit of performance. The buildup time is often considered, also, and the general relationships between these quantities which have been illustrated are very useful in the synthesizing of a system to meet given specifications.

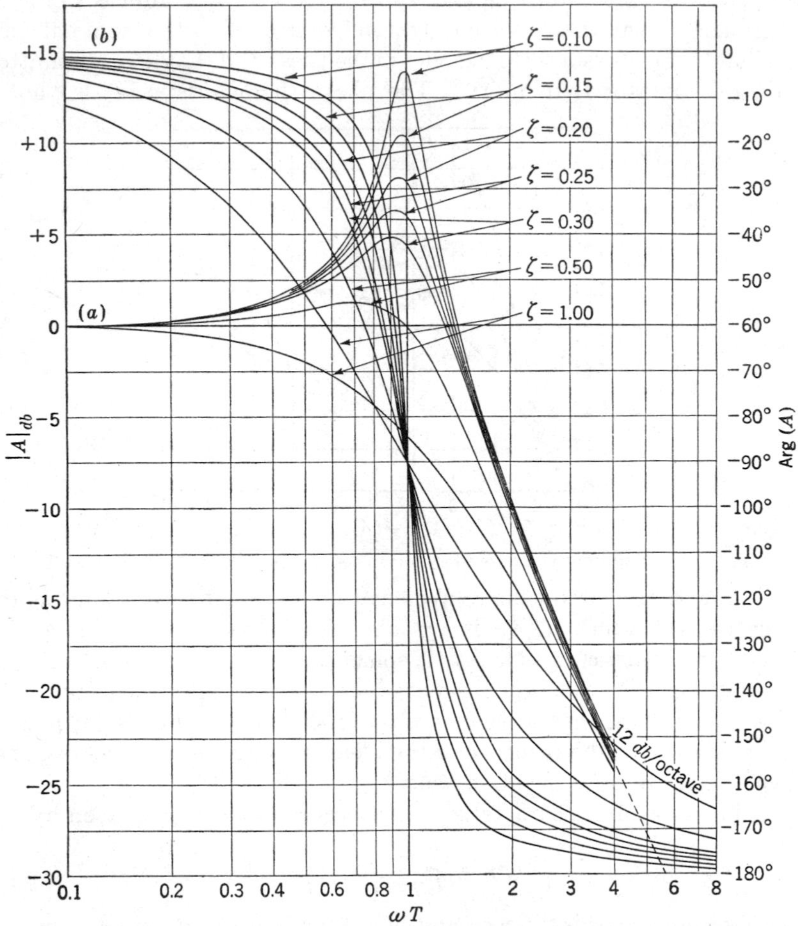

FIG. 4·8.—Frequency response for the transfer function $(T^2p^2 + 2\zeta Tp + 1)^{-1}$. (a) Gain curves; (b) phase-shift curves.

A constant-velocity input $\theta_I = \Omega t$ is a good approximation to many typical servomechanism inputs, and the response to such an input is of interest. Making use of Eq. (34), we can write the asymptotic form of $\epsilon(t)$, for large t, as

$$\lim_{t\to\infty} \epsilon(t) = \lim_{p\to 0} \left(\frac{\Omega}{p} - \frac{\Omega}{p}\,\frac{K_1p^{\alpha_1}}{1 + K_1p^{\alpha_1} + K_2p^{\alpha_2}}\right). \tag{45}$$

If $\alpha_1 = -1$ and $\alpha_2 = 0$, this reduces to

$$\lim_{t\to\infty} \epsilon(t) = \Omega \frac{1 + K_2}{K_1} = \frac{\Omega}{K_v}. \tag{46}$$

The output thus follows the input with a constant position error equal to the input velocity divided by a constant called for obvious reasons the "velocity-error constant." This is a characteristic of all zero-static-error servomechanisms. If $\alpha_1 = -2$ and $\alpha_2 \geqq 0$, the servomechanism is said to have zero velocity error, since a calculation similar to the preceding one shows that for a constant velocity input $\theta_I = \Omega t$,

$$\lim_{t\to\infty} \epsilon(t) = 0.$$

If a constant acceleration input $\theta_I = \frac{1}{2}At^2$ is applied to this servomechanism, and if $\alpha_1 = -2$ and $\alpha_2 = 0$, then

$$\lim_{t\to\infty} \epsilon(t) = A \frac{1 + K_2}{K_1} = \frac{A}{K_a}. \tag{47}$$

This equation defines the "acceleration-error constant" for this particular system. The definition and interpretation of velocity and acceleration-error constants and other error constants will be discussed more thoroughly in Sec. 4·4.

4·3. Output Disturbances.—The performance of a servomechanism may be influenced by many extraneous "inputs" to the system. Changes

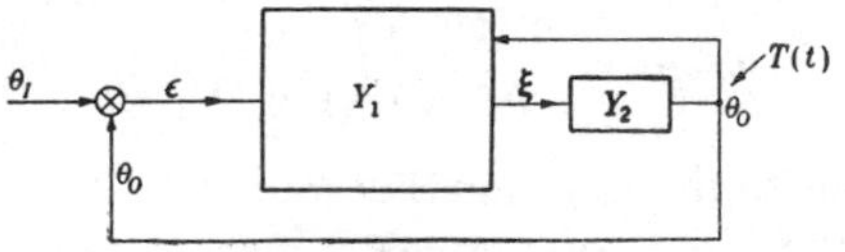

FIG. 4·9.—Two-loop servomechanism.

in the gain of vacuum tubes, changes in the values of resistors and condensers, ripple on the plate-supply voltage of vacuum tubes, changes in friction of bearings, and transient torque loads are all examples of such external influences. It can be shown with great generality that the presence of feedback in a system results in a reduction of the effects of such influences. Rather than attempt such a general treatment, we shall discuss only the important case of transient torque loading on the output of a servomechanism.

Suppose that we have a two-loop servomechanism, as shown in Fig. 4·9, where the output of Element 2 is the servomechanism output θ_O. Element 2 is assumed to be a motor characterized by inertia J and a viscous damping coefficient f_m. An external torque $T(t)$ acts on the output shaft. The input signal to the motor is denoted by ξ. The differential equation for θ_O can then be written

$$Jp^2\theta_O + f_m p\theta_O = K_m f_m \xi + T(p) \tag{48a}$$

or

$$\theta_O = Y_2\xi + Y_2\frac{T(p)}{K_m f_m},$$

where

$$Y_2 = \frac{K_m}{p(T_m p + 1)}. \tag{48b}$$

From the basic equations for a two-loop system we have

$$\xi = \frac{\dfrac{Y_{11}^0}{Y_2}\,\theta_I - Y_{11}^0\,\dfrac{T(p)}{K_m f_m}}{1 + Y_{11}^0 + Y_{22}^0}. \tag{49}$$

If θ_I is set equal to zero, then

$$\theta_O(p) = \frac{Y_2 T(p)}{K_m f_m}\left(\frac{1 + Y_{22}^0}{1 + Y_{11}^0 + Y_{22}^0}\right). \tag{50}$$

Note that the response of the system *without feedback* to $T(t)$ is simply

$$\theta_O(p) = \frac{Y_2 T(p)}{K_m f_m}; \tag{51}$$

the presence of feedback modifies the response by the function (or operator) in the parentheses in Eq. (50). For a single-loop servo Eq. (50) reduces to

$$\theta_O(p) = \frac{Y_2 T(p)}{K_m f_m}\left(\frac{1}{1 + Y_{11}}\right). \tag{52}$$

This result is similar to the familiar theorem of feedback-amplifier theory which states that the effects of changes in parameters and external influences are reduced by feedback in the ratio $1/(1 + \mu\beta)$, where $\mu\beta$ is the gain around the feedback loop.

As an example, let us use Eq. (50) to compute the asymptotic response of a zero-static-error servomechanism to a sustained torque T_0 suddenly applied to the output shaft. We have as before

$$\lim_{t\to\infty} \theta_O(t) = \lim_{p\to 0} \frac{Y_2 T_0}{K_m f_m}\left(\frac{1 + Y_{22}^0}{1 + Y_{11}^0 + Y_{22}^0}\right).$$

Using the characteristics of Y_{11}^0 and Y_{22}^0 discussed in Sec. 4·2, we find

$$\lim_{t\to\infty} \theta_O(t) = \frac{T_0}{f_m}\left(\frac{1 + K_2}{K_1}\right) = \frac{T_0}{f_m K_v} = \frac{T_0}{K_T}. \tag{53}$$

The quantity K_T is called the "torque-error constant" and is directly proportional to the velocity-error constant. It follows that a zero-velocity-error system will have an infinite torque-error constant; that is, a constant load torque will not cause an error in output position.

Equation (50) can be used to compute the response of a system to any arbitrary torque loading if such a calculation is necessary in a given application. Usually, however, a computation of K_T gives enough information. Since we are dealing with linear systems, the errors resulting from torque loading or other external influences add directly to the errors that are caused by the dynamics of the system when following any input signal.

It should be noted that the response to a torque disturbance $T(t)$ is identical with the response to an equivalent input signal

$$[\theta_I(p)]_{\text{equivalent}} = \frac{Y_2T(p)}{K_mf_m}\left(\frac{1 + Y_{22}^0}{Y_{11}^0}\right). \tag{54}$$

Frequently, particularly for simple systems, this equivalent input is easily calculated and is of such a nature that the response is readily estimated from a knowledge of the step-function response of the system.

4·4. Error Coefficients.—The discussion in the preceding sections led naturally to the definition of certain system parameters called "error coefficients," which characterized the performance of a given system to some given input. Specifically, we have defined the velocity-, acceleration-, and torque-error constants for several simple systems. The concept of error coefficient can be considerably generalized, and such a generalization provides a very useful and simple way of considering the nature of the response of a system to almost any arbitrary input.

We consider the Laplace transform of the quantity ϵ/θ_I for a general servomechanism and assume that it can be expanded as a power series in p, valid at least for small p. Calling this function $M(p)$, we have

$$\frac{\epsilon}{\theta_I}(p) = M(p) = \sum_{m=0}^{\infty} \frac{C_n p^n}{n!}. \tag{55}$$

Proceeding in a formal manner, we have

$$\epsilon(p) = M(p)\theta_I(p) = C_0\theta_I(p) + C_1p\theta_I(p) + \frac{C_2}{2}p^2\theta_I(p) + \cdots. \tag{56}$$

The region of convergence of the power series for $M(p)$ and $\epsilon(p)$ is the neighborhood of $p = 0$. These series can therefore be used to obtain an expression for $\epsilon(t)$ that is valid for large values of t, that is, for the steady-state response. This result is

$$\underset{t\to\infty}{\epsilon(t)} = C_0\theta_I(t) + C_1\frac{d\theta_I}{dt} + \frac{C_2}{2}\frac{d^2\theta_I}{dt^2} + \cdots. \tag{57}$$

The error is seen to consist of terms proportional to the input, the input velocity, input acceleration, and, in general, still higher derivatives of the input signal. The constants C_n, defined by Eq. (55), are clearly a series of error coefficients which can be used to calculate the steady-state error of the servomechanism. Assuming that the C_n's are known, let us examine a few typical calculations. If $\theta_I(t)$ is a unit-step function of position, then the steady-state error is simply C_0. If $\theta_I(t)$ is a step function of velocity, then C_0 must be zero for a finite error; this finite error is then simply $C_1\Omega$, where Ω is the input velocity. If $\theta_I(t) = \frac{1}{2}At^2$,

$$\epsilon(t)_{t\to\infty} = \frac{C_0}{2} At^2 + C_1At + \frac{C_2}{2} A; \tag{58}$$

for a finite error, C_0 and C_1 must be zero. Comparing these results with Eqs. (46) and (47), Sec. 4·2, we see that the C's are related simply to the error coefficients previously defined. For instance,

$$C_1 = \frac{1}{K_v}, \qquad C_2 = \frac{2}{K_a}. \tag{59}$$

Let the input be a single-frequency sinusoid: $\theta_I(t) = \theta \sin \omega_0 t$. Equation (57) formally gives the result

$$\epsilon(t) = \theta \left[\left(C_0 - \frac{C_2\omega_0^2}{2!} + \frac{C_4\omega_0^4}{4!} - \cdots \right) \sin \omega_0 t + \left(C_1\omega_0 - \frac{C_3\omega_0^3}{3!} + \cdots \right) \cos \omega_0 t \right]. \tag{60}$$

The error is sinusoidal, and its amplitude is given by θ times the square root of the sum of the squares of the two quantities in parentheses in Eq. (60). The restriction to small values of p, considered earlier as a restriction to large values of t, corresponds in this case to a restriction to small values of ω_0. This is perhaps more easily seen if we go back to Eq. (55) and consider $\frac{\epsilon}{\theta_I}(j\omega)$ rather than $\frac{\epsilon}{\theta_I}(p)$. We would then have

$$\frac{\epsilon}{\theta_I}(j\omega) = C_0 + C_1 j\omega - \frac{C_2\omega^2}{2!} - \frac{C_3}{3!} j\omega^3 + \frac{C_4}{4!}\omega^4 + \cdots. \tag{61}$$

Taking the absolute value of both sides, we find

$$|\epsilon| = |\theta_I| \left[\left(C_0 - \frac{C_2\omega^2}{2!} + \frac{C_4\omega^4}{4!} - \cdots \right)^2 + \left(C_1\omega - \frac{C_3\omega^3}{3!} + \cdots \right)^2 \right]^{\frac{1}{2}}. \tag{62}$$

Equation (61) will converge if the C's are bounded. In this event

Eq. (62) is also a reasonable expression and yields the same amplitude and phase of ϵ as Eq. (60). In most cases of practical importance the static-error coefficient C_0 is identically zero. Furthermore, the series in Eqs. (55) and (61) usually converges sufficiently rapidly to allow reasonably accurate calculation of errors using only the first few terms; very often C_1 and C_2 are entirely sufficient.

It can be concluded from the above discussion that Eq. (57) can be used to compute the errors resulting from any arbitrary input signal, providing the Fourier spectrum of the input signal contains only very low frequencies or at least is heavily predominant in low frequencies. This is very often the case in practical applications. The input signal to the elevation servo of an automatic-tracking radar gun director following a plane on a crossing course, for instance, is of this general nature. Examples of calculations for such a signal, using the results of this section, will be given in Sec. 4·19 of this chapter.

So far in the discussion it has been assumed that the coefficients in the power-series expansion in Eq. (55) are known. We must now consider the general nature of the function $M(p)$ and the manner in which the C_n's are determined. In Sec. 4·2 the loop transfer function of a single-loop zero-static-error servo was seen to be of the form

$$Y_{11} = K_1 \frac{f_1(p)}{p^n g_1(p)}, \tag{63}$$

where $n = +1$. We can then write

$$\frac{\epsilon}{\theta_I}(p) = \frac{1}{1 + Y_{11}} = \frac{p^n g_1}{p^n g_1 + K_1 f_1} = \sum_{m=0}^{\infty} \frac{C_m}{m!} p^m. \tag{64}$$

If f_1 and g_1 are relatively uncomplicated functions of p, the first few terms of the series can often be written down by inspection. If this is not the case, then the C's may be computed from the formula for the usual Taylor series expansion

$$C_m = \left[\frac{d^m}{dp^m}\left(\frac{1}{1 + Y_{11}}\right)\right]_{p=0}. \tag{65}$$

Taking $n = 1$ and assuming $f(p)$ and $g(p)$ to be in the form of Eq. (33), we easily find from Eq. (64),

$$\left.\begin{aligned} C_0 &= 0,\ C_1 = \frac{1}{K_1}, \qquad C_2 = \frac{b_1 - a_1}{K_1} - \frac{1}{K_1^2}, \\ C_3 &= \frac{2}{K_1^3} + \frac{4(a_1 - b_1)}{K_1^2} + \frac{2(a_1^2 - a_1 b_1 + b_2 - a_2)}{K_1}. \end{aligned}\right\} \tag{66}$$

Entirely similar results can be derived for the more complicated cases. For multiple-loop systems the resulting expressions are often very valuable in indicating desired gain levels in the subsidiary loops for optimum values of the C's, that is, for minimum error.

In a later section there will be given a very simple way of determining approximate values of the first few C_n's, at least, directly from the frequency-response curves of the system.

The error coefficients can be given a still different physical significance which is sometimes useful and of more than academic interest. Let us suppose that a unit-step function of position is applied to a general servc. Then

$$\epsilon(p) = \frac{M(p)}{p}, \tag{67}$$

and

$$\mathcal{L}\left[\int_0^t dt\, \epsilon(t)\right] = \frac{M(p)}{p^2}. \tag{68}$$

Furthermore,

$$\int_0^\infty dt\, \epsilon(t) = \lim_{t\to\infty} \int_0^t dt\, \epsilon(t) = \lim_{p\to 0} \frac{M(p)}{p}. \tag{69}$$

We are familiar with the fact that a zero-static-error servo is characterized by an $M(p)$ that has a zero of order one at $p = 0$; that is,

$$M(p) = pN(p). \tag{70}$$

Substituting in Eq. 65, we get

$$C_n = \left[\frac{d^n}{dp^n}\, pN(p)\right]_{p=0}. \tag{71}$$

This gives immediately

$$C_0 = 0 \qquad \text{(as assumed)}$$

and

$$C_1 = \lim_{p\to 0}\left[N(p) + p\frac{dN}{dp}\right] = \lim_{p\to 0} N(p), \tag{72}$$

$$N(p) = \frac{M(p)}{p}, \tag{73}$$

which is precisely the expression in Eq. (69) for the integral of the error for a step-function input. It follows that C_1 or K_v^{-1} is a good measure of the speed of response of a servo that has an aperiodic or nearly aperiodic response but may easily be a very poor figure of merit for a servo having a damped oscillatory response, because a very poor system of this type could conceivably be adjusted to give a very low C_1 (very high K_v). In a similar manner one can show that C_2 or K_a^{-1}, for a zero-static-error and zero-velocity-error servo, is

$$K_a^{-1} = \tfrac{1}{2}C_2 = -\int_0^\infty dt\, t\epsilon(t); \tag{74}$$

that is, the acceleration-error constant is the reciprocal of the time integral of the step-function error weighted by the time. Similarly C_3 is proportional to the integral of the step-function error weighted by the square of the time and so on for the higher error coefficients. The interpretation of the error coefficients in this manner is often instructive. Similar correlations may be derived if the input is considered as a step function in velocity.

Most of the results of this section have been obtained in a purely formal way, proceeding from Eq. (55), and the conscientious reader will observe many steps involving operations that are open to question. The inversion of Eq. (56) in order to pass to Eq. (57), for instance, results not only in the terms given in the latter but also in a whole series of higher-order impulse functions (delta functions) that have been discarded. The justification for this procedure, as well as for the validity of the term-by-term inversion of the transform in Eq. (55), is too involved to be presented here. The reader interested in these questions, as well as in the general subject of the asymptotic behavior of functions and their Laplace transforms, is referred to Part III of G. Doetsch's excellent book[1] *Theorie und Anwendung der Laplace Transformation.*

BASIC DESIGN TECHNIQUES AND APPLICATION TO A SIMPLE SERVO

4·5. Introduction.—In the following sections we shall consider a typical servo design problem and examine the various procedures or techniques available for its solution, attempting to emphasize the advantages and limitations of the different modes of approach.

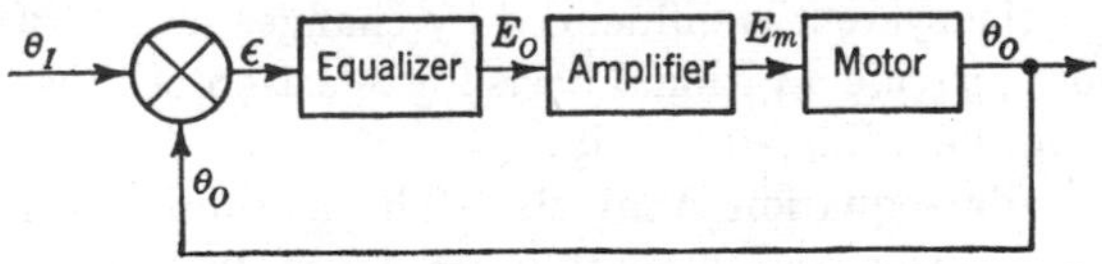

FIG. 4·10.—Simple servo loop.

Figure 4·10 is a block diagram of the system to be analyzed. The error-measuring device is assumed to give a voltage proportional to the error. The transfer function of the equalizing network is taken to be

$$\frac{E_O}{\epsilon}(p) = \frac{1 + Tp}{1 + aTp}, \tag{75}$$

which is the transfer function of the network shown in Fig. 4·11, where $T = R_1C_1$ and $a = (R_1 + R_2)/R_1$. The reasons for using this so-called "integral" type of equalization will be evident from the results of the analyses in the following sections; a discussion of integral equalization

[1] G. Doetsch, *Theorie und Anwendung der Laplace Transformation,* Dover Publications, New York, 1943.

is given in Sec. 4·16. The amplifier can be characterized by a constant gain G_a. The motor is characterized by an inertia J_m and a viscous damping coefficient f_m; its transfer function is

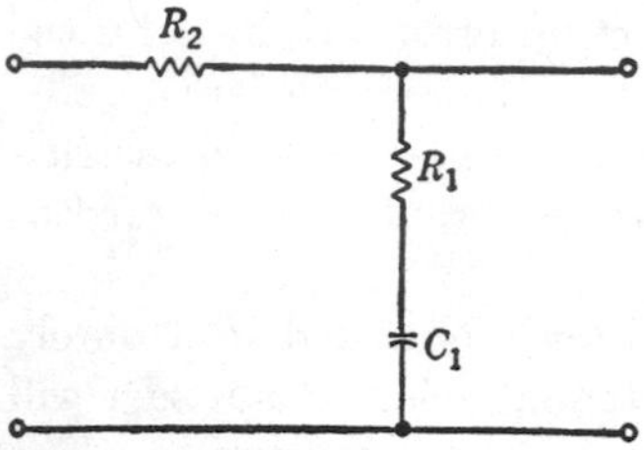

FIG. 4·11.—Equalizing network.

$$\frac{\theta_O}{E_m}(p) = \frac{K_m}{p(T_m p + 1)}, \tag{76}$$

where $T_m = J_m/f_m$ and K_m has the dimensions of angular velocity per volt. The study of this system is important because simple servos of this kind are frequently used and because many more complicated systems can be approximated by this simple system for the purpose of studying the effect of adding integral equalization.

The important physical parameters of the complete system can now be listed:

T_m = the motor time constant,
K_m = the motor gain,
G_a = the amplifier gain,
T = the integral time constant,
a = the attenuation factor of the equalizer.

In a given design problem the motor characteristics are usually considered as being given, while a, T, and G_a are parameters that we can vary in any way we choose in order to improve the performance of the system. In general any "solution" to the design problem should tell us how the performance of the system is influenced by changes in any of the parameters and should provide a rational basis for selection of those parameters whose values can be adjusted at will.

4·6. Differential-equation Analysis.—The method of direct solution of differential equations is commonly employed in the study of most physical systems and immediately suggests itself in connection with the servo problem. Following the basic outline given in the first section of this chapter, we can write for our chosen example

$$\frac{\theta_O}{\theta_I}(p) = \frac{Y_{11}(p)}{1 + Y_{11}(p)}, \tag{77}$$

where

$$Y_{11}(p) = \left(\frac{1 + Tp}{1 + aTp}\right)(G_a)\left[\frac{K_m}{p(T_m p + 1)}\right] = \frac{K_v(1 + Tp)}{p(T_m p + 1)(aTp + 1)}. \tag{78}$$

It is important to note that the product $G_a K_m$ appears in these equations in such a way that it can immediately be identified with K_v, the velocity-error constant. The differential equation for this system is clearly

$$aT\,T_m \frac{d^3\theta_O}{dt^3} + (aT + T_m)\frac{d^2\theta_O}{dt^2} + (1 + K_vT)\frac{d\theta_O}{dt} + K_v\theta_O = K_v\theta_I + K_vT\frac{d\theta_I}{dt}. \tag{79}$$

This differential equation is to be solved subject to the condition that the system is initially at rest. The Laplace transform method of solution is the most convenient approach, since Eq. (79) is a simple ordinary differential equation with constant coefficients. The transform of the output is

$$\mathfrak{L}[\theta_O(t)] = \frac{K_v(1 + Tp)}{p(T_mp + 1)(aTp + 1) + K_v(1 + Tp)}\,\theta_I(p). \tag{80}$$

We now assume some representative or at least interesting form of input function, the most commonly used one being a suddenly applied displacement of velocity, as discussed in Sec. 4·2. For a suddenly applied velocity Ω_0, Eq. (80) can be written as

$$\mathfrak{L}[\theta_O(t)] = \frac{K_v\Omega_0(1 + Tp)}{p^2[p(T_mp + 1)(aTp + 1) + K_v(1 + Tp)]}, \tag{81}$$

or

$$\theta_O(p) = \frac{\Omega_0(1 + Tp)}{p^2\left(\frac{\alpha}{\zeta}\frac{p}{\omega_n} + 1\right)\left(\frac{p^2}{\omega_n^2} + 2\zeta\frac{p}{\omega_n} + 1\right)}, \tag{82}$$

where the denominator has been factored and the parameters α, ζ, and ω_n introduced. The inversion of Eq. (82) to find $\theta_O(t)$ can be performed in general by means of the inversion integral and the calculus of residues, or it may be expanded in partial fractions, and the separate inversions looked up in a standard table of Laplace transform pairs (see Chap. 2).[1] The result is

$$\begin{aligned}\theta_O(t) = {} & \Omega_0 t + \frac{\Omega_0}{\omega_n}\left(\omega_nT - \frac{\alpha}{\zeta} - 2\zeta\right) - \frac{\Omega_0}{\omega_n}\frac{\left(\omega_nT - \frac{\alpha}{\zeta}\right)}{\left(1 - \frac{2\zeta^2}{\alpha} + \frac{\zeta^2}{\alpha^2}\right)}e^{-\frac{\zeta}{\alpha}\omega_nt} \\ & - \frac{\Omega_0}{\omega_n}\left[\omega_nT - \frac{\alpha}{\zeta} - 2\zeta - \frac{\left(\omega_nT - \frac{\alpha}{\zeta}\right)}{1 - \frac{2\zeta^2}{\alpha} + \frac{\zeta^2}{\alpha^2}}\right]e^{-\zeta\omega_nt}\cos\sqrt{1 - \zeta^2}\,\omega_nt \\ & + \frac{\Omega_0}{\omega_n}\frac{\zeta}{\sqrt{1 - \zeta^2}}\left[\frac{\left(1 - \frac{1}{\alpha}\right)\left(\omega_nT - \frac{\alpha}{\zeta}\right)}{\left(1 - \frac{2\zeta^2}{\alpha} + \frac{\zeta^2}{\alpha^2}\right)} - \omega_nT + \frac{\alpha}{\zeta} - \frac{1}{\zeta} + 2\zeta\right]e^{-\zeta\omega_nt}\sin\sqrt{1 - \zeta^2}\,\omega_nt.\end{aligned} \tag{83}$$

[1] See, for instance, M. F. Gardner and J. L. Barnes, *Transients in Linear Systems*, Wiley, New York, 1942, Table C.

Limiting forms of this expression must be used for the cases $\zeta = 1$ and $\alpha = 1$. The errors resulting from this suddenly applied velocity are plotted in Figs. 4·12 and 4·13 for different values of ζ and α. The motor time constant, a fixed system characteristic, is used as the normalization constant. It is necessary to select a value of the parameter a before drawing these curves; the figures are drawn for $a = 10$. It will be apparent later that changes in the value of a have a direct effect on the magnitude of the steady-state following error but practically no effect on the transient nature of the response.

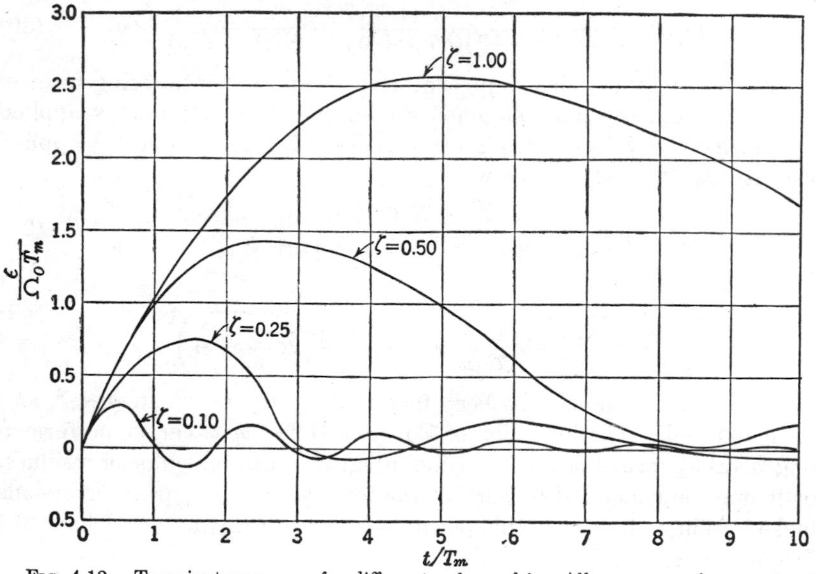

FIG. 4·12.—Transient responses for different values of ζ. All curves are for $\alpha = 1$.

We have not as yet defined the parameters α, ζ, and ω_n in terms of the parameters of the actual system, so that our results are of no practical value as yet. For any given single set of data, of course, the system parameters corresponding to a set of values of α, ζ, and ω_n can be calculated, but it requires a considerable number of such calculations to determine the effects of general variations in system constants. This is an inherent difficulty of the differential equation approach—even in this simple example it shows up quite strongly.

Since the characteristic equation is here of the third order, we can expect to find no simple relationship between the system parameters and the coefficients of the factored cubic in Eq. (82); we are thus led naturally to some sort of graphic presentation of this relationship. Charts relating the coefficients of the general cubic

$$a_3x^3 + a_2x^2 + a_1x + 1 = 0 \tag{84}$$

to the values of α, ζ, and ω_n in the factored cubic

$$\left(\frac{x^2}{\omega_n 2} + \frac{2\zeta}{\omega_n} x + 1\right)\left(\frac{\alpha}{\zeta\omega_n} x + 1\right) = 0 \tag{85}$$

have been prepared in connection with this same problem,[1,2,3] but their use involves a fair amount of calculation, since the coefficients a_1, a_2, and a_3 are still not related in any simple way to the actual system parame-

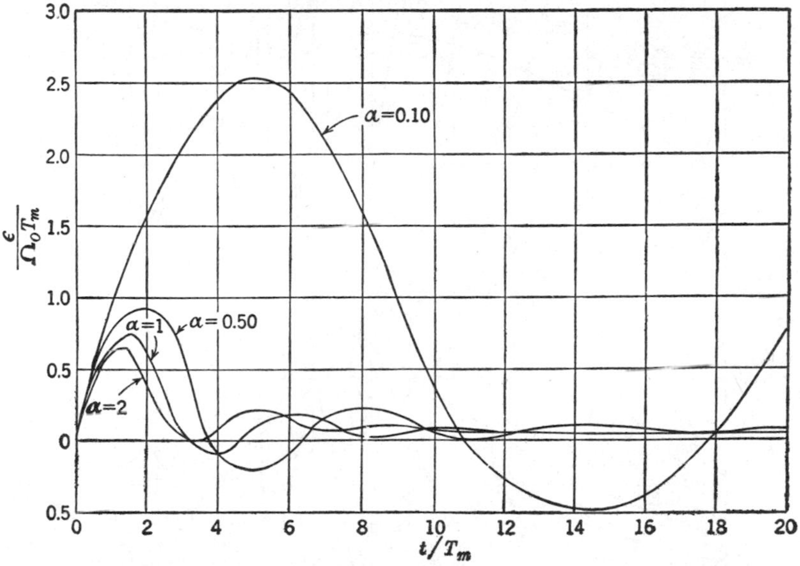

FIG. 4·13.—Transient responses for different values of α. All curves are for $\zeta = 0.25$.

ters. It is apparent that the only satisfactory answer is a chart that directly relates the system parameters to α, ζ, and $\omega_n T_m$. Such a chart can be prepared using the equations that result when coefficients of powers of p in Eq. (81) are equated to coefficients of like powers in Eq. (82):

$$\frac{\alpha}{\zeta} = \frac{a\omega_n^3 T T_m}{K_v}; \qquad 1 + 2\alpha = \frac{\omega_n^2(aT + T_m)}{K_v}; \qquad \frac{\alpha}{\zeta} + 2\zeta = \frac{\omega_n}{K_v} + \omega_n T. \tag{86}$$

[1] Y. J. Liu, *Servomechanisms: Charts for Verifying Their Stability and for Finding the Roots of Their Third and Fourth Degree Characteristic Equations*, privately printed by Massachusetts Institute of Technology, Department of Electrical Engineering, 1941.

[2] Also, L. W. Evans, *Solution of the Cubic Equation and the Cubic Charts*, privately printed by Massachusetts Institute of Technology, Department of Electrical Engineering, 1943.

[3] Also, E. Jahnke and F. Emde, *Funktionentafeln (Tables of Functions)*, Dover, New York, 1943, pp. 21–30 of the Addenda.

The three dimensionless parameters a, T/T_m, and K_vT_m represent the actual constants of the physical system; and in order to present corresponding values of α, ζ, and ω_nT_m it is convenient to assign a fixed value to one of a, T/T_m, and K_vT_m and plot the remaining two against each other. Figure 4·14 is such a chart drawn for $a = 10$, in which T_m/T is plotted

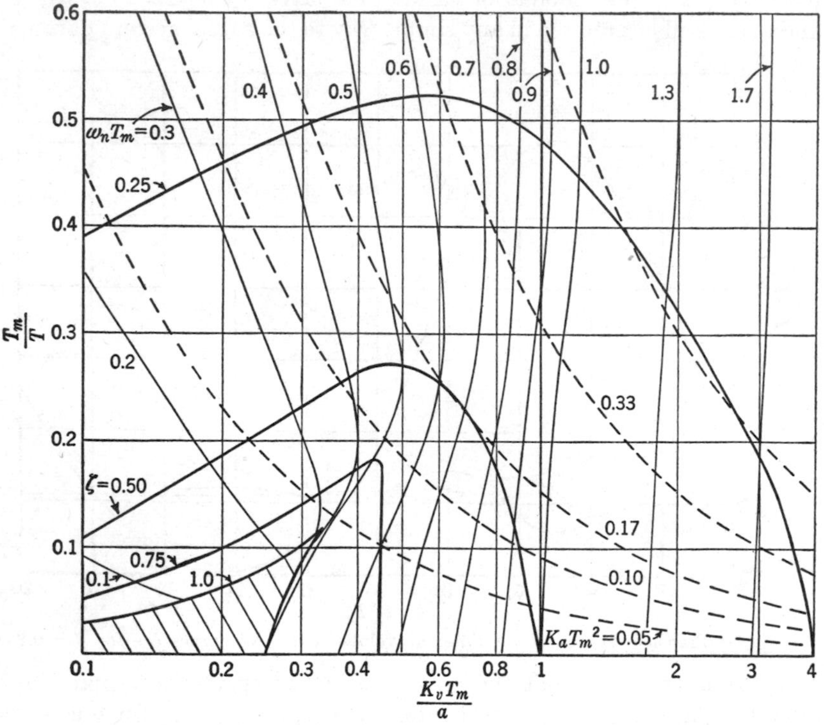

FIG. 4·14.—Design chart for single-time-lag servo with integral equalization. Heavy solid lines are for constant values of ζ; light solid lines are for constant values of ω_nT_m; dashed lines are for constant values of $K_aT_m^2$. The entire family of curves is drawn for $a = 10$.

against K_vT_m and the curves are for constant values of ζ and ω_nT_m. This is, then essentially a plot of the reciprocal of the integral time constant against the loop gain or velocity-error constant. Figure 4·15 is a similar figure drawn for $a = 5$.

We know from the response curves of Figs. 4·12 and 4·13 that values of ζ in the range from 0.25 to 0.75 result in reasonable transient response and that it is desirable to have as high a value of K_vT_m (velocity-error constant) as is consistent with satisfactory transient response. The design charts then show that the integral time constant should be between four and eight times as large as the motor time constant and that loop gains of the order of $K_vT_m = a$ can be used. If the integral equalizer were not used, a maximum usable value of K_vT_m would be 1 or 2; thus the equalizer enables us to increase the velocity-error constant by roughly the attenuation factor a of the network or possibly by as much as twice this factor. Values of $K_aT_m^2$, a dimensionless parameter proportional to

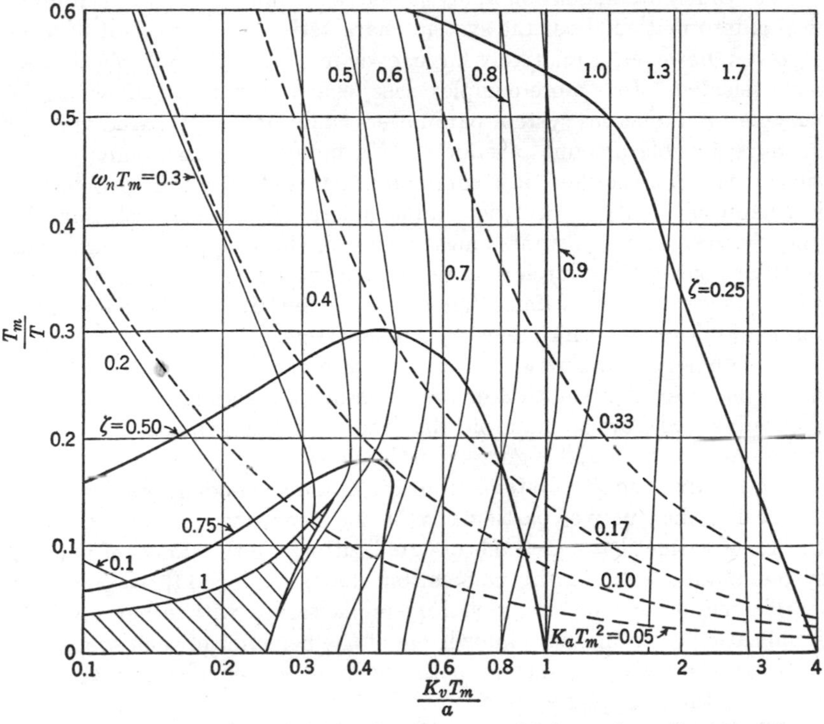

FIG. 4·15.—Design chart for single-time-lag servo with integral equalization. Heavy solid lines are for constant values of ζ; light solid lines are for constant values of ω_nT_m; dashed lines are for constant values of $K_aT_m{}^2$. The entire family of curves is drawn for $a = 5$.

the acceleration-error constant (see Secs. 4·2 and 4·4), have been plotted on the design charts; they indicate clearly an optimum value of integral time constant; optimum, that is, if acceleration errors are considered important. It can be shown that such optimum adjustment corresponds to making the parameter α equal to roughly unity.

Examination of the transient response curves show that if the system is adjusted to $\zeta = 0.25$ and $\alpha = 1 (K_vT_m = 2a)$, then the rise time or buildup time of the step-function response will be about $1.5T_m$ sec and the period of the oscillatory part of the response will be about $5T_m$ sec. According to Eq. (43), the cutoff frequency of this servo, considered as a low-pass filter, is about $2/T_m$ radians per second. We can conclude that (as long as a is chosen greater than about 5) the maximum usable gain for this system is between $K_vT_m = a$ and $K_vT_m = 2a$ and that a value of T equal to approximately $4T_m$ is required for optimum operation at these gain levels. The buildup time is not materially affected by changes in the value of a.

The differential equation analysis[1] carried out in detail yields a great deal of information about the system characteristics; the amount of work involved, however, is relatively large, even in the simple example that we have selected. In a more complex case, charts displaying the effects of varying the numerous system parameters could not be prepared without an unreasonable amount of effort. If a detailed transient analysis of such a system is required, it is common practice to set up the problem on a differential analyzer and determine a large number of solutions by varying the system constants one at a time or (hopefully!) in appropriate combinations. More often than not such a procedure leaves the designer with a large amount of data that are extremely difficult to interpret in terms of optimum performance from the system.

Fortunately, more powerful and convenient design procedures not based on an explicit solution of the differential equations are available; their advantages are so manifold that the differential-equation approach is seldom used by servo engineers at the present time.

The study of simple systems from the differential-equation viewpoint, however, is instructive, particularly to the neophyte, in demonstrating the use of various basic methods of equalization and the effects of varying system parameters. In this connection, charts similar to those presented in this section can be prepared for simple servos with other kinds of equalization. An intimate knowledge of the behavior of such systems is useful to the designer, since so many complex systems can be approximated by these simpler systems.

4·7. Transfer-locus Analysis. The Nyquist Diagram.—The transfer-locus analysis is a study of the steady-state response of the servo system to sinusoidal input signals. It is common practice, for the sake of simplicity and convenience of interpretation, to study the loop transfer function rather than the over-all transfer function, that is, to study the transmission of signals around the servo loop. The essential advantage of this method arises from the familiar fact that the sinusoidal steady-state solution of the differential equation can be written down immediately if the transfer function of the system is known.

[1] G. S. Brown and A. C. Hall, "Dynamic Behavior and Design of Servomechanisms," *Trans. ASME*, **68**, 503 (1946). S. W. Herwald, "Considerations in Servomechanism Design," *Trans. AIEE*, **63**, 871 (1944). A. Callender, D. R. Hartree, and A. Porter, "Time Lag in a Control System," *Trans. Roy. Soc.* (*London*), **235A**, 415 (1936).

We now take up the transfer-locus analysis of the simple system shown in Fig. 4·10. The transfer function defining the transmission of signals around the servo loop is evidently given by

$$\frac{\theta_O}{\epsilon}(p) = \frac{K_v(1 + Tp)}{p(1 + T_m p)(1 + aTp)}. \tag{87}$$

To find the sinusoidal steady-state solution we simply replace p by $j\omega$ in Eq. (87), obtaining

$$\frac{\theta_O}{\epsilon}(j\omega) = \frac{K_v(1 + j\omega T)}{j\omega(1 + j\omega T_m)(1 + ja\omega T)}. \tag{88}$$

This is, in general, a complex number that can be expressed in its polar form, that is, in terms of its magnitude and phase. A polar plot of this

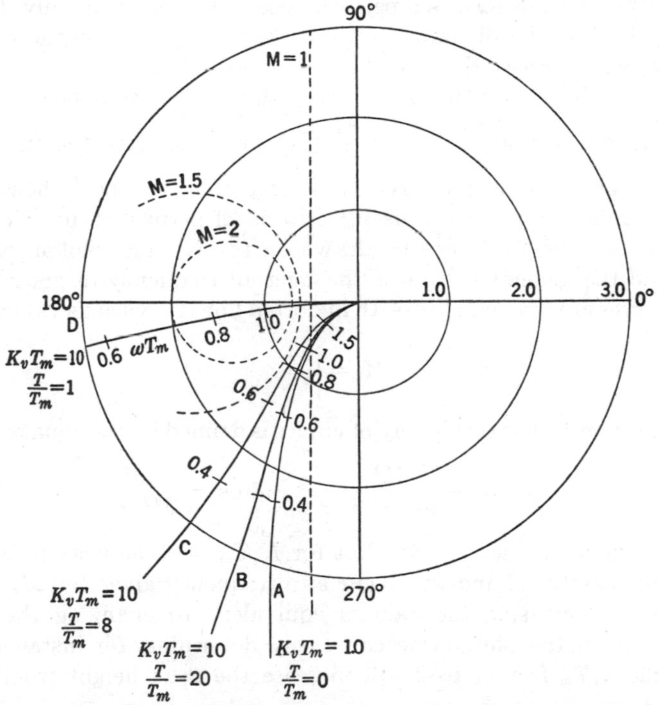

FIG. 4·16.—Nyquist diagram for single-time-lag servo. (a) No equalization, (b), (c), (d) with integral equalization.

function with the driving frequency ω as a parameter is called a transfer-locus plot or, more commonly, a Nyquist diagram.

Let us first consider the Nyquist diagram corresponding to the servo with no equalization, which is simply a plot of

$$\frac{\theta_O}{\epsilon}(j\omega) = \frac{K_vT_m}{j\omega T_m(1 + j\omega T_m)}. \tag{89}$$

The real factor K_vT_m affects only the magnitude and not the phase of this quantity and hence is simply a radial scale factor on the plot. We will take K_vT_m, which is proportional to the loop gain (or velocity-error constant), equal to unity for the purpose of plotting Eq. (89). Curve A in Fig. 4·16 is the Nyquist plot of Eq. (89). The values of ωT_m corresponding to various points of the curve are labeled in the figure.

The loop phase angle at any frequency (taken as positive) diminished by 180° is defined as the "phase margin" at that frequency, and the frequency at which the curve crosses the $|\theta_O/\epsilon| = 1$ circle is termed the "feedback cutoff frequency."

In this extremely simple system we have just one adjustable parameter at our disposal, namely, the loop gain, and we must determine what values of gain will result in tolerable performance. This is commonly done by relating the Nyquist diagram to the over-all frequency-response curves of the system, a process that is rather easily carried out.

It was pointed out in Sec. 4·2 that the over-all frequency-response curves defined by the function $\frac{\theta_O}{\theta_I}(j\omega)$ are similar to the frequency-response curves of a low-pass filter and that the peak height and corresponding frequency are useful criteria of performance. Curves of constant value of $|\theta_O/\theta_I|$ can be drawn on the Nyquist plot in order to determine the general nature of the over-all frequency-response curve. These curves are drawn in Fig. 4·16 in dotted lines for various values of

$$M = \left|\frac{\theta_O}{\theta_I}\right|.$$

It is easily shown that this family of circles is defined by the equations

$$\text{Center} = -\frac{M^2}{M^2 - 1}, \qquad \text{radius} = \frac{M}{M^2 - 1}. \tag{90}$$

From the figure we see clearly that for $K_vT_m = 1$ the peak height will be approximately 1.2 and will occur at a frequency given by ωT_m equals about 0.8. Increasing the gain is equivalent to changing the radial scale factor on the plot. One can easily determine, for instance, that increasing K_vT_m from 1 to 2 will increase the peak height from 1.2 to about 1.5.

Now let us examine what happens when the integral equalizer is added to the system. The quantity $\frac{\theta_O}{\epsilon}(j\omega)$ is then multiplied by the factor

$$G(j\omega T_m) = \frac{1 + j\frac{T}{T_m}\omega T_m}{1 + ja\frac{T}{T_m}\omega T_m}. \tag{91}$$

This transfer locus of the integral network is plotted in Fig. 4·17; it is always a semicircle, the zero frequency point being at $r = 1$, $\theta = 0$ and the infinite frequency point at $r = a^{-1}$, $\theta = 0$. The parameter T/T_m determines the distribution of frequencies along the arc of the semicircle. To combine this curve with the transfer locus A of Fig. 4·16, we must first select values of a and T/T_m, then "multiply" the two loci in the way in which complex numbers are multiplied, that is, by multiplying the

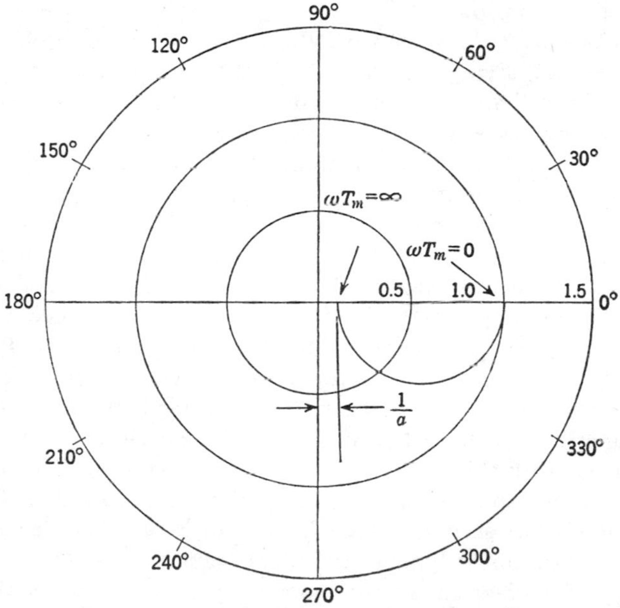

FIG. 4·17.—Nyquist diagram for integral equalizer.

magnitudes of the radius vectors at a given frequency and adding their phase angles. The curves in Fig. 4·16 show the results of such a process when a is taken to be 10 and the curves are for various values of T/T_m. These curves are drawn with $K_vT_m = 10$, as compared with $K_vT_m = 1$ in the case of the curve for the unequalized servo. If $T/T_m = 1$, we see that the transfer locus passes very near the critical point $-1 + j0$; the servo is decidedly unstable when $K_vT_m = 10$. If, however, T/T_m is increased to 8, a gain of $K_vT_m = 10$ can be used, giving a frequency-response peak height of less than 1.5 at ωT_m equal to approximately 0.8. The gain could be increased to 20 without causing the peak height to grow to more than 1.8. If T/T_m is increased to 20, this same high gain can be used, and the performance will not differ essentially from the performance obtained with $T/T_m = 8$. Further analysis would show that T/T_m could be decreased to about 4 and that a gain of $K_vT_m = 20$ could still be used.

It is quite clear from these curves that the phase margin at feedback cutoff is a good criterion of stability when the transfer locus is more or less parallel or tangent to one of the circles of constant M in the vicinity of feedback cutoff. This condition obtains in many, if not most, actual systems. More than 30° phase margin at feedback cutoff is usually desirable; more than 60° will usually result in a system that is greater than critically damped.

Assuming that $K_vT_m = 20$ with $T/T_m = 8$, feedback cutoff occurs at about $\omega T_m = 1.3$, giving a buildup time of $2.4T_m$ (see Sec. 4·2)—somewhat larger than the value found from the differential-equation analysis in the preceding section; if T/T_m were reduced to about 4 (we have already mentioned that this is possible), the frequency of feedback cutoff would be increased, resulting in a somewhat shorter buildup time.

It is instructive to interpret the curves of Fig. 4·16 in terms of the Nyquist stability criterion developed in Chap. 2. The transfer loci have been drawn only for the range of frequencies from 0 to ∞; and since the stability criterion requires the curves for the complete range of all real frequencies, $-\infty$ to $+\infty$, we must imagine the curves of Fig. 4·16 to be completed by drawing in their complex conjugates, *i.e.*, their reflections about the real axis. We can see that no matter how high the gain is raised, the critical point $-1 + j0$ will never be enclosed, so that in the mathematical sense the system never becomes unstable. This apparent paradox and its explanation have already been discussed in Chap. 2, and we have already seen in this section how more detailed considerations of stability set an upper limit to the usable gain.

The Nyquist diagram is most commonly used in conjunction with curves of constant magnitude of $|\theta_O/\theta_I|$ to determine parameter values that result in a satisfactory over-all frequency response rather than for determining stability in the absolute mathematical sense. For more complicated systems, additional factors will appear in the expression for θ_O/ϵ, and these can be combined one at a time in the same way that the two simple factors were combined in our example; thus the effects of additional equalization or more complex motive elements are easily studied. The economy of thought and time inherent in this approach, as compared with the direct solution of the differential equations, is much more striking in more complex examples where the differential-equation method is all but unfeasible; even in our simple example, however, the transfer-locus method is much more convenient and less time-consuming, as the reader can verify by going through the detailed calculations involved in solving the same or a similar problem by the two different techniques. The principal advantage of the transfer-locus technique is the manner in which the results of varying system parameters can be determined.

This type of analysis has been exhaustively treated by A. C. Hall,[1] who gives a detailed account of the basic philosophy of the method and treats many different practical examples. The treatment of multiple-loop systems by this method is somewhat involved, since the loop transfer function is then no longer a product of simple factors. Several writers have pointed out the advantages of using a diagram in which ϵ/θ_O is plotted rather than θ_O/ϵ for such multiple-loop systems. Since the general approach to the design problem to be discussed in the following section is ideally suited for multiple-loop systems, these inverse Nyquist diagrams are not described here in any detail.

4·8. Attenuation-phase Analysis.—The "attenuation-phase" or "decibel–log-frequency" type of analysis to be introduced in this section has been found to be the most satisfactory approach to the servo design problem and is the method that will be used in the later sections which deal with the general servo design problem in detail.

The general theoretical foundations of this type of analysis are discussed in Sec. 4·9, and the present section is intended to give no more than a brief introduction to the method, which, like the transfer-locus method, is basically a study of the steady-state transmission of sinusoidal signals around the servo loop. The real and imaginary parts of the logarithm of the loop transfer function are plotted as functions of the frequency, on a logarithmic frequency scale. Writing

$$\ln \frac{\theta_O}{\epsilon}(j\omega) = \ln \left|\frac{\theta_O}{\epsilon}(j\omega)\right| + j \operatorname{Arg} \frac{\theta_O}{\epsilon}(j\omega), \tag{92}$$

we see that the real part is the logarithm of the magnitude of $\frac{\theta_O}{\epsilon}(j\omega)$ and the imaginary part is simply the phase of the same function. The quantity $20 \log_{10} \left|\frac{\theta_O}{\epsilon}\right|$, proportional to the real part of the above expression, is usually plotted rather than just $\ln \left|\frac{\theta_O}{\epsilon}\right|$ and is then called the loop attenuation in decibels. It should be remarked here that the terms "attenuation" and "gain" are used interchangeably in this text for the same quantity, even though the gain in decibels is the negative of the

[1] A. C. Hall, *The Analysis and Synthesis of Linear Servomechanisms*, Technology Press, Massachusetts Institute of Technology, May 1943. A. C. Hall, "Application of Circuit Theory to the Design of Servomechanisms," J. Franklin Inst., **242**, 279 (1946).

See also: H. Lauer, R. Lesnick, and L. E. Matson, *Servomechanism Fundamentals*, McGraw-Hill, New York, 1947.

attenuation in decibels. The context in any particular instance will prevent confusion. The significance of this seemingly trivial modification of the usual Nyquist diagram stems from certain asymptotic properties of the resulting curves and from certain relationships between the two diagrams. It will be shown later that for a large class of transfer functions, the so-called minimum-phase class, the attenuation characteristic is completely determined when the phase characteristic is prescribed, and vice versa. A knowledge of the nature of this functional relationship between the attenuation and phase characteristics often makes it possible to carry through a large portion of the design procedure using only the attenuation curve, which is extremely simple to construct, even for very complex systems.

Let us now consider the attenuation and phase diagrams for the transfer function of Eq. (88). First we notice that the real part of the logarithm of this expression can be written

$$A = 20 \log_{10} K_v T_m + 20 \log_{10} |(1 + j\omega T)| - 20 \log_{10} |j\omega T_m| \\ -20 \log_{10} |(1 + j\omega T_m)| - 20 \log_{10} |(1 + ja\omega T)|; \quad (93)$$

the attenuation characteristic is the sum of the characteristics of the individual factors of the complete expression. The first term is simply an additive constant; we therefore take $K_v T_m = 1$ and eliminate this term for the time being. The attenuation characteristic corresponding to a typical term, say $A_1 = 20 \log_{10} |(1 + j\omega T)|$, is easily constructed. For very low frequencies this term approaches $20 \log_{10} 1$, or zero. For very large frequencies we have

$$20 \log_{10} |(1 + j\omega T)| \sim 20 \log_{10} \omega T. \quad (94)$$

Thus

$$A_1 \sim 0, \qquad \omega T < 1,$$
$$A_1 \sim 20 \log \omega T, \qquad \omega T > 1. \quad (95)$$

In this asymptotic relation A_1 is obviously a linear function of the logarithm of the frequency and becomes zero at a frequency $\omega = 1/T$. To determine the slope of the linear plot of A_1 as a function of $\log_{10} \omega T_m$, we notice that if a given value of ω is doubled, that is, if the frequency is raised one octave, then A_1 is increased by $20 \log_{10} 2$. Thus the slope may be expressed as 6 db per octave. These high- and low-frequency asymptotes are shown in Fig. 4·18, where $x = \omega T$. The exact function 20 $\log_{10} |(1 + j\omega T)|$ is also plotted, in dashed lines, and is seen to differ from the asymptotic curve by at most 3 db, at the corner frequency $\omega = 1/T$. The term $20 \log_{10} |j\omega T_m|$ in Eq. (93) is easily seen to have an attenuation characteristic that is simply a straight line with a slope of 6 db per octave passing through zero at the frequency $\omega = 1/T_m$.

If we now assume that $T/T_m > 1$, we can draw the asymptotic curves for each of the terms in Eq. (93) all on one drawing and finally take the sum of these curves to find the asymptotic attenuation characteristic

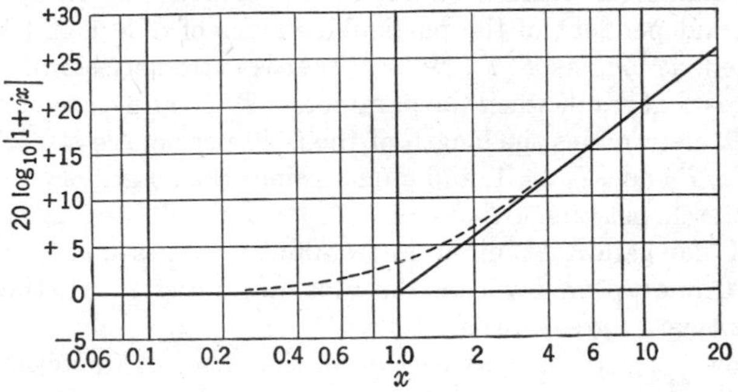

FIG. 4·18.—Attenuation of $1 + jx$.

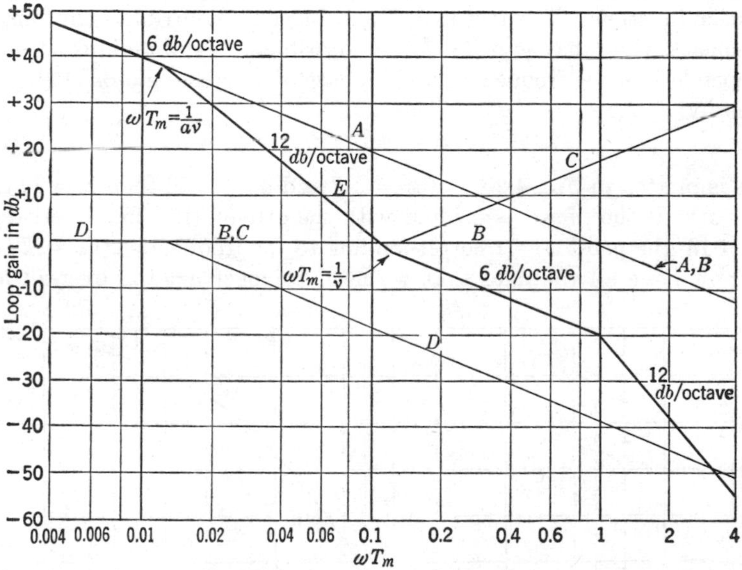

FIG. 4·19.—Asymptotic attenuation characteristic. Curves are drawn for $\nu = 8$, $a = 10$, and $K_v T_m = 1$.

$A \sim -20 \log_{10} |j\omega T_m|$,
$B \sim -20 \log_{10} |(1 + j\omega T_m)|$,
$C \sim 20 \log_{10} |(1 + j\omega T)|$,
$D \sim -20 \log_{10} |(1 + ja\omega T)|$,
$E \sim$ sum of the above.

for the entire loop. This is shown in Fig. 4·19. In this and the following figures the symbol ν has been used to denote the quantity T/T_m. Actually, of course, the individual curves A, B, C, D need not be drawn in order to draw the complete curve E once a little insight into the nature of the process is gained.

Several important features of the over-all curve E should be noted. (1) The final break from 6 to 12 db per octave will always occur at $\omega T_m = 1$, independent of the particular values of $a > 1$ and T/T_m that are selected, as long as $T/T_m > 1$. (2) It is extremely simple to observe the changes that result when the parameters T/T_m and a are varied. The ratio T/T_m determines the length of the 6-db per octave stretch between $\omega T_m = T_m/T$ and $\omega T_m = 1$, and a determines the length of the 12-db per octave stretch between $\omega T_m = (aT/T_m)^{-1}$ and $\omega T_m = T_m/T$. Finally, a value of loop gain $K_v T_m$ different from unity results simply in a shift of the $A = 0$ line up or down on the plot, according to whether $K_v T_m$ is made less than or greater than unity.

We now take up the construction of the phase characteristics. It is evident that the complete phase angle for the loop transfer function is equal to the sum of the phases of each of the separate factors of the transfer function. The factor $K_v T_m$, being real, contributes nothing to the phase, while the factor $(j\omega T_m)^{-1}$ contributes $-\pi/2$ radians or $-90°$, independent of the frequency. The phase of a typical factor $(1 + jx)$ is given by

$$\phi = \tan^{-1} x. \tag{96}$$

This is plotted in Fig. 4·20. If $x = \omega T$ and $\omega = 1/T$, then $x = 1$; thus this curve is the phase associated with the attenuation characteristic of Fig. 4·18, the point $x = 1$ corresponding to the frequency $\omega T_m = T_m/T$. We now have all the data that we need to construct the over-all loop

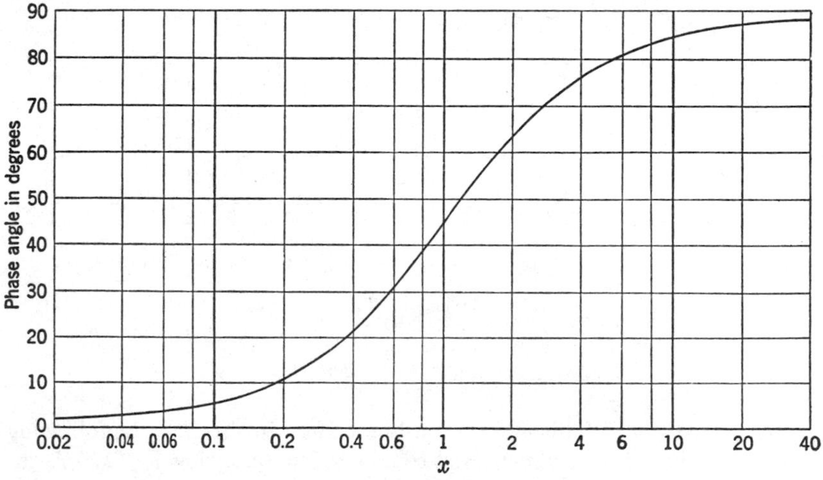

FIG. 4·20.—Phase of $1 + jx$.

phase characteristic. It should be noticed that rapid changes in phase can occur only in the vicinity of those frequencies at which the slope of the attenuation characteristic changes and that if the attenuation characteristic has a constant slope over any appreciable frequency range, then the associated phase will be essentially constant. This is illustrated in Fig. 4·21, where the phases of the individual factors of the transfer function are sketched (A, B, C, D) along with their sum E. Comparing

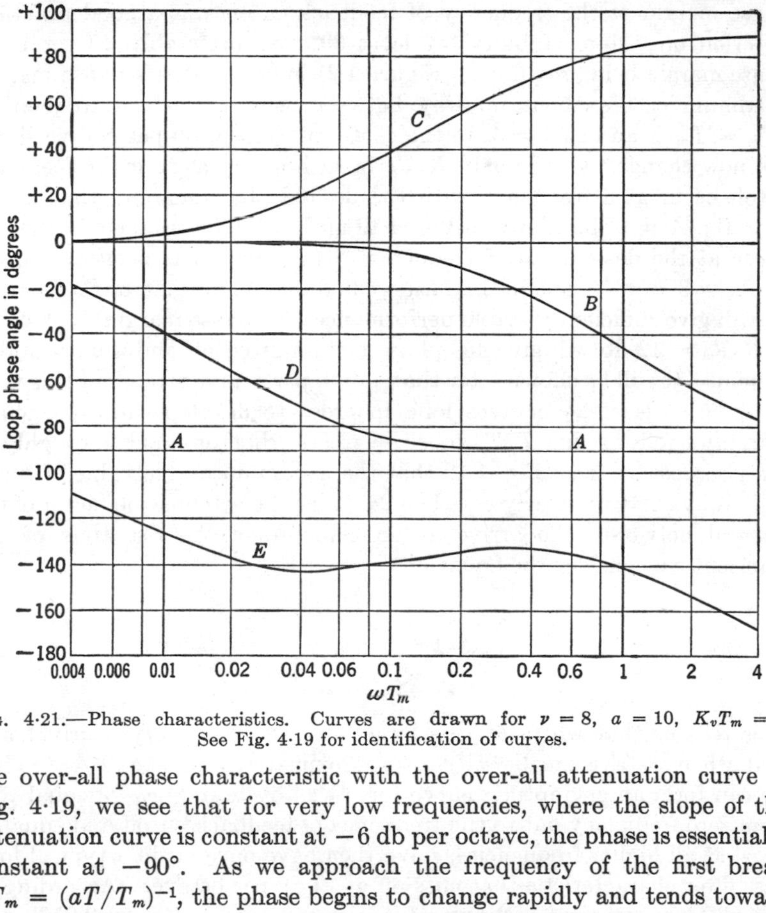

FIG. 4·21.—Phase characteristics. Curves are drawn for $\nu = 8$, $a = 10$, $K_vT_m = 1$. See Fig. 4·19 for identification of curves.

the over-all phase characteristic with the over-all attenuation curve of Fig. 4·19, we see that for very low frequencies, where the slope of the attenuation curve is constant at -6 db per octave, the phase is essentially constant at $-90°$. As we approach the frequency of the first break $\omega T_m = (aT/T_m)^{-1}$, the phase begins to change rapidly and tends toward a new constant value of $-180°$, associated with the long -12-db per octave stretch of the attenuation curve. As the attenuation curve breaks back to -6 db per octave, the phase once again changes rapidly back toward the $-90°$ value always associated with a -6-db per octave slope. However, since the frequencies $\omega T_m = T_m/T$ and $\omega T_m = 1$ are relatively close together (the 6-db per octave portion of the curve is relatively short), the phase does not reach $-90°$ again but rather decreases asymptotically to $-180°$ under the influence of the break from -6 to -12 db per octave at the frequency $\omega T_m = 1$. It is evident from Fig. 4·21 that as long as the frequencies at which the breaks occur are fairly well separated, the phase changes associated with the breaks are more or less independent of one another.

The discussion in the previous section showed that the amount of phase margin at the frequency of feedback cutoff was a good practical criterion of system stability, at least 30° and preferably 45° or more phase margin being required. Figure 4·21 indicates that a phase-margin maximum occurs about midway between the two critical frequencies $\omega T_m = T_m/T$ and $\omega T_m = 1$, in the center of the -6-db per octave slope. We now change the loop gain $K_v T_m$ in such a way as to make feedback cutoff occur at a frequency with the desired phase margin, that is, we slide the $A = 0$ line down in Fig. 4·19 until it intersects the attenuation curve at the desired cutoff frequency. The curve has been drawn for $T/T_m = 8$, $a = 10$, and in this case we find that a loop gain of $K_v T_m = 26$ db will give sufficiently stable performance (30° phase margin). A value of $K_v T_m = 12$ db will give 45° phase margin at cutoff and a more stable system. It will be shown later that a 6-db per octave stretch of this type must be at least $2\frac{1}{2}$ octaves long in order to develop sufficient phase margin; it follows that T/T_m must be greater than or equal to roughly 4. We also observe from Fig. 4·19 that the maximum usable value of $K_v T_m$ will always be very nearly equal to $2a$, twice the attenuation factor of the integral network. To arrive at an estimate of the rise time of the transient we consider the equation

$$\frac{\theta_O}{\theta_I}(j\omega) = \frac{\dfrac{\theta_O}{\epsilon}(j\omega)}{1 + \dfrac{\theta_O}{\epsilon}(j\omega)}. \tag{97}$$

This tells us that when $|\theta_O/\epsilon|$ is large, then $|\theta_O/\theta_I|$ is very nearly 1 and that when $|\theta_O/\epsilon|$ is small, $|\theta_O/\theta_I|$ is approximately equal to $|\theta_O/\epsilon|$. Thus we can form an asymptotic curve for $|\theta_O/\theta_I|$ by taking $|\theta_O/\theta_I|$ equal to 1 from zero frequency out to the frequency of feedback cutoff and equal to $|\theta_O/\epsilon|$ at all higher frequencies. We then have once again a typical low-pass filter characteristic that cuts off at 12 db per octave. According to Eq. (43), the rise time of the step function response is π/ω_0, or $2.25T_m$ sec, when $T/T_m = 8$, $a = 10$, $K_v T_m = 26$ db.

The acceleration-error constant is easily found from the attenuation curve. Equation (66) gives us

$$\frac{1}{K_a} = \frac{aT + T_m - T}{K_v} - \frac{1}{K_v^2}, \tag{98}$$

and we can write, approximately,

$$K_a = \frac{K_v}{aT}. \tag{99}$$

If we extend the 12-db per octave slope in the low-frequency region until it intersects the line of selected gain level, the frequency of intersection will give the acceleration-error constant through the formula

$$\omega_c^2 = \frac{K_v}{aT}, \tag{100}$$

where ω_c is the frequency of intersection.

The reader should observe that given a certain amount of prior knowledge of attenuation-phase relationships, it would not have been necessary to compute the phase characteristic in detail and that most of the design procedure is based on the attenuation characteristic, which can be drawn in asymptotic form with no computation and negligible effort. The more complex examples considered later in the chapter will illustrate even more strikingly the superiority of the attenuation-phase concepts.

ATTENUATION-PHASE RELATIONSHIPS FOR SERVO TRANSFER FUNCTIONS

4·9. Attenuation-phase Relationships.—A complete mathematical treatment of attenuation-phase relationships will not be presented here because the detailed results of the theory are not actually used in this book, and the theory has been exhaustively treated elsewhere.[1] A brief survey of the theory is given, followed by a detailed exposition of the practical procedures involved in the analysis of servo problems.

The transfer functions considered may represent the physical characteristics of many different kinds of devices. For example, they may be over-all loop transfer functions, subsidiary loop transfer functions, or perhaps the transfer functions of simple passive equalizing networks. In general, we consider the logarithms of these functions, the real part $A(\omega)$ being the attenuation, or gain, and the imaginary part $\phi(\omega)$ being the phase. The general symbol $Y(p)$ is used here to represent the transfer function, considered as a function of the complex frequency $p = \alpha + j\omega$. We can divide the class of transfer functions considered into two subclasses, depending on the location of the zeros and poles of $Y(p)$. If $Y(p)$ has no poles or zeros in the right half of the p-plane, then

[1] See, in particular, H. W. Bode, *Network Analysis and Feedback Amplifier Design*, Van Nostrand, New York, 1945; a brief readable treatment is given by F. E. Terman, *Radio Engineers' Handbook*, McGraw-Hill, New York, 1943; L. A. MacColl, *Fundamental Theory of Servomechanisms*, Van Nostrand, New York, 1945; R. E. Graham, "Linear Servo Theory," *Bell System Technical Journal*, **XXV**, 616 (1946). E. B. Ferrell, "The Servo Problem as a Transmission Problem," *Proc. IRE*, **33**, 763 (1945).

$Y(p)$ is called a "minimum-phase" function. The great majority of the functions encountered in servo theory belong to this class, which possesses the following important property: If the attenuation $A(\omega)$ is known over the entire range of frequencies, then the phase $\phi(\omega)$ is uniquely determined; and similarly, if $\phi(\omega)$ is known over the entire range of frequencies, then $A(\omega)$ is uniquely determined. This property is not possessed by functions $Y(p)$ having poles or zeros in the right half of the p-plane, and this case, which arises occasionally in connection with systems having more than one feedback loop, must be treated differently.

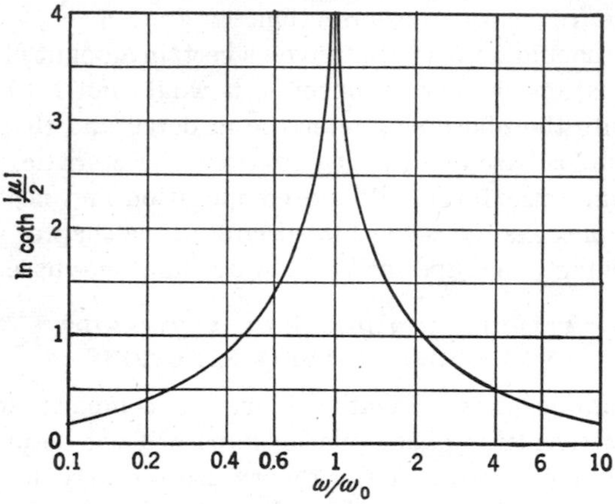

FIG. 4·22.—Weighting function.

The formula expressing the minimum phase associated with a given attenuation characteristic can be given in a variety of forms, and numerous other attenuation-phase relationships can be derived by function-theory considerations. One form of the relation is

$$\phi(\omega_0) = \frac{\pi}{12}\left(\frac{dA}{d\mu}\right)_{\omega=\omega_0} + \frac{1}{6\pi}\int_{-\infty}^{\infty} d\mu \left[\left(\frac{dA}{d\mu}\right) - \left(\frac{dA}{d\mu}\right)_{\omega=\omega_0}\right] \ln \coth \frac{|\mu|}{2}, \quad (101)$$

where $\mu = \ln \omega/\omega_0$. This formula places in direct evidence the important characteristics of the attenuation-phase relationship. The phase in radians at any frequency ω_0, $\phi(\omega_0)$, is expressed in terms of the slope of the attenuation diagram and a weighting function, where

$$\left(\frac{dA}{d\mu}\right) = \text{slope of attenuation curve in decibels per octave.}$$

The weighting function $\ln \coth |\mu|/2$ is plotted in Fig. 4·22; it has a total weight, with respect to integration over μ, of 1. Several important results, obtained in a more experimental manner in the last section, can be derived from Eq. (101). It is clear, for instance, that the phase associated with a constant attenuation slope of $6n$ db per octave is just $n\pi/2$ radians. It is also clear from the form of the weighting function that the phase must always change most rapidly in the vicinity of changes in slope of the attenuation characteristic and that the phase at any given frequency is influenced appreciably only by the changes in attenuation slope near that given frequency. The actual use of Eq. (101) for computational purposes would be extremely involved; and when a phase characteristic must be computed from a given attenuation characteristic, it is more convenient to approximate the given curve with straight-line asymptotes and to compute the corresponding phase by means of the procedures and charts developed by Bode[1] for this purpose. In servo problems it is nearly always possible to approximate the attenuation characteristic with sufficient accuracy, using only straight lines with slopes that are integral multiples of 6 db per octave; consequently the phase can be computed using the simplified techniques and charts presented in the following section.

Occasionally a nonminimum-phase network may be used for a passive equalizer. The transfer function for such a network will have one or more zeros in the right half of the p-plane and will thus have, for instance, a factor of the form $(-1 + Tp)$, which has the same attenuation characteristic as $(1 + Tp)$ but a reversed phase characteristic. Another nonminimum-phase situation arises in the case of an unstable subsidiary loop, for which the transfer function has a factor $(T^2p^2 - 2\zeta Tp + 1)^{-1}$; this again has the same attenuation characteristic as $(T^2p^2 + 2\zeta Tp + 1)^{-1}$ but a reversed phase characteristic. The occurrence of these special cases is not troublesome in servo problems if the techniques of the following sections are employed, since we have always sufficient knowledge of the origin of the attenuation characteristic to know whether or not such nonminimum-phase structures are present. Clearly, however, if one is simply given an attenuation characteristic, it cannot be assumed automatically that it is the characteristic of a minimum-phase structure, and the phase cannot be computed with certainty. Obviously the attenuation and phase may be computed from the transfer function.

4·10. Construction and Interpretation of Attenuation and Phase Diagrams.—For the construction of attenuation and phase diagrams the feedback transfer function θ_O/ϵ is expressed, as far as possible, as the product or quotient of factors of the form $(Tp + 1)$; its decibel magnitude $|\theta_O/\epsilon|_{db}$ and phase angle Arg (θ_O/ϵ) are then plotted on semilog coordinates as a function of frequency. In this type of plot an asymptotic method can be used to approximate the curves.

[1] Bode, *op. cit.*, Chap. XV.

As an illustration of the construction of decibel–log-frequency graphs let us take the transfer function

$$\frac{\theta_O}{\epsilon} = \frac{K_v}{p(Tp + 1)}. \tag{102}$$

As $\omega \rightarrow 0$, $|\theta_O/\epsilon|_{\text{db}} \rightarrow 20 \log_{10} K_v - 20 \log_{10} \omega$. The argument then proceeds as in Sec. 4·8. Since doubling the frequency diminishes the value of $|\theta_O/\epsilon|$ by a factor of 2, the asymptote to the actual curve for small values of ω has a slope of -6 db/octave [the log of 2 is 0.30103;

$$20(0.30103) = 6.0206 \text{ db},$$

which is usually approximated by 6 db]. When $\omega \gg 1/T$, that is, $\omega T \gg 1$, $|\theta_O/\epsilon|$ varies inversely as the square of the frequency. Therefore the asymptote has a slope of -12 db/octave. If $|\theta_O/\epsilon|$ is represented by these two asymptotes intersecting at $\omega = 1/T$, the maximum departure from the actual curve is only 3 db and occurs at the intersection. For one octave above or below this point the departure is 1 db.

When more time constants are present, the approximate plot is made similarly, with a change of 6 db in its slope at each value of ω for which ω times one of the time constants equals unity. The slope is decreased for time constants in the denominator but increased for those in the numerator. The departure from the actual curve near each slope-change point is the same as that for Eq. (102) if the time constants are not too close to each other.

The plot of Arg (θ_O/ϵ) for Eq. (102) is approximated from the following:

$$\text{As } \omega \rightarrow 0, \text{ Arg}\left(\frac{\theta_O}{\epsilon}\right) \rightarrow -90°,$$

$$\omega \rightarrow \infty, \text{ Arg}\left(\frac{\theta_O}{\epsilon}\right) \rightarrow -180°.$$

$$\text{At } \omega = \frac{1}{T}, \text{ Arg}\left(\frac{\theta_O}{\epsilon}\right) = -135°,$$

$$\omega = \frac{1}{2T}, \text{ Arg}\left(\frac{\theta_O}{\epsilon}\right) \text{ is } -26.5° \text{ from the } -90°\text{-phase asymptote},$$

$$\omega = \frac{2}{T}, \text{ Arg}\left(\frac{\theta_O}{\epsilon}\right) \text{ is } +26.5° \text{ from the } -180°\text{-phase asymptote}.$$

For convenience, the "decibel–log-frequency" and "Arg–log-frequency" plots are usually made on the same sheet.

In using this method of plotting transfer functions for servo design, numerous short-cut methods can be devised.

The attenuation plot may be constructed entirely by projecting the line at one slope to the next break point and then projecting the new slope to the next break point and so on. However, since the errors in this process are cumulative, better accuracy is obtained for the asymptotic-attenuation plot if the value of the attenuation at each break point in the asymptotic curve is computed directly. The following procedure has been found useful: The decibel value is computed at the first break point ($\omega = 1/T_1$). If $|\theta_o/K\epsilon|$ (K being the gain term) is being plotted and the low-frequency asymptote has a slope of 6 db/octave, the required value is $-20 \log_{10} (1/T_1)$. If the asymptote preceding the next break point ($\omega = 1/T_2$) has a slope of $6m$ db/octave, the decibel value at this break point is computed by subtracting $20 \log_{10} (T_1/T_2)^m$ from the decibel at the previous break point. The decibel values at the other break points are similarly computed.

A log-log duplex vector slide rule is useful for calculation of the decibel magnitude or phase contributed by any of the $(Tp + 1)$-terms and of the departure of the asymptotic plot from the actual curve.

In calculating the magnitude $\sqrt{\omega^2T^2 + 1}$, use is made of the relation $1/\tanh \mu = \sqrt{1 + 1/\sinh^2 \mu}$, with $\sqrt{\omega^2T^2 + 1} = 1/\tanh \mu$ and

$$\omega T = \frac{1}{\sinh \mu}.$$

In detail, the procedure involves

1. Computation of $1/\omega T$.
2. Determination of $\mu = \sinh^{-1} (1/\omega T)$.
3. Determination of $\tanh \mu$.
4. Computation of $1/\tanh \mu$.
5. Determination of $\log (1/\tanh \mu)$.

By leaving the slide exactly in the mid-position these operations are completed by only two settings of the cursor. To illustrate the method, let $\omega T = 0.5$.

1. Set the cursor to 0.5 on the *CI*-scale and read the value $\mu = 1.442$ on the *Sh*2-scale. (The *Sh*1-scale is used if $\omega T > 1$.)
2. Set the cursor to 1.442 on the *Th*-scale. The figure 1.12 on the *CI*-scale is the magnitude $\sqrt{\omega^2T^2 + 1}$, but 0.05, the log of the magnitude, may be read directly on the *L*-scale by reading this linear scale as if the zero gradation were at its right-hand end and the one gradation at the left end. Mental multiplication by 20 gives 1 db for the contribution of this time constant.

Since the asymptotic plot uses 0 db/octave for a $(Tp + 1)$-term when $\omega T < 1$, the magnitude of 1 db obtained in the example is also that of the departure of the asymptotic plot from the actual curve for $\omega T = 0.5$; and since the departures are symmetrical about $\omega T = 1$, this is also the departure at $\omega T = 2$.

The phase angle is obtained for $\omega T < 1$ by setting the cursor to ωT on the C-scale and reading the angle on the T-scale; for $\omega T > 1$ it is obtained by setting the cursor to ωT on the CI-scale and reading the angle on the T-scale, but using the complement, which is usually given in red numbers on this scale. The ST-scale is used for $\omega T > 10$ or < 0.1.

When two time constants of the transfer function are close together and one is in the numerator and the other in the denominator, the maximum departure of the approximate plot from the actual curve is less than the 3 db resulting from one time constant alone. Figure 4·23 shows both plots for $T_1 = 2T_2$.

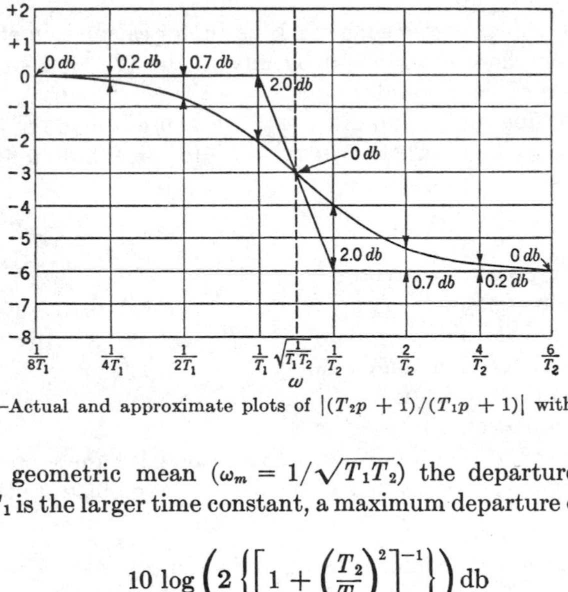

FIG. 4·23.—Actual and approximate plots of $|(T_2p + 1)/(T_1p + 1)|$ with $T_1 = 2T_2$.

At the geometric mean ($\omega_m = 1/\sqrt{T_1T_2}$) the departure is always zero. If T_1 is the larger time constant, a maximum departure of

$$10 \log \left(2\left\{\left[1 + \left(\frac{T_2}{T_1}\right)^2\right]^{-1}\right\}\right) \text{db}$$

occurs both at $\omega = 1/T_1$ and at $\omega = 1/T_2$. The phase angle is zero for small ω, increasing to a maximum of $-\pi/2 + 2 \tan^{-1} \sqrt{T_2/T_1}$ at the geometric mean (T_1 being the larger time constant) and then decreasing to zero for higher frequencies.

When two time constants are close together and both are either in the numerator or in the denominator of the transfer function, the maximum departure of the approximate plot from the actual curve is greater than the 3 db resulting from one time constant alone. If the two time constants are equal, the maximum departure is 6 db at $\omega = 1/T$. If there are n equal time constants, the maximum departure is $3n$ db at $\omega = 1/T$. For two time constants, with $T_1 = 2T_2$, the maximum departure is 4 db. This is shown in Fig. 4·24.

If T_1 is the larger time constant, a maximum departure of

$$10 \log \left\{2\left[1 + \left(\frac{T_2}{T_1}\right)^2\right]\right\} \text{ db}$$

occurs both at $\omega = 1/T_1$ and at $\omega = 1/T_2$. At the geometric mean ($\omega_m = 1/\sqrt{T_1T_2}$), the phase angle is $-90°$; the departure of the approximate curve reaches a local minimum and is $20 \log [1 + (T_2/T_1)]$ db. The phase-angle asymptotes are 0° for low frequencies and $\pm 180°$ at high frequencies for the time constants in the numerator or denominator

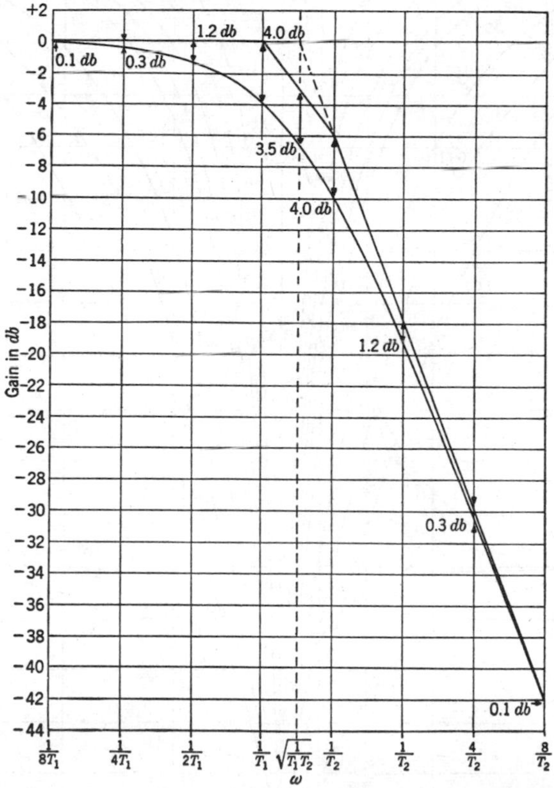

FIG. 4·24.—Actual and approximate plots of $|1/[(T_1p + 1)(T_2p + 1)]|$ with $T_1 = 2T_2$.

respectively. The dotted projection of the 0- and the 12-db asymptotes in Fig. 4·24 indicates that the region above $\omega = 1/T_2$ may be approximated by a 12-db break at $\omega = 1/\sqrt{T_1T_2}$.

When a quadratic factor having a pair of conjugate complex roots appears in the transfer function, the shape of the actual curve is that shown in Fig. 4·8. This plot is for the dimensionless quadratic factor

$$\frac{1}{T^2p^2 + 2\zeta Tp + 1}.$$

Only the cases where $\zeta < 1$ need be considered, since when $\zeta = 1$ the denominator $= (Tp + 1)^2$ and, when $\zeta > 1$ it may be factored into $(T_1p + 1)(T_2p + 1)$.

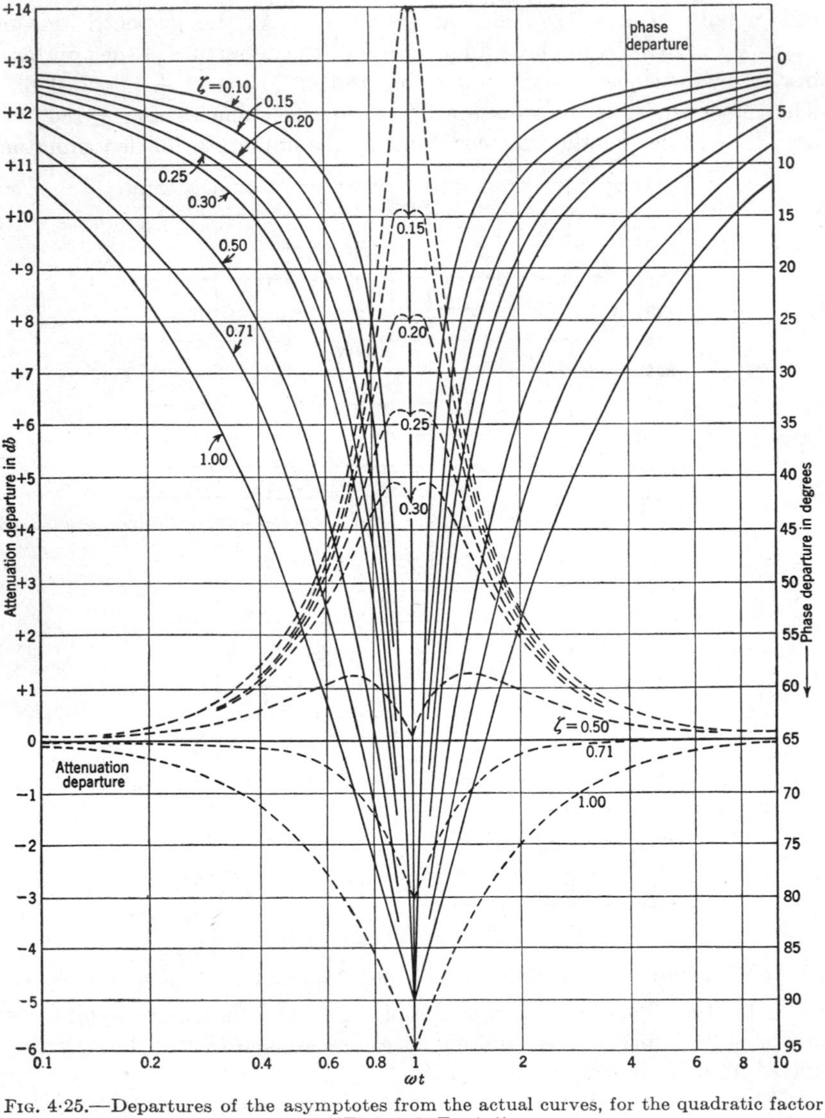

FIG. 4·25.—Departures of the asymptotes from the actual curves, for the quadratic factor $1/(T^2p^2 + 2\zeta Tp + 1)$.

The asymptotic plot is constructed as for $\zeta = 1$, using a 12-db change in slope at $\omega = 1/T$. The phase-angle asymptotes are 0° for low frequencies and $-180°$ for high frequencies with $-90°$ at $\omega = 1/T$. The departures of the asymptotes from the actual curve both for attenuation and phase are given on Fig. 4·25. When the quadratic factor occurs in the numerator of the transfer function, the signs of the departures on this plot are reversed. The departure curves are symmetrical about $\omega = 1/T$. For the frequencies not covered by the plot, below $\omega T = 0.1$ and above $\omega T = 10$, the phase-angle departure may be computed very closely by using a change of a factor of 2 for each change of one octave in frequency.

When nonminimum-phase terms such as $(Tp - 1)$ or

$$(T^2p^2 - 2\zeta Tp + 1)$$

(resulting, for example, from an unstable internal loop) appear in the transfer function, the approximate attenuation plot is constructed in the same way as for $(Tp + 1)$ or $(T^2p^2 + 2\zeta Tp + 1)$, and the departure from the actual curve is also the same. The associated phase angle is, however, not the same as for the minimum-phase terms. (The actual curves can, of course, always be computed directly.) Since these factors are seldom encountered, they are neglected in this discussion.

For construction of the actual curve from the asymptote lines, it is convenient to use the following relations that hold true for all of the factors considered in this section.

1. For both phase angle and attenuation the departure contributed by a single time constant or by a quadratic factor is symmetrical about $\omega = 1/T$ and that from two time constants close together is symmetrical about $\omega = 1/\sqrt{T_1T_2}$ but may be treated as two separate time constants if desired.
2. The phase-angle departure decreases by a factor of approximately 2 for each octave along the ω-scale in the direction away from the maximum departure point. From the data given in the previous discussions it is seen that this approximation does not hold in the region close to the maximum departure point.
3. The attenuation departure decreases by a factor of approximately 4 for each octave along the ω-scale in the direction away from the maximum departure point. Since the attenuation departure decreases at a more rapid rate, this approximation may be used closer to the maximum departure point than that for phase but it is not satisfactory less than 1 octave from this point or 2 octaves if more accuracy is required.

To illustrate an approximate method for computing total phase angles, let the equation for the phase angle be

$$\text{Arg}\,\frac{\theta_0}{\epsilon} = -n\frac{\pi}{2} + \tan^{-1}\omega T_1 + \tan^{-1}\omega T_2 + \tan^{-1}\omega T_3. \tag{103}$$

This may be approximated by

$$\text{Arg}\,\frac{\theta_0}{\epsilon} \approx -n\frac{\pi}{2} + \omega\sum_l T_l + k\frac{\pi}{2} - \frac{1}{\omega}\sum_h \frac{1}{T_h}, \tag{104}$$

where $\sum_l T_l$ includes only the time constants for which $\omega T < 1$, $\sum_h \frac{1}{T_h}$ those with $\omega T > 1$, and k is the number of those in $\Sigma 1/T_h$. For $\omega T = 0.5$ or 2, the error is about 2°; and for $\omega T = 0.25$ or 4, the error is about 0.4°. The maximum error is 12.4° for $\omega T = 1$. The terms for which $0.5 < \omega T < 2$ would ordinarily be handled separately by more accurate methods.

A pair of dividers may be used to facilitate the calculation of the phase-angle and attenuation departure for any frequency, using the asymptotic attenuation plot. Suppose that the attenuation plot consists of 6-db attenuation to $\omega = 1/T_1$, 12 db to $\omega = 1/T_2$, and 24 db for the higher frequencies and that the phase angle is desired at a certain frequency ω_x, lying between $\omega = 1/T_1$ and $\omega = 1/T_2$. The dividers are set to the distance along the ω-axis between $1/T_1$ and ω_x. Then one point of the divider is placed on 1 on the ω-scale, and the value of $\omega_x T_1$ is read where the other point on the divider lies on the ω-scale, $\omega_x T$ being greater than 1 when $1/T$ is less than ω_x and less than 1 when $1/T$ is greater than ω_x. From the value of $\omega_x T$ the phase angle or attenuation departure may then be computed by the methods previously suggested. The same procedure may be used with all the time constants but would not be necessary with those for which $1/T$ differs by several octaves from ω_x, since their contribution is close to the asymptotic value. If the double time constant T_2 in the example is due to a quadratic factor, the angle is obtained by use of Fig. 4·25. The total phase angle is the sum of the angles for the terms in the numerator minus the sum for the denominator terms, with $90n°$ for p^n.

The attenuation diagram for a transfer function may be constructed before determination of the value of the gain term K associated with it. Frequently $|\theta_o/K\epsilon|$ is plotted. At very low frequencies the expression reduces to $|p^n|$ where n is a positive or negative integer. Zero db is located on the scale at the point where the low-frequency asymptote crosses $\omega = 1$ on the frequency scale.

The case where $n = -1$ is frequently encountered. In this case K is the velocity-error coefficient K_v, which may be read off the plot in two ways. On the attenuation diagram the line representing a unit value of $|\theta_o/\epsilon|$ is usually located for optimum phase-angle conditions. Its position on the decibel scale of the $|\theta_o/K\epsilon|$ plot gives the decibel value of

K_v for the gain setting chosen. The value of ω at which the projection of the 6-db/octave low-frequency asymptote crosses the unit line is the value of K_v.

When the low-frequency asymptote has a slope of -12 db/octave, the intersection of its projection with the unit line in the plot of $|\theta_O/K\epsilon|$ occurs at $\omega_c = \sqrt{K_a}$, where K_a is the acceleration-error coefficient. If a 6-db/octave low-frequency asymptote is followed by a long 12-db/octave section due to a $(T_1p + 1)$-term in the denominator $(K_vT_1 \gg 1)$, the projection of the 12-db section may be used in the same way to obtain $K_a \approx \omega_c^2$. Under the same conditions $K_a \approx K_v/T_1$.

The error $\epsilon(t)$ for an input $\theta_I(t)$ can be obtained with sufficient accuracy from the equation

$$\epsilon(t) = C_0\theta_I(t) + \frac{1}{K_v}\frac{d\theta_I}{dt} + \frac{1}{K_a}\frac{d^2\theta_I}{dt^2}, \tag{105}$$

when the frequency components of the input are low enough so that the higher-order terms are negligible. This is usually the case, for example, in a servo loop used for automatic tracking of an airplane.

4·11. Decibel–phase-angle Diagrams and Frequency-response Characteristics.—This section contains a discussion of methods that facilitate

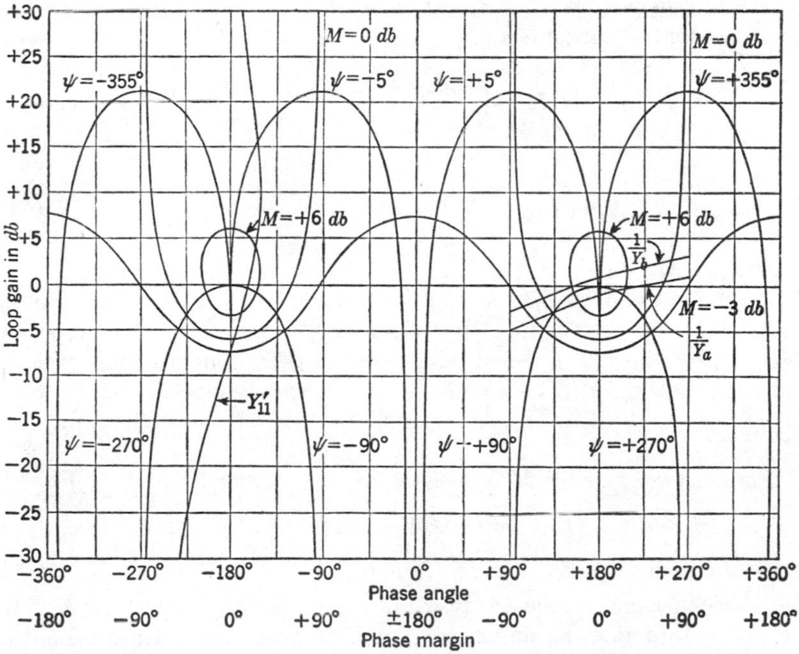

FIG. 4·26.—Constant-amplification and phase-angle contours on the loop-gain phase-angle diagram and illustrative plots of Y'_{11}, $1/Y_a$, and $1/Y_b$.

the determination of control-system constants compatible with good frequency-response characteristics. By means of a study of the transfer function relating the output θ_O to the input θ_I, we shall see how to adjust the servo parameters so that the ratio $M = |\theta_O/\theta_I|$ has a limited departure from the ideal $|\theta_O/\theta_I| = 1.0$ over a suitable bandwidth of operation. To do this it is convenient to plot both M-contours and the loop transfer function θ_O/ϵ on the same diagram. The contours are analogous to the M-circles in the complex plane of the transfer-locus plots.

If $\theta_O/\theta_I = Y_1$ and $\theta_O/\epsilon = Y_{11}$, then

$$Y_1 = \frac{Y_{11}}{1 + Y_{11}}. \tag{106}$$

Contours of constant $M = |Y_1|$ in decibels and contours of constant $\psi = \text{Arg } (Y_1)$ in degrees are plotted on Fig. 4·26,[1] against $|Y_{11}|_{\text{db}}$ on the vertical axis (loop gain in decibels), and Arg (Y_{11}) on the horizontal axis (angle in degrees). Since these plots repeat for each successive 360° section of Arg (Y_{11}) and are symmetrical about the middle of each section, it is possible to use a larger and more accurate plot showing only a 180° region of Arg (Y_{11}), as in Fig. 4·27.

For convenience the angle is also indicated on both figures in terms of the degrees departure from $-180°$ and labeled "phase margin." The equations for the contours are

$$|Y_{11}|_{\text{db}} = 20 \log_{10} \left(\frac{\cos \phi \pm \sqrt{\cos^2 \phi + M^{-2} - 1}}{M^{-2} - 1} \right) \tag{107a}$$

and

$$|Y_{11}|_{\text{db}} = 20 \log_{10} \left[\frac{\sin (\phi - \psi)}{\sin \psi} \right], \tag{107b}$$

where $\phi = \text{Arg } Y_{11}$, $\psi = \text{Arg } Y_1$.

On Fig. 4·27 the M-contours are given from $+12$ to -24 db. Below -24 db, since $|Y_{11}| \ll 1$, Eq. (106) yields $|Y_1| \approx |Y_{11}|$. At the same time Arg $(Y_1) \approx$ Arg (Y_{11}) also; the Arg (Y_1)-contours asymptotically approach the Arg (Y_{11})-lines and are not separately labeled, except those for $-5°$ and $-2°$. As Y_{11} increases, $Y_1 \rightarrow 1$, $|Y_1| \rightarrow 0$ db, and Arg $(Y_1) \rightarrow 0°$.

For each contour for $M > 1$ there are two values,

$$|Y_{11}|_{\text{db}} = -20 \log_{10} (1 \pm M^{-1}),$$

where the phase margin is zero. When $|Y_{11}|_{\text{db}} = -10 \log_{10} (1 - M^{-2})$, the phase margin reaches a maximum and is $\cos^{-1} \sqrt{1 - M^{-2}}$. (In the above formulas the numerical value of M is used rather than the

[1] The examples Y_b, Y_a, and Y'_{11} are discussed later in this section.

decibel value.) For the ψ-contours the highest value of $|Y_{11}|$ is reached where the phase margin is equal to $90° + \psi \pm n\pi$ and in decibels equals $20 \log_{10} |1/\sin \psi|$.

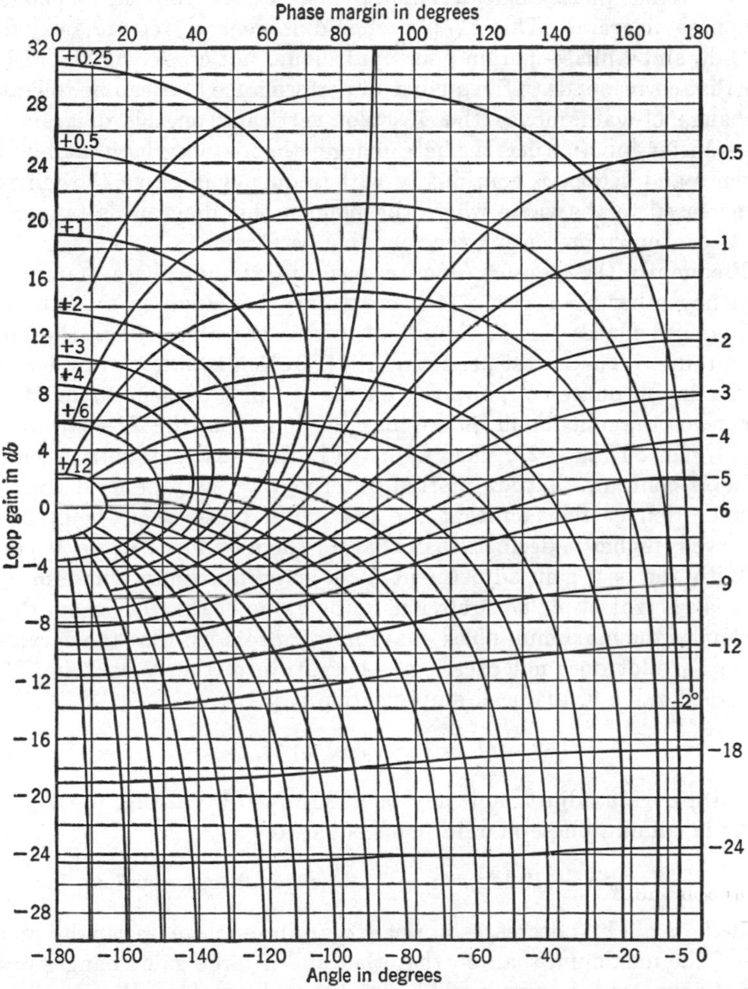

FIG. 4·27.—Constant-phase-angle and constant-amplification contours on the decibel–phase-angle loop diagram.

It is obviously possible to transfer the M-contours and the ψ-contours from this decibel–phase-angle diagram to the type of decibel–log-frequency graph discussed in Sec. 4·10. Then, after a study of the manner in which the attenuation curve crosses the M-contours, it is possible to alter the gain and, if necessary, the shape of the attenuation plot to obtain a satisfactory frequency-response characteristic. Since a large number of M-curves must be plotted, it is easier (if the designer has available enlarged copies of Fig. 4·27) to plot the transfer locus of Y_{11} on this decibel–phase-angle diagram, by use of data from the attenuation and phase diagram. This Y_{11} plot should, in general, remain away from the 0-db and 0-phase-margin point and should not cross over the M-contour that corresponds to the quality of performance that can be tolerated. A change of gain moves the Y_{11} plot vertically on this diagram. If this transfer function has a phase margin that is very large at low frequencies and decreases continually with frequency increase, the gain may be increased to the value where the plot on this diagram is tangent to the M-contour representing the tolerable performance.

Frequently the transfer function has a maximum phase margin at a frequency other than zero. It is customary to design so that the gain that is used places this in the region where the plot crosses the larger M-contours. The lowest peak amplitude in $|Y_1|$ is obtained by locating the maximum phase-margin point on the Y_{11} plot tangent to an M-contour near the maximum phase-margin point on the M-contour. If the Y_{11} plot on Fig. 4·27, when adjusted in this way, passes between two of the M-contours that are plotted, interpolation may be used with due consideration of the fact that the maximum phase-angle point on an M-curve is higher in decibels than that for the next lower value M-curve.

With the best gain adjustment for a given maximum phase-margin, the peak height of $|\theta_O/\theta_I|$ is obviously the value of the M-contour that is tangent to the maximum phase-margin line, provided that the curvature of the Y_{11} plot does not exceed the curvature of the M-contour. The numerical value of the peak amplification is then

$$M = (1 - \cos^2 \phi)^{-1/2}. \tag{108}$$

The proper gain adjustment may be determined by setting the Y_{11} gain at the maximum phase-margin point equal to

$$|Y_{11}|_{\text{db}} = -10 \log_{10} (1 - M^{-2}) = -10 \log_{10} (\cos^2 \phi). \tag{109}$$

If the Arg (Y_{11}) decreases in phase margin much more rapidly on one side of the maximum than on the other and if large gain changes in the loop are expected, a gain should be used that differs from the adjustment mentioned above in that it provides equal performance (that is, the same maximum M is reached) at both extremes of the gain variation.

In order to illustrate the details of these methods and interpretation of the results, two examples will be given, using the loop transfer functions

$$Y_{11} = \frac{K(T_1p + 1)}{p^2(T_2p + 1)} \tag{110a}$$

and

$$Y'_{11} = \frac{K(T_1p + 1)}{p^2(T_2p + 1)^2}, \tag{110b}$$

with $T_1 = \frac{1}{10}$ sec and $T_2 = \frac{1}{60}$ sec.

The attenuation and phase diagrams for these transfer functions are given in Fig. 4·28. The asymptotes from which the actual attenuation curves were plotted by the departure method (see Sec. 4·10) are shown dotted. The curve for $M = +3$ db for Y_{11} [that is, plotted against Arg (Y_{11})] illustrates the use of these curves on this type of diagram. It has

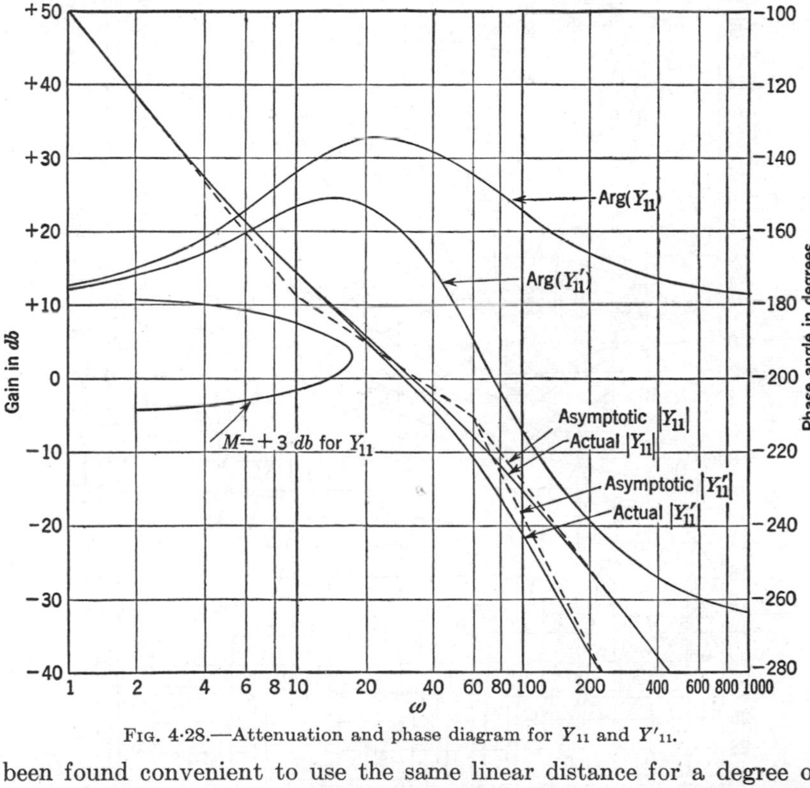

FIG. 4·28.—Attenuation and phase diagram for Y_{11} and Y'_{11}.

been found convenient to use the same linear distance for a degree of angle on this attenuation and phase diagram as on the decibel–phase-angle diagram of Fig. 4·27. A pair of dividers can then be used in transferring either M-curves to the decibel–log-frequency diagram or a transfer locus to the decibel–phase-angle diagram. In either case the dividers are set to the distance corresponding to the phase margin at ω for a given value of decibels on the attenuation diagram and then used to mark off that distance along the corresponding decibel line on the decibel–phase-angle diagram.

Figure 4·29 shows plots of Y_{11} and Y'_{11} on the decibel–phase-angle diagram. The ω-parameter values are marked along these plots.

The decibel scale on the attenuation plot corresponds to a correct gain setting for Y_{11} but is not correct for Y'_{11}. A third curve shows that a

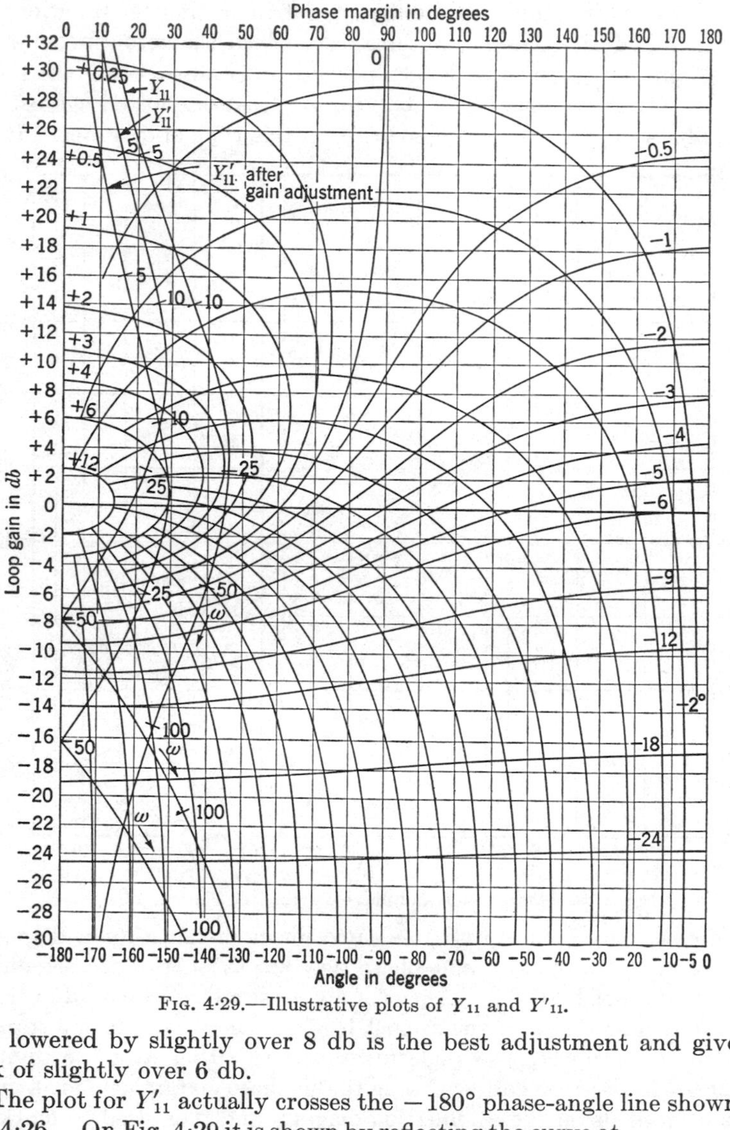

FIG. 4·29.—Illustrative plots of Y_{11} and Y'_{11}.

gain lowered by slightly over 8 db is the best adjustment and gives a peak of slightly over 6 db.

The plot for Y'_{11} actually crosses the $-180°$ phase-angle line shown on Fig. 4·26. On Fig. 4·29 it is shown by reflecting the curve at

$$\text{Arg } (Y'_{11}) = -180°$$

and plotting back across the same set of contours, with $-170°$ for $-190°$, $-150°$ for $-210°$, and so on. The phase margin is then the negative of that read on the diagram, but the decibel scale applies unchanged.

The plots on the decibel–phase-angle diagram approach an asymptote of an integral multiple of 90° for both low and high decibel values. The plot of Y'_{11} approaches $-180°$ at high decibel values and $-270°$ at low decibel values. In constructing the plot, use may be made of the approximate rate of approach, which is such that the departure from a $90n°$ asymptote changes by a factor of 2 for a change of $6n$ db.

It is a general rule that a fairly long 6-db/octave section between two long 12-db/octave sections on the attenuation plot will provide a region of positive phase margin that varies in extent directly with the length of the 6-db/octave section. In the case of Y_{11} this section is about 15 db long; best servo performance results when the unity gain line crosses the 6-db/octave section about a third of its length from its high-frequency end. Since this type of plot is frequently obtained from lead or derivative equalization, a further discussion of it is given in Sec. 4·15, where Table 4·1 gives the maximum phase-angle contribution toward positive phase margin for various lengths of the 6-db/octave section.

When the 6-db/octave section is followed by an 18-db/octave section, the phase margin is less than with the 12-db/octave section, and the gain must be lowered, as is illustrated in the case of Y'_{11}. If desired, the values of M from the diagram can be plotted against ω, as is done in Sec. 4·15, but usually the shape of this plot can be seen with sufficient detail directly from the decibel–phase-angle diagram. With a knowledge from past experience of the attenuation and form of phase diagram required for satisfactory performance, it is possible to omit also the decibel–phase-angle plot in the early design stages. This plot is generally made only after the gain has been determined roughly by inspection of the attenuation and phase diagram.

The decibel–phase-angle diagram may be used for functions other than those of the type of Eq. (106) by plotting and/or reading reciprocal values. As examples, we may take

$$\frac{\epsilon}{\theta_I} = \frac{1}{1 + \dfrac{\theta_O}{\epsilon}} = \frac{\dfrac{\epsilon}{\theta_O}}{1 + \dfrac{\epsilon}{\theta_O}} \tag{111}$$

or

$$1 + Y_a = \left(\frac{\dfrac{1}{Y_a}}{1 + \dfrac{1}{Y_a}}\right)^{-1}. \tag{112}$$

The reciprocal functions are handled by changing the signs of both the decibel and phase angle of the function or changing the signs (on the decibel–phase-angle diagram) of the scales that apply. On Fig. 4·26 the plot of $1/Y_a$ represents this quantity with the signs on the loop-gain and phase-angle scales as labeled. If the signs of these two scales are reversed, the plot is that for Y_a. To read $1 + Y_a$ from the M- and ψ-contours, the signs on the scales must be reversed.

It is of interest to study the case where the plot on the decibel–phase-margin diagram passes close to or through a 0-db and 0-phase-margin point. The relation of Eq. (112) is used as an example, with the plots of $1/Y_a$ and $1/Y_b$ on Fig. 4·26 representing a transfer locus for two different gain adjustments. With $|Y_a|$ increasing, Arg $(1 + Y_a)$ changes rapidly from $-270°$ to $-90°$ and, if the gain of Y_a is reduced by 1 db, will make the change instantaneously, since the new plot passes through the $-180°$ phase angle and 0-db point. This is seen to be the actual case by inspection of Fig. 4·30. Further reduction of the gain by 1 db leads to the plot of $1/Y_b$ in Fig. 4·26. Here Arg $(1 + Y_b)$ appears to jump from $-360°$ to $0°$ at the 0-phase-margin point. This does not actually happen, as may be seen from Fig. 4·30.

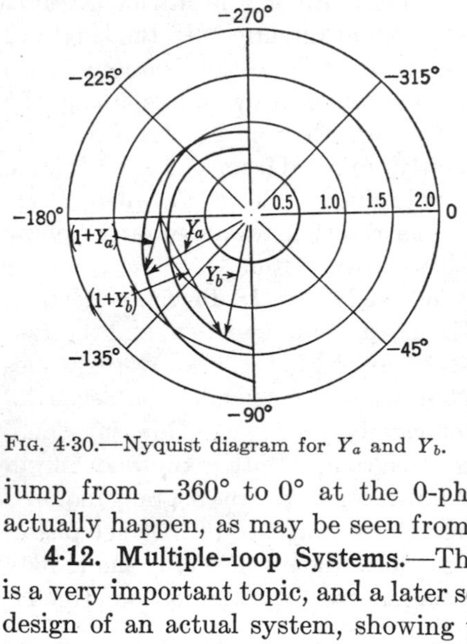

FIG. 4·30.—Nyquist diagram for Y_a and Y_b.

4·12. Multiple-loop Systems.—The design of multiple-loop systems is a very important topic, and a later section will carry through a detailed design of an actual system, showing the advantages of equalization by means of subsidiary loops. In this section we shall consider a simple double-loop system in order to introduce the techniques that will be needed in a later analysis and in order to illustrate further the ideas developed in the preceding sections. The equations for a general two-loop system are given in Sec. 4·1, Eqs. (13) to (15), and the schematic diagram is given in Fig. 4·2. As a simple example let us take

$$Y_{11}^0 = \frac{K_v T}{Tp(Tp + 1)} \tag{113}$$

and

$$Y_{22} = \frac{K_{22}T^3p^3}{(Tp + 1)^3(0.25Tp + 1)}. \tag{114}$$

The transfer function of the principal loop when the subsidiary loop is

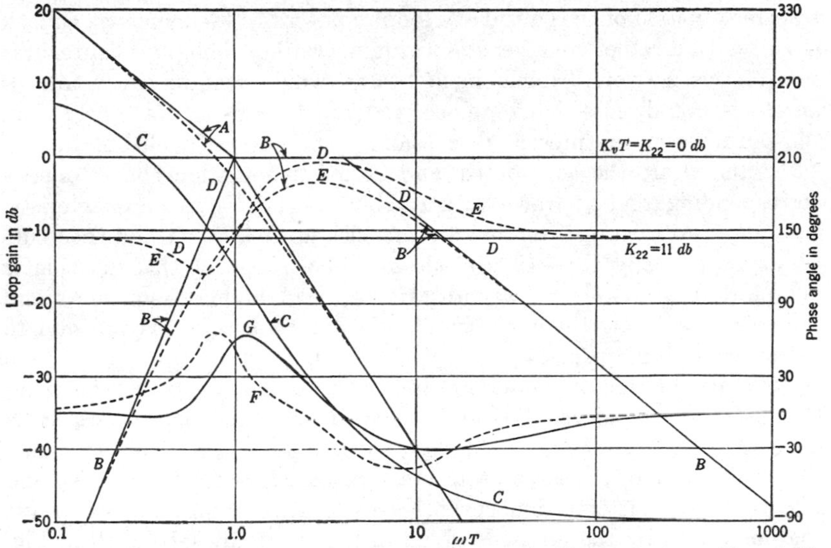

FIG. 4·31*a*.—Phase and attenuation characteristics for a double-loop system with a stable subsidiary loop.

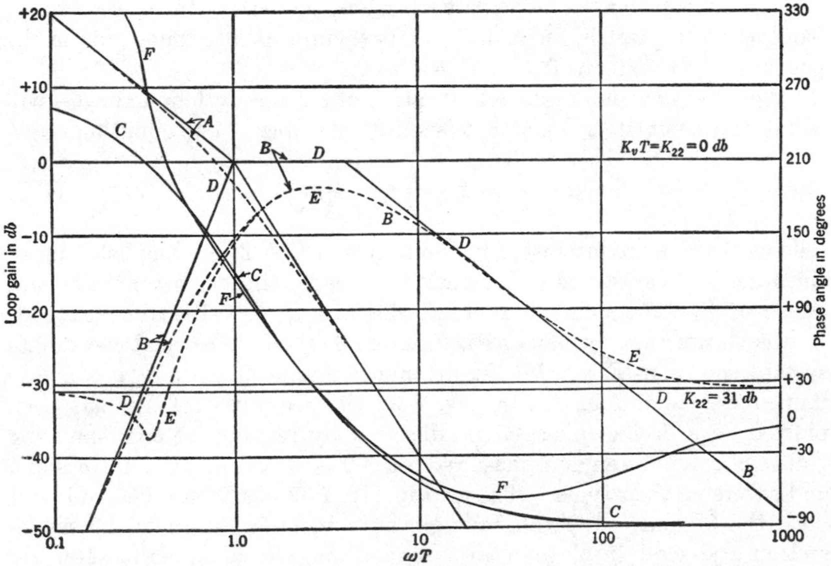

FIG. 4·31*b*.—Phase and attenuation characteristics for a double-loop system with an unstable subsidiary loop.

open, Y_{11}^0, represents a simple amplifier and motor combination, and the transfer function of the subsidiary loop represents a tachometer feedback circuit with a rather complex equalizing network. The physical realization of this network (which, incidentally, would require active impedances) is not discussed here, since it would take us too far afield from the purposes of the present discussion. The curves labeled A in Fig. 4·31a and b are the asymptotic and actual attenuation characteristics corresponding to Y_{11}^0, drawn with $K_vT = 1$. This simple characteristic falls at -6 db/octave from low frequencies up to $\omega T = 1$ and then cuts off asymptotically to -12 db/octave. The phase of this function is not plotted but is clearly asymptotic to $-90°$ at low frequencies and changes rapidly in the vicinity of $\omega T = 1$ to become asymptotic to $-180°$ at high frequencies.

The attenuation characteristic for the subsidiary-loop transfer function is proportional to T^3p^3 at low frequencies and hence rises at 18 db/octave toward $\omega T = 1$. At high frequencies Y_{22} cuts off at a rate of -6 db/octave, the asymptote starting at $\omega T = 4$. This curve and also the actual attenuation curve, easily plotted from the asymptotic characteristics by the methods given in Sec. 4·10, are labeled B in Fig. 4·31a and b. The phase of Y_{22}, which again is easily computed using the methods already referred to, is labeled C in the same figure. The subsidiary-loop transmission characteristics, we see, are those of a typical bandpass filter, which, for $K_{22} = 1$, has asymptotically unity gain in the pass band that extends from $\omega T = 1$ to $\omega T = 4$.

We must now determine what values of subsidiary-loop gain K_{22} will result in a complete system that is suitably stable. The equation

$$\frac{\theta_O}{\epsilon} = Y_{11} = \frac{Y_{11}^0}{1 + Y_{22}} \tag{115}$$

tells us that we are interested in the function $1 + Y_{22}$. The behavior of this function is most easily investigated by replotting the attenuation and phase of Y_{22} on a gain–phase-angle diagram as described in Sec. 4·11. It was shown that by plotting a function $1/F$ on the special coordinate system shown in Fig. 4·26, the attenuation and phase of $1/(1 + F)$ are immediately determined. In Fig. 4·32 the reciprocal of Y_{22} has been plotted on a decibel–phase-angle diagram by reading off corresponding values of attenuation and phase from the Y_{22} curves in Figs. 4·31a and b and reversing their signs. The grid in Fig. 4·32 has been reflected about both the 0° and $-180°$ phase-angle lines in order to make the single-section grid serve in place of an extended diagram of the kind shown in Fig. 4·26. The upper curve in Fig. 4·32 is for $K_{22} = 11$ db, while the lower curve is for $K_{22} = 31$ db, a 20-db increase in loop gain as compared with the upper curve. The two curves are, of course, identical in shape.

As mentioned in Sec. 4·11, caution must be exercised when reading values of the magnitude and phase of $(1 + Y_{22})^{-1}$ from the labeled curves in any such plot in which the extreme phase change in Y_{22} is greater than

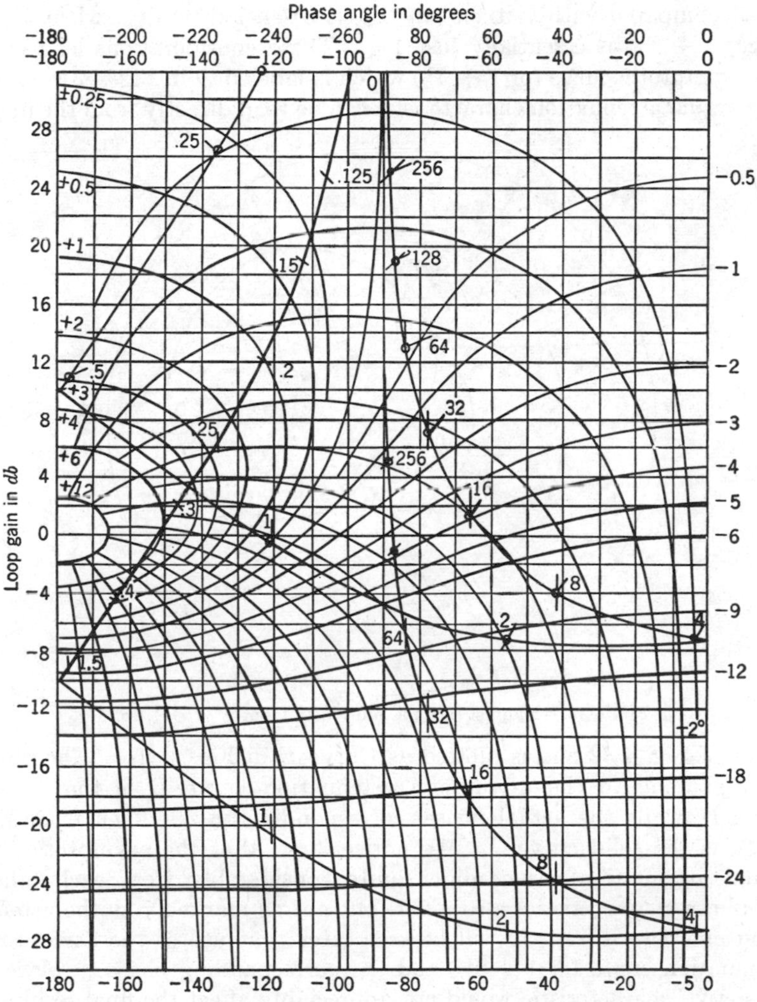

FIG. 4·32.—Gain—phase-angle diagram for subsidiary loop.

180°. The observation that the phase of $1 + Y_{22}$ must be continuous as long as $1 + Y_{22}$ is continuous is usually sufficient to resolve any question as to what phase should be assigned any given value of $1 + Y_{22}$. A crude sketch of the Nyquist diagram for Y_{22} can always be made with no difficulty, either by inspection of Y_{22} itself or from the Y_{22} curves of

Fig. 4·31*a* and *b*; such a diagram will always show clearly the behavior of the phase of $1 + Y_{22}$. The Nyquist diagram for Y_{22}, drawn for $K_{22} = 11$ db, is given in Fig. 4·33. Let us now consider the asymptotic behavior of $1 + Y_{22}$ when the gain K_{22} is set at a level of 11 db. When Y_{22} is small compared with 1, then $1 + Y_{22}$ is essentially unity; when Y_{22} is large, $1 + Y_{22}$ is essentially just Y_{22}. These considerations lead us to the asymptotic curve for $1 + Y_{22}$ which is labeled D in Fig. 4·31*a* and *b*. The actual attenuation characteristic can be read directly from the upper

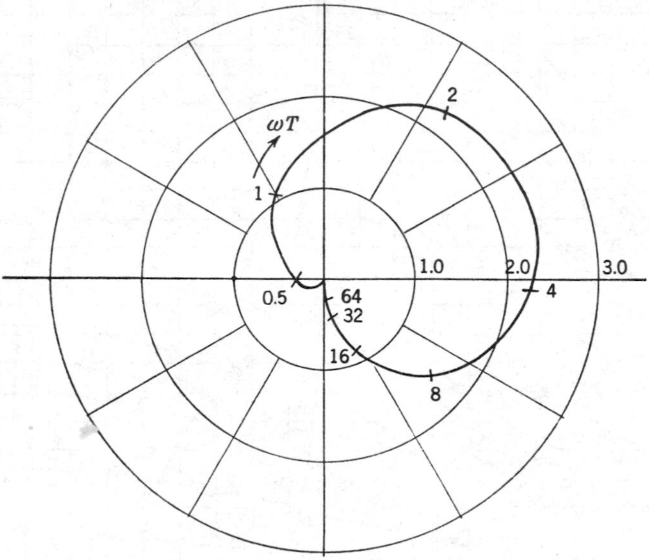

FIG. 4·33.—Nyquist plot for subsidiary loop, $K_{22} = 11$ db.

curve of Fig. 4·32 and is plotted as Curve E in Fig. 4·31*a*. The phase corresponding to the asymptotic attenuation curve D is the dashed curve F, while the actual phase, corresponding to E (taken from Fig. 4·32), is the solid curve G. We notice, first, that the asymptotic and actual attenuation curves differ quite considerably from each other; the phase characteristics also differ, but not as markedly as the attenuation characteristics. It will be seen later that use of the asymptotic attenuation curve for $1 + Y_{22}$ and the corresponding phase in place of the actual characteristic would not appreciably affect the final results of the analysis.

Inspection of the form of Y_{22} shows that it has no poles in the right half of the p-plane, and, therefore, neither does $1 + Y_{22}$. Application of the usual Nyquist test to the transfer locus of Fig. 4·33 then shows that $1 + Y_{22}$ has no zeros or poles in the right half plane; we conclude that the subsidiary loop is stable and, furthermore, that the usual simple form of the Nyquist criterion will suffice to test the stability of the over-all system.

From Eq. (115) we see that the attenuation characteristic for the over-all loop transfer function Y_{11} is found simply by subtracting the attenuation (in decibels) and phase of $1 + Y_{22}$ from the attenuation and phase of Y_{11}^0. The results of this procedure are shown in Fig. 4·34, where the Curves A are the asymptotic and actual characteristics for the case $K_{22} = 11$ db, $K_vT = 0$ db. The actual characteristic was computed using the Curve E from Fig. 4·31a, not directly from the asymptote,

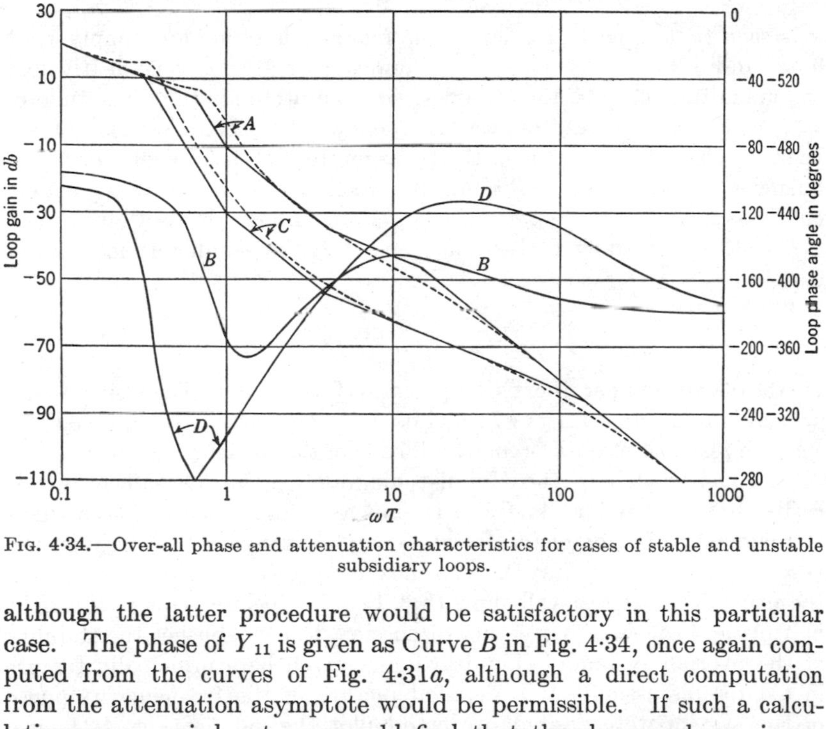

FIG. 4·34.—Over-all phase and attenuation characteristics for cases of stable and unstable subsidiary loops.

although the latter procedure would be satisfactory in this particular case. The phase of Y_{11} is given as Curve B in Fig. 4·34, once again computed from the curves of Fig. 4·31a, although a direct computation from the attenuation asymptote would be permissible. If such a calculation were carried out, we would find that the phase-angle maximum that occurs near $\omega T = 10$ on Curve B would be shifted to $\omega T = 8$ and would be about $-132°$ instead of $-145°$. It will be seen that this change would have only a slight effect on the value of loop gain K_v that is to be selected. Examination of the over-all characteristics shows that if we select K_vT equal to 44 db, then feedback cutoff (the point at which the attenuation characteristic crosses the 0-db line) will occur approximately in the center of a -6-db/octave slope and near the phase-angle maximum of $-145°$, corresponding to a phase margin of $+45°$. According to the discussion given in the preceding section this represents a satisfactory adjustment of gain, and we see that we can obtain a dimensionless velocity-error constant (K_vT) of 44 db, or 158, a great improvement over the value of 1 or 2 obtainable with the simple unequalized single-loop system. A good approximation to the speed of response is easily obtained by forming the asymptotic curve for the magnitude of θ_O/θ_I. From the equation

$$\frac{\theta_O}{\theta_I} = \frac{\dfrac{\theta_O}{\epsilon}}{1 + \dfrac{\theta_O}{\epsilon}} \tag{116}$$

it is seen that when θ_O/ϵ is large, the magnitude of θ_O/θ_I is simply 1, or 0 db, and when θ_O/ϵ is small, the magnitude of θ_O/θ_I is very nearly just the magnitude of θ_O/ϵ; thus the desired asymptote for the magnitude of θ_O/θ_I is flat (zero slope) from zero frequency out to the frequency of feedback cutoff and is identical with the asymptote of θ_O/ϵ at all higher frequencies. Having set $K_vT = 44$ db, we find that the -12-db/octave cutoff asymptote of the θ_O/θ_I characteristic intersects the 0-db line at $\omega_cT = 13$. According to Eq. (43), Sec. 4·2, the buildup time is given closely by

$$\tau_b = \frac{1}{2f_c} = \frac{\pi}{\omega_c} = \frac{\pi}{13}T. \tag{117}$$

In the same manner the buildup time of the unequalized single-loop system is found to be $\tau_b = \pi T$. Thus we have materially improved the speed of response of the system by addition of the subsidiary loop.

A rough sketch of the Nyquist diagram of the over-all system is easily drawn from Fig. 4·34 and is shown in Fig. 4·35*a*. If this curve is imagined to be completed for the complete range of real frequencies, $-\infty$ to $+\infty$, by adding the complex conjugate of the curve shown, the usual Nyquist test will show that $1 + Y_{11}$ has no zeros in the right half plane; in view of our earlier discussion, this establishes the stability of the over-all system. This drawing is given here principally for use in a later discussion. If a detailed picture of the frequency response of the system were desired, we could plot the data of Fig. 4·34 on a gain–phase-angle diagram. This is not actually necessary, however, since we have already obtained the asymptotic θ_O/θ_I curves, and we know that with the system adjusted to give a 45° phase margin in the vicinity of feedback cutoff, the resonance curve will have a peak of certainly not more than 6 db.

We now consider the effects on the over-all system of changes in value of the subsidiary loop gain K_{22}. Referring to Fig. 4·32, we see that increasing K_{22} over 11 db simply slides the upper curve down on the diagram. In particular, if K_{22} is increased to 21 db, the curve passes through the singular point of the diagram, corresponding to an infinite attenuation value of $1 + Y_{22}$. This situation corresponds to increasing the radial scale factor in Fig. 4·33 until the transfer locus passes exactly through the critical point $-1 + j0$. If K_{22} is increased still more, say to 31 db, we arrive at the lower curve in Fig. 4·32, and we find the behavior of $1 + Y_{22}$ for this case in the same way that we determined the behavior of $1 + Y_{22}$ with $K_{22} = 11$ db. The solid curve D in Fig. 4·31b is the asymptotic behavior of the attenuation of $1 + Y_{22}$ with $K_{22} = 31$ db, and the dashed curve E is the actual attenuation char-

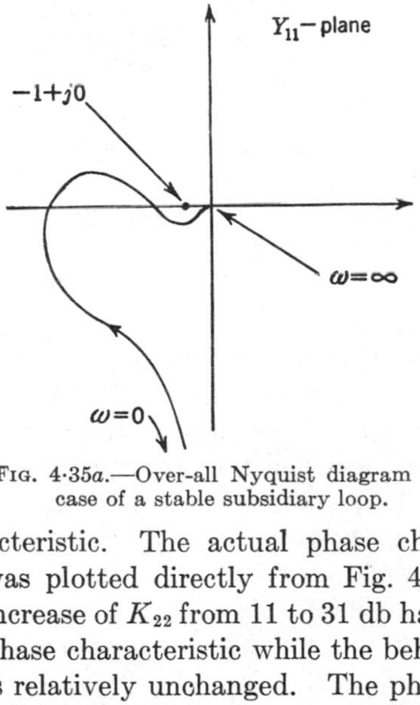

FIG. 4·35a.—Over-all Nyquist diagram for case of a stable subsidiary loop.

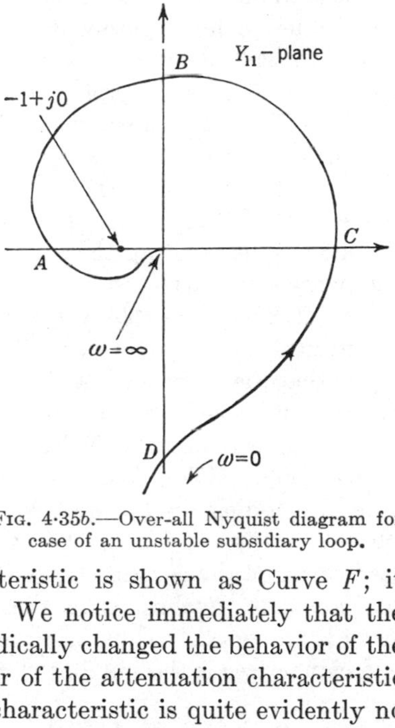

FIG. 4·35b.—Over-all Nyquist diagram for case of an unstable subsidiary loop.

acteristic. The actual phase characteristic is shown as Curve F; it was plotted directly from Fig. 4·32. We notice immediately that the increase of K_{22} from 11 to 31 db has radically changed the behavior of the phase characteristic while the behavior of the attenuation characteristic is relatively unchanged. The phase characteristic is quite evidently no longer the minimum phase shift associated with the given attenuation characteristic. This situation is further clarified by consideration of the Nyquist diagram of Y_{22} (Fig. 4·33). The diagram as drawn is for $K_{22} = 11$ db; by allowing the tip of the vector $1 + Y_{22}$, drawn from the point $-1 + j0$ to the curve, to traverse the curve as ω varies from 0 to ∞, we easily verify the general behavior of the phase characteristic G in Fig. 4·31a. Increasing K_{22} to 31 db changes the scale factor in Fig. 4·33 so that the critical point $-1 + j0$ is enclosed by the transfer locus; we see that the behavior of the phase of the vector $1 + Y_{22}$ is indeed changed and is as given by Curve F in Fig. 4·31b. We now apply the Nyquist stability criterion to this subsidiary loop. We easily see that the function $1 + Y_{22}$ has no poles in the right half plane. The curve of Fig. 4·33 (with the changed radial scale factor) is completed by adding the complex conjugate curve, corresponding to frequencies from $-\infty$ to 0, and the Nyquist test is applied. The vector $1 + Y_{22}$ undergoes two complete revolutions in the clockwise sense as the tip of the vector traces the curve from $\omega = -\infty$ to $\omega = +\infty$; we conclude that $1 + Y_{22}$ has two zeros in the right half of the p-plane, or, in other words, that the subsidiary loop is unstable. This brings out clearly the nonminimum-phase character of $1 + Y_{22}$ when K_{22} is large and shows why its phase characteristic is so radically altered when K_{22} is increased.

Now let us investigate what happens to the over-all system when the gain of the subsidiary loop is increased enough to make it unstable. At first sight, at least, it appears intuitively obvious that the complete system will become unstable, but closer analysis will show that this is another of many situations in which intuition fails one. The attenuation and phase functions for the over-all systems are obtained from the curves of Fig. 4·31*b* in the same way as in the earlier case and are shown in Fig. 4·34, C designating the attenuation curves and D the phase curve. The phase-shift curve has been reflected about the $-280°$ line, since the phase shift exceeds $-450°$ at low frequencies and is asymptotic to $-450°$ at extremely low frequencies. Selecting a value of K_v equal to 86 db, we see that the phase shift at feedback cutoff will be $-130°$, or the phase margin will be 50°. So far, we apparently have a satisfactory system. Now let us examine the Nyquist diagram, a rough sketch of which is given in Fig. 4·35*b*. Again, we must imagine this diagram to be completed by adding the complex conjugate curve and a large semicircle in the right half plane joining the two zero frequency portions of the curve. Application of the Nyquist test shows that the vector $1 + Y_{11}$ undergoes two complete revolutions in the counterclockwise sense as the entire curve is traversed. Thus, the number of poles of $1 + Y_{11}$ in the right half plane exceeds the number of zeros in that region by two. Since

$$1 + Y_{11} = 1 + \frac{Y_{11}^0}{1 + Y_{22}} \tag{118}$$

and an earlier Nyquist test of the subsidiary loop has disclosed two zeros of $1 + Y_{22}$ in the right half plane, we see that $1 + Y_{11}$ has two poles in this region; it follows that $1 + Y_{11}$ has no zeros in the critical region and that the over-all system is stable. The selected gain level of 86 db gives a velocity-error constant of approximately $20{,}000T^{-1}$ and a buildup time of $\tau_b = (\pi/140)T$, representing substantial improvements in system performance.

The reader should appreciate that a designer with a certain background of experience with these methods could carry through the above design procedure almost completely, using only the asymptotic attenuation characteristics that can be constructed in a matter of minutes. The detailed curves have been presented in an effort to supply the reader with some of the requisite insight into the design procedure.

4·13. Other Types of Transfer Loci.—Occasionally there arise special problems in servo design that are best treated by procedures other than those already presented. The vast majority of problems, however, are readily handled using the "standard" techniques. The ingenious designer will continue to develop new procedures ad infinitum to suit his own out-of-the-ordinary problems, and it would be futile to attempt to give any comprehensive discussion here of all the special methods that have been devised. A few, however, are perhaps worth mentioning.

Several writers[1] have proposed the use of the reciprocal of the usual Nyquist diagram for the treatment of multiple-loop systems and systems in which there are elements in the feedback path or paths such that a true error signal does not actually exist in the system. The advantage of this reciprocal diagram in discussing multiple-loop systems is readily appreciated by writing the equation for ϵ/θ_O for a double-loop system. Using the notation of Sec. 4·1, we have

$$\frac{\epsilon}{\theta_O} = \frac{1}{Y_{11}^0} + \frac{Y_{22}}{Y_{11}^0}. \tag{119}$$

Thus the ϵ/θ_O diagram can be constructed by a simple vector addition of two preliminary diagrams rather than by a process of "multiplying" two diagrams together, as with the usual Nyquist diagram. The interested reader will find ample discussion of these ideas in the references already cited.

The drawing of Nyquist diagrams is often complicated by the extreme range of values of the radial coordinate that must be plotted. The example in the previous section serves as a good illustration of this difficulty. Referring to Fig. 4·35*b*, a simple calculation will show that if the sketch were actually drawn to scale, the following values of radius would have to be plotted:

At the point A, r = approximately 100.
At the point B, r = approximately 5000.
At the point C, r = approximately 115,000.
At the point D, r = approximately 150,000.
At feedback cutoff, $r = 1$.

The obvious difficulty is usually surmounted by plotting various portions of the curve with different scale factors. This is a satisfactory solution,

[1] H. T. Marcy, "Parallel Circuits in Servomechanisms," *Trans. AIEE*, **65,** 521 (1946), H. Harris, Jr., "The Frequency Response of Automatic Control Systems," *Trans. AIEE*, **65,** 539 (1946).

especially since one is usually interested in the detailed shape of the locus only in the vicinity of the feedback cutoff frequency. A detailed drawing can be made of this portion of the locus, while crude sketches of the remaining portion will suffice. Some workers, however, prefer to use a logarithmic radial scale, effectively giving a polar form of the decibel–phase-angle diagram already discussed in this chapter.

Diagrams similar to Nyquist diagrams can also be used in the treatment of servo problems involving pulsed or discontinuous data. These problems are discussed in Chap. 5.

EQUALIZATION OF SERVO LOOPS

4·14. General Discussion of Equalization.—Equalization circuits and networks are employed in servo circuits in order to obtain a desired behavior for the complete system. In the usual design some of the parts of the system are selected with an eye to availability, cost, ease of maintenance, or other reasons. For example, a synchro data transmission is quite often specified because the completed system may have to tie into a shipboard fire-control system where the synchro system has already been standardized. The power-supply frequency is often specified as, for example, 60 cps. If in addition the use of 1- and 36-speed ordnance synchros is specified, the error signal will consist of a 60-cycle voltage with an error gain for small errors of 1 volt per degree on the 36-speed shaft or 36 volts per degree on the 1-speed shaft. Other considerations may have dictated the choice of an amplidyne and d-c motor as the power drive element. This last choice will then require a servoamplifier capable of accepting a 60-cycle error signal and delivering a d-c current to the control field of the amplidyne; this demands the use of a phase-sensitive detector in the servoamplifier.

The pertinent constants presented to the servo designer will then be approximately the following:

1. Combined motor-amplidyne time constant, 0.25 sec $= T_m$.
2. Effective time constant of the phase-sensitive detector, 0.02 sec $= T_r$.
3. Amplidyne quadrature-field time constant, 0.02 sec $= T_q$.

The loop transfer function with a flat frequency-response amplifier may be written

$$\frac{\theta_O}{\epsilon} = \frac{K_v}{p(T_m p + 1)(T_r p + 1)(T_q p + 1)}, \tag{120}$$

where $K_v = \dfrac{K_\epsilon K_A K_a K_m}{N}$ = velocity-error constant, deg/sec per deg,

K_ϵ = error-measuring element sensitivity, volts/deg,

K_A = amplifier gain, ma/volt,

K_a = amplidyne open-circuit gain, volts/ma,
K_m = motor speed-voltage ratio, deg/sec per volt,
$1/N$ = motor-load gear ratio, deg/deg.

This transfer function has a slope of −6 db/octave from zero to $\omega = 1/T_m$ and −12 db/octave to $\omega = 1/T_r = 1/T_q$ and then decreases at 24 db/octave. It has a 180° lag and thus zero phase margin at

$$\omega \approx \frac{2.5}{T_m} = 1.6 \text{ cps}.$$

A value of $K_v \approx 6.25/T_m = 25 \text{ sec}^{-1}$ will make the system unstable; a value of $K_v = 0.75/T_m = 3 \text{ sec}^{-1}$ is required in order that the phase margin be 45° at the feedback-cutoff frequency $\omega_c = 0.75/T_m = 0.48$ cps. The buildup time will then be approximately $\tau_b = 1/(2f_c) = 1$ sec. This system would have a maximum error of 10° when the input is a 30°-amplitude 6-sec sine wave and would ordinarily not be acceptable.

Hysteresis in the amplidyne magnetic circuit may also cause considerable error in a system with as small a velocity-error constant as the above. An amplidyne may commonly have a hysteresis loop as wide as $\pm E_{ah} = \pm 20$ volts. The resulting hysteresis standoff error, $\epsilon_h = K_m E_{ah}/NK_v$, with $K_m = 85°$ per sec/volt and $N = 300$, is then $\epsilon_h = 2°$.

Three more or less general methods may be used to modify the above system in order to improve its performance at either high or low frequencies.

1. The proportional integral method is applicable when a buildup time and cutoff frequency of the same order of magnitude as that of the simple system are acceptable or desirable. In this method, the loop transfer function is left substantially unchanged for frequencies above one-fourth the frequency of the −6 to −12-db/octave transition (that is, above a point 2 octaves below $1/T_m$) and its magnitude is increased in the lower frequency range.
2. Lead or derivative equalization is used to improve the system performance at all frequencies; in particular, the feedback-cutoff frequency is increased with a corresponding reduction in the buildup time.
3. One or more subsidiary loops may be introduced in order to improve the servo performance. This constitutes a very powerful method of equalization and decreases the effects of variations in some of the elements.

4·15. Lead or Derivative Control.—Lead or derivative equalization is used to raise the feedback-cutoff frequency. It will, in general, increase the velocity-error constant while keeping a satisfactory stability or phase margin in the region of cutoff. The feedback transfer function of the simple servo mentioned in Chap. 1 may be written

$$\frac{\theta_O}{\epsilon} = \frac{K_v}{p} \frac{1}{T_m p + 1}. \tag{121}$$

This transfer function has an asymptotic characteristic of -6 db/octave for $\omega < 1/T_m$ and -12 db/octave for $1/T_m < \omega$. The phase angle is $-135°$ at $\omega = 1/T_m$, decreasing to $-153.5°$ at $\omega = 2/T_m$. For $K_vT_m = 1$ the height of the resonance peak will be $+1.25$ db (1.15 ratio) and the feedback-cutoff frequency will be $\omega_c = 0.78/T_m$. For $K_vT_m = 2(+6 \text{ db})$ the resonance peak will be 3.6 db with $\omega_c = 1.25/T_m$, and for

$$K_vT_m = 4\ (+12 \text{ db})$$

the resonance peak will be $+6.3$ db with $\omega_c = 1.75/T_m$. Thus the usual stability requirement of a resonance peak between $+3$ and $+6$ db would allow a K_v between $2/T_m$ and $4/T_m$. Assuming $T_m = 0.25$ sec, this would correspond to K_v between 8 and 16 sec^{-1}.

Adding either an a-c or d-c proportional-derivative equalizer of the type discussed in Chap. 3 makes the feedback transfer function

$$\frac{\theta_O}{\epsilon} = \frac{K_{v1}}{p} \frac{1}{T_m p + 1} \frac{G_0(T_d p + 1)}{G_0 T_d p + 1}, \tag{122a}$$

$$\frac{\theta_O}{\epsilon} = \frac{K_v}{p} \frac{1}{T_m p + 1} \frac{T_d p + 1}{G_0 T_d p + 1}, \tag{122b}$$

where T_d = derivative time constant,
G_0 = d-c or carrier gain ($G_0 < 1$),
$K_v = K_{v1}G_0$ = velocity-error constant.

The complete study of this transfer function involves the two parameters T_d/T_m and G_0 as well as the velocity-error constant K_v. It will be most convenient to study first the case where $T_d/T_m \ll 1$. With this assumption, Eq. (122) can be approximated as

$$\frac{\theta_O}{\epsilon} \approx \frac{K_v T_m}{(T_m p)^2} \frac{T_d p + 1}{G_0 T_d p + 1}. \tag{123}$$

The first factor in Eq. (123) produces a phase lag of 180° at all frequencies; thus the proportional-derivative equalizer must supply all of the lead required to give the desired phase margin near feedback cutoff. Inspection of the decibel–phase-margin contour diagram (Fig. 4·27) shows that the over-all frequency response is $|\theta_O/\theta_I| = +3$ db and the loop phase margin is $+45°$ where the loop gain is $+3$ db, whereas $|\theta_O/\theta_I| = +6$ db and the loop phase margin is $+30°$ when the loop gain is $+1.3$ db.

The proportional-derivative equalizer has an asymptotic characteristic of $(G_0)_{\text{db}}$ up to $\omega = 1/T_d$, increases at 6 db/octave to $\omega = 1/G_0T_d$, and is then constant at 0 db for higher frequencies. Its phase angle is zero for small ω, increasing to a maximum at the geometric mean of the two above frequencies, $\omega_m = 1/(T_d \sqrt{G_0})$, and then decreasing to zero for higher frequencies. The maximum phase angle is easily shown to be

$$\phi_m = \frac{\pi}{2} - 2 \tan^{-1} \sqrt{G_0}; \tag{124}$$

solving for G_0, we find

$$G_0 = \tan^2 \left(\frac{\pi}{4} - \frac{\phi_m}{2} \right). \tag{125}$$

The gain at the geometric mean frequency is $\sqrt{G_0}$. Table 4.1 gives a few corresponding values of G_0 and ϕ_m. An equalizer with $G_0 = -15.31$

TABLE 4·1.—MAXIMUM PHASE ANGLE FOR PROPORTIONAL-DERIVATIVE EQUALIZER

ϕ_m	75°	60°	45°	30°	15°	7.5°
$(G_0)_{db}$	−35.22	−22.88	−15.310	−9.5400	−4.600	−2.280
$\frac{1}{G_0}$	57.70	13.93	5.827	3.000	1.698	1.300

db will therefore have a resonance peak of +3 db when K_vT_m is adjusted to put the maximum phase margin at a loop gain of +3 db. When this is the case,

$$\frac{K_vT_m}{\left(\dfrac{T_m}{T_d\sqrt{G_0}}\right)^2} \frac{1}{\sqrt{G_0}} = 1.414 = (+3 \text{ db}), \tag{126}$$

or

$$(K_vT_m)_{db} = +3.0 + 2\left(\frac{T_m}{T_d}\right)_{db} - \frac{1}{2}(G_0)_{db}, \tag{127}$$

$$(K_{v1}T_m)_{db} = +3.0 + 2\left(\frac{T_m}{T_d}\right)_{db} - \frac{3}{2}(G_0)_{db}. \tag{128}$$

Figure 4·36 is a decibel–log-frequency plot of this system for $T_m/T_d = 10$. Curve a is the attenuation—log-frequency plot. The lower phase-angle curve c is drawn from the approximate Eq. (123); there is relatively little difference between curve c and the exact phase-angle curve b in regions near the phase-margin maximum for a value of $T_m/T_d = 10$. The main difference is a slightly lower maximum phase margin in the approximate curve. To obtain the desired phase margin of 45° it would suffice to use a lead equalizer with G_0 so chosen that the approximately computed phase margin is $45° - \tan^{-1} T_d \sqrt{G_0}/T_m$ instead of 45°. To evaluate this expression the approximate value $G_0 = -15.31$ db may be used; one finds that the required approximate maximum lead is 42.5°. The correction of G_0 for this small change in maximum phase margin is ordinarily not necessary.

Using Eq. (127), one computes a value of $K_vT_m = +50.7$ db for the velocity-error constant. If $T_m = \frac{1}{4}$ sec, this corresponds to

$$K_v = 340 \text{ sec}^{-1}$$

and $T_d = 0.025$ sec. The notch width (see Sec. 3·14) of this lead equalizer for a-c use is then $40/2\pi = \pm 6.4$ cps. It should be pointed out, however, that a parallel-T lead equalizer used with a 60-cps carrier will yield a lower value of G_0 than is required in this example and will thus

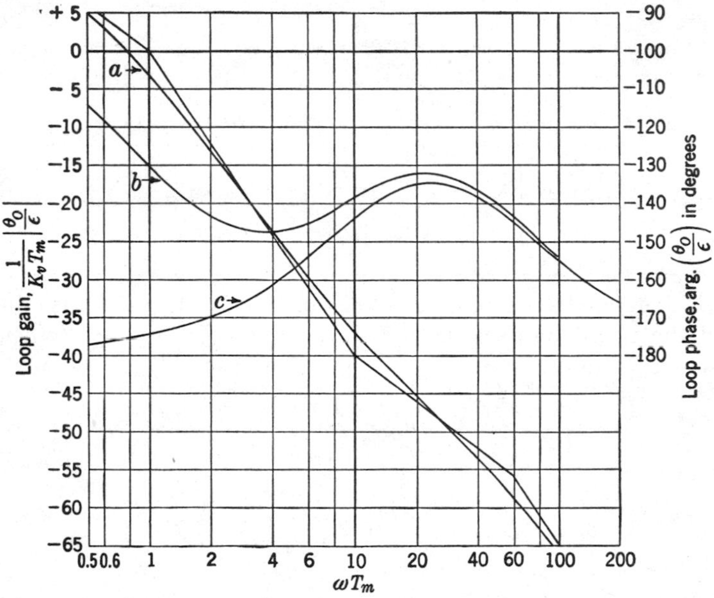

FIG. 4·36.—Lead equalization applied to a single–time-lag servomotor. (a) Attenuation; (b) phase angle; (c) approximate phase angle by Eq. (123).

provide a larger phase margin than is necessary for the +3-db resonance peak.

Figure 4·37 is a decibel–phase-margin diagram for the system with K_v and T_d/T_m selected as above. Frequency parameter values have been marked on the curve. The frequency response $|\theta_O/\theta_I|$ can then be plotted from this curve by observing the frequencies at which the decibel–phase-margin curve crosses the respective resonance contours. The resulting curve is shown in Fig. 4·38. The asymptotic frequency response is, of course, constant for frequencies less than feedback cutoff and follows the $|\theta_O/\epsilon|$ asymptote for frequencies above feedback cutoff.

Use of the lead equalizer has thus resulted in an increase of K_vT_m by $50.7 - 3.0 = 47.7$ db (increase of K_v from 5.7 sec^{-1} to 340 sec^{-1}). The feedback-cutoff frequency has been raised from $\omega_c = 1/T_m$ to $\omega_c = 32/T_m$ ($\omega_c = 128$ radians/sec $= 20$ cps).

It would appear that a higher value of K_v could be obtained through the use of a smaller value of T_d, with a corresponding further increase in the cutoff frequency. In the usual case, however, Eq. (121) will require modification because of the presence of other time constants which will begin to make their influence felt as the cutoff frequency is raised. In the use of a 60-cps carrier frequency there appear to be limitations

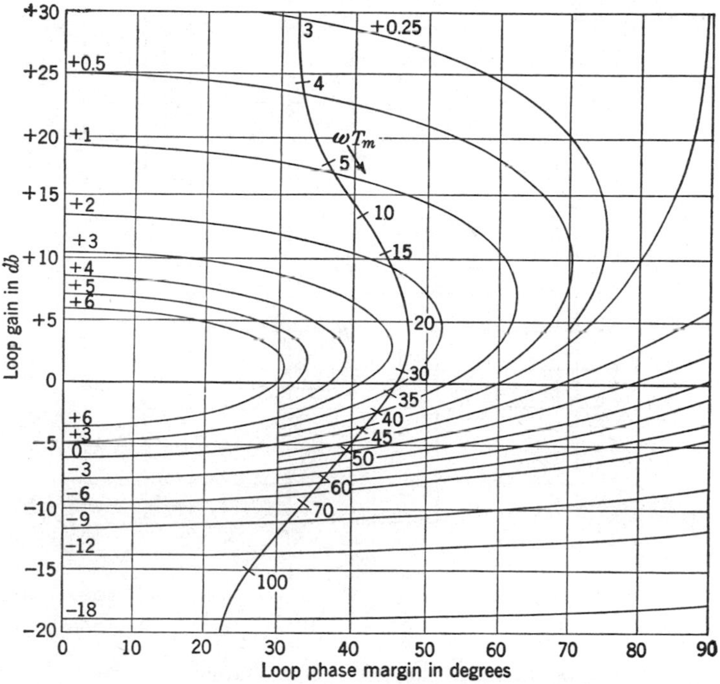

FIG. 4·37.—Lead equalization applied to a single-time-lag servomotor. $K_v = 340$ sec^{-1}; $T_d/T_m = 0.1$.

placed on the use of cutoff frequencies that approach the carrier frequency or, in some instances, even one-half of the carrier frequency. Another source of difficulty arises when a phase-sensitive detector is used. A ripple filter is then required to decrease the ripple voltage, in order not to overload the output stages of the power amplifier. This ripple filter must have appreciable attenuation at twice the carrier frequency in a full-wave rectifier and will thus contribute appreciable phase shift at frequencies above one-half of the carrier frequency.

Inspection of Fig. 4·37 shows that an increase in loop gain of approximately 12 db will increase the resonance peak to +6 db, and a reduction in loop gain of approximately 27 db will increase the resonance peak to 5.4 db—the largest resonance peak that can be obtained by reducing the loop gain. These two quantities give the magnitude of the amplification tolerances that should be placed on the system in order to maintain satisfactory stability if the other quantities are constant. The velocity-error constant would, of course, change by the same factor, and over-all system specifications may not permit a reduction in K_v of more than 12

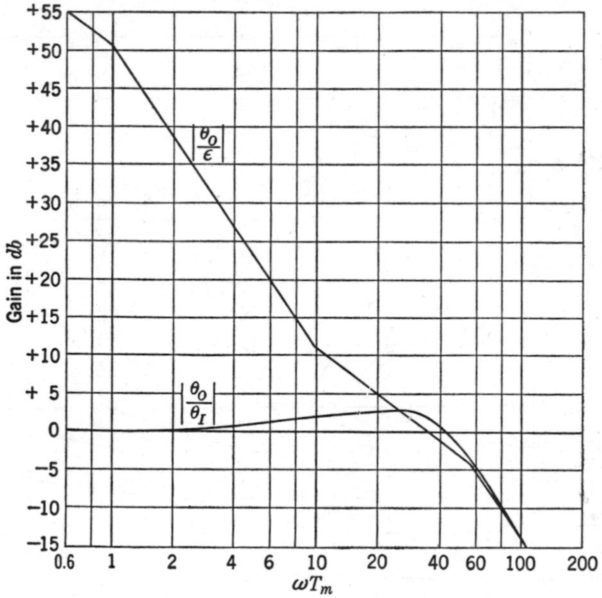

FIG. 4·38.—Frequency response for a single–time-lag servomotor with lead equalization. $K_v = 340\ \text{sec}^{-1}$; $T_d/T_m = 0.1$.

db. A check can be made on the effect of a change in T_m on the system stability by use of Figs. 4·36 and 4·37. Change in T_m is practically equivalent to a change in gain, since the T_m–phase-margin contribution near feedback cutoff is small. An increase of T_m by a factor of 2 would require a factor of 4 (+12 db) increase in K_v to keep the phase-margin maximum in the gain region for maximum stability since it would increase the length of the −12-db/octave section by 1 octave. Allowing an increase of T_m by a factor of 2 without changing the velocity-error constant would correspond approximately to a reduction in gain of 12 db and would increase the resonance peak to +3.9 db.

No attempt will be made at this time to make a complete tolerance discussion of the above circuit. The following equations for the lead equalizer will be useful in a further study:

$$\frac{E_O}{E_I} = G_0 \frac{T_d p + 1}{G_0 T_d p + 1}, \tag{129}$$

$$\phi_m = \frac{\pi}{2} - 2 \tan^{-1} \sqrt{G_0}, \tag{130}$$

where

$$G_0 = \frac{R_1}{R_1 + R_2},$$

$$T_d = R_2 C_2,$$

$$\frac{\delta T_d}{T_d} = \frac{\delta R_2}{R_2} + \frac{\delta C_2}{C_2}, \tag{131}$$

$$\frac{\delta G_0}{G_0} = \frac{R_2}{R_1 + R_2} \frac{\delta R_1}{R_1} - \frac{R_2}{R_1 + R_2} \frac{\delta R_2}{R_2}, \tag{132}$$

$$\delta\phi_m = -\frac{1}{2} \cos \phi_m \frac{\delta G_0}{G_0}. \tag{133}$$

4·16. Integral Equalization.—Integral equalization is used in a servo loop in order to increase the loop gain at relatively low frequencies; it may be used in conjunction with lead equalization in a loop.

For the moment we shall assume that a given transfer function has been selected and that it is then desired to increase the loop gain at low frequencies. One example of this type arises in connection with a servomotor having a quadratic lag factor,

$$\frac{\theta_O}{\epsilon} = \frac{K_v}{p} \frac{1}{T^2 p^2 + 2\zeta T p + 1}. \tag{134}$$

This basic loop equation could arise from a tachometer-equalized servomotor of the type discussed in the next section. An equation of approximately this form also arises in the design of a gyro-stabilized fire-control director. In the latter case Eq. (134) represents the transfer function relating the precession torque applied to the gyro and the angle through which the director turns in response to error signals between the gyro and the director.

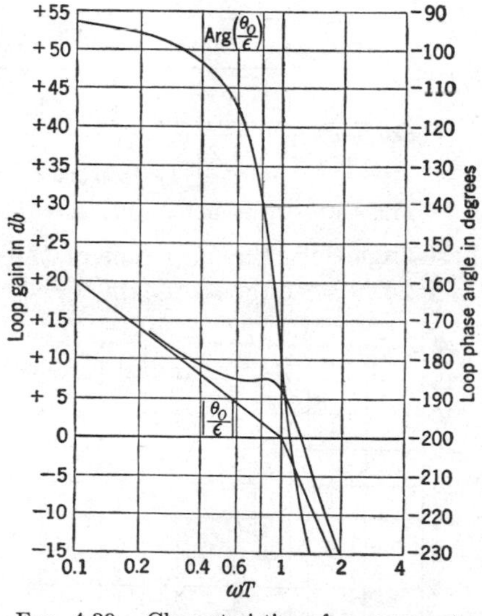

FIG. 4·39.—Characteristics of a servomotor with quadratic lag. $\zeta = 0.25$.

The feedback transfer function of Eq. (134) has an asymptotic characteristic of −6 db/octave for frequencies below $\omega = 1/T$ and −18 db/octave for frequencies above $1/T$. The usual design for the subsidiary loop would yield a value of ζ of the order of 0.25, resulting in a resonance peak in $|p\theta_O/\epsilon|$ of $+6$ db. Figure 4·39 is a decibel–log-frequency and

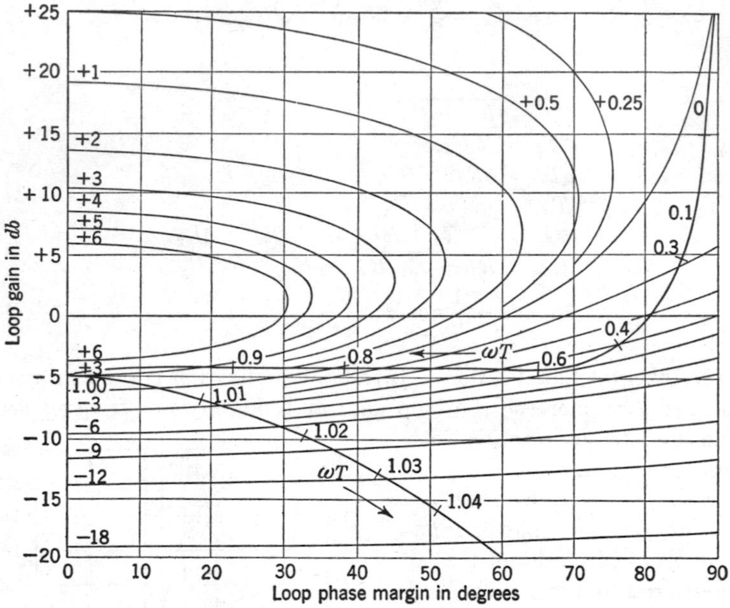

FIG. 4·40.—Characteristics of a servomotor with quadratic lag. $\zeta = 0.25$.

phase-angle–log-frequency plot of the transfer function of Eq. (134), for $\zeta = 0.25$. Since the loop gain is relatively constant in the region where the phase angle is going through $-180°$ (0 phase margin), it will be necessary to choose a value of K_vT that will give a loop gain of -5 db or less when the phase margin goes through zero, in order to have a resonance peak of $+3$ db or less in the frequency-response curve. A value of $K_vT = -11$ db will satisfy this requirement. Figure 4·40 is a decibel–phase-margin plot of this system with over-all frequency-response contours drawn in for $K_vT = -11$ db; a part of the curve has been reflected in the zero-phase-margin line. The frequency-response maximum increases to $+6$ db with a further $+1.5$-db increase in K_vT. The servo becomes unstable for an increase in K_vT of only $+5$ db and would be

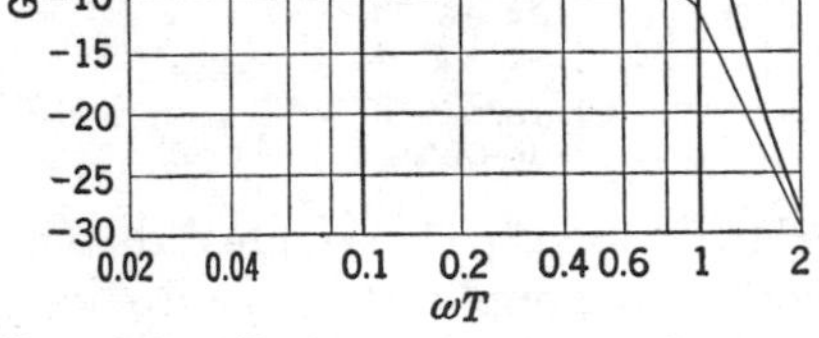

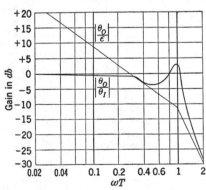

FIG. 4·41.—Frequency response of servomotor with quadratic lag. $\zeta = 0.25$.

rather unsatisfactory. Figure 4·41 is the corresponding over-all frequency response $|\theta_O/\theta_I|$.

Feedback cutoff occurs at $\omega_c = 0.3/T$, although the resonance peak occurs at $\omega_r = 1/T$. The frequency response exhibits a fairly deep minimum at a frequency between feedback cutoff and the resonance peak. If one assumes $T = \frac{1}{15}$ sec, then $K_v = 5.3$ sec^{-1}, $\omega_c = 0.7$ cps, and $\omega_r = 2.4$ cps.

This system can be equalized by the use of a proportional-integral network having the transfer characteristic

$$\frac{E_O}{E_I} = \frac{T_1 p + 1}{A_0 T_1 p + 1}, \qquad (A_0 > 1). \tag{135}$$

This has an asymptotic characteristic of 0 db for $\omega < 1/(A_0T_1)$, -6 db/octave for $1/(A_0T_1) < \omega < 1/T_1$ and is constant at $1/A_0$ for higher frequencies. The attenuation A_0 will be chosen quite large, and the time constant T_1 will be larger than the time constant T appearing in the quadratic factor. The phase angle of the proportional-integral equalizer will be zero for low and high frequencies and will approach a maximum negative value at the geometric mean of the frequencies $1/(A_0T_1)$ and $1/T_1$.

Addition of the equalizer phase angle to that of the original loop will give an over-all phase angle having a maximum negative value of about $-180°$ at $\omega = (\sqrt{A_0}/T_1)^{-1}$ and a minimum negative value between the frequencies $\omega = 1/T_1$ and $\omega = 1/T$; it then decreases toward $-270°$ at higher frequencies. It will then be desirable to place feedback cutoff near the minimum negative phase angle between $\omega = 1/T_1$ and $\omega = 1/T$. The phase angle near cutoff should be in the neighborhood of $-135°$. The phase-angle contribution of the proportional-integral equalizer is

$$\text{Arg}\,\frac{E_O}{E_I} = -\tan^{-1}\omega A_0 T_1 + \tan^{-1}\omega T_1. \tag{136}$$

For large A_0 ($A_0 = 40 = +32$ db in the present example) we have approximately

$$\text{Arg}\,\frac{E_O}{E_I} = -\frac{\pi}{2} + \tan^{-1}\omega T_1. \tag{137}$$

From Fig. 4·40 it appears that the phase margin of the original loop can be decreased by approximately 30° at $\omega = 0.3/T$. This would mean that we can set

$$\tan^{-1} 0.3\,\frac{T_1}{T} = 60° \tag{138}$$

or

$$\frac{T_1}{T} = 5.7. \tag{139}$$

The feedback transfer function can then be written

$$\frac{\theta_O}{\epsilon} = \frac{K_vT}{Tp}\,\frac{T_1p+1}{A_0T_1p+1}\,\frac{1}{(Tp)^2+2\zeta Tp+1}. \tag{140}$$

Figure 4·42 is a decibel–log-frequency and phase-angle–log-frequency plot for $A_0 = +32$ db, $T_1/T = 5.62 = +15$ db, $\zeta = 0.25$. The factor A_0/K_vT has been taken out in order to facilitate comparison with the previous system. The loop gain curve is still flat in the region of zero

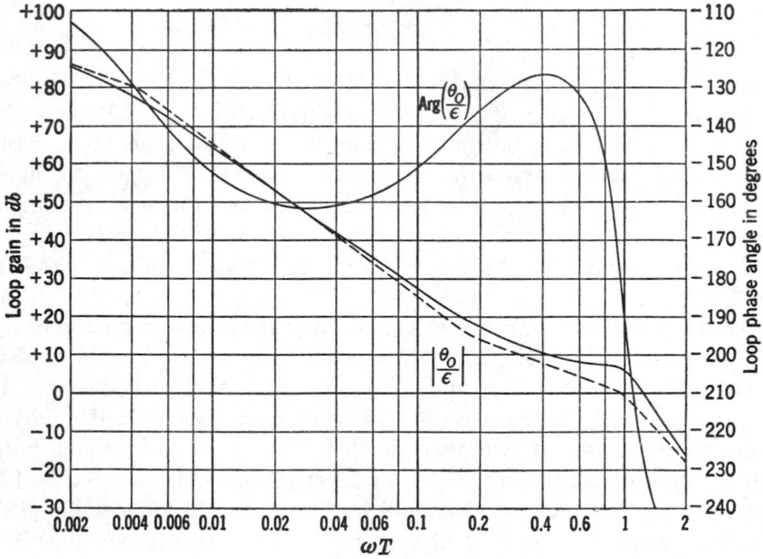

FIG. 4·42.—Characteristics of integral-equalized servomotor with quadratic lag. $A_0 = 32$ db; $T_1/T = 15$ db; $\zeta = 0.25$.

phase margin; it will again be desirable to set K_vT at such a value that the loop gain will be -5 db when the phase margin is zero. This will correspond to $K_vT/A_0 = -12$ db ($K_vT = +20$ db) for this example. Figure 4·43 is then the decibel–phase-margin diagram, with the appropriate $|\theta_O/\theta_I|$ contours. Figure 4·44 shows the frequency-response curve and the asymptotic $|\theta_O/\epsilon|$-curve. The $|\theta_O/\epsilon|$-curve is useful for estimating the magnitude of the error at low frequencies where $|\theta_O/\epsilon|$ and $|\theta_I/\epsilon|$ are nearly equal. The frequency response is seen to have two maxima of $+3$ db, one below and one above feedback cutoff. Inspection of the decibel–phase-margin diagram shows that any smaller value of T_1 would make the phase-margin maximum so narrow that either one or both of the frequency-response maxima would be larger than $+3$ db. The choice of $T_1/T = +15$ db has also made this system quite sensitive to a change in K_vT. A change in K_vT of $+1.5$ or -12.5 db will raise one of the frequency-response maxima to $+6$ db.

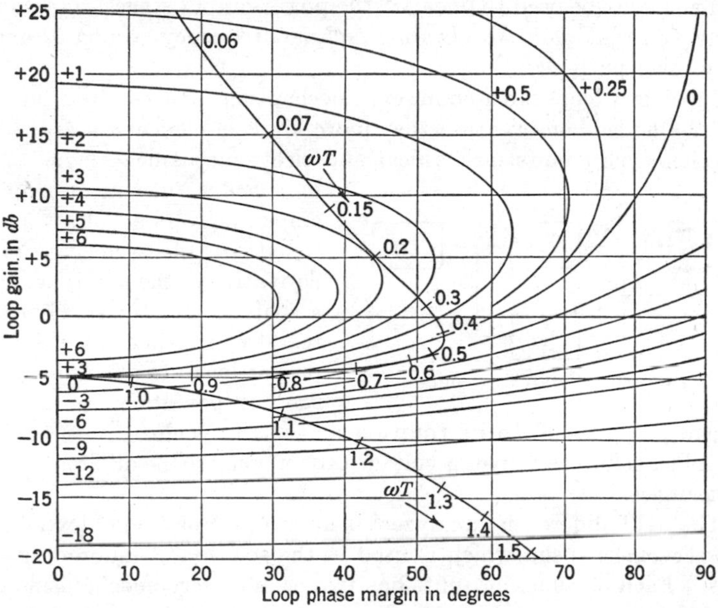

FIG. 4·43.—Characteristics of integral-equalized servomotor with quadratic lag.

Comparing this with the original system, we see that the addition of an integral equalizer with an attenuation A_0 of $+32$ db has increased K_vT from -11 to $+20$ db, an increase of $+31$ db. The feedback cutoff frequency is now $\omega_c = 0.34/T$, as compared with the previous $\omega_c = 0.3/T$. In other words, the low-frequency loop gain has been increased without an appreciable change in cutoff frequency. This is the usual result obtained with integral equalization.

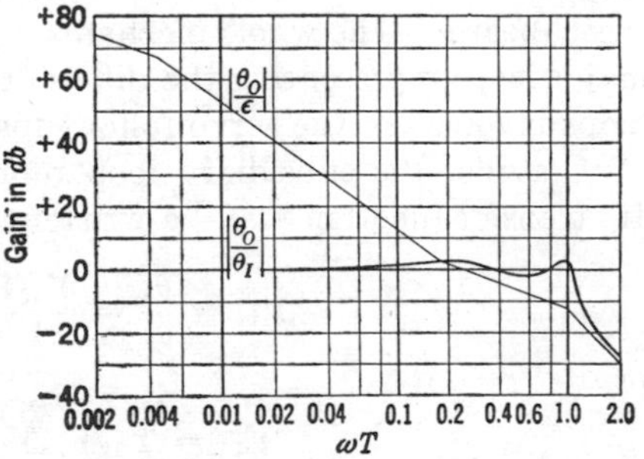

FIG. 4·44.—Frequency response of servo with integral-equalized servomotor with quadratic lag.

It should be pointed out, however, that the use of $\zeta = 0.25$ and $T_1/T = +15$ db has made this system more sensitive to changes in K_vT than would ordinarily be desired. The most straightforward method of improvement would call for a larger value of ζ (perhaps 0.5) and a slight increase in the ratio T_1/T.

4·17. Equalization Using Subsidiary Loops.—Feedback has long been used to change and improve the performance of electronic amplifiers. Feedback may be used to linearize the power-output stages, to hold more nearly constant gain, to obtain a special frequency response, and for many other purposes.

Subsidiary loops are used in servomechanisms for these same purposes, with the added complication that more kinds of elements are available, since here one admits mechanical and electromechanical devices. The tachometer generator, for example, delivers a voltage proportional to the velocity, or the derivative of the rotation angle of a shaft. A motor acts like an integrator in that its velocity is proportional to its applied voltage. A potentiometer delivers a voltage proportional to its rotation angle. A synchro transmitter and control transformer deliver a voltage proportional to the difference in their shaft angles.

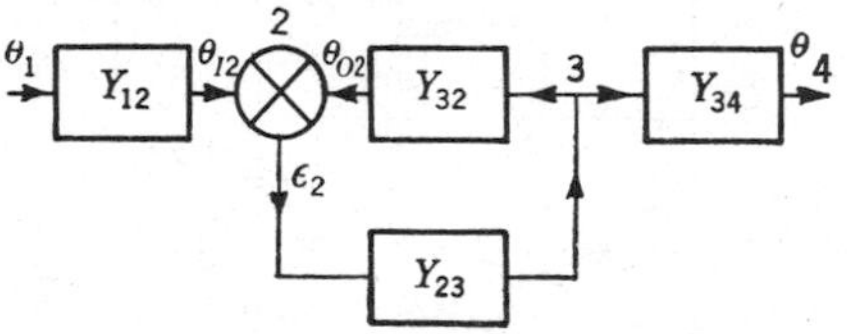

FIG. 4·45.—Subsidiary loop.

The MIT differential analyzer[1] is an example of a complex multiple-loop servomechanism which is used in the solution of differential equations. Each of its major units has two or more servomechanisms incorporated in it. The integrator, for example has two servo follow-ups which receive electrical data and drive the lead screw and integrator disk. The integrating wheel merely turns an electrical transmitter which is followed up by another servo at the point where the integrator wheel angle is used. The various units are interconnected through an electrical switchboard. The whole mechanism may be looked upon as one or more major loops representing the differential equation, with many subsidiary loops involved in the servo follow-ups.

Consider the subsidiary loop represented symbolically in Fig. 4·45. Its transfer function may be written

$$Y_{14} = \frac{\theta_4}{\theta_1} = \frac{Y_{12}Y_{34}}{Y_{32}} \frac{Y_{23}Y_{32}}{1 + Y_{23}Y_{32}} \tag{141}$$

or

$$Y_{14} = Y_{12}Y_{23}Y_{34}\frac{1}{1 + Y_{23}Y_{32}}. \tag{142}$$

Equation (142) is convenient to use in the frequency region where

$$Y_{23}Y_{32} = Y_{22}$$

is small compared with 1; it indicates that the subsidiary loop has practic-

[1] V. Bush and S. H. Caldwell, "A New Type of Differential Analyzer," *J. Franklin Inst.*, **240,** 255 (1945).

ally no effect on the direct transmission through its element Y_{23}. In the frequency region where Y_{22} is large compared with 1, the direct-transmission element Y_{23} is replaced by the reciprocal of the reverse-transmission element Y_{32}, as can be seen from Eq. (141). The above will be recognized as the usual result: one can obtain the reciprocal of a network over a given frequency range by placing it in the β-portion of a feedback amplifier.

It should be pointed out that although it is usually convenient, it is not necessary that a transfer function be stable when it is used as an element in a larger feedback loop. The function Y_{14}, for example, could have a negatively damped quadratic factor in its denominator, arising from the function $(1 + Y_{22})^{-1}$. The use of such an element will, however, require careful use of the general Nyquist criterion as discussed in Chap. 2.

Proceeding to an example, let us consider an amplidyne coupled to a d-c motor with a d-c tachometer driven by the motor. Figure 4·2*a* of Sec. 4·1 is the corresponding symbolic diagram, with

$$\frac{\theta_m}{\epsilon_2} = Y_{23} = \frac{K_A K_a K_m}{p(T_{ma}p + 1)(T_q p + 1)(T_f p + 1)}, \tag{143}$$

$$\frac{\theta_{02}}{\theta_m} = Y_{32} = K_g p, \tag{144}$$

$$\frac{\theta_O}{\theta_m} = Y_{31} = \frac{1}{N}, \tag{145}$$

$$\frac{\theta_{12}}{\epsilon} = Y_{12} = \frac{K\epsilon}{T_r p + 1}; \tag{146}$$

θ_m has been used in place of the θ_3 of Fig. 4·2*a*. The over-all feedback-transfer function associated with differential 1 is then

$$\frac{\theta_O}{\epsilon} = \frac{Y_{11}^0}{1 + Y_{22}} = Y_{11}, \tag{147}$$

where

$$Y_{11}^0 = Y_{12}Y_{23}Y_{31} = \frac{K_{11}T_{ma}}{T_{ma}p(T_{ma}p + 1)(T_q p + 1)(T_r p + 1)(T_f p + 1)}, \tag{148}$$

$$Y_{22} = Y_{23}Y_{32} = \frac{K_{22}}{(T_{ma}p + 1)(T_q p + 1)(T_f p + 1)}, \tag{149}$$

$$K_{11} = \frac{K_\epsilon K_A K_a K_m}{N}, \tag{150}$$

$$K_{22} = K_A K_a K_m K_g. \tag{151}$$

Equation (148) has been partially nondimensionalized through the use of T_{ma}. This is usually a relatively fixed parameter and cannot be varied in the solution of a particular design problem. The following time-constant values will be assumed:

T_{ma} = motor-amplidyne time constant = 0.25 sec,
T_q = amplidyne-quadrature time constant = 0.02 sec,
T_f = amplidyne-control-field time constant = 0.002 sec,
T_r = ripple-filter time constant = 0.04 sec.

The constant K_{11} has the dimensions of $\sec^{-1}$ and is related to the velocity-error constant. The constant K_{22} is dimensionless; it has been called the

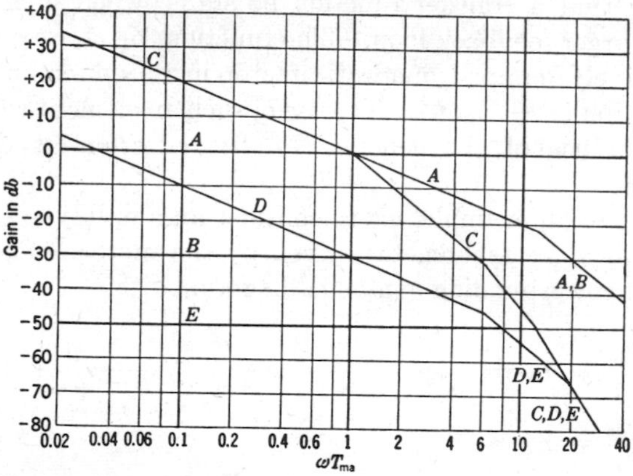

FIG. 4·46.—Asymptotic characteristics of amplidyne with direct tachometer equalization

antihunt gain. Equation (147) may be rewritten as follows:

$$Y_{11} = \frac{Y_{11}^0}{Y_{22}} \frac{Y_{22}}{1 + Y_{22}}. \tag{152}$$

It will be useful to make first a decibel–log-frequency plot of both Y_{11}^0 and Y_{22} on the same piece of paper, as shown in Fig. 4·46. Curve A, the asymptotic plot of Y_{22}, has a break from -6 to -12 db/octave at $\omega T_{ma} = 12.5$; its corresponding phase margin at this break would be approximately 45°, decreasing to approximately 30° at $\omega T_{ma} = 25$. This would mean that the largest useful value of K_{22} would be between $+22$ and $+34$ db since it is most convenient in this case to make the subsidiary loop stable. The value of $K_{22} = +30$ db gives the asymptotic Curve B for $Y_{22}/(1 + Y_{22})$; this coincides with Y_{22} for frequencies above $\omega_{c2} = 19.5/T_{ma}$. The 0-db axis for Curve B has been set at -30 db. From Eq. (152), the asymptotic Curve D for Y_{11} is $|Y_{11}^0|_{\text{db}}$ (Curve C) minus $|Y_{22}|_{\text{db}}$ (Curve A) plus $[Y_{22}/(1 + Y_{22})]_{\text{db}}$ (Curve B); this coincides with Y_{11}^0 (Curve C) at frequencies above ω_{c2}. The resulting $Y_{11} = \theta_o/\epsilon$ asymptote has a break from -6 to -12 db/octave at $\omega = 1/T_r$ and a break from -12 to -18 db/octave at $\omega = \omega_{c2}$. The subsidiary loop has shifted the break in Y_{11}^0 at $1/T_{ma}$ up to its cutoff frequency ω_{c2}.

The phase margin associated with the Y_{11} asymptote would then be approximately 45° at $\omega = 1/T_r$; the complete system would probably be operated with feedback cutoff occurring at a slightly higher frequency of perhaps $\omega_{c1} = 8/T_{ma}$. This would correspond to a value of

$$K_{11}T_{ma} = +50 \text{ db}.$$

Curve E is the asymptote for θ_O/θ_I, with its 0 db at -50 db. Curve D, when referred to this axis, is then the loop gain θ/ϵ; it gives an indication of the error for low-frequency sinusoidal inputs. The low-frequency -6 db/octave, if extended to higher frequencies, will intersect the -50-db ordinate at a frequency equal to the velocity-error constant: $K_vT_{ma} = 10$ or $K_v = 40 \text{ sec}^{-1}$. The single-loop system with $Y_{11} = Y_{11}^0$ would have been operated with feedback cutoff at approximately

$$\omega_{c0} = 2/T_{ma}$$

and with a velocity-error constant of $K_vT_{ma} = 2$ or $K_v = 8 \text{ sec}^{-1}$. The addition of the subsidiary loop has thus made an appreciable improvement in the system.

It may be remarked that a reduction in T_q that would permit a larger antihunt gain and higher feedback-cutoff frequency in the tachometer loop would not make an appreciable improvement in the over-all system; the -6 to -12-db/octave break will still occur at $\omega = 1/T_r$, and this sets an upper limit on the feedback-cutoff frequency for the combined system. The feedback transfer function Y_{11} could, of course, be modified by a lead equalizer in Y_{12}, and in this way a higher cutoff frequency could be obtained for the complete system.

A more accurate computation of the over-all feedback transfer function Y_{11} can be obtained by plotting the tachometer transfer function Y_{22} on the decibel–phase-margin diagram with the appropriate contours for $|Y_{22}/(1 + Y_{22})|$ and Arg $[Y_{22}/(1 + Y_{22})]$. These curves can then be used together with Y_{11}^0/Y_{22} to give accurate values of Y_{11}. This procedure will be illustrated in the the next section.

The feedback transfer function Y_{11} can be increased for low frequencies by including in Y_{32} a high-pass filter that will reduce Y_{22} to zero at low frequencies. The cutoff frequency of this high-pass filter should be made so low that the -6-db/octave asymptote in Y_{11} is at least 2.5 octaves in length (15 db). A single-section high-pass RC-filter gives

$$Y_{32} = \frac{T_hp}{T_hp + 1} K_gp, \tag{153}$$

which changes Y_{22} into

$$Y_{22} = Y_{23}Y_{32} = \frac{K_{22}T_hp}{(T_hp + 1)(T_{ma}p + 1)(T_qp + 1)(T_fp + 1)}. \tag{154}$$

The transfer function Y_{11}^0 is left unchanged.

Equation (152) can also be used to construct the asymptotic decibel–log-frequency curves for Y_{11}. Figure 4·47 is constructed with the same upper cutoff frequency for the tachometer loop and with

$$T_h = 0.28 \text{ sec} = 1.1T_{ma}.$$

The various curves have been lettered in the same manner as Fig. 4·46.

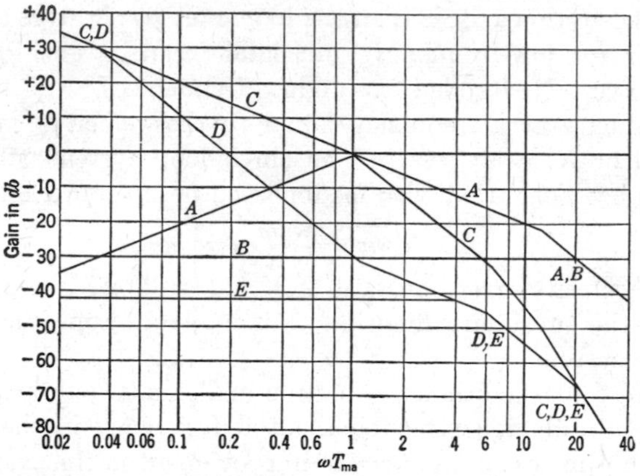

FIG. 4·47.—Asymptotic characteristics of amplidyne with high-pass tachometer equalization.

Curve E is the $|\theta_O/\theta_I|$ asymptote. Feedback cutoff has been reduced to $\omega_{c1} = 4/T_m$, and the system would be operated with

$$(K_vT_m)_{\text{db}} = (K_{11}T_m)_{\text{db}} = +39 \text{ db},$$

as compared with the previous value of +20 db. A comparison of the loop-gain Curve D with the previous result shows that the two systems have equal gains, +28 db, at $\omega = 4/T_{ma}$; the high-pass system has the higher loop gain at lower frequencies and the lower loop gain at higher frequencies.

APPLICATIONS

4·18. SCR-584 Automatic-tracking Loop.—This system serves as a good illustration of the decibel–log-frequency design techniques because of the availability of the considerable amount of experimental data contained in Radiation Laboratory Report 370.[1] The Nyquist locus and differential-equation methods were used in the design of this equipment.

The system[2] comprises a radar transmitter and a receiver which delivers a modulated video signal to a diode detector. A so-called "slow" automatic gain control operates on the radar receiver gain in

[1] G. J. Plain and S. Godet, "Data on SCR-584 Control Equipment," Dec. 17, 1942.

[2] "The SCR-584 Radar," *Electronics*, **18**, 104 (1945).

such a way that the amplitude of the video modulation envelope is proportional to the angle between the parabolic-reflector axis and the target, that is, to the angular error in tracking the target. The signal is modulated at 30 cps, since reception takes place through a conical-scanning antenna placed at the parabola focus and rotated at this speed by an 1800-rpm induction motor; this motor also drives a two-phase permanent-magnet reference generator. The 30-cps reference generator is used in the commutating or phase-sensitive detector to enable separation of the elevation and traverse (or azimuth) error signals.

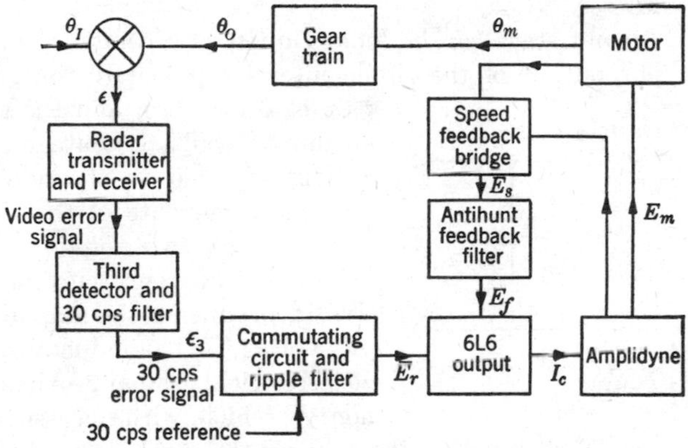

FIG. 4·48.—SCR-584 tracking-servo block diagram.

In what follows it will be assumed that the commutating detector has performed its function and that the analysis can be carried out separately for the elevation and azimuth channels. The circuits of the two channels are identical and can therefore be considered separately. Figure 4·48 is a block diagram of the servo system. The torque limit circuits will not be discussed in the following and have not been included in Fig. 4·48. Neglecting noise modulation effects, the modulation envelope is a true representation of the antenna misalignment and will be assumed to be in phase with the actual error ϵ. Radiation Laboratory Report 370 gives an over-all frequency response for the third detector and 30-cps filter. The data are fairly well fitted by a single-lag transfer function with $T_3 = 0.013$ sec:

$$\frac{\epsilon_3}{\epsilon} = \frac{K_3}{T_3p + 1}, \tag{155}$$

where ϵ_3 is the amplitude of the 30-cps error signal. The commutating circuit can be considered as producing a slowly varying voltage with superimposed ripple. Most of the ripple power is 60 cps and higher, since it is full wave. The average value of the commutator output is equal to the amplitude of the 30-cps error signal associated with the azimuth or elevation error. The commutator output is then fed through a ripple filter of the type illustrated in Fig. 4·49. The nominal values indicated would give a quadratic lag with $\zeta = 0.35$ and a cutoff frequency of 71 radians/sec or 11.3 cps. Actual measurement indicates that the frequency response depends on the amplitude of the input voltage E_r but is fairly accurately represented by the transfer characteristic

$$\frac{\bar{E}_r}{E_r} = \frac{1}{(T_r p + 1)^2}, \tag{156}$$

with $T_r = 0.01$ sec.

The 6L6 output stage can be looked upon as a combined mixer and amplifier. The output of the ripple filter is applied to the grids of a pair of 6L6 tubes, and the amplified antihunt feedback voltage is differentially applied to the screen grids. The plate currents of the two 6L6's flow through two amplidyne control fields; the difference current is effective in producing the amplidyne output voltage. The inductance of each control field is approximately 30 henrys, which, with the assumption of 100 per cent coupling between the two control fields and a 30,000-ohm plate resistance for the 6L6, gives

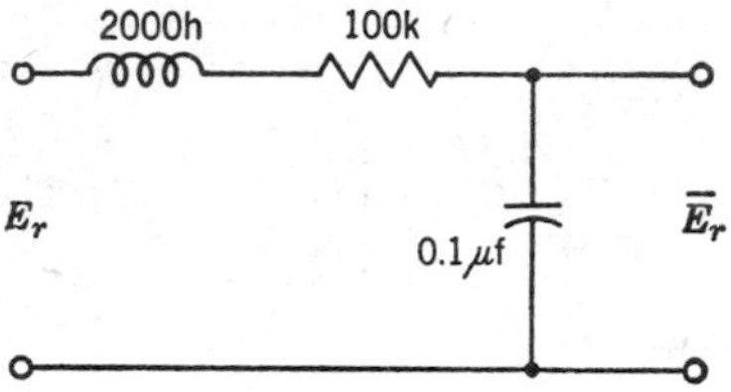

FIG. 4·49.—SCR-584 commutator-ripple filter.

$$\Delta I_c = \frac{K_r E_r}{T_c p + 1} - \frac{K_f E_f}{T_c p + 1}, \tag{157}$$

with the control-field time constant $T_c = 0.002$ sec. The quadrature-field time constant T_q was measured and found to be 0.02 sec. Using the armature resistance of 6.9 ohms, rotor inertia of 7 lb in^2, and the name-plate data of 0.5 hp, 3450 rpm, 250 volts, 1.9 amp, one obtains $T_m = 0.041$ sec. Combining the motor and amplidyne and using the armature circuit resistance of 11 ohms together with the motor resistance of 6.9 ohms, one finds the combined motor-amplidyne time constant $T_{ma} = 0.10$ sec. This compares with a measured value of 0.11 sec for the combined time constant in the system. Using Eq. (157) and the above time constants, one then obtains

$$(T_{ma}p + 1)(T_q p + 1)(T_c p + 1)p\theta_m = K_m K_r E_r - K_m K_f E_f. \tag{158}$$

The speed-feedback bridge is of the type discussed in Sec. 3·15. It is redrawn in Fig. 4·50, along with the connections between the motor and amplidyne. Referring to Fig. 3·24, we see that

$$R_c = R_5 + R_6 = 3.1 \quad \text{ohms},$$
$$R_m = R_3 + R_4 = 5.8 \quad \text{ohms},$$
$$R_a = R_7 + R_8 = 10.1 \quad \text{ohms}.$$

The speed-feedback voltage is then related to θ_m by the equation

$$E_s = K_g(T_{m0}p + 1)p\theta_m, \tag{159a}$$

where

$$K_g = \frac{R_1}{R_1 + R_2} K_e$$

is the effective tachometer constant, and

$$T_{m0} = \frac{R_m - \dfrac{R_2}{R_1} R_c}{R_a + R_m + R_c} T_{ma};$$

the loading effect of C_1 in Fig. 4·50 has been neglected. On substituting in the numerical values, one obtains $T_{m0} = 0.22$, $T_{ma} = 0.024$ sec.

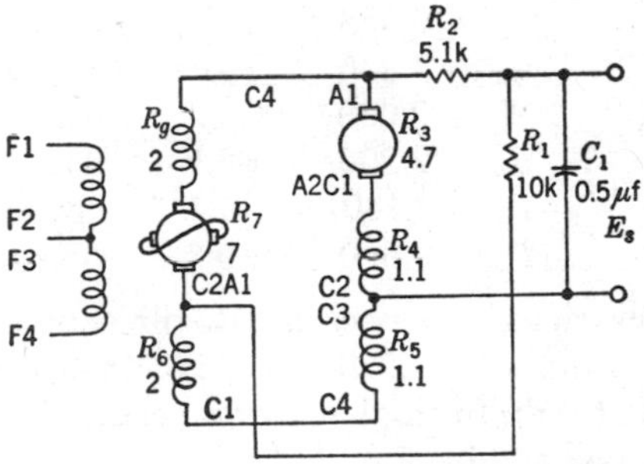

FIG. 4·50.—Amplidyne-motor connections and speed-feedback bridge.

The capacitor C_1 in Fig. 4·50 is a capacity load on the divider resistors R_1 and R_2. It looks into a very high impedance at the input to the feedback filter. Equation (159a) then becomes

$$E_s = K_g \frac{T_{m0}p + 1}{T_x p + 1} p\theta_m, \tag{159b}$$

where $T_x = (R_1R_2/R_1R_2)C_1 = 0.0017$ sec. This capacitor is introduced to provide a high-frequency cutoff and prevent brush noise and general pickup in the system from activating the feedback-amplifier stages.

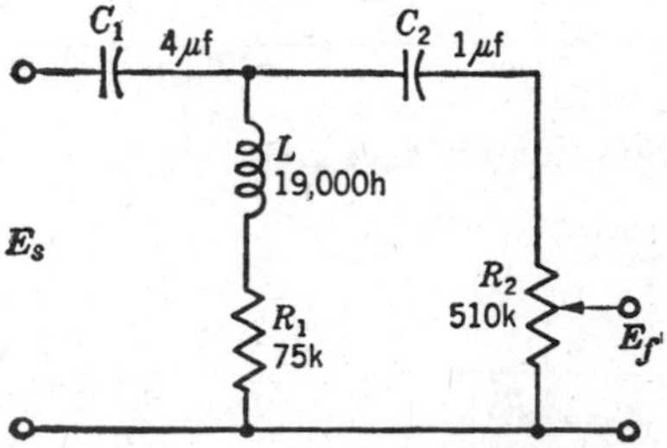

FIG. 4·51.—SCR-584 antihunt filter.

Figure 4·51 is a schematic diagram of the high-pass equalizer or antihunt filter used in this system. The voltage E_s is supplied by the low-impedance bridge and may be considered to have a zero source impedance. The voltage E_f is applied to a vacuum-tube control grid R_2 can then be taken as the only load. The transfer function can be shown to be

$$\frac{E_f}{E_s} = \frac{R_2C_2R_1C_2p^2\left(\frac{L}{R_1}p + 1\right)}{R_1C_1p\left(R_2C_2p + 1 + \frac{C_2}{C_1}\right)\left(\frac{L}{R_1}p + 1\right) + R_2C_2p + 1}. \quad (160)$$

This transfer function can be factored and rewritten as

$$\frac{E_f}{E_s} = \frac{T_1}{T_L}\,\frac{\left(\frac{p}{\omega_n}\right)^2(T_Lp + 1)}{(T_1p + 1)\left[\left(\frac{p}{\omega_n}\right)^2 + 2\zeta\frac{p}{\omega_n} + 1\right]}, \quad (161)$$

where $T_L = L/R_1$ and T_1, ω_n, ζ are obtained by factoring the denominator. Putting in the constants given in Fig. 4·50, one finds

$$\begin{aligned} T_L &= 0.253 \quad \text{sec},\\ T_1 &= 0.558 \quad \text{sec},\\ \omega_n &= 3.835 \quad \text{radians/sec},\\ \zeta &= 0.608,\\ T_1/T_L &= 2.206 = +6.9 \quad \text{db},\\ \omega_nT_1 &= 2.140 = +6.6 \quad \text{db},\\ \omega_nT_L &= 0.970 = -0.3 \quad \text{db}. \end{aligned}$$

The asymptotic characteristic rises at 12 db/octave to $\omega = 1/T_1$, at 6 db/octave for $1/T_1 < \omega < \omega_n$, at -6 db/octave for $\omega_n < \omega < 1/T_L$; it is then constant at 0 db for higher frequencies. Using the previously defined quantities, one obtains

$$\theta_m = \frac{\frac{K_mK_rK_3}{(T_3p + 1)(T_rp + 1)^2}\epsilon - \frac{K_mK_fK_g(T_1/T_L)(p/\omega_n)^2(T_Lp + 1)(T_{m0}p + 1)}{(T_1p + 1)\left[\left(\frac{p}{\omega_n}\right)^2 + 2\zeta\frac{p}{\omega_n} + 1\right](T_xp + 1)}\theta_m}{p(T_{ma}p + 1)(T_qp + 1)(T_cp + 1)}. \quad (162)$$

Solution for θ_m/ϵ gives

$$\frac{\theta_m}{\epsilon} = \frac{\left[\frac{K_mK_rK_3}{p(T_{ma}p + 1)(T_qp + 1)(T_cp + 1)(T_3p + 1)(T_rp + 1)^2}\right]}{1 + \frac{K_mK_fK_g\frac{T_1}{T_L}\left(\frac{p}{\omega_n}\right)^2(T_Lp + 1)(T_{m0}p + 1)}{(T_xp+1)(T_{ma}p+1)(T_qp+1)(T_cp+1)(T_1p+1)\left[(p/\omega_n)^2+2\zeta(p/\omega_n)+1\right]}}. \quad (163)$$

In terms of the gear ratio N between θ_O and θ_m and the loop-transfer functions Y_{11}^0 and Y_{22}, one can write

$$\frac{\theta_O}{\epsilon} = Y_{11} = \frac{Y_{11}^0}{1 + Y_{22}}, \tag{164}$$

where

$$Y_{11}^0 = \frac{K_v}{p(T_{ma}p + 1)(T_q p + 1)(T_c p + 1)(T_3 p + 1)(T_r p + 1)^2}, \tag{165}$$

$$Y_{22} = \frac{K_{22}\frac{T_1}{T_L}\left(\frac{p}{\omega_n}\right)^2 (T_L p + 1)(T_{m0} p + 1)}{(T_x p + 1)(T_{ma}p + 1)(T_q p + 1)(T_c p + 1)(T_1 p + 1)\left[\left(\frac{p}{\omega_n}\right)^2 + 2\zeta\frac{p}{\omega_n} + 1\right]}, \tag{166}$$

$K_v = K_m K_r K_3/N$ = velocity-error constant,
$K_{22} = K_m K_f K_q$ = antihunt gain.

The antihunt gain K_{22} has been so defined that it is the zero-frequency loop gain around the speed-feedback loop when the capacitors in the antihunt filter are short-circuited out (the filter then has unity gain at all frequencies). The antihunt gain is a dimensionless number; the antihunt gain control on the servoamplifier can be adjusted to a maximum value of $K_{22} = 70$. The forward gain control on the servoamplifier could be adjusted to make K_v a maximum of 540 sec^{-1}.

The following is a summary of the constants for the system:

$$\begin{aligned}
T_1 &= 0.558 \text{ sec} = \frac{1}{1.8},\\
\omega_n &= 3.8 \text{ radians/sec},\\
T_L &= 0.253 = \frac{1}{3.9},\\
T_{ma} &= 0.11 \text{ sec} = \frac{1}{9.0},\\
T_{m0} &= 0.022 = \tfrac{1}{45},\\
T_q &= 0.02 = \tfrac{1}{50},\\
T_3 &= 0.013 = \tfrac{1}{77},\\
T_r &= 0.01 = \tfrac{1}{100},\\
T_c &= 0.002 = \tfrac{1}{500},\\
T_x &= 0.0017 = \tfrac{1}{590},\\
\zeta &= 0.608.
\end{aligned}$$

Figure 4·52 is an asymptotic decibel–log-frequency plot of Y_{11}^0/K_v and Y_{22}/K_{22}. A value of $K_{22} = +26$ db or an antihunt gain of 20 was chosen in drawing the combined curve for $Y_{11}^0/(1 + Y_{22})$.

As long as the antihunt loop is reasonaby stable (perhaps 15° phase margin at cutoff), it is possible to construct a phase-angle–log-frequency

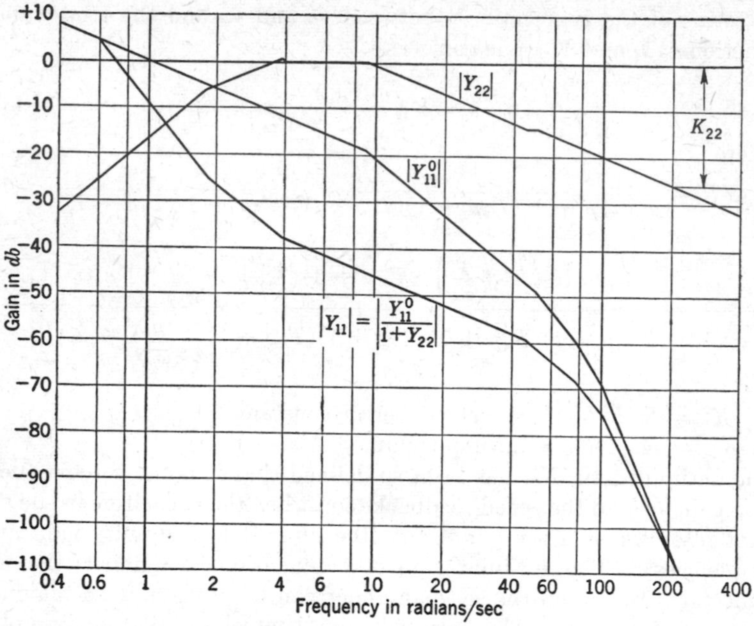

FIG. 4·52.—Asymptotic loop gains.

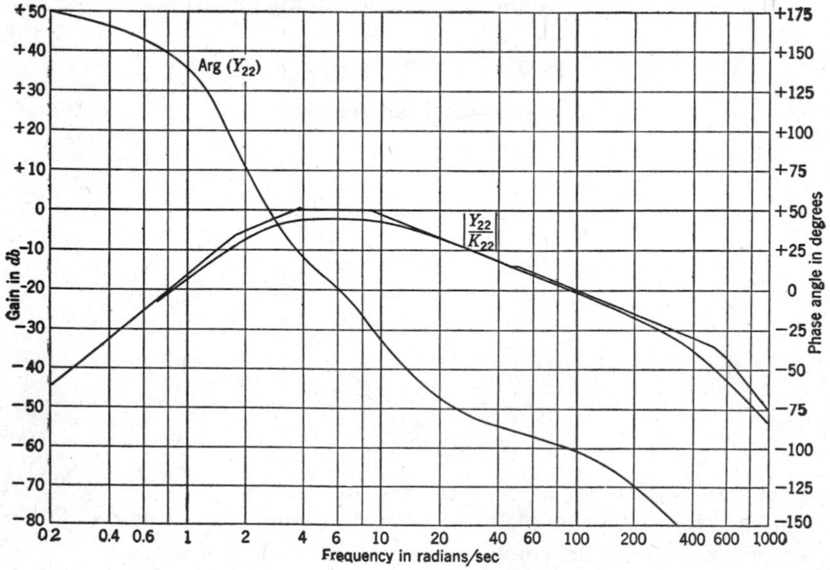

FIG. 4·53.—SCR-584 antihunt loop gain and phase angle.

curve from the asymptotic curve for Y_{11} and to use this phase-angle curve along with the asymptotic decibel–log-frequency curve in selecting the value of K_v that will give satisfactory system stability. In the present example, however, all of the steps will be carried through in detail, in order to illustrate the general method.

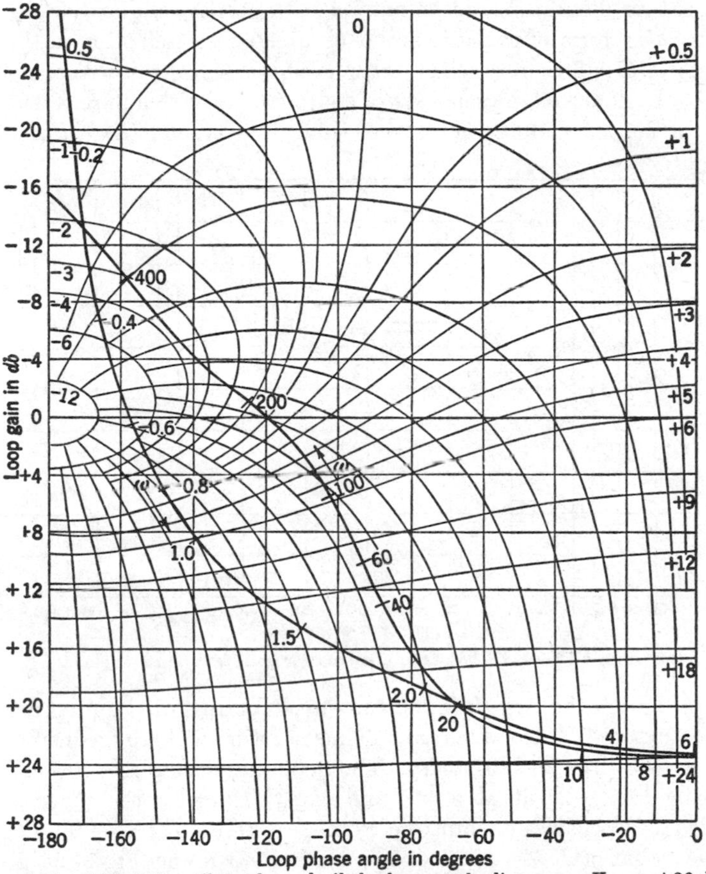

FIG. 4·54.—SCR-584 antihunt-loop decibel–phase-angle diagram. $K_{22} = +26$ db.

Figure 4·53 is a plot of the exact decibel–log-frequency and phase-angle–log-frequency curves for antihunt-loop transfer function Y_{22}. Examination of this curve indicates that $K_{22} = +26$ db will give a stable system. The loop gain and loop phase angle can now be plotted on the decibel–phase-angle diagram (Fig. 4·54). The contours on this diagram permit (the sign having been changed as discussed in Sec. 4·11) a determination of the transfer gain and phase angle for the function

$$Y_2 = 1 + Y_{22}. \tag{167}$$

The loop gain $|Y_{22}|_{db}$, is plotted against Arg (Y_{22}), with the radian frequency ω as a parameter. The contours are those of $|Y_2|$ and Arg (Y_2) and are correctly marked in decibels and degrees, for

$$-180° < \text{Arg } (Y_{22}) < 0°.$$

The contour diagram could be extended to positive values of Arg (Y_2); but since the form of the contours is obtained by a reflection in the loop-gain axis, it is sufficient to reflect the curve for Y_{22} in the line Arg $(Y_{22}) = 0$ and plot back across the same set of contours. For this part of the curve the $|Y_2|$ contours then retain the same values, but the values to be

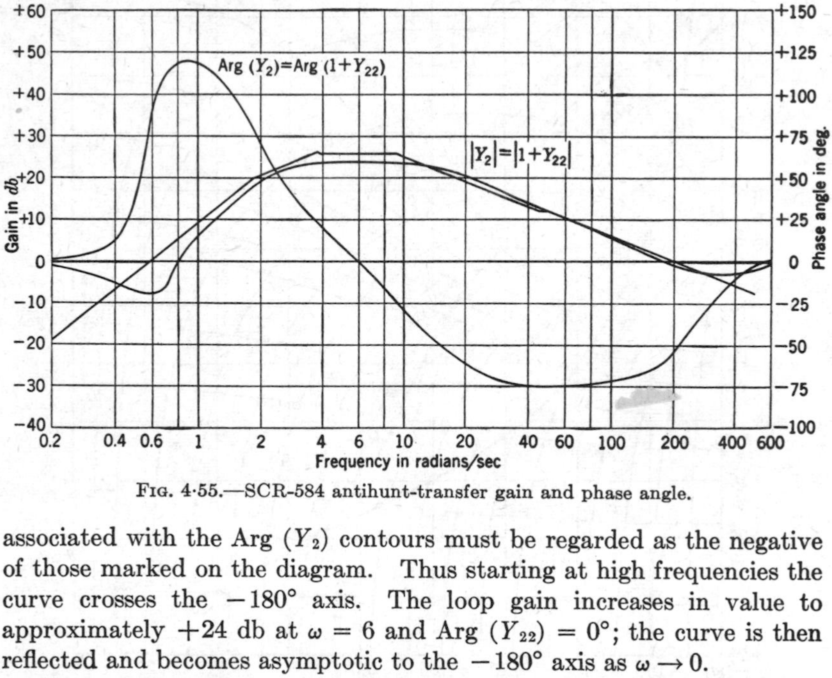

FIG. 4·55.—SCR-584 antihunt-transfer gain and phase angle.

associated with the Arg (Y_2) contours must be regarded as the negative of those marked on the diagram. Thus starting at high frequencies the curve crosses the $-180°$ axis. The loop gain increases in value to approximately $+24$ db at $\omega = 6$ and Arg $(Y_{22}) = 0°$; the curve is then reflected and becomes asymptotic to the $-180°$ axis as $\omega \rightarrow 0$.

The value of $K_{22} = +26$ db used in constructing Fig. 4·54 gives a stable antihunt loop with approximately 12° phase margin at low-frequency feedback cutoff and a peak gain of approximately -9 db. Increasing K_{22} by 16 db would make the antihunt loop unstable at the high-frequency end.

Figure 4·55 is constructed by reading off the values of the transfer gain $|Y_2|_{db}$ and the transfer phase angle Arg (Y_2) from the contours for $Y_2 = 1 + Y_{22}$.

Figure 4·56 gives the loop phase angle for the loop transfer function Y_{11}^0 that remains when the antihunt loop is inactive $(Y_{22} = 0)$. The

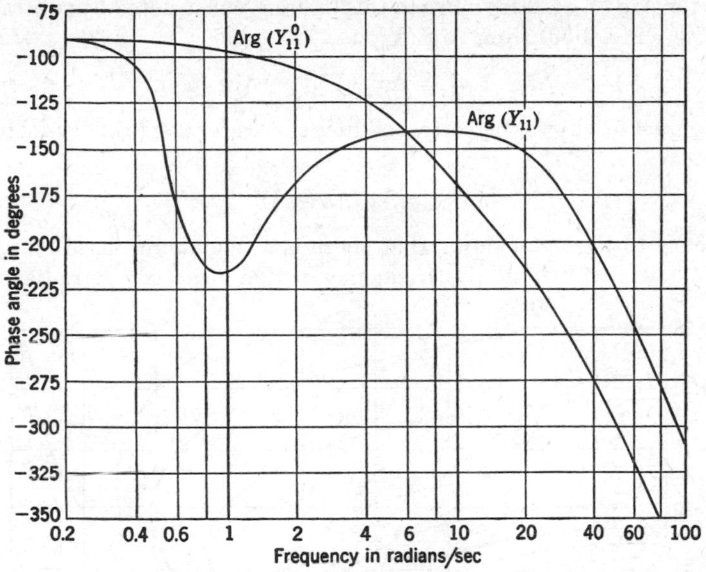

FIG. 4·56.—Primary-loop phase angles.

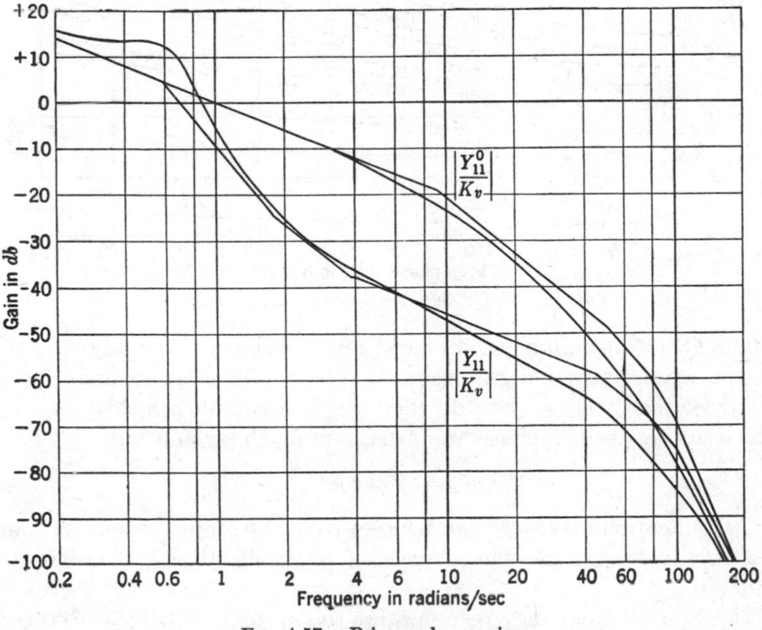

FIG. 4·57.—Primary-loop gains.

curve for Arg (Y_{11}), also shown in this figure is constructed by subtracting Arg (Y_2) (Fig. 4·55) from Arg (Y_{11}^0):

$$\text{Arg}\,(Y_{11}) = \text{Arg}\,(Y_{11}^0) - \text{Arg}\,(Y_2). \tag{168}$$

Figure 4·57 shows the corresponding curves for the primary-loop gain and for

$$|Y_{11}|_{\text{db}} = |Y_{11}^0|_{\text{db}} - |Y_2|_{\text{db}}. \tag{169}$$

Reference to Fig. 4·56 shows that there is a maximum phase margin of +40° (180° − 140°) in the frequency region near $\omega = 8$ radians/sec.

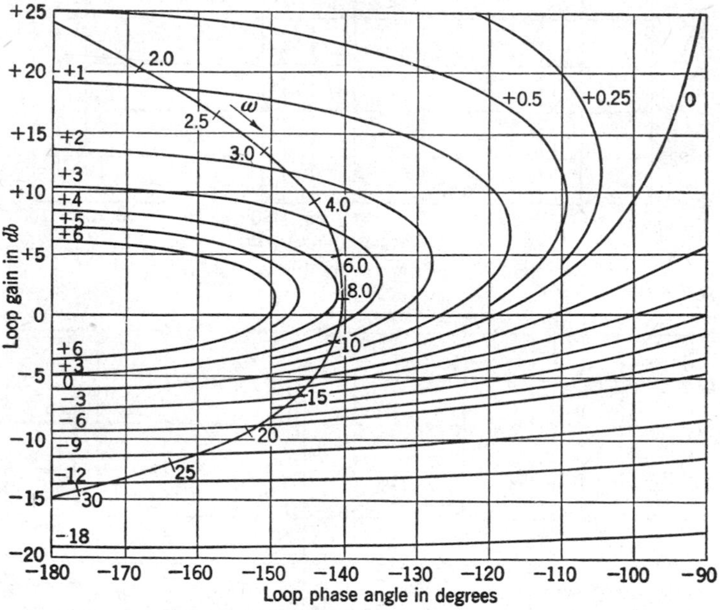

FIG. 4·58.—SCR-584 decibel–phase-angle diagram.

It follows that optimum stability will result when K_v is so adjusted that this maximum phase margin occurs at a loop gain of approximately +2 db. Selection of K_v = +46 db (200 sec^{-1}) accomplishes this; Fig. 4·58 is the resulting decibel–phase-angle diagram for the system with

$$K_v = 200 \text{ sec}^{-1}.$$

The amplification for $|\theta_O/\theta_I|$ can be read from the amplification contours; it is seen to have a resonance peak of +3.8 db at $\omega = 8$ radians/sec (1.3 cps).

The over-all frequency response for the system with $K_v = 200$ sec^{-1} and $K_{22} = 20$ is given in Fig. 4·59. It will be seen that the extension of the low-frequency −6-db/octave slope for $|\theta_o/\epsilon|$ intersects the 0-db axis at $\omega = 200 = K_v$.

It follows from Fig. 4·58 that an 11-db decrease or an 8-db increase in K_v will raise the resonance peak to +6 db. This means that the over-all system does not have much sensitivity to changes in the error-signal gain—one of the requirements for an automatic-tracking system of the type of the SCR-584.

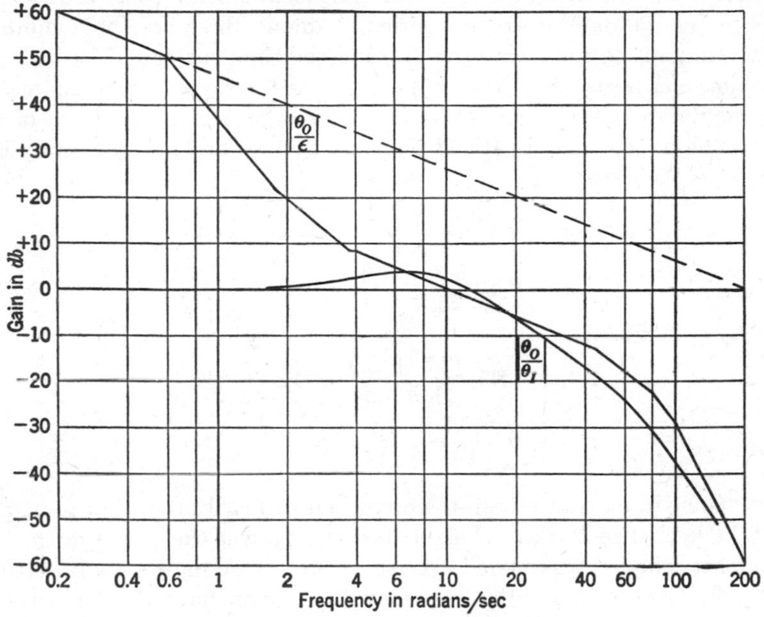

FIG. 4·59.—SCR-584 frequency response.

One observes from Fig. 4·58 that the stability of the system is determined by the phase angle and gain of Y_{11} in the frequency range

$$3 < \omega < 20.$$

Changes in K_{22} and K_v will obviously have no effect on Arg (Y_{11}^0). Reference to Fig. 4·54 shows that a change in K_{22} will have little effect on Arg (Y_2), since the contours of Arg (Y_2) are almost parallel to the contours of Arg (Y_{22}). The contours of $|Y_2|_{db}$ are also almost parallel to the contours of $|Y_{22}|_{db}$ in this frequency region. Thus an increase in K_{22} will merely move the complete curve of Fig. 4·58 downward by the same number of decibels, assuming that K_v remains constant. Also, increasing K_v and K_{22} by the same factor will leave the stability and cutoff frequency unchanged.

A study of the power spectrum of the angular error in automatic tracking with the SCR-584, by the method of Chap. 6, indicates that the location of the peak varied during normal operation from 0.4 to 0.9 cps (2.5 to 5.6 radians/sec) and that the peak height was approximately +8 db when the resonant frequency was 0.9 cps, with greater peak heights occurring as the resonant peak shifted to lower frequencies. This is precisely the behavior that would be expected from Fig. 4·58 as either K_v is decreased or K_{22} is increased from the value used there.

Referring to Fig. 4·52, one can investigate the behavior of the system as some of the parameters are varied. Among these are the combined motor-amplidyne time constant T_{ma} and the time constant T_{m0}. These two time constants can change appreciably as the regulation resistance of the amplidyne[1] is changed through its manufacturing tolerance of 25 to 42.5 ohms (compared with 11 ohms as used in the foregoing analysis). For $R_a = 25$ ohms,

$$T_{ma} = 0.11\,\frac{25 + 6.9}{11 + 6.9} = 0.19 \qquad \text{sec},$$

$$T_{m0} = 0.19\,\frac{5.8 - 1.6}{25 + 6.9} = 0.025 \qquad \text{sec}.$$

For $R_a = 42.5$ ohms,

$$T_{ma} = 0.11\,\frac{42.5 + 6.9}{11 + 6.9} = 0.3 \qquad \text{sec},$$

$$T_{m0} = 0.3\,\frac{5.8 - 1.6}{42.5 + 6.9} = 0.026 \qquad \text{sec}.$$

The change in R_a is thus seen to correspond primarily to a change in T_{ma} with little change in T_{m0}. The change in T_{ma} over the above range can be almost completely removed from the over-all system by a readjustment of K_{22} that leaves K_v and the frequency response unchanged. This would indicate that, as has been shown by experience, the manufacturing tolerance on R_a is sufficiently precise. Variation of amplification in the various elements can, of course, be corrected by adjustment of the two gain controls that change K_v and K_{22}.

The time parameters that could give trouble are T_q, ω_n, and T_L; these determine the length of the −6-db/octave slope in the Y_{11} asymptote. The manufacturing tolerances on these parameters are not known to the authors, but it would seem reasonable to require T_q to be less than 0.03 sec, T_L to be greater than 0.35 sec, and ω_n to be less than 5.6 radians/sec. These tolerances were probably held in production, since they correspond to a 40 per cent change from the nominal value.

4·19. Servo with a Two-phase Motor.—The two-phase motors mentioned in Chap. 3 are quite useful in low-power servo applications. They

[1] GE amplidyne model 5AM65FB2A, 500-watt, 250-volt, 115-volt, three-phase drive motor.

have been widely used in computing mechanisms and remote positioning applications. As an example, we may consider a servo system designed originally to drive a computer shaft in synchronism with train angle data provided by an antiaircraft director. This uses a Diehl[1] two-phase

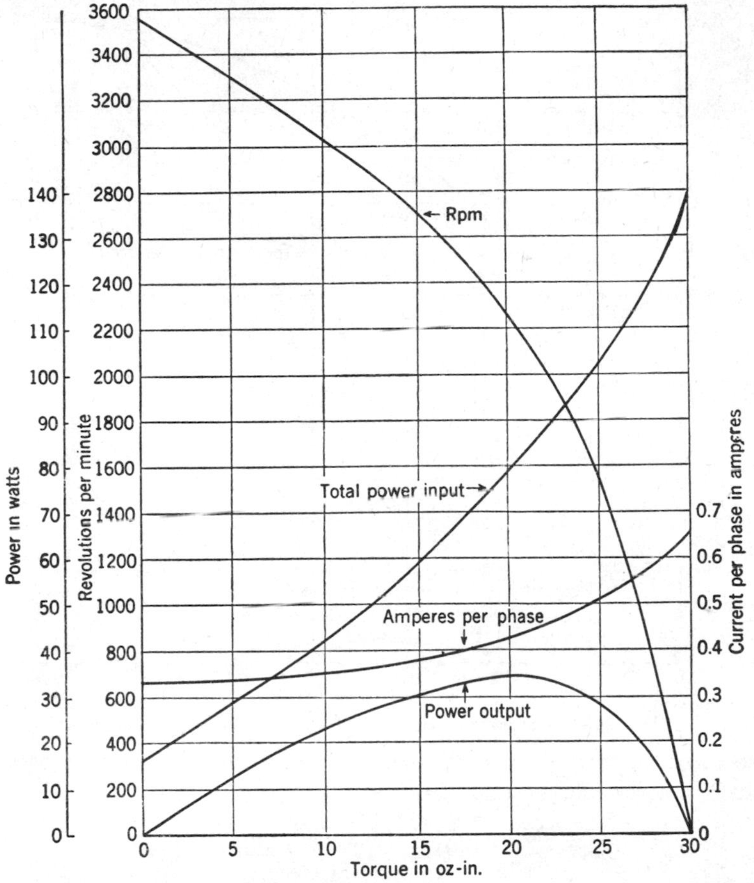

FIG. 4·60.—Brake test at 115 volts, 60 cps of Diehl motor FPF49-7.

servomotor. First a brief outline will be given of the experimental procedure involved in obtaining the motor characteristics.

The motor rating is 22 mechanical watts output at 2200 rpm; Fig. 4·60 is a copy of the manufacturer's data. The rotor inertia is 0.66 oz-in.^{2}, and the impedance looking into either of the phases varies from 350 ohms at no load and maximum speed to 180 ohms when stalled. Each winding takes 70 watts or 75 volt-amperes when the motor is stalled, with 115 volts on each winding.

[1] S.S. No. FPF49-7, 115 volts, 60 cps, Diehl Manufacturing Co., Somerville, N. J.

Figure 4·61 shows the free-running speed and the stalled torque as a function of the control phase voltage with 115 volts on the fixed phase. Inspection of these curves shows that $K_m = 840°$ per second per volt and $K_t = 0.25$ oz-in./volt. The measured inertia of the motor and its

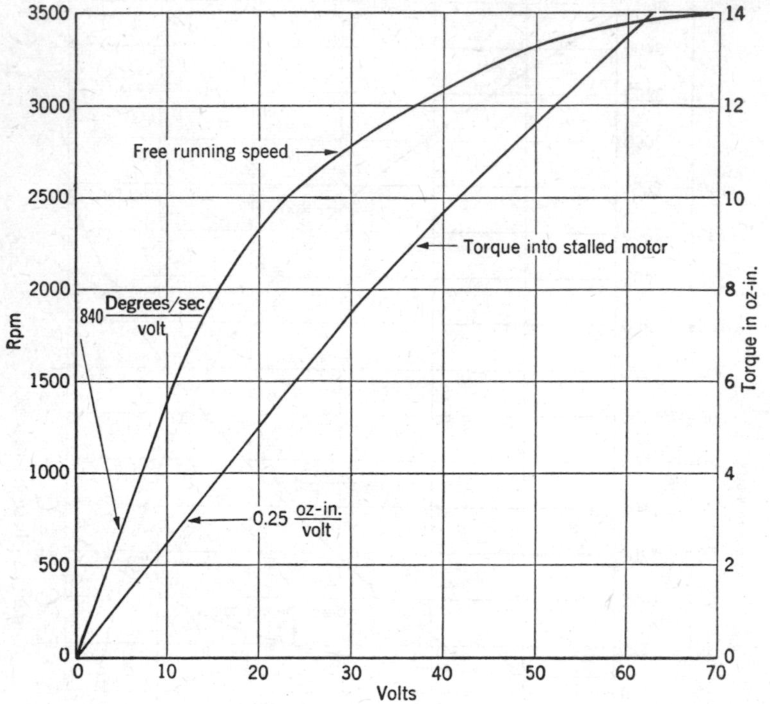

FIG. 4·61.—Characteristics of Diehl FPF49-7 two-phase motor.

associated gear train gave an inertia of 1 oz-in.² Conversion of these values to a common system of units gives

$$f_m = \frac{K_t}{K_m} = 0.018 \qquad \text{oz-in. radian per sec,} \tag{170}$$

$$T_m = \frac{J_m}{f_m} = 0.15 \qquad \text{sec.}$$

The speed-torque curve of Fig. 4·60 gives $f_m = 0.022$ oz-in./radian per sec for the internal damping coefficient, that is, the slope of the speed-torque curve at zero speed point. Assuming that the stalled torque is linear with voltage, one obtains from Fig. 4·60 $K_t = 0.26$ oz-in./volt.

The value of K_m can then be obtained from Eq. (170). All of the quantities are seen to be in fair agreement, an indication that the common brake test data can be used to obtain the motor time constant T_m and the speed voltage constant K_m.

The error signal in the system we shall consider is obtained from a synchro control transformer that is geared down from the motor by a ratio of 10. The error signal is then a 60-cps voltage with a gradient of 0.1 volt per degree, referred to the motor shaft. The fixed phase of the

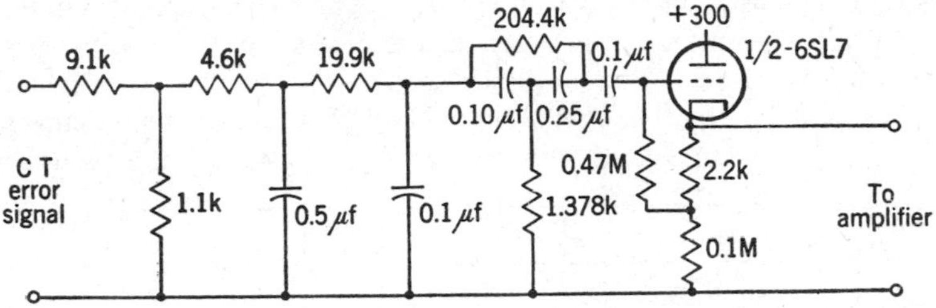

FIG. 4·62.—Phase-lag network and bridged-T equalizer.

motor is put across the 115-volt a-c line, and the error is made to lag the line by 90° through the use of a two-section RC phase-lag network. A conventional a-c amplifier is used with a pair of push-pull 807's in the output; the amplifier has a voltage gain of 22,000 (+86.5 db). It

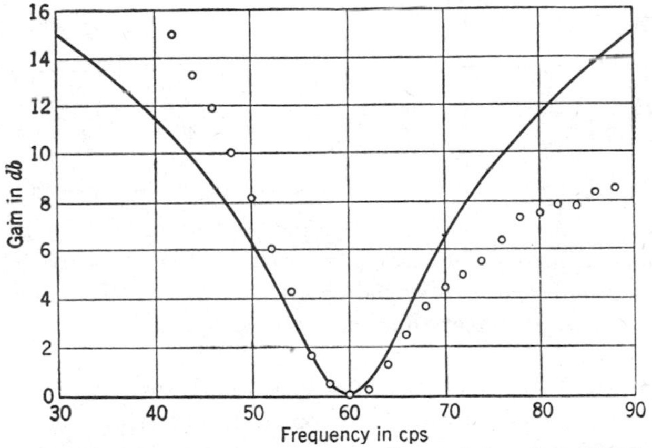

FIG. 4·63.—Frequency response of equalizer and phase-lag network.

delivers approximately 45 watts into the stalled motor—enough to drive the motor to its maximum power output at 2200 rpm. Inverse feedback is used in the amplifier in order to keep its output impedance at a low value (approximately 350 ohms). The phase-shifted error signal is passed through a bridged-T equalizer with a notch width of 5.5 cps ($T_d\omega_0 = 11$). Figure 4·62 is a schematic diagram of the filter and phase-lag network. Figure 4·63 gives a plot of the frequency response of this filter and phase-lag network, together with a plot of $1 + j(\omega - \omega_0)T_d$, which is the exact response for a lead equalizer in a carrier-frequency system with carrier frequency $f_0 = \omega_0/2\pi$ and derivative time constant T_d. In each curve the gain has been plotted with its 60-cps value as a reference level. The input attenuator and output cathode follower are included in Fig. 4·62 as an example of one method of coupling the equalizer into the circuit; in this example the over-all voltage attenuation at 60 cps in 69 db. The input attenuator has a loss of 9 db; the phase-lag network a loss of 20 db; and the bridged-T attenuation is 40 db. The amplifier used in this particular application was also used in 11 other servo channels with different equalizing networks. This arrangement required cabling between the equalizing

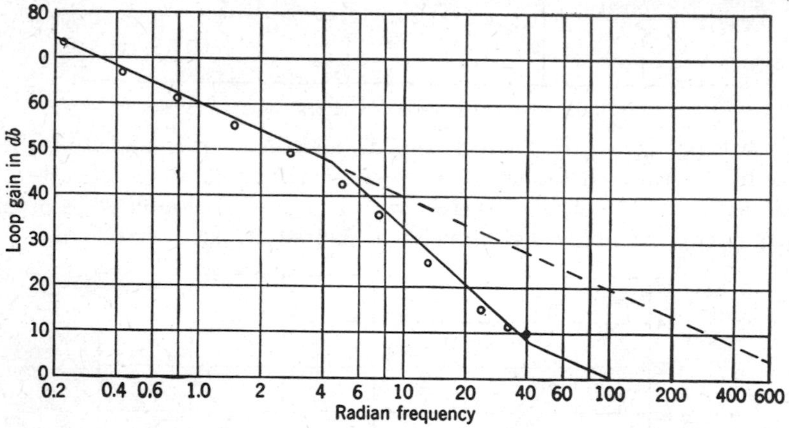

FIG. 4·64.—Experimental decibel–log-frequency plot of the loop transfer function.

network and the servoamplifier. Since a low-impedance line is less likely to pick up signals from adjacent circuits, it was advantageous to use the cathode follower as an impedance transformer. The line from the servoamplifier to equalizer thus operates with approximately 500 ohms impedance to ground.

Figure 4·64 is a plot of the loop gain for this system. The experimental setup made use of a synchro-control transformer as a generator of a modulated 60-cps signal which was connected to the input terminals of the network shown in Fig. 4·62. A constant 60-cycle voltage was impressed on its stator; and as the rotor was turned, its voltage was

$$E_R = E \cos \omega_m t \cos \omega_0 t, \tag{171}$$

where E = maximum value of the 60-cycle carrier,

$f_0 = \dfrac{\omega_0}{2\pi}$ = carrier frequency, cycles per second,

$f_m = \dfrac{\omega_m}{2\pi}$ = rotation speed, revolutions per second.

The voltage E_R is of the same form as that which would be produced by a small-amplitude sinusoidal motion of a synchro-control transformer in a synchro data-transmission system. The magnitude of E was changed throughout the course of the experiment in order to maintain the maximum voltage applied to the control phase of the motor at 50 volts rms. The amplitude of oscillation of the motor shaft or a geared-down shaft was observed optically at the low frequencies and electrically at high frequencies. The ratio of the motor-shaft amplitude in degrees to the voltage E of Eq. (171) is plotted in Fig. 4·64.

The system was operated with a velocity-error constant $K_v = 500\ \text{sec}^{-1}$ which placed feedback cutoff at 96 radians/sec (15.3 cps). The intercept of the -12-db/octave section on the 0-db axis of the loop gain curve occurred at 57.7 radians/sec and gave an acceleration-error constant of $(57.7)^2$, or 3330 sec^{-2}. Experimental over-all frequency-response curves show a rapid falling off at frequencies above 15 cps and thus verify the above analysis.

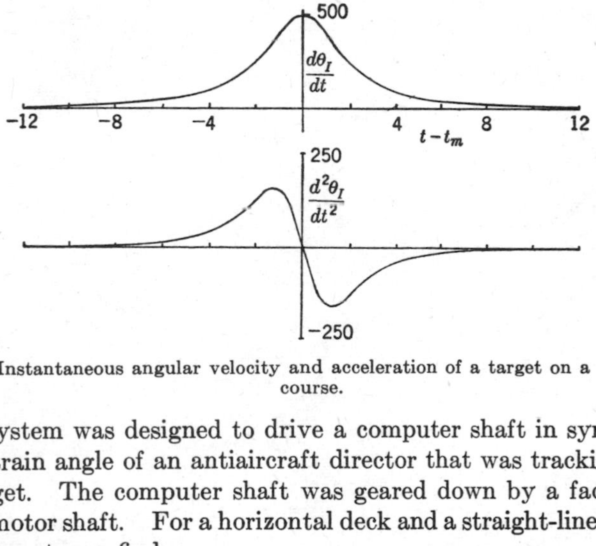

FIG. 4·65.—Instantaneous angular velocity and acceleration of a target on a straight-line course.

This system was designed to drive a computer shaft in synchronism with the train angle of an antiaircraft director that was tracking an airplane target. The computer shaft was geared down by a factor of 360 from the motor shaft. For a horizontal deck and a straight-line constant-velocity target, one finds

$$\theta_I = \tan^{-1} \frac{V_h(t - t_m)}{R_m}, \tag{172}$$

where θ_I = input train angle,
V_h = horizontal velocity,
R_m = minimum horizontal range,
t_m = time at crossover.

The angular velocity and angular acceleration are

$$\frac{d\theta_I}{dt} = \frac{V_h}{R_m} \cos^2 \theta_I, \tag{173}$$

$$\frac{d^2\theta_I}{dt^2} = -2\left(\frac{V_h}{R_m}\right)^2 \sin \theta_I \cos^3 \theta_I. \tag{174}$$

The angular velocity reaches a maximum of V_h/R_m at crossover, or $\theta_I = 0$. The angular acceleration reaches a maximum positive value of

$$\left(\frac{3\sqrt{3}}{8}\right)\left(\frac{V_h}{R_m}\right)^2$$

at 30° before crossover and a corresponding maximum negative value at 30° after crossover. Figure 4·65 is a plot of the angular velocity and acceleration when V_h/R_m is $\frac{1}{2}$ radian/sec (500 angular mils per second). This corresponds to a target with R_m = 500 yd and V_h = 250 yd/sec (450 knots). Using the values of K_v and K_a previously determined, one computes for the servo following of such a target a maximum velocity error of 1 mil and a maximum acceleration error of 0.05 mils.

CHAPTER 5

FILTERS AND SERVO SYSTEMS WITH PULSED DATA

BY W. HUREWICZ

5·1. Introductory Remarks.—Servos considered so far in this book operate on the basis of error data supplied *continuously*, in an uninterrupted flow. The present chapter is concerned with servos that are actuated by error data supplied *intermittently*, at discrete moments equally spaced in time. In other terms, the error data are supplied in the form of pulses, and the servo receives no information whatsoever about the error during the period between two consecutive pulses.

As an extremely simple example of a servo with pulsed data, let us consider a system for which the input and the output are shaft rotations. We denote as usual by θ_I and θ_O the angles determining the position of the shafts and suppose that the action of the servo consists in (1) measuring the error $\epsilon = \theta_I - \theta_O$ at specified, equally spaced moments, say once every second, and (2) instantaneously rotating the output shaft immediately after each measurement by the angle $K\epsilon$, where K is a fixed positive constant. In order to study the performance of the servo, we may suppose that the system begins operating with an initial error ϵ_0 and that the angle θ_I is kept fixed thereafter. Immediately following the first error measurement, the error will acquire the value

$$\epsilon_1 = (1 - K)\epsilon_0. \tag{1}$$

Immediately after the next measurement the error will have the value

$$\epsilon_2 = (1 - K)\epsilon_1 = (1 - K)^2\epsilon_0. \tag{2}$$

Denoting by ϵ_n the value of the error immediately after the nth measurement, we have

$$\epsilon_n = (1 - K)^n\epsilon_0. \tag{3}$$

When $0 < K < 2$, the error approaches zero with increasing n; the servo is therefore stable. On the other hand, for $K > 2$ the error increases indefinitely and the servo is unstable. It is to be noted that instability is caused in this case by *overcorrection.* This kind of instability is quite typical for servos with pulsed data.

A less trivial example will be obtained by the following modifications of the preceding example: Instead of assuming that the errors are corrected by instantaneous rotations of the output shaft, let us now assume that the corrective action of the servo consists in continually exerting a *torque* on the output shaft in such a fashion that the torque is always proportional to the error found at the immediately preceding measurement. The torque then remains constant during the interval between two measurements, changing stepwise at each measurement. Again it is clear that overcorrection and instability will occur when the corrective torque per unit error is too large. In this case a quantitative analysis of stability conditions is not simple, nor can it be obtained by methods used in the theory of servos with continuous error data. The complete analysis will be given at the end of this chapter. Another example of a servo with pulsed data is the automatic gain control system for radar tracking systems.

In the following we shall denote by the *repetition period* of a servo the time interval T_r between two consecutive moments at which error data are received. The quantity $1/T_r$ will be called the "repetition frequency f_r" (in cycles per second). It is almost needless to mention that when T_r is very small compared with other time constants involved in the system, the servo can be treated to within a sufficiently good approximation as a servo with continuous data. The need for a different treatment arises when the length of the repetition period cannot be neglected in comparison with the remaining time constants of the servo.

In analogy with the procedure adopted in Chap. 2, we shall base the theory of servos with pulsed error data on the theory of *filters with pulsed input data;* this will be the subject of the following sections.

FILTERS WITH PULSED DATA

5·2. The Weighting Sequence.—By a linear filter with pulsed data (abbreviated in the following discussion to pulsed filter) we shall mean a transmission device that is supplied with input data at specified equally spaced moments and, in response, furnishes output data at the same moments in such a way that (1) the output data depend linearly on the input data received previously and (2) the performance of the device does not change with time. An example of such a device is a four-terminal passive network that receives its input voltage in the form of *pulses;* if we consider the values of the voltage at the output terminals only at the instants when a pulse is applied to the input terminals, this network can be regarded as a filter with pulsed data.

In order to formulate mathematically the conditions 1 and 2 of the preceding paragraph, let us assume that input data are received at the moments $t = nT_r$ ($n = 0, \pm 1, \pm 2, \pm 3, \cdots$). Let x_n be the value of the input and y_n the value of the output at the time $t = nT_r$. Condition 1 states that

$$y_n = \sum_{k=1}^{\infty} c_{n,k}x_{n-k}, \qquad n = 0, \pm 1, \pm 2, \cdots, \tag{4}$$

where the $c_{n,k}$ are real constants. Condition 2 states that the coefficients $c_{n,k}$ depend only on k, since x_{n-k} must enter y_n in the same way as x_{m-k} enters the expression for y_m. Setting

$$w_k = c_{n,k}, \tag{5}$$

we write Eq. (4) as

$$y_n = \sum_{k=1}^{\infty} w_k x_{n-k}. \tag{6}$$

In order to avoid difficulties caused by the fact that the infinite series in the right-hand term of Eq. (6) may not converge, let us assume for the time being that the input up to a certain moment is zero; that is, $x_n = 0$ for sufficiently large negative values of n. Then there are only a finite number of terms in the sum which are different from zero, and the question of convergence does not arise.

The sequence (w_n) is quite analogous to the weighting function $W(t)$ introduced in Chap. 2; it will be called the *weighting sequence* of the filter. It may be noted in passing that a pulsed filter can be regarded as a continuous filter with the weighting function

$$W(t) = \sum_{n=1}^{\infty} w_n \delta(t - nT_r), \tag{7}$$

where $\delta(t)$ denotes the Dirac delta function.

The meaning of the numbers w_n will be made clearer by the following remark. Let the input to the filter be a single unit pulse applied at $t = 0$:

$$x_0 = 1, \qquad x_n = 0 \qquad \text{for } n \neq 0. \tag{8}$$

Then by Eq. (6)

$$y_n = w_n \qquad (n = 1, 2, 3, \cdots). \tag{9}$$

In words, the number w_n represents the response to the unit pulse n repetition periods after the pulse has been received.

If for a sufficiently large n, say for $n > N$, all the w_n are zero, then the output at a given moment depends only on the N input data received immediately preceding this moment. One can say in this case that the filter has a "finite memory" limited to N pieces of information.

5·3. Stability of Pulsed Filters.—In complete analogy with the concept of stability developed in Chap. 2, a pulsed filter will be called *stable* if to a bounded input there always corresponds a bounded output. We shall see that a *necessary and sufficient condition for stability* is the absolute convergence[1] of the series $\sum_{n=1}^{\infty} w_n$, where (w_n) is the weighting sequence of the filter.

We first prove the sufficiency. Suppose that the sum $\sum_{n=1}^{\infty} |w_n|$ is finite, and let A denote its value. Let the input sequence (x_n) be bounded; that is, for a certain positive number M,

$$|x_n| < M \tag{10}$$

for every integer n. From Eq. (6) we obtain

$$|y_n| < \sum_{k=1}^{\infty} M|w_k| = MA. \tag{11}$$

The output is therefore bounded by the number MA.

In order to prove the necessity of the condition let us assume that the filter is stable. It was remarked in the preceding section that the weighting sequence (w_n) can be regarded as the output sequence corresponding to the unit-pulse input. Hence (by the definition of stability) the sequence (w_n) is bounded. Let M be a positive number such that

$$|w_n| < M \qquad (n = 1, 2, 3, \cdots). \tag{12}$$

Suppose now that the series $\sum_{n=1}^{\infty} |w_n|$ diverges. There certainly exists a positive integer N_1 such that

$$\sum_{n=1}^{N_1} |w_n| > 1. \tag{13}$$

We further select an integer $N_2 > N_1$ such that

$$\sum_{n=1}^{N_2-N_1} |w_n| > MN_1 + 2. \tag{14}$$

The existence of such an integer follows from the divergence of the series. We continue the process ad infinitum. After having selected the integers $N_1, N_2, \ldots, N_{i-1}$, we choose an integer $N_i > N_{i-1}$ satisfying

[1] A series $\sum_{n=1}^{\infty} w_n$ is said to be absolutely convergent if $\sum_{n=1}^{\infty} |w_n| < \infty$.

$$\sum_{n=1}^{N_i - N_{i-1}} |w_n| > MN_{i-1} + i. \tag{15}$$

We now define a bounded input sequence as follows:

$$\left.\begin{aligned} x_n &= 0 && \text{for } n \leqq 0, \\ x_n &= \operatorname{sgn} w_{N_1-n}{}^{1} && \text{for } 1 \leqq n < N_1, \\ x_n &= \operatorname{sgn} w_{N_2-n} && \text{for } N_1 \leqq n < N_2, \\ &\cdots\cdots && \cdots\cdots \\ x_n &= \operatorname{sgn} w_{N_i-n} && \text{for } N_{i-1} \leqq n < N_i. \end{aligned}\right\} \tag{16}$$

Let (y_n) be the corresponding output sequence. By Eq. (6)

$$y_{N_i} = \sum_{k=1}^{N_i-1} w_k x_{N_i-k}. \tag{17}$$

For $1 \leqq k \leqq N_i - N_{i-1}$, the kth term in this sum has (in accordance with the definition of the numbers x_n) the value $|w_k|$. Then by Eq. (15)

$$\sum_{k=1}^{N_i - N_{i-1}} w_k x_{N_i-k} > MN_{i-1} + i. \tag{18}$$

On the other hand, for any n we have $|w_n| < M$, and hence

$$\sum_{k=N_i-N_{i-1}+1}^{N_i-1} w_k x_{N_i-k} > -MN_{i-1}. \tag{19}$$

Adding the last two inequalities, we obtain

$$y_{N_i} > i. \tag{20}$$

Thus (y_n) is an unbounded sequence, contrary to the assumption that the filter is stable. This concludes the proof.

An important property of stable filters is the existence of a steady-state response to a step-function input. Let a unit-step function be applied to the filter at the time $t = 0$. The input x_n has then the value zero for $n < 0$ and the value one for $n \geqq 0$ For the corresponding output data we have, by Eq. (6),

$$y_n = \sum_{k=1}^{n} w_k. \tag{21}$$

Since the absolute convergence of the series $\sum_{n=1}^{\infty} w_n$ implies ordinary con-

[1] The symbol "sgn b" denotes the number that is 0 if $b = 0$, is 1 if $b > 0$, and is -1 if $b < 0$.

vergence, the output y_n in Eq. (21) approaches with increasing n the finite value

$$S = \sum_{k=1}^{\infty} w_k. \tag{22}$$

The constant S represents the steady-state output corresponding to a unit-step input. It should be remarked that the steady-state response S may exist even for an unstable filter, since the series $\sum w_n$ may converge without converging absolutely.

So far we have always assumed that the input x_n is zero up to a certain moment. In the case of a *stable* filter the series in the right-hand term of Eq. (6) converges for any *bounded* infinite sequence (x_n). This follows from the fact that if M is an upper bound for the absolute values $|x_n|$, the convergent series $\sum_{n=1}^{\infty} M|w_n|$ is a majorant series for the series in Eq. (6); the output sequence is well defined even if x_n is different from zero for arbitrarily large negative values of n. In the case of stable filters one may therefore speak of an output for a bounded input which has been "going on forever." In particular, the response to the constant unit input $x_n = 1$ $(n = 0, \pm 1, \pm 2, \cdots)$ is the constant output

$$y_n = \sum_{k=1}^{\infty} w_k = S, \tag{23}$$

which is, of course, equal to the steady-state response to the unit-step input.

We shall call a filter *normalized* if

$$\sum_{n=1}^{\infty} w_n = 1. \tag{24}$$

In this case a constant input is faithfully reproduced by the filter, without either attenuation or amplification. In the case of a normalized filter, each of the output data y_n can be regarded as a *weighted average* of previously applied input data $x_{n-1}, x_{n-2}, x_{n-3}, \cdots$.

5·4. Sinusoidal Sequences.—Let (x_n) $(n = 0, \pm 1, \pm 2, \cdots)$ be a two-sided discrete sequence of data observed at equally spaced moments nT_r where T_r is fixed once for all. (In this section it is not necessary to assume that the members of the sequence are input data of a filter.) We shall call (x_n) a *sinusoidal sequence* with a frequency of ω radians per second or $f = \omega/2\pi$ cps if

$$x_n = A \sin (n\omega T_r + \phi) = A \sin (2\pi n f T_r + \phi), \tag{25}$$

where A and ϕ ("amplitude" and "phase," respectively) are constants and $A > 0$.

We observe first of all that unlike the continuous function, the sequence of Eq. (25) is *not periodic* unless the frequencies f and $f_r = 1/T_r$ are commensurable.[1]

We further note that the amplitude A does not necessarily represent the maximum value attained by the members of the sequence.[2] For instance, if $f/f_r = \frac{1}{4}$ and $\phi = \pi/4$ each number in the sequence of Eq. (25) has one of the two values $\pm(\sqrt{2}/2)A \approx \pm 0.7A$. If, however, f and f_r are incommensurable, the amplitude A is always the upper bound (although not necessarily the maximum) of the sequence; that is, there are members of the sequence arbitrarily near to but less than A.

The following remark is of the greatest importance: The sequence of Eq. (25) remains unchanged if the frequency f is replaced by the frequency $f + kf_r$, where k is an integer. *No distinction can be made between two frequencies that differ by an integral multiple of the repetition frequency.* For instance, a sinusoidal sequence of frequency f_r obviously consists of a single number repeated infinitely many times and is hence the same as a sequence of the frequency zero. It is clear from the foregoing that by varying f between 0 and f_r the entire range of frequencies is covered.

As a matter of fact, every sinusoidal sequence can be written as a sequence with the *frequency not exceeding one-half of the repetition frequency.* In order to show this, let us consider two frequencies f and f', such that $f + f' = f_r$; such frequencies will be called complementary to each other. Clearly one of these frequencies, say f', is $\leqq f_r/2$. Hence it is sufficient to demonstrate that every sinusoidal sequence with the frequency f can also be written as a sinusoidal sequence with the frequency f'. Now

$$\begin{aligned} A \sin (2\pi n f T_r + \phi) &= A \sin (-2\pi n f' T_r + \phi) \\ &= A \sin (2\pi n f' T_r + \pi - \phi). \end{aligned} \tag{26}$$

Thus a sinusoidal sequence with the frequency f can also be represented as a sequence with the frequency f', with the phase changed from ϕ to $(\pi - \phi)$.

As in the discussion of continuous sinusoidal data, it is convenient to

[1] By a periodic sequence is meant a sequence such that for a certain fixed m, $x_{n+m} = x_n$ for all integers n. A sinusoidal sequence always belongs to the class of sequences called "almost periodic" regardless of whether or not it is periodic.

[2] It is, of course, clear that no member of the sequence can exceed A.

substitute for the sequence of Eq. (25) a sequence of complex numbers,

$$\sigma_n = ce^{jn\omega T_r}, \tag{27}$$

where c is a complex constant. With suitably selected c the real parts of the numbers σ_n are the members of the sequence of Eq. (25). The sequence (27) can be written in an even simpler way if we make the substitution

$$z = e^{j\omega T_r}; \tag{28}$$

it now becomes

$$\sigma_n = cz^n. \tag{29}$$

In this representation z can be an arbitrary complex number of absolute value 1. *Each frequency ω is represented by a definite point z of the unit circle;* moreover, equivalent frequencies (that is, frequencies differing by multiples of the repetition frequency) are represented by the same point on the unit circle. (Hence the advantage of using a circle instead of a straight line for representing the continuum of frequencies.) The frequency $\omega = 0$ corresponds to the number $z = 1$, and the frequency equal to one-half of the repetition frequency corresponds to the point $z = -1$, which is one-half of the circumference away from the point $z = 1$. The frequency equal to one-fourth of the repetition frequency is represented by the point $z = j$, which is one-fourth of the total circumference away from the reference point $z = 1$, and so on. When ω is varied from 0 to $2\pi f_r$, the point z makes a complete turn around the unit circle in the counterclockwise direction. It should be noted that two points on the unit circle symmetric with respect to the real axis (or, what amounts to the same thing, two conjugate complex numbers of absolute value 1) represent complementary frequencies, which, as was pointed out before, are not essentially different. Hence the points of the upper (or the lower) semicircle, including +1 and −1, suffice to represent the entire range of frequencies.

5·5. Filter Response to a Sinusoidal Input.—Since a sinusoidal sequence is necessarily bounded, it follows that a sinusoidal sequence of data applied as the input to a *stable* filter will produce a well-defined output. In computing the output it is convenient to replace the sequence in Eq. (25) by an imaginary input sequence of the type in Eq. (27) or, equivalently, by a sequence of the type in Eq. (29). The "response" to such a complex input sequence is a sequence of complex output data with real parts representing the output data corresponding to the real parts of the input data.

From the input sequence

$$\sigma_n = cz^n = ce^{jn\omega T_r} \qquad (n = 0, \pm 1, \pm 2, \cdots) \tag{29}$$

one obtains the output sequence

$$\xi_n = \sum_{k=1}^{\infty} c w_k z^{n-k} = c z^n \sum_{k=1}^{\infty} w_k z^{-k} = c \mathcal{Y} z^n, \tag{30}$$

where the complex number

$$\mathcal{Y} = \sum_{k=1}^{\infty} w_k z^{-k} = \sum_{k=1}^{\infty} w_k e^{-j\omega k T_r} \tag{31}$$

depends only on the frequency ω. The sequence (ξ_n) determined by Eq. (30) is of exactly the same form as the sequence in Eq. (29). Translated into "real" terminology, this yields the fundamental result that (in complete analogy with the theory of continuous filters) the *response of a stable filter to a sinusoidal input is a sinusoidal output of the same frequency.* The change in the amplitude and phase is obtained in a familiar way from the complex number $\mathcal{Y}$: The ratio of the amplitude of the output to that of the input is the absolute value of $\mathcal{Y}$; the difference between the phase of the output and the phase of the input is the angular coordinate of $\mathcal{Y}$. One sees that for $z = 1$, that is, for the input frequency zero, the response factor is $\mathcal{Y} = w_1 + w_2 + w_3 + \cdots$; whereas for $z = -1$, that is, for the input frequency $\frac{1}{2}f_r$, the response factor assumes the value $\mathcal{Y} = -w_1 + w_2 - w_3 + \cdots$. Since the latter value is always a real number, we are led to the following important conclusion: *The phase shift at the input frequency of* $\frac{1}{2}f_r$ *is either* 0° or 180°.

Example.—Let $w_n = K^n$, where K is a real constant and $|K| < 1$. For the frequency-response ratio $\mathcal{Y}$ we obtain from Eq. (31)

$$\mathcal{Y} = \sum_{n=1}^{\infty} K^n z^{-n} = \frac{K}{z - K} = \frac{K}{e^{j\omega T_r} - K} = \frac{K}{\cos \omega T_r - K + j \sin \omega T_r}. \tag{32}$$

The ratio of output amplitude to input amplitude is

$$|\mathcal{Y}| = \frac{K}{\sqrt{(\cos \omega T_r - K)^2 + \sin^2 \omega T_r}} = \frac{K}{\sqrt{K^2 + 1 - 2K \cos \omega T_r}}. \tag{33}$$

The output lags behind the input in phase by an angle

$$\phi = \tan^{-1} \frac{\sin \omega T_r}{\cos \omega T_r - K}. \tag{34}$$

Regarded as a function of the frequency ω, $\mathcal{Y}$ is, of course, periodic with the period $2\pi/T_r = 2\pi f_r$, and according to Eq. (31) the weighting numbers w_n are coefficients in the Fourier expansion of $\mathcal{Y}$ as a function of ω. This implies incidentally that the numbers w_n (and consequently the performance of the filter) are completely determined by its frequency response.

Before concluding this section, let us consider a bounded input that becomes sinusoidal only from a certain moment on and is completely arbitrary up to this moment (subject merely to the condition of boundedness). Suppose, for instance, that Eq. (25) is satisfied only for $n \geqq 0$ whereas, if $n < 0$, the numbers x_n form an arbitrary bounded sequence. Let y_n be the output in the present case, and let (y_{sn}) denote the sinusoidal response to the sequence that satisfies Eq. (25) for all positive and negative values of n. By using the absolute convergence of the series $\sum w_n$ it is easily shown that

$$\lim_{n \to \infty} (y_n - y_{sn}) = 0. \tag{35}$$

In other terms, the sequence (y_{sn}) represents the *steady-state output* corresponding to an input that is sinusoidal only after a certain moment, without having been sinusoidal "forever." The difference $y_n - y_{sn}$ represents the *transient* part of the output, which gradually disappears.

5·6. The Transfer Function of a Pulsed Filter.—In the preceding section the quantity

$$\mathcal{Y} = \sum_{k=1}^{\infty} w_k z^{-k} \tag{31}$$

was considered only for values z on the unit circle $|z| = 1$. In a purely formal way we can consider $\mathcal{Y}$ as being defined for any complex number z for which the power series $\sum_{k=1}^{\infty} w_k z^{-k}$ converges; for any such number the sequence $\mathcal{Y} z^n$ $(n = 0, \pm 1, \pm 2, \pm 3, \cdots)$ can be regarded (again from a purely formal point of view) as the output sequence that corresponds by Eq. (6) to the input sequence[1] z^n $(n = 0, \pm 1, \pm 2, \pm 3, \cdots)$. These formal considerations are valid even if the filter is unstable.

It is well known from the elements of function theory[2] that the series $\sum_{k=1}^{\infty} w_k z^{-k}$ converges for $|z| > R$ and diverges for $|z| < R$, where the convergence radius of the series R is the upper limit of the sequence

$$|w_n|^{1/n} \; (n = 1, 2, \cdots).$$

[1] We shall speak in this case of the "output sequence" despite the fact that the sequence z is unbounded unless $|z| = 1$ (previously we agreed to consider output sequences only in the case of bounded input sequences).

[2] See, for instance, E. C. Titchmarsh, *The Theory of Functions*, Oxford, New York, 1932.

In extreme cases R may have the value 0, which means that the series converges everywhere except at the point $z = 0$, or R may have the value ∞, which means that the series diverges everywhere except at the point $z = \infty$. In the following we shall always assume that $R < \infty$ or, equivalently, that a finite positive number M can be determined in such a way that

$$|w_n| \leqq M^n \tag{36}$$

for every n. Observe that this condition is automatically satisfied if the weighting sequence is bounded and, in particular, if the filter is stable.[1]

For $|z| > R$ the quantity $\mathcal{Y}$ is an *analytic* function of z with the value zero at $z = \infty$. By using the process of analytic continuation[2] one may be able to assign values of $\mathcal{Y}$ even to points with $|z| < R$ (for such points $\mathcal{Y}$ will not be represented by the power series $\sum_{k=1}^{\infty} w_k z^{-k}$). The complete analytic function obtained by the process of analytic continuation from the power series may very well turn out to be a multivalued function; for example, setting $w_n = (-1)^n/n$, we obtain

$$\mathcal{Y}(z) = -\ln(1 + z^{-1}),$$

with infinitely many values assigned to each z.

The transfer function of a filter is defined as follows: *Given a filter (stable or unstable) with the weighting sequence* (w_n), *the function of the complex variable* z *defined by*

$$\mathcal{Y}(z) = \sum_{k=1}^{\infty} w_k z^{-k} \tag{37}$$

and extended by the process of analytical continuation is called the transfer function of the filter.

Example 1.—Let $w_n = K^n$, where K is an arbitrary real constant. Then (see the example at the end of the preceding section)

$$\mathcal{Y}(z) = \frac{K}{z - K}. \tag{38}$$

We observe that $\mathcal{Y}(z)$ is defined over the entire complex plane [if the value ∞ is included among the values of $\mathcal{Y}(z)$], despite the

[1] It has been shown in Sec. 5·3 that stability implies the absolute convergence of the sum $\sum_{n=1}^{\infty} w_n$ and, consequently, the boundedness of the sequence (w_n).

[2] Titchmarsh, *op. cit.*

fact that the power series by which $\mathcal{Y}$ is defined converges only for $|z| > |K|$. The point $z = K$ is a pole of the function $\mathcal{Y}(z)$; at all the remaining points of the plane $\mathcal{Y}(z)$ is regular.

Example 2.—Let $w_n = 1/n!$. Then

$$\mathcal{Y}(z) = e^{1/z} - 1. \tag{39}$$

In this case $\mathcal{Y}(z)$ has an essential singularity at $z = 0$.

Example 3.—Consider a filter such that $w_n = 0$ for sufficiently large n, say for $n > n_0$. Then

$$\mathcal{Y}(z) = P(z)z^{-n_0}, \tag{40}$$

where $P(z)$ is a polynomial in z; conversely, when $\mathcal{Y}(z)$ is of this form, then all sufficiently high terms in the weighting sequence vanish and the filter has a "finite memory."

It is worth remarking that the substitution

$$z = e^{T_r p} \tag{41}$$

transforms the function $\mathcal{Y}(z)$ into the function of p defined by the series $\sum_{k=1}^{\infty} w_k e^{-kT_r p}$. This series is quite analogous to the Laplace integral $\int_{0-}^{\infty} dt\, W(t)e^{-pt}$, which served to define the transfer function of a "continuous" filter in terms of its weighting function $W(t)$. In the case of pulsed servos it is much more convenient to use the variable z than p, since in most important cases the function $\mathcal{Y}(z)$ turns out to be a *rational function* of z, whereas $\mathcal{Y}$, regarded as a function of p, can never be rational or even algebraic. This last remark follows from the fact that z and consequently $\mathcal{Y}$ are periodic in p with the imaginary period $2\pi j/T_r$.

5·7. Stability of a Pulsed Filter, and the Singular Points of Its Transfer Function.—This section relates only to filters with single-valued transfer functions. This restriction is made to avoid terminological complications; the following discussion could easily be extended to the case of multivalued transfer functions by substituting for the complex plane the Riemann surface[1] determined by the transfer function.

With the assumption that $\mathcal{Y}$ is single valued, it is clear that the weighting sequence is completely determined by the transfer function $\mathcal{Y}(z)$, since the numbers w_n are coefficients in the Taylor expansion of $\mathcal{Y}(z)$ at the point $z = \infty$. It follows that all the properties of the filter are determined by the function $\mathcal{Y}(z)$. The most important property of a filter is its stability or lack of stability. We shall now prove that the stability properties of a pulsed filter, like those of continuous filters, depend on the location of the *singular points* of its transfer function.

[1] E. C. Titchmarsh, *The Theory of Functions*, Oxford, New York, 1932.

We consider first a stable filter. According to Sec. 5·3, the series $\sum_{k=1}^{\infty} w_k$ converges absolutely. In other words, the series $\sum_{k=1}^{\infty} w_k z^{-k}$ converges for $z = 1$. Hence the convergence radius R must be $\leqq 1$. The function $\mathcal{Y}(z)$ is regular for $|z| > R$ and a fortiori for $|z| > 1$ (including $z = \infty$); all the singularities[1] of $\mathcal{Y}(z)$ are therefore contained inside the unit circle or on its boundary.

On the other hand, if the filter is unstable, then the series $\sum_{k=1}^{\infty} w_k z^{-k}$ does not converge absolutely for $z = 1$, and hence $R \geqq 1$. We now recall that by a fundamental theorem of function theory, there is at least one singular point (which may be either a pole or an essential singularity of $\mathcal{Y}$) on the boundary $|z| = R$ of the convergence circle. Since $R \geqq 1$, this point is located either in the exterior or on the boundary of the unit circle.

Combining these remarks, we obtain the following fundamental theorem: *If all the singular points of the transfer function are located inside the unit circle, the filter is stable. If at least one singular point lies outside the unit circle, the filter is unstable.*

It should be observed that there is one ambiguous case which is not covered by the preceding theorem, the case of a transfer function with all singularities inside or on the boundary of the unit circle and at least one singularity located exactly on the boundary. In this case the filter may be stable or unstable. From the physical point of view such a filter should be regarded as unstable, since a very small change in the physical constants of the filter may throw the critical singularity from the boundary into the exterior of the unit circle, causing actual instability. In this connection we may further remark that for a stable filter the position of the singularities of the transfer function indicates the degree of stability; the further the singularities are from the boundary of the unit circle the more stable is the filter.

The above theorem can be illustrated by the example $w_n = K^n$. We have found for this case

$$\mathcal{Y}(z) = \frac{K}{z - K}. \tag{38}$$

The only singularity of $\mathcal{Y}(z)$ is the point $z = K$, and the theorem indicates stability for $|K| < 1$ and instability for $|K| > 1$. The same result follows immediately from the definition of stability or from the result of Sec. 5·3.

In the following sections we shall deal for the most part with filters with transfer functions that are rational functions of z:

[1] Since $\mathcal{Y}(z)$ is not a constant, there must be at least one singular point.

$$\mathcal{Y}(z) = \frac{P(z)}{Q(z)}, \tag{42}$$

where $P(z)$ and $Q(z)$ are polynomials[1] that may be assumed to be without common factors. The singularities of $\mathcal{Y}(z)$ are the roots of the algebraic equation

$$Q(z) = 0. \tag{43}$$

The filter is stable if all the roots of this equation are contained inside the unit circle. For example, the filter with the transfer function

$$\mathcal{Y}(z) = \frac{z + 1}{z^2 - \frac{1}{2}z} \tag{44}$$

is stable, whereas the filter with the transfer function

$$\mathcal{Y}(z) = \frac{1}{z^2 - 2z} \tag{45}$$

is unstable.

Comparing the result of this section with the theory developed in Chap. 2, we recognized that in our present considerations the unit circle plays the role that the half plane to the left of the imaginary axis played in the theory of continuous filters. This is in accordance with the fact that the substitution

$$z = e^{T_r p} \tag{41}$$

mentioned at the end of the preceding section transforms the unit circle of the z-plane into the left half plane of the p-plane.

5·8. The Transfer Function Interpreted as the Ratio of Generating Functions.—It was shown in Chap. 2 that the transfer function of a continuous filter can be interpreted as the ratio of the Laplace transform of the output to the Laplace transform of the input. In order to gain an analogous interpretation for transfer functions of pulsed filters, let us consider an input sequence (x_n) with $x_n = 0$ for sufficiently large negative values of n. Suppose, furthermore, that there exists a constant $M > 0$ such that

$$x_n < M^n \tag{46}$$

for every n (this condition is certainly satisfied if the input is bounded). Then the function

$$g_I(z) = \sum_{k=-\infty}^{\infty} x_k z^{-k} \tag{47}$$

of the complex variable z is defined when $|z|$ is sufficiently large. We

[1] Observe that $Q(z)$ must be of higher degree than $P(z)$, since by its definition the transfer function has the value zero at $z = \infty$.

shall call this function the *generating function* of the input. In the same way we associate with the output (y_n) the function

$$g_O(z) = \sum_{k=-\infty}^{\infty} y_k z \tag{48}$$

called the generating function of the output. We now obtain, using Eq. (6),

$$g_I(z)\mathcal{Y}(z) = \sum_{m=-\infty}^{\infty} x_m z^{-m} \sum_{k=1}^{\infty} w_k z^{-k} = \sum_{n=-\infty}^{\infty} z^{-n} \sum_{k=1}^{\infty} w_k x_{n-k}$$

$$= \sum_{n=-\infty}^{\infty} y_n z^{-n} = g_O(z)^1. \tag{49}$$

It follows that the transfer function $\mathcal{Y}(z)$ can be expressed as the ratio

$$\mathcal{Y}(z) = \frac{g_O(z)}{g_I(z)}. \tag{50}$$

This result will be useful in the theory of pulsed servos. It can also be applied to the treatment of two filters in series, where the output of the first filter is the input of the second filter. In such cases the *transfer function of the total filter is the product of the transfer functions of its components.* Let $g_I(z)$, $g_O(z)$, and $g'(z)$ be the generating functions, respectively, of the input to the total filter, the output of the total filter, and the output of the first component; then we can write

$$\frac{g_O(z)}{g_I(z)} = \frac{g_O(z)}{g'(z)} \frac{g'(z)}{g_I(z)}. \tag{51}$$

This proves our assertion, since by the above theorem the two factors in the right-hand term are the transfer functions of the component filters.

FILTERS WITH CLAMPING

5·9. The Concept of Clamping.—Let us suppose that pulsed data measured at the moments $t = 0, T_r, 2T_r, \cdots$, are fed into a device that yields an output with value at any time equal to the values of the input at the immediately preceding pulse. Electrical circuits that perform this function are often referred to as "clamping circuits"; we shall speak of their action as "clamping."

Denoting by x_n the value of the pulsed input to a clamping circuit at

[1] This shows, incidentally, that the series defining $g_O(z)$ converges in the region in which the series defining $g_I(z)$ and $\mathcal{Y}(z)$ are both convergent.

the time $t = nT_r$ and by $x(t)$ the value of the output at the time t, we have

$$x(t) = x_n \qquad \text{for } nT_r < t \leqq (n + 1)T_r. \tag{52}$$

The function $x(t)$ changes discontinuously at the moments $t = nT_r$, and its graph is of staircase form. It will be noted that the value of $x(t)$ at the discontinuity point nT_r has been set equal to $x(nT_r - 0) = x_{n-1}$ [and not to $x(nT_r + 0) = x_n$]. This is, of course, an arbitrary convention.

Suppose now that the output $x(t)$ of the clamping device is fed in turn into a linear filter of the continuous type dealt with in earlier chapters. Let $y(t)$ be the output of this filter, and let $y_n = y(nT_r)$. We can regard the combination of filter and clamping device as a single *pulsed filter* transforming the input data x_n into the output data y_n. An example of such a filter with clamping is the so-called "boxcar" detector used in radar devices. Filters with clamping occur in many applications.

In the following discussion we shall let $Y(p)$ be the transfer function of a continuous filter, to distinguish it from the transfer function $\mathcal{Y}(z)$ of a pulsed filter. The question arises: How may one compute the transfer function $\mathcal{Y}(z)$ of the pulsed filter obtained by combining a continuous filter with a storage device as described above? Since the behavior of the pulsed filter is completely determined by the nature of the continuous filter and the time constant T_r of the clamping device, it follows that the transfer function $\mathcal{Y}(z)$ is completely determined by the function $Y(p)$ and the time constant T_r. In studying the problem of computing the function $\mathcal{Y}(z)$ we shall confine ourselves to cases in which $Y(p)$ is a *rational function*, that is, to the case of continuous filters described by a finite system of linear differential equations with constant coefficients. Such a filter can always be visualized as an *RLC*-network.

5·10. Transfer Functions of Some Special Filters with Clamping.— Before passing to the general treatment of filters with clamping, we shall consider some important special cases.

Example 1.—Let $Y(p)$ be constant;

$$Y(p) = K. \tag{53}$$

The action of the filter without the storage device consists merely in multiplying the input by the constant K. For pulsed input and output we have

$$y_n = Kx(nT_r) = Kx_{n-1}. \tag{54}$$

Hence the pulsed filter has the weighting sequence

$$w_1 = K, \qquad w_2 = 0, \qquad w_3 = 0, \cdots, \tag{55}$$

and the transfer function is

$$\mathcal{Y}(z) = Kz^{-1}. \tag{56}$$

Example 2.—Let

$$Y(p) = \frac{\beta}{p - \alpha}, \tag{57}$$

where α and β are constants. If the filter is stable, then $\alpha < 0$. A concrete realization of a filter with transfer functions of this type is the simple RC-network of Fig. 5·1. The weighting function corresponding to the transfer functions $Y(p)$, that is, the function with Laplace transform equal to $Y(p)$, is

$$W(t) = \beta e^{\alpha t}. \tag{58}$$

Let the pulsed input be the unit pulse

$$x_0 = 1, \qquad x_n = 0 \qquad \text{for } n \neq 0. \tag{59}$$

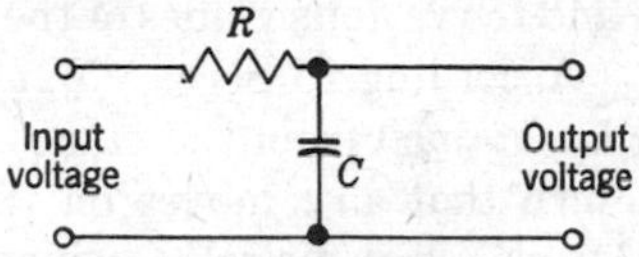

FIG. 5·1.—Simple RC-network.

After having been passed through the storage device, this input becomes

$$x(t) = 1 \qquad \text{for } 0 < t \leqq T_r, \qquad x(t) = 0 \qquad \text{for } t \leqq 0 \text{ or } t > T_r. \tag{60}$$

The continuous output of the filter is[1]

$$y(t) = \int_{0-}^{\infty} d\tau\, W(\tau)x(t - \tau) = \int_{t-T_r}^{t} d\tau\, W(\tau). \tag{61}$$

The values of $y(t)$ for $t = T_r, 2T_r, 3T_r, \cdots$, constitute the pulsed output sequence $y_1, y_2, y_3, \cdots$. As has been shown (see Sec. 5·2), the output sequence of the pulsed filter for a unit-pulse input is identical with the weighting sequence (w_n). Hence

$$w_n = \int_{(n-1)T_r}^{nT_r} W(\tau)\, d\tau = \int_{(n-1)T_r}^{nT_r} \beta e^{\alpha\tau}\, d\tau = \frac{\beta}{\alpha}(e^{\alpha T_r} - 1)e^{(n-1)\alpha T_r}. \tag{62}$$

From this result we obtain for the transfer function $\mathcal{Y}(z)$ of the pulsed filter

$$\begin{aligned}\mathcal{Y}(z) = \sum_{k=1}^{\infty} w_k z^{-k} &= \frac{\beta}{\alpha}(e^{\alpha T_r} - 1)z^{-1} \sum_{k=0}^{\infty} (e^{\alpha T_r} z^{-1})^k \\ &= \frac{\beta}{\alpha}(e^{\alpha T_r} - 1)z^{-1}(1 - e^{\alpha T_r} z^{-1})^{-1}, \end{aligned} \tag{63}$$

or in more symmetric form

$$\mathcal{Y}(z) = -\frac{\beta}{\alpha}\frac{1 - e^{\alpha T_r}}{z - e^{\alpha T_r}}. \tag{64}$$

This formula is correct even for $\alpha = 0$, provided the factor $(1 - e^{\alpha T_r})/\alpha$ in Eq. (64) is replaced by its limiting value as $\alpha \to 0$, namely, $-T_r$; hence corresponding to $Y(p) = \beta/p$, one has $\mathcal{Y}(z) = \beta T_r/(z - 1)$. Let us remark further that Example 1 discussed above can be treated as the

[1] For $\tau < 0$ we set $W(\tau) = 0$.

limiting case of Example 2 for α and β increasing indefinitely, with constant ratio β/α.

Suppose now that $\alpha < 0$ and consequently $e^{\alpha T_r} < 1$. The filter is then stable both with and without the storage device. Suppose, in addition, that the filter is normalized; that is, $-\alpha = \beta$, and consequently $\mathcal{Y}(1) = Y(0) = 1$. It is quite instructive to consider the *frequency response* of the pulsed filter, as thus restricted, for fixed filtering constant α and for various values of the clamping time constant T_r.

According to Secs. 5·5 and 5·6, the frequency response at frequency ω is obtained from the values of $\mathcal{Y}(z)$ for $z = e^{j\omega T_r}$. Now it can easily be shown that as z moves on the unit circle, the point $\mathcal{Y}(z)$ given by Eq. (64) moves on a circle C which has its center on the real axis and cuts that axis at the points

$$\mathcal{Y}(1) = 1,$$

$$\mathcal{Y}(-1) = -\frac{1 - e^{\alpha T_r}}{1 + e^{\alpha T_r}} = \tanh\left(\frac{\alpha T_r}{2}\right) \tag{65}$$

(see Fig. 5·2). When the point z moves clockwise, the point $\mathcal{Y}(z)$ moves counterclockwise. A complete 360° rotation of z corresponds to a complete 360° rotation of $\mathcal{Y}(z)$; a rotation of 180° of z from $z = 1$ to $z = -1$ corresponds to a 180° rotation of $\mathcal{Y}(z)$ from $\mathcal{Y}(1) = 1$ to $\mathcal{Y}(-1)$. If we denote the point $\mathcal{Y}(e^{j\omega T_r})$ by P, then the length of the segment OP gives the attenuation factor and the angle XOP gives the phase shift corresponding to the frequency ω. It is clear from Fig. 5·2 that the attenuation factor has its smallest value, $\tanh(\alpha T_r/2)$, for $\omega T_r = \pi$, that is, for ω equal to one half of the repetition frequency. The phase shift at this frequency is 180°.

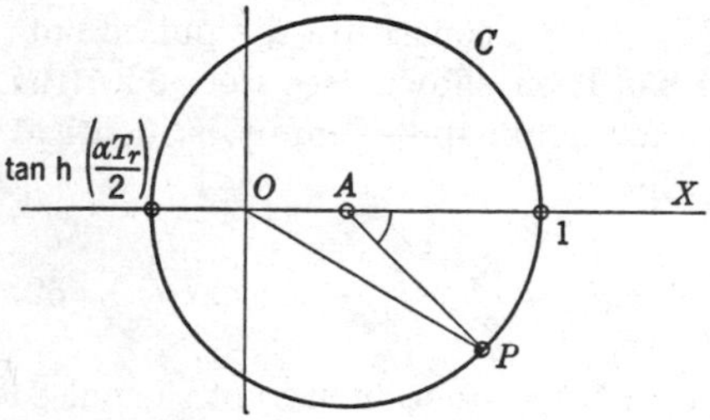

FIG. 5·2.—Transfer function locus for Example 2.

Suppose now that T_r is very small compared with the time constant $-(1/\alpha)$ of the filter. Then the circle C is practically tangent to the imaginary axis at the origin. In this limiting position C coincides with the locus of the points $[-\alpha/(j\omega - \alpha)]$ with $(-\infty < \omega < \infty)$, which represent the frequency response of the filter without the storage device. It is, of course, to be expected that for very small T_r the introduction of the storage device cannot make any appreciable difference.

If the time constant T_r is increased, the center of the circle C moves nearer and nearer to the origin; there is less and less attenuation. In the limit case $\alpha T_r = -\infty$ the circle C coincides with the unit circles around the origin. By Eq. (64) the transfer function in this case becomes $\mathcal{Y}(z) = z^{-1}$, which is the same as in Example 1 with $K = 1$. This is again evident a priori, since when T_r is large, the filter remembers only the last piece of information supplied and consequently y_n is determined by x_{n-1} alone.

Example 3.—Let

$$Y(p) = \frac{\beta}{(p - \alpha)^n}, \tag{66}$$

where n is an arbitrary positive integer. The corresponding weighting function

$$W(t) = \frac{1}{(n-1)!}\beta t^{n-1}e^{\alpha t} = \frac{1}{(n-1)!}\frac{\partial^{n-1}}{\partial \alpha^{n-1}}(\beta e^{\alpha t}) \tag{67}$$

is obtained by applying the operator $[1/(n-1)!](\partial^{n-1}/\partial\alpha^{n-1})$ to the weighting function of Example 2. By going through all the steps of the computation of Example 2, one sees very easily that the resulting transfer function $\mathcal{Y}(z)$ is obtained by applying the same operator to the transfer function computed in Example 2. Hence, by Eq. (64),

$$\mathcal{Y}(z) = \frac{1}{(n-1)!}\frac{\partial^{n-1}}{\partial\alpha^{n-1}}\left(-\frac{\beta}{\alpha}\frac{1 - e^{\alpha T_r}}{z - e^{\alpha T_r}}\right). \tag{68}$$

For example, if $n = 2$,

$$\begin{aligned}\mathcal{Y}(z) &= -\beta\frac{\partial}{\partial\alpha}\left[\frac{1 - e^{\alpha T_r}}{\alpha(z - e^{\alpha T_r})}\right]\\ &= \beta\frac{(z - e^{\alpha T_r})(1 - e^{\alpha T_r} + \alpha T_r e^{\alpha T_r}) - (1 - e^{\alpha T_r})\alpha T_r e^{\alpha T_r}}{\alpha^2(z - e^{\alpha T_r})^2}.\end{aligned} \tag{69}$$

5·11. Transfer Function of a Filter with Clamping; Stability.—We are now prepared to compute the transfer function when $Y(p)$ is an arbitrary rational function,

$$Y(p) = \frac{N(p)}{D(p)}, \tag{70}$$

where $N(p)$ and $D(p)$ are polynomials in p without common factors and the degree of the numerator does not exceed the degree of the denominator. Let $\alpha_1, \alpha_2, \ldots, \alpha_m$, be the different zeros of the denominator, that is, the different poles of $Y(p)$. We can then decompose $Y(p)$ into a finite number of simple partial fractions

$$Y(p) = K + \sum_{k,s}\frac{\beta_{ks}}{(p - \alpha_k)^s}. \tag{71}$$

Using the same methods as above, we find that the transfer function $\mathcal{Y}(z)$ is obtained by adding up the corresponding expressions as given by Eq. (68). That is,

$$\mathcal{Y}(z) = \frac{K}{z} + \sum_{k,s} \frac{1}{(s-1)!} \frac{\partial^{s-1}}{\partial \alpha_k^{s-1}} \left(-\frac{\beta_{ks}}{\alpha_k} \frac{1 - e^{\alpha_k T_r}}{z - e^{\alpha_k T_r}} \right). \tag{72}$$

(The fact that the numbers α_k and β_{ks} are not necessarily real has, of course, no effect on the formal computations.)

It should be noted that $\mathcal{Y}(z)$ is a *rational* function of z, the poles of which, aside from a possible pole at $z = 0$,[1] are at the points[2] $z_k = e^{\alpha_k T_r}$. The degree of the denominator of $\mathcal{Y}(z)$ cannot exceed the degree of the denominator of $Y(p)$ by more than 1.

When $Y(p)$ has no multiple poles, the decomposition of $Y(p)$ into partial fractions assumes the simpler form

$$Y(p) = K + \sum_k \frac{\beta_k}{p - \alpha_k}, \tag{73}$$

and Eq. (72) simplifies to

$$\mathcal{Y}(z) = \frac{K}{z} + \sum_k -\frac{\beta_k}{\alpha_k} \frac{1 - e^{\alpha_k T_r}}{z - e^{\alpha_k T_r}}. \tag{74}$$

Example 1.—Let

$$Y(p) = \frac{p}{p+1} = 1 - \frac{1}{p+1}. \tag{75}$$

One obtains

$$\mathcal{Y}(z) = \frac{1}{z} - \frac{1 - e^{-T_r}}{z - e^{-T_r}}. \tag{76}$$

Example 2.—Consider next a resonant filter. Denoting the resonant frequency of the filter by ω_n, we can write

$$Y(p) = \frac{\omega_n^2}{p^2 + \omega_n^2}. \tag{77}$$

In order to compute $\mathcal{Y}(z)$ we first decompose $Y(p)$ into partial fractions:

$$Y(p) = \frac{j\omega_n}{2} \left(\frac{1}{p + j\omega_n} - \frac{1}{p - j\omega_n} \right). \tag{78}$$

Applying Eq. (74), one obtains

$$\begin{aligned} \mathcal{Y}(z) &= \frac{j\omega_n}{2} \left(\frac{1}{j\omega_n} \frac{1 - e^{j\omega_n T_r}}{z - e^{j\omega_n T_r}} + \frac{1}{j\omega_n} \frac{1 - e^{-j\omega_n T_r}}{z - e^{-j\omega_n T_r}} \right) \\ &= \frac{1}{2} \left(\frac{1 - e^{j\omega_n T_r}}{z - e^{j\omega_n T_r}} + \frac{1 - e^{-j\omega_n T_r}}{z - e^{-j\omega_n T_r}} \right) \\ &= (1 - \cos \omega_n T_r) \frac{1 + z}{1 + z^2 - 2z \cos \omega_n T_r}. \end{aligned} \tag{79}$$

[1] This pole occurs if and only if $N(p)$ has the same degree as $D(p)$.

[2] Observe that two different poles α_1, α_2 of Y yield the same pole of $\mathcal{Y}$ if $\alpha_1 - \alpha_2 = 2\pi k j / T_r$, where k is an integer.

Suppose first that $\omega_n T_r$ is not an integral multiple of π; the resonant frequency is then not an integral multiple of half of the repetition frequency. The formula above shows $\mathcal{Y}(e^{j\omega_n T_r}) = \infty$ and $\mathcal{Y}(-1) = 0$. This means that the filter with the storage device still resonates at the frequency ω_n and in addition gives *complete attenuation* at one-half of the repetition frequency. The attenuation factor of the filter operating without the storage device is, of course, different from zero for all frequencies. In case $\omega_n T_r = k\pi$, where k is an odd integer, one has

$$\mathcal{Y}(z) = \frac{2}{z+1}. \tag{80}$$

The pulsed filter resonates in this case at half of the repetition frequency. All frequencies except the zero frequency are amplified, since $|2/(z+1)| > 1$ when $|z| = 1$ and $z \neq 1$. Suppose finally that $\omega_n T_r = k\pi$, where k is an even number. In this case

$$\mathcal{Y}(z) = 1 \quad \text{for } z = 1, \qquad \mathcal{Y}(z) = 0 \quad \text{for } z \neq 1. \tag{81}$$

This means that the filter rejects all the frequencies except the zero frequency. In an actual physical system (which can only approximate this ideal case) such a pulsed filter will act as a low-pass filter with an extremely sharp cutoff at a low frequency.

We conclude this section with the following important remark. We have seen that to every pole α of the function $Y(p)$ corresponds a pole $e^{\alpha T_r}$ of the function $\mathcal{Y}(z)$. If the real part of α is negative, the point $e^{\alpha T_r}$ is inside the unit circle, and conversely. Recalling the stability criteria for continuous and discontinuous filters, we conclude that if a filter is stable without the storage device, it will remain stable with the storage device, and conversely.

5·12. Simplified Transfer Functions for $|\alpha_k T_r| \gg 1$.—The expressions occurring on the right in Eqs. (72) and (74) can be rewritten as follows:

$$-\frac{\beta_{ks}}{\alpha_k}\frac{1 - e^{\alpha_k T_r}}{z - e^{\alpha_k T_r}} = \frac{\beta_{ks}}{\dfrac{z-1}{T_r}\dfrac{\alpha_k T_r}{e^{\alpha_k T_r} - 1} - \alpha_k}. \tag{82}$$

Setting

$$\gamma_k = \frac{\alpha_k T_r}{e^{\alpha_k T_r} - 1}, \tag{83}$$

and introducing the new variable

$$p = \frac{z-1}{T_r}, \tag{84}$$

one can write Eq. (72) as

$$\mathcal{Y}(z) = \mathcal{Y}(1 + T_r p) = \frac{K}{1 + T_r p} + \sum_{k,s} \frac{1}{(s-1)!}\frac{\partial^{s-1}}{\partial \alpha_k^{s-1}}\frac{\beta_{ks}}{\gamma_k p - \alpha_k}. \tag{85}$$

It should be noted that the new variable p has the dimension of frequency whereas z was dimensionless. Observe also that by Eq. (84) the unit circle of the z-plane is transformed into the circle C of the p-plane with center at the point $p = -1/T_r = -f_r$ and radius f_r; this circle is tangent to the imaginary axis at the origin (see Fig. 5·3).

Let us now make the following *assumptions*:

1. $Y(\infty) = 0$; that is, $N(p)$ has lower degree than $D(p)$.
2. All the numbers $|\alpha_k T_r|$ corresponding to different poles of $Y(p)$ are *very small* compared with 1.

Physically, Assumption 2 means that all the time constants involved in our filter are *large* compared with the repetition period T_r of the pulses. It follows from Eq. (83) that under this condition all the numbers γ_k are close to 1 and their successive derivatives $(\partial^s\gamma_k)/(\partial\alpha_k^s)$ are close to zero. Thus, instead of the exact Eq. (85) one may use the approximate formula[1]

$$\mathcal{Y}(z) = \mathcal{Y}(1 + T_r p) \approx \sum_{k,s} \frac{1}{(s-1)!} \frac{\partial^{s-1}}{\partial\alpha_k^{s-1}} \left(\frac{\beta_{ks}}{p - \alpha_k}\right) = \sum_{k,s} \frac{\beta_{ks}}{(p - \alpha_k)^s} \tag{86}$$

or

$$\mathcal{Y}(z) = \mathcal{Y}(1 + T_r p) \approx Y(p). \tag{87}$$

If the above assumptions are valid, *then the transfer function of the pulsed filter can be identified with the transfer function of the continuous filter by introduction of the variable p defined by* Eq. (84). This result is of great practical importance, since, under the conditions specified above, the transfer function of the pulsed filter can be obtained immediately from the function $Y(p)$; one thus avoids the tedious process of decomposing $Y(p)$ into partial fractions, which involves the solution of the algebraical equation $D(p) = 0$. When using this simplified formula one fact should always be kept in mind: Although the frequency response of the continuous filter is obtained from the values of $Y(p)$ on the imaginary axis, the frequency response of the pulsed filter is computed from the values of $Y(p)$ along the circle C. In particular, the response corresponding to a given frequency $\omega \leqq \pi f_r$ is approximately determined by the value of $Y(p)$ at a point P of the circle C, at a linear distance ω from the origin, measured counterclockwise along the circle. If ω is small compared with the repetition frequency f_r, then the point P is very close

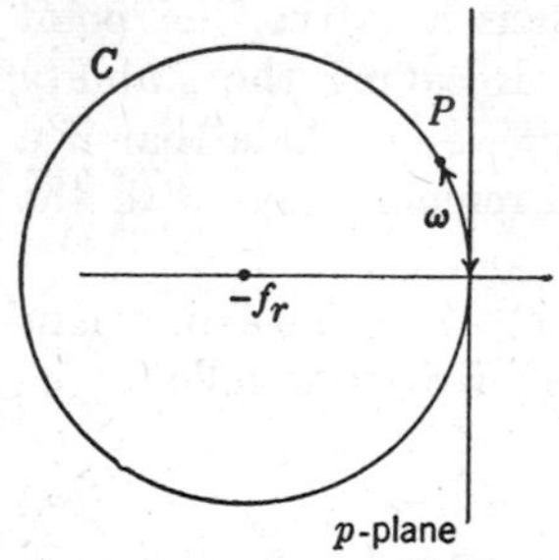

FIG. 5·3.—The circle C.

[1] Since $Y(\infty) = 0$, the constant term in the decomposition of $Y(p)$ in partial fractions vanishes.

to the point $j\omega$ on the imaginary axis and can be identified with it. This is in accord with the expectation that for frequencies that are low compared with the repetition frequency there should be practically no difference between the responses of the filter with or without storage device. It would, however, be entirely wrong to identify the two responses for high frequencies. For instance, the response of the continuous filter to the frequency $\omega = \pi f_r$, which is one-half of the repetition frequency, is determined by the value $Y(\pi j f_r)$, whereas the response of the pulsed filter to the same frequency is (approximately) determined by the value $Y(-2f_r)$. This latter value is always real, corresponding to a phase shift of either 0° or 180° (see Sec. 5·5).

The formula of Eq. (87) can be used only when T_r is small compared with all the time constants of the filter. One might object that this condition can never be satisfied in a concrete physical device, since there always remains the possibility of small unpredictable time lags which may be comparable to the time period T_r or even smaller. In order to meet this objection, let us consider the simplest filter with a single time constant T_1, having the transfer function

$$Y(p) = \frac{1}{T_1 p + 1}. \tag{88}$$

Suppose now that this filter has an additional time lag T_2 which is small compared with T_1. The exact transfer function is then

$$Y(p) = \frac{1}{T_1 p + 1} \frac{1}{T_2 p + 1} = \frac{1}{T_1 - T_2} \left(\frac{T_1}{T_1 p + 1} - \frac{T_2}{T_2 p + 1} \right). \tag{89}$$

By Eq. (85) we have, exactly,

$$\mathcal{Y}(z) = \mathcal{Y}(1 + T_r p) = \frac{T_1}{T_1 - T_2} \frac{1}{\gamma_1 T_1 p + 1} - \frac{T_2}{T_1 - T_2} \frac{1}{\gamma_2 T_2 p + 1}, \tag{90}$$

where $|\gamma_1 - 1|$ is a small number if the ratio T_r/T_1 is small. The number γ_2 is not necessarily close to 1. The second term in the expression for $\mathcal{Y}(z)$ is, however, very small compared with the first term because of the small coefficient $T_2/(T_1 - T_2)$; it therefore does not make any appreciable difference whether this term is left unchanged, simplified by replacing γ_2 by 1, or left out altogether. The same reasoning can be applied in the general case, where it leads to the conclusion that the simplified Eq. (87) can be applied without regard for "parasitic" time lags, provided the "essential" time constants are large compared with T_r.

5·13. Filters with Switches.—Instead of assuming a storage device that holds the pulsed-input value for the entire repetition period T_r, we could consider a storage device that retains the pulse during only a fraction of the repetition period. It is not hard to derive in this more general case formulas for the transfer function $\mathcal{Y}(z)$ that are analogous to those derived in Secs. 5·10 through 5·12. We shall treat in some detail only the extreme case in which the pulse is held for a period T_s small compared with the repetition period T_r. Such a system can best be visualized as a filter fed by a continuous input and supplied with a *switch* that is closed only during very short periods of length T_s following each of the moments $t = 0, T_r, 2T_r, \cdots$

During the short period T_s we may regard as constant the finite weighting function $W(t)$ of the filter without the switch. When the switch is in operation, the input received at the time $t = 0$ has the weight $T_sW(nT_r)$ at the time $t = nT_r$. In other terms, the filter with the switch, regarded as a pulsed filter, has the weighting sequence

$$w_n = T_sW(nT_r) \tag{91}$$

and the transfer function

$$\mathcal{Y}(z) = T_s \sum_{n=1}^{\infty} W(nT_r)z^{-n}. \tag{92}$$

For example, if

$$Y(p) = \frac{\beta}{p - \alpha}, \qquad W(t) = \beta e^{\alpha t}, \tag{93}$$

we have

$$\mathcal{Y}(z) = T_s \sum_{n=1}^{\infty} \beta e^{n\alpha T_r} z^{-n} = T_s\beta \frac{e^{\alpha T_r}}{z - e^{\alpha T_r}}. \tag{94}$$

In the more general case when $Y(p)$ is a rational transfer function satisfying $Y(\infty) = 0$, we have, in the notation of Eq. (72),

$$\mathcal{Y}(z) = \sum_{k,s} \frac{T_s}{(s-1)!} \frac{\partial^{s-1}}{\partial\alpha_k^{s-1}} \frac{\beta_{ks}e^{\alpha_k T_r}}{z - e^{\alpha_k T_r}}. \tag{95}$$

If all the numbers $\alpha_k T_r$ are small, we can replace the exponential $e^{\alpha_k T_r}$ in this formula by the approximation $(1 + \alpha_k T_r)$; with the substitution of Eq. (84) this yields, after obvious simplifications, the approximate formula

$$\mathcal{Y}(z) = \mathcal{Y}(1 + T_r p) \approx \frac{T_s}{T_r} Y(p). \tag{96}$$

Except for the factor T_s/T_r this is the same as Eq. (87).

SERVOS WITH PULSED INPUT

5·14. General Theory of Pulsed Servos: Feedback Transfer Function, Stability.—In a pulsed servo the input and the output are considered only at discrete times $t = nT_r$ ($n = 0, \pm 1, \pm 2, \cdots$). We shall denote by θ_{In} the input and by θ_{On} the output at the time $t = nT_r$. The servo output is activated by the pulsed error

$$\epsilon_n = \theta_{In} - \theta_{On}. \tag{97}$$

As in the theory of continuous servos, we shall assume that the output sequence (θ_{On}) is related to the error sequence (ϵ_n) as output and input of a linear filter. In this case, however, the filter will be a pulsed filter. The transfer function $\mathcal{Y}(z)$ of this filter will be called the *feedback transfer function* of the servo. In order to obtain the relation between the output and the input, we shall assume that up to a certain moment both the input and the output are zero:

$$\theta_{In} = 0, \qquad \theta_{On} = 0, \qquad \epsilon_n = 0. \tag{98}$$

for sufficiently large negative values of n.

Following the ideas of Sec. 5·8, we set

$$g_I(z) = \sum_{-\infty}^{\infty} \theta_{In} z^{-n}, \tag{99a}$$

$$g_O(z) = \sum_{-\infty}^{\infty} \theta_{On} z^{-n}, \tag{99b}$$

$$g_\epsilon(z) = \sum_{-\infty}^{\infty} \epsilon_n z^{-n} = g_I(z) - g_O(z). \tag{99c}$$

By the interpretation of the transfer function discussed in Sec. 5·8 we have

$$g_O(z) = \mathcal{Y}(z) g_\epsilon(z) = \mathcal{Y}(z)[g_I(z) - g_O(z)] \tag{100a}$$

or

$$g_O(z) = \frac{\mathcal{Y}(z)}{1 + \mathcal{Y}(z)}\, g_I(z). \tag{100b}$$

The relation between the sequence (θ_{In}) and the sequence (θ_{On}) is thus the same as that between the input and output of a pulsed filter with the transfer function

$$\mathcal{Y}_O(z) = \frac{\mathcal{Y}(z)}{1 + \mathcal{Y}(z)}; \tag{101}$$

$\mathcal{Y}_O(z)$ is the *over-all transfer function* of the servo.

Since the pulsed servo is, in effect, a pulsed filter with the transfer function $\mathcal{Y}_O(z)$, it is clear that the theory of stability of pulsed servos is contained in the theory of stability of pulsed filters developed in the preceding sections of this chapter. Hence the servo will be stable if all the singular points of the over-all transfer function $\mathcal{Y}_O(z)$ are located inside the unit circle. If at least one singular point lies outside the unit circle, then the servo is unstable.

We shall suppose, in what follows, that the feedback transfer function $\mathcal{Y}(z)$ is a rational function of z. The singularities (poles) of the over-all transfer function $\mathcal{Y}_O(z)$ are then the roots of the algebraic equation

$$1 + \mathcal{Y}(z) = 0. \tag{102}$$

The stability criterion becomes this: *If all the roots of Eq.* (102) *are inside the unit circle, the servo is stable. If at least one of the roots of Eq.* (102) *lies in the exterior of the unit circle, then the servo is unstable.*

The stability criterion for pulsed servos is, of course, very similar to the stability criterion for continuous servos; in fact one need only replace the unit circle by the left half plane in order to obtain the criterion (see Chap. 2) for the continuous case. As in the continuous case, the stability criterion for the pulsed servo can be brought into geometric form. To this end we define the *transfer locus* of the pulsed servo to be the closed curve described by the point $\mathcal{Y}(z)$, as the point z describes the boundary of the unit circle in a counterclockwise direction. If any points exterior to the unit circle are mapped onto the point -1 by $\mathcal{Y}(z)$, then at least one of the roots of Eq. (102) is in the exterior of the unit circle and the servo is unstable. In such a case, the boundary of the exterior of the unit circle will enclose the point -1; this boundary is, of course, the transfer locus. One can, in fact, show that the number of roots minus the number of poles of $\mathcal{Y}(z) + 1$ is precisely equal to the number of times that the transfer locus encircles the point -1 in a clockwise direction. This is, of course, the analogue of the continuous case, except that the circumference of the unit circle is used instead of the imaginary axis. If, in particular, the function $\mathcal{Y}(z)$ has no poles outside the unit circle (which means that the servo is stable when the feedback is cut off), one can use a modified form of the Nyquist criterion: *The servo is stable if and only if*[1] *the transfer locus does not surround the point* -1. The procedure to be used when $\mathcal{Y}(z)$ has poles on the boundary of the unit circle is analogous to that developed in Chap. 2.

If $\mathcal{Y}(z)$ is a rational function of degree 2, Eq. (102) can be written in the form

$$P(z) \equiv z^2 + Az + B = 0, \tag{103}$$

where A and B are real. In this case the stability criterion, that the roots of Eq. (103) lie inside the unit circle, reduces to the following simple form: The servo is stable if and only if

[1] In this and in the remainder of the chapter if a root of Eq. (102) lies *on* or outside the circle of convergence, then the servo is considered to be unstable.

$$\left.\begin{aligned} P(1) &= 1 + A + B > 0, \\ P(-1) &= 1 - A + B > 0, \\ P(0) &= B < 1. \end{aligned}\right\} \tag{104}$$

The last condition excludes imaginary roots of absolute value $\geqq 1$ and, together with the first two conditions, excludes real roots outside the interval $-1 < z < +1$.

Similar but more complicated criteria can be derived for equations of higher order.

5·15. Servos Controlled by Filter with Clamping.—The discussion of the preceding section applies in particular to a servo controlled by a *filter with clamping*. Such a servo can be regarded as a continuous servo containing a clamping device that holds the error signal at a constant value during the period $nT_r < t < (n + 1)T_r$; the rest of the servo is then activated by the errors measured at the instants $T_r, 2T_r, 3T_r, \ldots,$ instead of by the errors measured continuously.

Let $Y(p)$ be the feedback transfer function of the servo without the clamping device. If $Y(p)$ is a *rational function* of p, the feedback transfer function $\mathcal{Y}(z)$ of the pulsed servo can be computed from $Y(p)$ by the method developed in Secs. 5·9 through 5·12. The stability equation

$$1 + \mathcal{Y}(z) = 0 \tag{102}$$

can then be handled either algebraically or geometrically.

Especially simple is the case when the time interval T_r is small compared with all the numbers $|\alpha_k|^{-1}$, the α_k's being the poles of the function $Y(p)$. As was pointed out in Sec. 5·12, in this case one obtains the approximate formula

$$\mathcal{Y}(1 + T_r p) \approx Y(p). \tag{87}$$

The variable p is related to z by

$$p = \frac{z - 1}{T_r}, \tag{84}$$

and the unit circle in the z-plane goes over into the circle C (see Fig. 5·3),

$$\left|p + \frac{1}{T_r}\right| = \frac{1}{T_r}. \tag{105}$$

The servo will be stable if and only if all roots of the equation

$$1 + Y(p) = 0 \tag{106}$$

lie within the circle C defined by Eq. (105). It is evident that the graphical procedure for determining the stability of the servo consists in tracing the locus of the points $Y(p)$ as the point p describes the circle

C in a counterclockwise direction. The number of times that this locus surrounds the point -1 in a clockwise direction gives the difference between the number of roots and the number of poles of Eq. (106) that lie outside the circle C. This procedure differs from the ordinary Nyquist procedure only in the fact that the circle C is used instead of the imaginary axis

As an illustration of various methods for determining the stability of a servo, we may consider the simple example in which

$$Y(p) = \frac{K}{T_1 p + 1}. \tag{107}$$

Aside from the clamping device, the controller of the servo is an exponential-smoothing filter with the time constant T_1 and the gain K. Substituting in Eq. (64), we obtain

$$\mathcal{Y}(z) = \frac{K(1 - e^{-\frac{T_r}{T_1}})}{z - e^{-\frac{T_r}{T_1}}}. \tag{108}$$

First we apply the stability criterion of Sec. 5·14. The root of the stability equation

$$1 + \mathcal{Y}(z) \equiv 1 + \frac{K(1 - e^{-\frac{T_r}{T_1}})}{z - e^{-\frac{T_r}{T_1}}} = 0 \tag{109}$$

is numerically less than 1 if and only if

$$1 + \mathcal{Y}(-1) > 0, \tag{110}$$

or

$$K < \coth \frac{T_r}{2T_1}; \tag{111}$$

the servo is stable only when the gain is thus limited.

The same condition can be obtained geometrically by considering the locus of the points $\mathcal{Y}(z)$, when z describes the unit circle. As has been shown in Sec. 5·10, this locus is the circle which has its center on the real axis and cuts the real axis at the points

$$\mathcal{Y}(1) = K, \text{ and } \mathcal{Y}(-1) = -K \tanh \frac{T_r}{2T_1}. \tag{112}$$

According to the geometrical-stability criterion, the servo will be stable if the point -1 is not contained in this circle,[1] that is, if

$$-K \tanh \frac{T_r}{2T_1} > -1. \tag{113}$$

This, of course, coincides with the stability condition derived analytically.

[1] The only pole of $\mathcal{Y}(z)$ does not lie exterior to the unit circle.

Suppose now that T_r is small compared with T_1. Then we can use the simplified geometrical criterion, which involves drawing the locus of

$$Y(p) = \frac{K}{T_1 p + 1} \tag{107}$$

for

$$\left|p + \frac{1}{T_r}\right| = \frac{1}{T_r}. \tag{105}$$

This locus is a circle in the p-plane, symmetric in respect to the real axis and intersecting the real axis at the points

$$Y(0) = K \qquad \text{and} \qquad Y\left(-\frac{2}{T_r}\right) = \frac{K}{-\frac{2T_1}{T_r} + 1}. \tag{114}$$

The point -1 lies in the exterior of this circle when

$$K < \frac{2T_1}{T_r} - 1. \tag{115}$$

This is an approximate stability condition, which, for the case $T_r/T_1 \ll 1$, is practically identical with the exact condition derived above, since it is permissible in this case to replace coth $(T_r/2T_1)$ by $2T_1/T_r$.

5·16. Clamped Servo with Proportional Control.—We now consider in some detail the servo mentioned in Sec. 5·1, in which the error (that is, the angular displacement between the input shaft and the output shaft) is measured at the moments T_r, $2T_r$, $3T_r$, . . . and in which the corrective torque is always proportional to the error obtained at the immediately preceding measurement.

If the error were measured continuously, we should have an ordinary servo with proportional gain control. The feedback transfer function of such a servo has the form

$$Y(p) = \frac{K}{p(T_m p + 1)}, \tag{116}$$

where T_m is the motor time constant and K is the velocity-error constant. The equalizer of the pulsed servo can be regarded as a filter with the transfer function $Y(p)$ combined with a clamping device. In order to compute the transfer function $\mathcal{Y}(z)$ of the equalizer (see Sec. 5·11) we first decompose $Y(p)$ into partial fractions:

$$Y(p) = \frac{K}{p} - \frac{K}{p + \frac{1}{T_m}}. \tag{117}$$

It now follows from Eq. (74) that

$$\mathcal{Y}(z) = \frac{KT_r}{z-1} - \frac{KT_m(1 - e^{-\frac{T_r}{T_m}})}{z - e^{-\frac{T_r}{T_m}}}. \tag{118}$$

The stability equation is

$$1 + \mathcal{Y}(z) = 0, \tag{102}$$

or, after clearing fractions,

$$P(z) \equiv (z-1)(z - e^{-\frac{T_r}{T_m}})\,[1 + \mathcal{Y}(z)] = 0. \tag{119}$$

This is a quadratic equation. According to the remark at the end of Sec. 5·14, the necessary and sufficient conditions for stability are

$$P(1) > 0, \qquad P(-1) > 0, \qquad P(0) < 1. \tag{104}$$

The first of these conditions is satisfied identically. The second and the third, after simple algebraic manipulations, yield, respectively,

$$\frac{1}{KT_r} > \frac{1}{2} - \frac{T_m}{T_r}\tanh\frac{T_r}{2T_m}, \tag{120}$$

$$\frac{1}{KT_r} > \frac{T_m}{T_r} + \frac{1}{1 - e^{T_r/T_m}}. \tag{121}$$

In Fig. 5·4 the values of T_r/T_m are marked on the horizontal, the values of $1/KT_r$ on the vertical axis. The two curves represent the functions on the right-hand sides of the above inequalities; the region of instability is shaded. The graph shows that when $T_r \ll T_m$ or $T_m \ll T_r$, the relation

$$KT_r < 2 \tag{122}$$

is the approximate condition for stability. For $T_r/T_m = 3.7$, one has the optimum stability condition $KT_r < 4.2$. For other ratios T_r/T_m, KT_r must be smaller than a number C that varies between 2 and 4·2. Let us consider a triple of values T_r, T_m, K, corresponding to a point on the boundary of the region of stability in Fig. 5·4. We shall distinguish between two cases.

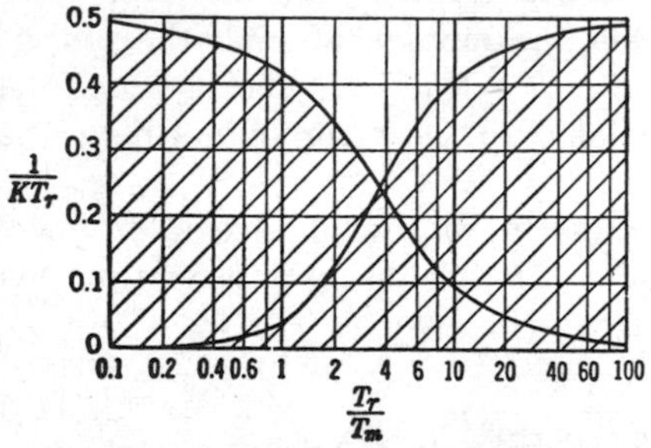

FIG. 5·4.—Region of instability.

1. $T_r/T_m \geqq 3.7$. In this case the point $(1/KT_r, T_r/T_m)$ is on the boundary of the curve represented by the right-hand side of the inequality (120); that is, the second inequality in (104) is replaced by the equation $P(-1) = 0$. In other words, the equation $\mathcal{Y}(z) + 1 = 0$ has the root $z = -1$, and the over-all transfer func-

tion $\mathcal{Y}_O(z)$ is infinite at $z = -1$. This indicates that the servo *resonates* at the frequency $\frac{1}{2}f_r$.

2. $T_r/T_m < 3.7$. In this case the third of the inequalities (104) is replaced by the equation $P(0) = 1$. It follows that the equation $\mathcal{Y}(z) + 1 = 0$ has a pair of conjugate complex roots on the boundary of the unit circle. The servo then resonates at the frequency corresponding to these roots, that is at a frequency different from $\frac{1}{2}f_r$.

CHAPTER 6

STATISTICAL PROPERTIES OF TIME-VARIABLE DATA

By R. S. Phillips

INTRODUCTION

6·1. The Need for Statistical Considerations.—Up to this point we have limited our design criteria for servomechanisms to considerations of stability, of suitable damping, and of the nature of the error for a step, constant-velocity, or constant-acceleration input. We have not considered the error that will result from the actual input that the servomechanism will be called upon to follow. Likewise nothing has been said about the effect on the servomechanism of uncontrolled load disturbances or of the effect of random noise sources, which are often found in the error-measuring device and the servoamplifier. Clearly the fundamental entity by which a servomechanism should be judged is the actual error that results from the actual input and these random disturbances. It is true that the design criteria already developed, together with ingenuity and common sense, will in most cases lead to a satisfactory solution of the design problem. It is, however, essential to come to grips with the basic problem, not only in order to obtain a good solution for the exceptional servo system but also to build up a rational and systematic science of servomechanisms.

The actual input to a servomechanism, the uncontrolled load disturbances, the noise interference, and the actual servo output can, in general, be described only statistically. Before developing the necessary machinery for such a description, we shall discuss some examples of these quantities.

Usually a servomechanism is required to follow many different input signals. If, on the contrary, the input were periodic, it would in general be simpler to drive the output by a cam than to use a servomechanism; the latter is most useful when its input is varied and to some extent unpredictable. The set of input signals for a single servomechanism is similar to the set of all messages transmitted by a single telephone in its lifetime. Like the telephone messages, the input signals will be confined to a limited frequency band but will be somewhat varied in detail. Furthermore, in neither case is it possible to predict the future with certainty on the basis of the past. On the other hand, the sounds in the telephone message are not completely unrelated. The remainder of an uncompleted sentence could in many cases be guessed; likewise, the possible future values of a servo input could be predicted if the extrapolation were not carried too far into the future. Hence, despite the fact that the lifetime input to a given servomechanism cannot be described in a straightforward way as a function of time, it is clear that there is a great deal that can be said about it.

As an example, consider an automatic-tracking radar system that is required to track all aircraft traveling through a hemisphere of radius 20,000 yd about the system. Because of the limited acceleration to which aircraft and pilot can be subjected, all the aircraft trajectories have about the same degree of smoothness. The location of certain aircraft objectives near the tracking system also induces a degree of uniformity in the trajectories. In order to assess precisely the demands on the system, one would need to know the probability of occurrence and the strategic importance of the different possible paths. It is well to remark that although an exact history of the system would furnish the probability of occurrence of the paths, this information could be much more easily deduced from other sources.

There are some servo systems, designed to follow a simple input, to which the above considerations apply in only a trivial sense. This is the case for a thermostat designed to maintain a constant temperature in a building; the input signal is simply a constant temperature. It is, however, necessary that the thermostat be a closed-cycle system in order that it may correct the random variations in the building temperature caused by fluctuations in the temperature of the atmosphere. This is an example of an uncontrolled load disturbance. Another example is the effect of a gusty wind on a heavy gun-mount servomechanism. It is clear that one could not hope to design an ideal thermostat-controlled heating system without knowing how the temperature of the atmosphere fluctuates; the system must be built to respond to the dominant frequency band of the atmospheric temperature fluctuations. In order to describe these fluctuations it is again necessary to use the language of statistics, since it is only certain probability functions of these fluctuations which are predictable.

There are many other uncontrolled disturbances operating on a servomechanism besides the load disturbance. The most troublesome are those which occur where the error signal is at a low power level, as it may be in the error-measuring device or in the first stage of the servoamplifier. For example, in the first stage of the servoamplifier it sometimes happens that small voltage fluctuations caused by thermal agitation of electrons in a metal or by the erratic passage of electrons through a vacuum tube (shot effect) are of the same order of magnitude as the error signal. Here again statistical considerations are called for.

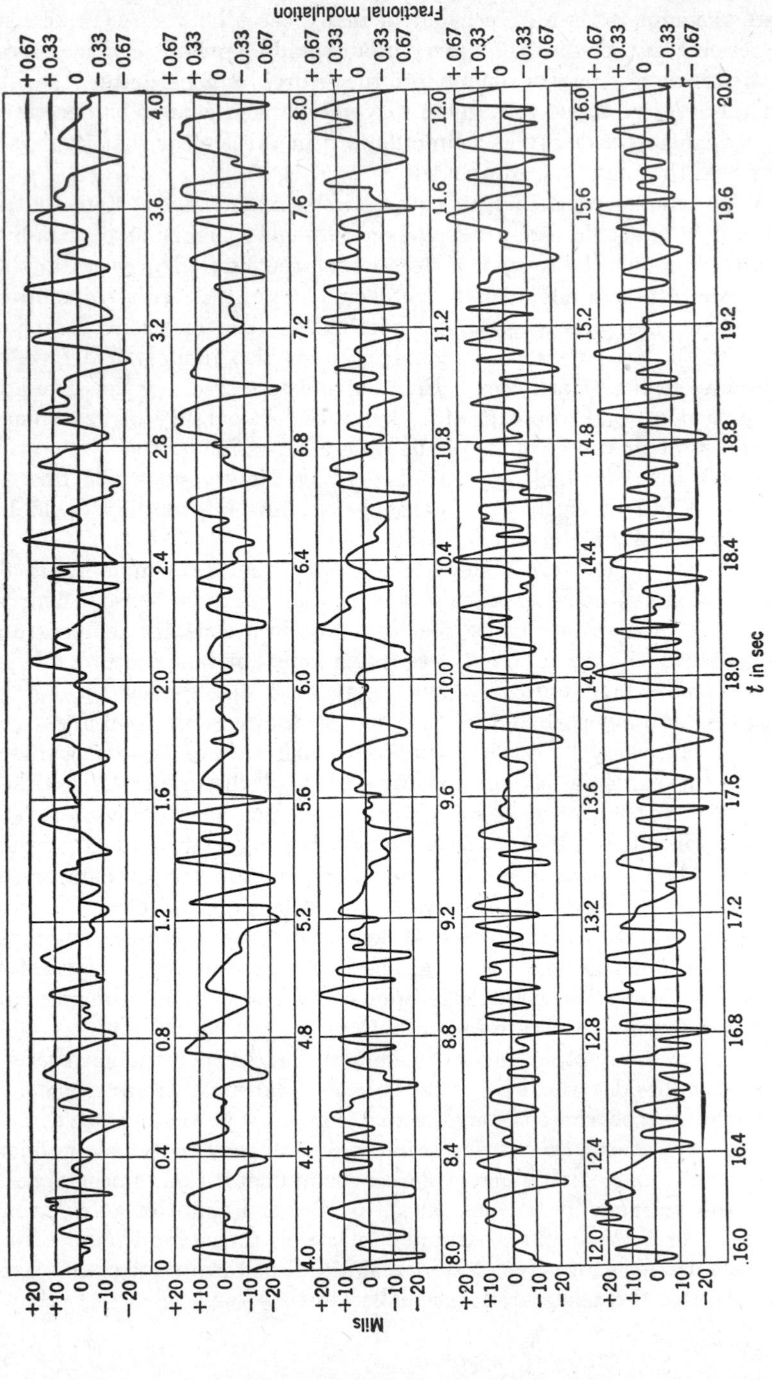

FIG. 6·1.—Record of fading in reflected radar signal.

An example of a noise source occurring in the error-measuring device is found in radar tracking systems. Here the radar beam scans conically about the axis of the tracking system. The resulting modulation of the radar signal reflected from a target provides information about the error with which that target is being tracked. The received signal is also modulated by fluctuations in the over-all reflection coefficient of the aircraft, caused by propeller rotation, engine vibration, and change in the airplane's aspect resulting from yaw, roll, and pitch. This type of disturbance is known as fading. An actual record of the fading in the received radar signal reflected from an aircraft in flight is shown in Fig. 6·1. The fading is given in terms of fractional modulation and the mils tracking error that would produce such a modulation in the absence of fading.

The performance of a servomechanism will depend both on its input and on these uncontrolled disturbances. Since the input can, in general, be expressed only in statistical terms, and since the disturbances certainly can be only thus expressed, it is clear that the output of the mechanism can be assessed only on a statistical basis. Thus what is of interest is not the exact performance of the mechanism but rather the average performance and the likely spread in performance.

The uncontrolled factors are not necessarily uncontrollable. In most cases one can, by proper design, control a disturbance so completely that its effect is negligible. In some instances, however, it is impossible to do this without badly impairing the mechanism's usefulness. For instance, if a filter in a telephone system is designed to transmit a message, it must of necessity transmit some of the ever-present noise; if the noise and the message are in about the same frequency band, one cannot eliminate the noise without at the same time preventing the transmission of the message. This same situation holds for servo systems. Here it is desired to follow a signal and at the same time to ignore the disturbances; as both are not simultaneously possible, a compromise must be made. It will be the purpose of the remainder of this book to present and discuss a method for making this compromise expediently.

This chapter will be devoted to developing the statistical tools of the theory. Sections 6·2 through 6·5 furnish background material—a discussion of stationary random processes. Although the concept of a random process is basic in what follows, it is actually used in the calculations only to obtain certain input examples; these sections can be omitted on a first reading. On the other hand, it is imperative that the reader understand the meaning of the autocorrelation function and the spectral density if he is to appreciate the developments in later chapters. The autocorrelation function is dealt with in Sec. 6·6; the spectral density in Sec. 6·7; and the relation between the two in Sec. 6·8. The spectral density and autocorrelation function of the filtered signal are derived in terms of the filter input in Sec. 6·9. In Sec. 6·10 the autocorrelation function for the error of a radar automatic-tracking system is derived; the results compare very favorably with experiment. The remainder of the chapter is devoted to examples.

6·2. Random Process and Random Series.—A *random process*[1] consists of an ensemble of functions of time having certain statistical properties.

The notion of a *function of time* $y(t)$ is familiar enough.[2] An *ensemble* of such functions is simply a given set of functions of time. This concept is most useful when these functions are typical records of some physical quantity taken from a set of essentially similar systems containing some uncontrolled elements. The member functions of a random-process ensemble need not be completely random, and, in fact, we do not exclude cases where the functions exhibit no randomness whatever.

In general, it will not be possible to predict the future values of a function of an ensemble from its past values; nor will the similarity between the physical systems, which generate the ensemble, imply that one can predict the values of one function by observing another function of the ensemble. It is not at all obvious that one can formulate a theory for such an ensemble of functions. In order to do so it is, in fact, necessary to place restrictions on the ensemble. Only those ensembles which meet the requirement that there exist certain probability distributions for the function values will be called random processes; the precise nature of these distribution functions will be discussed in the next section. Random processes are then subject to statistical discussion; one can make statistical predictions concerning the functions of the ensemble and the corresponding physical systems.

Examples of random processes are plentiful in nature. For instance, we can obtain a random process by recording the fluctuating voltages due to thermal "noise" between two points on a set of identically cut pieces of similar metal. The functions of another random process might describe the possible motions of the molecules of gas in a box. In this case we assume that we have a sufficiently large number of similar boxes of gas so that all possible initial conditions of the molecules are represented with equal likelihood. If we then record the position and velocity

[1] Several aspects and applications of the general theory of random processes are reviewed by Ming Chen Wang and G. E. Uhlenbeck, *Rev. Mod. Phys.* **17**, 323 (1945); by S. O. Rice, *Bell System Tech. Jour.* **23**, 282 (1944) and **25**, 45 (1945); and by S. Chandrasekhar, *Rev. Mod. Phys.* **15**, 1 (1943). These papers include rather complete references to the literature. A mathematical treatment of the subject can be found in a paper by N. Wiener, *Acta Math.* **55**, 118 (1930).

[2] For each value of t, y may consist of a set of numbers. In this case $y(t)$ can be considered as a vector function of time.

of each molecule in every box for all time, we shall have an ensemble of functions comprising a random process. The fading record shown in Fig. 6·1 is a sample of a function belonging to a random process, generated by the reflected radar signals from an ensemble of airplanes in all possible states of motion.

It is not difficult to devise function ensembles with the statistical properties of random processes. For example, consider functions that assume only the values 0 and 1 and are constant throughout successive unit intervals. We can define an ensemble containing all such functions by stating the probability of occurrence of every subclass of functions in the ensemble. For instance, we may state that—

1. All functions differing only by a translation in time are equally likely.
2. The function values 0 and 1 are equally likely in each interval.
3. The probability of a function taking on the value 0 or 1 in any interval does not depend on its values elsewhere.

These conditions can be stated more concisely as follows. Let

$$y_s(t) = a_n \qquad \text{for} \begin{Bmatrix} n + s \leqq t < n + 1 + s \\ n = 0, \ \pm 1, \ \pm 2, \ \cdot \cdot \cdot \end{Bmatrix}, \tag{1}$$

where the a_n's are independent random variables assuming the values 0 and 1 with equal likelihood. For each set of values of the a's (. . . , a_{-1}, a_0, a_1, . . . ,), let the probability that s lies in any region within the interval (0,1) be equal to the length of that region. Then the set of functions obtained by all possible choices of s and of the a's will constitute the random process. It is well to note that this definition does not explicitly describe any member function of the ensemble as a function of time. It is evident that there are functions in the ensemble, such as $y(t) \equiv 0$ or $y(t) \equiv 1$, that hold no interest for us, since we are concerned only with average properties. Such functions are very rare; in fact the probability of choosing one at random is zero.

A *random series* consists of an ensemble of functions defined over all positive and negative integral values of an index; often the integers represent equally spaced instants of time. Such an ensemble is a random process only if it meets statistical specifications entirely parallel to those placed on random processes; the properties of random series are exactly analogous to those of random processes.

An example of a random series can be generated by a very large group of men, each busily engaged in flipping his own coin. If the record of each man's flips is recorded (heads as 1 and tails as -1), then the resulting set of records will form a random series. The discrete random-walk problem in one dimension also involves a random series. Here each member of a large group of men takes a unit step either forward or backward, with equal likelihood, at successive unit intervals of time; the record of their positions as a function of the number of steps taken is a random series. The series obtained by taking the first differences of the member functions of this random series is precisely the random series generated by the coin flippers.

6·3. Probability-distribution Functions.—Before the concept of a random process can be fully understood it is necessary to discuss probability-distribution functions. Let us consider a finite ensemble of functions. At a definite time t, we can determine the fraction δ_1 of the total number of functions $y(t)$ that have a value in the interval between y_1 and $y_1 + \Delta y_1$. This will depend on the specified y_1 and t and will be roughly proportional to Δy_1 for small Δy_1; that is,

$$\delta_1 = P_1(y_1, t)\, \Delta y_1. \tag{2}$$

The function $P_1(y,t)$ is called the "first probability distribution." Next we can determine the fraction δ_2 of the member functions for which $y(t)$ lies in the range $(y_1, y_1 + \Delta y_1)$ at a given time t_1 and also lies in the range $(y_2, y_2 + \Delta y_2)$ at a given time t_2. This fraction is

$$\delta_2 = P_2(y_1, t_1; y_2, t_2)\, \Delta y_1\, \Delta y_2; \tag{3}$$

P_2 is called the "second probability distribution." We can continue in this fashion, defining the third probability distribution in terms of the fraction of functions that lie in three given ranges at three respectively given times, and so on.[1]

The probability-distribution functions so defined must fulfill the following obvious conditions.

1. $P_n \geqq 0$.
2. $P_n(y_1, t_1; y_2, t_2; \cdots ; y_n, t_n)$ is a symmetric function in the set of variables $y_1, t_1; y_2, t_2; \cdots ; y_n, t_n$. This is clear, since P_n is a joint probability.
3. $P_k(y_1, t_1; \cdots ; y_k, t_k)$

$$= \int \cdots \int dy_{k+1} \cdots dy_n P_n(y_1, t_1; \cdots ; y_n, t_n); \tag{4a}$$

$$1 = \int dy\, P_1(y,t). \tag{4b}$$

Since each function P_k can be derived from any P_n with $n > k$, the functions P_n describe the random process in more and more detail as n increases.

Although we have defined probability-distribution functions for

[1] If y takes on only a discrete set of values, then P_n will be defined as a probability itself and not as a probability density. Thus $P_1(y_1,t_1)$ will be the probability of $y(t)$ taking on the value y_1 at the time t_1, and so on.

finite ensembles, it is clear that the functions themselves have statistical meaning when applied to infinite ensembles. Thus $\int_a^b dy\, P_1(y,t)$ can be thought of as the probability that an arbitrary member function $y(t)$ of the ensemble lies in the interval $a < y < b$ at the time t. With this in mind it is now possible to define a random process precisely:

A random process consists of an ensemble of functions of time that can be characterized by a complete set of probability-distribution functions.

It is easy to see that an experimental determination of a probability-distribution function P_n is a tedious task. Frequently one can determine the functions P_n from statistical considerations. For example, this is the case for the random process described by Eq. (1). It is evident that at any time there is equal likelihood that y is either 0 or 1:

$$\left.\begin{aligned} P_1(y,t) &= \tfrac{1}{2} \qquad \text{for } y = 0 \text{ or } 1, \\ P_1(y,t) &= 0 \qquad \text{otherwise.} \end{aligned}\right\} \tag{5}$$

Since a_n is independent of a_m for $n \neq m$, it follows that

$$P_2(y_1, t_1; y_2, t_2) = P_1(y_1,t_1)P_1(y_2,t_2) \tag{6}$$

whenever $|t_1 - t_2| > 1$. On the other hand, if $|t_1 - t_2| \leqq 1$, then the probability that both t_1 and t_2 lie in the same unit interval is just $(1 - |t_1 - t_2|)$; the common value is then either 0 or 1 with equal likelihood. The probability that t_1 and t_2 do not lie in the same unit interval is clearly $|t_1 - t_2|$; in this case, as in the case described by Eq. (6), any of the four possible combinations of (y_1,y_2) occur with equal frequency. Hence, for $|t_1 - t_2| \leqq 1$,

$$\left.\begin{aligned} P_2(y_1, t_1; y_2, t_2) &= \tfrac{1}{2}(1 - |t_1 - t_2|) + \tfrac{1}{4}|t_1 - t_2| \\ &\qquad \text{for } y_1 = y_2 = 0 \text{ or } 1, \\ &= \tfrac{1}{4}|t_1 - t_2| \qquad \text{for } (y_1,y_2) = (0,1) \text{ or } (1,0). \end{aligned}\right\} \tag{7}$$

Thus P_2 depends on the difference between t_1 and t_2. The higher probability distributions can be discussed in the same way.

To take another example, consider the previously mentioned discrete random-walk problem in one dimension. Let us suppose that in all experiments the walker remains stationary at the origin for $n \leqq 0$ and thereafter takes a unit step either forward or backward with equal likelihood at successive unit intervals of time. Because of this initial condition we need to consider only $n > 0$. For this case it can be shown[1]

[1] See, for example, Ming Chen Wang and G. E. Uhlenbeck, *Rev. Mod. Phys.* **17**, 327 (1945). The conditional probability is usually derived in the literature. This is the probability that an individual will be at y at $t = n$ if it is known that at $t = 0$ he was at the origin. Because of our initial condition, this conditional probability is precisely our $P_1(y,n)$ for $n \geqq 0$.

that

$$P_1(y,n) = \frac{n!}{\left(\frac{n+y}{2}\right)!\left(\frac{n-y}{2}\right)!}\left(\frac{1}{2}\right)^n \tag{8}$$

if n and y are even or odd integers together; otherwise, $P_1(y,n) = 0$. It can likewise be shown for this problem that P_k can be written in terms of P_1; for instance,

$$P_2(y_1, n_1; y_2, n_2) = P_1(y_1,n_1)P_1[(y_2 - y_1), (n_2 - n_1)], \tag{9}$$

where $n_2 > n_1$. In words, the probability that an individual is at y_1 after n_1 steps and then at y_2 after n_2 steps is equal to the probability that he first walks to y_1 in n_1 steps, times the probability that he thereafter walks a distance $(y_2 - y_1)$ in $(n_2 - n_1)$ steps.

HARMONIC ANALYSIS FOR STATIONARY RANDOM PROCESSES

6·4. Stationary Random Process.—In most applications the underlying mechanism that generates the random process does not change in time. In addition, one is usually interested only in the steady-state output that occurs after the initial transients have died down. When this is the case, the basic probability distributions are invariant under shifts in time.

A random process characterized by probability-distribution functions that are invariant under a change in the origin in time is said to be a *stationary random process.* Such a process is described in increasing detail by the distribution functions:

$P_1(y_1)\,dy_1$ = probability of finding a value of a member of the ensemble between y_1 and $y_1 + dy_1$.

$P_2[y_1, (t_1 + \tau); y_2, (t_2 + \tau)]\,dy_1\,dy_2$ = joint probability of finding a pair of values of a member of the ensemble in the ranges $(y_1, y_1 + dy_1)$ and $(y_2, y_2 + dy_2)$ at respective times $t_1 + \tau$ and $t_2 + \tau$. This function will be independent of τ; it will be convenient to abbreviate it as $P_2(y_1, y_2, t)$, where $t = t_2 - t_1$.

$P_3[y_1, (t_1 + \tau); y_2, (t_2 + \tau); y_3, (t_3 + \tau)]\,dy_1\,dy_2\,dy_3$ = joint probability of finding values of a member of the ensemble in the ranges $(y_1, y_1 + dy_1)$, $(y_2, y_2 + dy_2)$, $(y_3, y_3 + dy_3)$, at the respective times $t_1 + \tau$, $t_2 + \tau$, $t_3 + \tau$; and so on.

This and all similar P's will be independent of τ.

The thermal motion of free electrons in a metal at constant temperature and the Brownian motion of molecules of gas in a box at constant temperature each generates a stationary random process. The random process described by Eq. (1) is also stationary.

The discrete random-walk problem, formulated at the end of the previous section, does not generate a stationary random series, since the set of possible positions continually increases with n; the dependence of P_1 upon n is shown explicitly in Eq. (8). On the other hand, the series produced by the coin flippers is stationary; in this case

$$\left.\begin{aligned} P_k[y_1, (n_1 + m); \cdots ; y_k, (n_k + m)] &= (\tfrac{1}{2})^k \quad \text{for} \\ y_i = \pm 1 \; (i = 1, \cdots, k), \\ P_k &= 0 \qquad \text{otherwise.} \end{aligned}\right\} \tag{10}$$

As has already been noted, the first difference of the series obtained by the discrete random-walk problem in one dimension is essentially the series produced by the coin flippers. Some of the servomechanism inputs to be considered later are similar to the random-walk series in that they are not themselves stationary random processes whereas their time derivatives are.

6·5. Time Averages and Ensemble Averages.—In dealing with stationary random processes it is usually assumed that time averages are equivalent to ensemble averages. This is the so-called "ergodic hypothesis" of statistical mechanics. It is usually applicable only to stationary random processes that are (or might be) generated by an ensemble of systems for which the uncontrolled elements of any one system approach arbitrarily near to every possible configuration in the course of time. In such cases it is expected that any one system can be taken as representative of a properly defined ensemble, not only as regards the nature of the possible configurations but also as regards the probability that any given set of configurations will be observed. In other words, since the nature of the underlying mechanism does not change with time, it is expected that a large number of observations made on a single system at randomly chosen times will have the same statistical properties as the same number of observations made on randomly chosen systems at the same time. A rigorous mathematical proof of the ergodic hypothesis has been found for very few systems.

A simple example will serve to clarify the meaning of this assumption. Consider an idealized billiard table with perfectly reflecting cushions and a mass point as a billiard ball. Once started, the idealized ball will maintain its speed forever and, except for certain special initial positions and directions, will eventually approach arbitrarily near to any given point on the table. Now let us define an ensemble of trajectories starting from all possible positions and directions with the probability of starting in any given region and in any given angular range being proportional to the area of that region times the magnitude of the angular range. The ergodic hypothesis will then state that the ensemble average of any physical quantity defined by position and direction of a trajectory will be equal to the time average for any one of the nonperiodic trajectories. For instance, the average time spent by any nonperiodic trajectory in a given region of the table is proportional to the area of that region; for this is certainly true of an average over the ensemble at the time when the ensemble is set up and likewise at any other time. In making an ensemble average in this case it is actually not necessary to exclude periodic trajectories from the ensemble, since they occur, in any case, with zero probability.

The ergodic hypothesis can be given a more formal statement as follows: Let $F(y_1, y_2, \ldots, y_n)$ be an arbitrary function of the variables $y_1, y_2, \ldots, y_n$, and let $y_1 = y(t + \tau_1), y_2 = y(t + \tau_2), \ldots, y_n = y(t + \tau_n)$, where $y(t)$ belongs to a random process. We shall denote the time average of F for $y_i = y(t + \tau_i)$ by $\overline{F}$, and the ensemble average by $\tilde{F}$. That is, by definition

$$\overline{F} = \lim_{T \to \infty} \frac{1}{2T} \int_{-T}^{T} dt\, F[y(t + \tau_1), \cdots, y(t + \tau_n)] \tag{11}$$

and

$$\tilde{F} = \int \cdots \int dy_1 \cdots dy_n F(y_1, y_2, \cdots, y_n) \times P_n[y_1, (t + \tau_1); \cdots; y_n, (t + \tau_n)]. \tag{12}$$

The average $\overline{F}$ is clearly independent of t; $\tilde{F}$ will be independent of t if the process is stationary. The ergodic hypothesis states:

If the random process is stationary, then

$$\overline{F} = \tilde{F} \tag{13}$$

with a probability of 1.

A few examples will serve to illustrate the significance of this hypothesis. We can determine for any random process the *ensemble average* or *mean* of y, at the time t, from the first probability distribution $P_1(y,t)$:

$$\tilde{y} = \int dy\, y P_1(y,t). \tag{14}$$

From the way in which P_1 is determined, it is clear that $\tilde{y}$ is the mean of all the $y(t)$'s of the ensemble. For a stationary random process, $P_1(y,t)$ and consequently $\tilde{y}$ do not depend on t. On the other hand, the *time average*, which is defined as

$$\overline{y} = \lim_{T \to \infty} \frac{1}{2T} \int_{-T}^{T} dt\, y(t), \tag{15}$$

will, in general, differ for the various functions of an ensemble. The ergodic hypothesis states that for a stationary random process these two methods of averaging give the same result, no matter at what time the ensemble average is made or with what function (except for a choice of zero probability) the time average is made. That is

$$\bar{y} = \tilde{y}. \tag{16}$$

The same thing can be said for the higher *moments* of the distribution P_1, which can be determined by setting $F(y) = y^n$. The nth moment is defined as

$$\widetilde{y^n} = \int dy\, y^n P_1(y,t). \tag{17}$$

For a stationary random process this is equal to the time average

$$\overline{y^n} = \lim_{T \to \infty} \frac{1}{2T} \int_{-T}^{T} dt\, [y(t)]^n. \tag{18}$$

The second moment is called the "mean-square" value of y, and its square root $\sqrt{\widetilde{y^2}}$ is called the "root-mean-square" (abbreviated rms) value of y. From the first and second moments one can derive the *variance*

$$\begin{aligned} \widetilde{(y - y)^2} &= \widetilde{y^2} - (\tilde{y})^2 \\ &= \int dy\, (y - \tilde{y})^2 P_1(y,t), \end{aligned} \tag{19}$$

which is a measure of the width of the distribution $P_1(y,t)$ about its average value $\tilde{y}$.

6·6. Correlation Functions.—The *autocorrelation function* of a function $y(t)$ is defined as the time average of $y(t)y(t + \tau)$. It is a function of the time interval τ and of the function y. It will be denoted by $R_y(\tau)$ or, where this is not ambiguous, by $R(\tau)$. By definition, therefore,

$$R(\tau) = \overline{y(t)y(t + \tau)} = \lim_{T \to \infty} \frac{1}{2T} \int_{-T}^{T} dt\, y(t)y(t + \tau). \tag{20}$$

As we have seen in the previous section, in the case of a stationary random process $R(\tau)$ will not (except for a choice of zero probability) depend on the member of the ensemble on which the time average is performed. Furthermore, the time average of $y(t)y(t + \tau)$ will be equal to the ensemble average

$$\widetilde{y(t)y(t + \tau)} = \int \int dy_1\, dy_2\, y_1 y_2 P_2(y_1,y_2,\tau) \tag{21}$$

with probability 1. Thus one can define an autocorrelation function for a stationary random process as well as for a single function. This function gives a measure of the correlation between $y(t_1)$ and $y(t_2)$, where $t_2 - t_1 = \tau$. In case $y(t_1)$ and $y(t_2)$ are independent of each other,

$$P_2(y_1, t_1; y_2, t_2) = P_1(y_1,t_1)P_1(y_2t_2) \tag{22}$$

and

$$R(t_2 - t_1) = \widetilde{y(t_1)y(t_2)} = \widetilde{y(t_1)}\ \widetilde{y(t_2)}. \tag{23}$$

For noise this situation is approximated when the time interval τ is sufficiently large.

Some of the properties of $R(\tau)$ are fairly evident.

1.

$$R(0) = \overline{y^2}. \tag{24}$$

2. $R(\tau)$ is an even function of τ, since

$$R(\tau) = \overline{y(t)y(t+\tau)} = \overline{y(t-\tau)y(t)} = \overline{y(t)y(t-\tau)} = R(-\tau). \tag{25}$$

3. $|R(\tau)| \leqq R(0)$. This results from the inequality

$$0 \leqq [y(t) \pm y(t+\tau)]^2 \equiv y^2(t) + y^2(t+\tau) \pm 2y(t)y(t+\tau). \tag{26}$$

Hence

$$\pm 2y(t)y(t+\tau) \leqq y^2(t) + y^2(t+\tau). \tag{27}$$

Averaging both sides of this equation gives

$$\pm 2R(\tau) \leqq \overline{y^2(t)} + \overline{y^2(t+\tau)} = 2R(0). \tag{28}$$

4. Given any set of τ's $(\tau_1, \tau_2, \ldots, \tau_n)$, the determinant

$$\begin{vmatrix} R(\tau_1 - \tau_1) & R(\tau_1 - \tau_2) & \cdots & \cdots & R(\tau_1 - \tau_n) \\ R(\tau_2 - \tau_1) & R(\tau_2 - \tau_2) & \cdots & \cdots & R(\tau_2 - \tau_n) \\ \cdots & \cdots & \cdots & \cdots & \cdots \\ \cdots & \cdots & \cdots & \cdots & \cdots \\ R(\tau_n - \tau_1) & R(\tau_n - \tau_2) & \cdots & \cdots & R(\tau_n - \tau_n) \end{vmatrix} \tag{29}$$

is symmetric and nonnegative in value. It can be shown that condition (4) is a necessary and sufficient condition that $R(\tau)$ be an autocorrelation function.[1]

It is sometimes convenient to work with the function

$$\rho(\tau) \equiv \frac{\overline{[y(t) - \bar{y}][y(t+\tau) - \bar{y}]}}{\overline{y^2} - \bar{y}^2}, \tag{30}$$

which will be called the *normalized autocorrelation function.* It is evident that $\rho(0) = 1$ and that for noise $\rho(\tau) \to 0$ as $\tau \to \infty$.

The autocorrelation function for a random series is defined as

$$R(m) = \lim_{N\to\infty} \frac{1}{2N+1} \sum_{n=-N}^{N} y_n y_{n+m}. \tag{31}$$

It is clear that $R(m)$ has properties analogous to those of $R(\tau)$.

[1] A. Khintchine, "Korrelationstheorie der Stationären Stochastischen Prozesse," *Math. Ann.* **109**, 608 (1934).

Examples.—It will be instructive to consider a few examples. In the case of the purely incoherent stationary random series generated by the coin flippers one would expect $R(m)$ to decrease very rapidly with increasing m. As was seen in Sec. 6·4, $P_1(y_1) = \frac{1}{2}$ and $P_2(y_1,y_2,m) = \frac{1}{4}$, where y_1 and y_2 take on the values ± 1. It follows from Eq. (21) that

$$R(0) = \sum y_i^2 P_1(y_i) = 1^2 \times \tfrac{1}{2} + (-1)^2 \times \tfrac{1}{2} = 1, \tag{32}$$

and that for $m \neq 0$

$$\left.\begin{aligned} R(m) &= \sum y_i y_j P_2(y_i,y_j,m). \\ &= (1)(1)\tfrac{1}{4} + (1)(-1)\tfrac{1}{4} + (-1)(1)\tfrac{1}{4} + (-1)(-1)\tfrac{1}{4} \\ &= 0. \end{aligned}\right\} \tag{33}$$

The other extreme is represented by the function $y(t) \equiv 1$, for which

$$R(\tau) = \lim_{T\to\infty} \frac{1}{2T} \int_{-T}^{T} dt\, 1 \times 1 \equiv 1. \tag{34}$$

If $y(t)$ is periodic, then the periodicity persists in $R(\tau)$. For example, let

$$y(t) = A \sin(\omega t + \phi). \tag{35}$$

Then

$$\begin{aligned} R(\tau) = \overline{y(t)y(t+\tau)} &= \lim_{T\to\infty} \frac{1}{2T} \int_{-T}^{T} dt\, A \sin(\omega t + \phi) A \sin(\omega t + \omega\tau + \phi) \\ &= \lim_{T\to\infty} \frac{1}{2T} \int_{-T}^{T} dt \frac{A^2}{2} [\cos \omega\tau - \cos(2\omega t + \omega\tau + 2\phi)] \\ &= \lim_{T\to\infty} \frac{A^2}{2} \left[\cos \omega\tau - \frac{1}{2T} \frac{\sin(2\omega T + \omega\tau + 2\phi)}{2\omega} \right. \\ &\qquad \left. - \frac{1}{2T} \frac{\sin(2\omega T - \omega\tau - 2\phi)}{2\omega} \right] \\ &= \frac{A^2}{2} \cos \omega\tau. \end{aligned} \tag{36}$$

Although $R(\tau)$ has the period of $y(t)$, it is an even function independent of the phase ϕ of $y(t)$. For the function

$$y(t) = A_0 + \sum A_k \sin(\omega_k t + \phi_k), \tag{37}$$

where $\omega_n \neq \omega_m$ for $n \neq m$, the autocorrelation function is

$$R(\tau) = A_0^2 + \sum \frac{A_k^2}{2} \cos \omega_k \tau. \tag{38}$$

Here again the periods of y are present in $R(\tau)$, but the phase relations have been lost. If an apparently random function contains hidden periodicities, $R(\tau)$ will approach asymptotically an oscillating function like that in Eq. (38).

In the case of the stationary random process described by Eq. (1), we can obtain the autocorrelation as an ensemble average by means of Eq. (21). The second probability distribution P_2 is given in Eqs. (6) and (7). If $\tau = t_1 - t_2$ is greater in absolute value than 1, then, applying Eq. (6), we obtain

$$\begin{aligned} R(\tau) &= \sum y_1 y_2 P_2(y_1, t_1; y_2 t_2) \\ &= \tfrac{1}{4}(0 \times 0 + 0 \times 1 + 1 \times 0 + 1 \times 1) = \tfrac{1}{4}. \end{aligned} \tag{39}$$

On the other hand, if $|\tau| \leqq 1$, we make use of Eq. (7):

$$\begin{aligned} R(\tau) &= [\tfrac{1}{2}(1 - |\tau|) + \tfrac{1}{4}|\tau|](0 \times 0 + 1 \times 1) + \tfrac{1}{4}|\tau|(0 \times 1 + 1 \times 0) \\ &= \tfrac{1}{2} - \tfrac{1}{4}|\tau|. \end{aligned} \tag{40}$$

It follows from Eq. (5) that $\tilde{y} = \frac{1}{2} = \widetilde{y^2}$. Hence the normalized autocorrelation function is

$$\left.\begin{aligned} \rho(\tau) &= 0 \qquad &&\text{for } |\tau| > 1, \\ &= 1 - |\tau| &&\text{for } |\tau| \leqq 1. \end{aligned}\right\} \tag{41}$$

To obtain an autocorrelation function from experimental data, one of necessity starts with a record $y(t)$ of finite length: $0 \leqq t \leqq T$. If the data are not discrete, it is possible to consider them as such by using only the values at times $t = n\Delta$ $(n = 1, 2, \cdots, N = T/\Delta)$. The time interval Δ should be chosen so small that the function $y(t)$ does not vary significantly in any interval Δ. If $y(t)$ is to be used as an input to some mechanism, it is sufficient that Δ be small with respect to the system time constants. Setting $y_n = y(n\Delta)$, then

$$R(m) \approx \frac{1}{N - m} \sum_{n=1}^{N-m} y_n y_{n+m}, \qquad \text{for } m \geqq 0. \tag{42}$$

Equation (42) loses its reliability for very large m. For, as can be seen from Eq. (36), in working with a finite interval T a relative fractional error of about $1/\omega T$ is introduced for each periodicity present. The error in determining the contribution of a period P to the autocorrelation function will be less than 2 per cent if $2\pi[(N - m)\Delta/P] \geqq 50$. Hence for this purpose $T = N\Delta$ should be about $10P$, and m should not exceed $\frac{1}{5}T/\Delta$.

The normalized autocorrelation function of the fading data shown in Fig. 6·1 was obtained by use of Eq. (42). The period of observation was $T = 20$ sec. The value of Δ was chosen to be $\frac{2}{125}$ sec. The resulting function $\rho(\tau)$, calculated over the range $0 \leqq \tau \leqq 1.28$ sec, is shown in Fig. 6·2. As can be seen, there is very little correlation between data more than 0.1 sec apart. It follows from this that a very conservative choice of T was made; 2 or 3 sec would have been adequate.

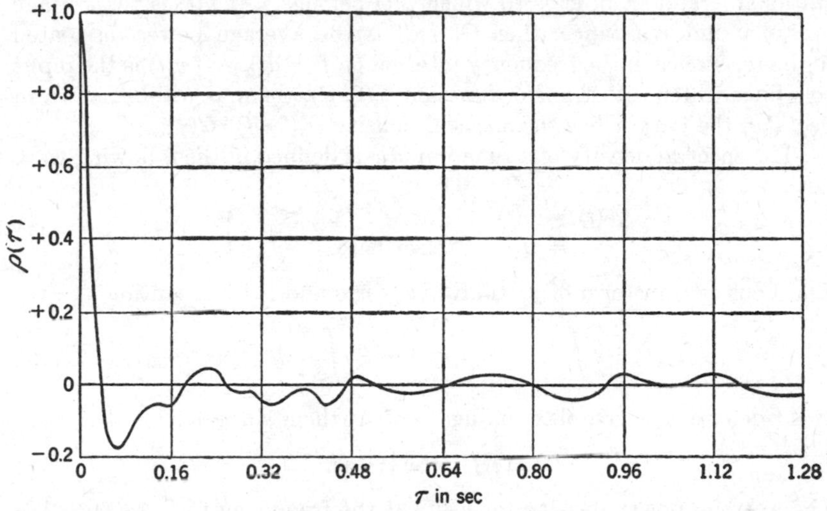

FIG. 6·2.—Normalized autocorrelation function for fading record. The rms value is 10.3 mils.

Correlation Matrix.—If y is a two-dimensional vector (u,v), one defines a correlation matrix instead of a correlation function. For a stationary random process, the ergodic hypothesis gives

$$\begin{Vmatrix} \overline{u(t)u(t+\tau)} & \overline{u(t)v(t+\tau)} \\ \overline{v(t)u(t+\tau)} & \overline{v(t)v(t+\tau)} \end{Vmatrix} = \begin{Vmatrix} \widetilde{u(t)u(t+\tau)} & \widetilde{u(t)v(t+\tau)} \\ \widetilde{v(t)u(t+\tau)} & \widetilde{v(t)v(t+\tau)} \end{Vmatrix}. \tag{43}$$

The function of τ, $\overline{u(t)v(t+\tau)}$, is called the *cross-correlation function* and will be designated as $R_{uv}(\tau)$.

The cross-correlation function is not symmetric, nor can one interchange the order of u and v without changing its value. There does, however, exist the relationship

$$R_{uv}(\tau) = R_{vu}(-\tau). \tag{44}$$

By using the inequality

$$0 \leqq \left[\frac{u(t)}{\sqrt{\overline{u^2}}} \pm \frac{v(t+\tau)}{\sqrt{\overline{v^2}}}\right]^2 \tag{45}$$

and averaging over time, one finds that

$$|R_{uv}(\tau)| \leqq \sqrt{R_u(0)}\,\sqrt{R_v(0)}. \tag{46}$$

$R_{uv}(\tau)$ is a measure of the coherence between $u(t)$ and $v(t+\tau)$.

6·7. Spectral Density.—We shall have occasion to consider the effect of a filter on the functions of a random process. It is natural, therefore, to attempt to resolve the functions of a stationary random process into their Fourier components. Such an attempt will, in turn, lead us to the concept of the spectral density $G(f)$ of a function $y(t)$ and of a stationary random process to which $y(t)$ belongs. If $y(t)$ is the voltage across a unit resistance, then $G(f)\,df$ is the average power dissipated in the resistance in the frequency interval $(f, f + df)$. If $y(t)$ is the input to a linear filter with transfer function $Y(2\pi jf)$, then, as will be shown in Sec. 6·9, the output has the spectral density $|Y(2\pi jf)|^2 G(f)$.

The spectral density of a function $y(t)$ is defined in the following way. Let

$$\left.\begin{aligned} y_T(t) &= y(t) \qquad \text{for } -T \leqq t \leqq T, \\ &= 0 \qquad \text{elsewhere.} \end{aligned}\right\} \tag{47}$$

The Fourier transform of $y_T(t)$ always exists and is by definition

$$A_T(f) = \int_{-\infty}^{\infty} dt\, y_T(t) e^{-2\pi jft} = \int_{-T}^{T} dt\, y(t) e^{-2\pi jft}. \tag{48}$$

If A^* denotes the complex conjugate of A, then, since y_T is real valued,

$$A_T(f) = A_T^*(-f). \tag{49}$$

The average power density for $y_T(f)$ at the frequency f is$[|A_T(f)|^2]/2T$; both positive and negative f must be taken into account. Since $|A_T(f)| = |A_T(-f)|$, one can limit attention to positive values of f and take the average power density to be $[|A_T(f)|^2]/T$. The *spectral density* of the function $y(t)$ is defined as the limit of this quantity as T goes to infinity;

$$G(f) = \lim_{T\to\infty} \frac{1}{T} |A_T(f)|^2. \tag{50}$$

As should be expected, one can obtain the average power in y by integrating the average power density $G(f)$ over all positive frequencies. In symbols

$$\overline{y^2} = \int_0^{\infty} df\, G(f). \tag{51}$$

This can be proved as follows. From Eqs. (48) and (49)

$$\int_{-\infty}^{\infty} df\, |A_T(f)|^2 = \int_{-\infty}^{\infty} df \left[A_T(-f) \int_{-\infty}^{\infty} dt\, y_T(t) e^{-2\pi jft} \right]. \tag{52}$$

Interchanging the order of integration gives

$$\int_{-\infty}^{\infty} df\, |A_T(f)|^2 = \int_{-\infty}^{\infty} dt \left\{ y_T(t) \left[\int_{-\infty}^{\infty} df\, A_T(-f) e^{-2\pi jft} \right] \right\}. \tag{53}$$

It follows from the Fourier integral theorem (see Chap. 2) that the quantity inside the brackets is just $y_T(t)$. Hence

$$\int_{-\infty}^{\infty} dt\, y_T^2(t) = \int_{-T}^{T} dt\, y^2(t) = \int_{-\infty}^{\infty} df\, |A_T(f)|^2$$
$$= 2 \int_0^{\infty} df\, |A_T(f)|^2. \quad (54)$$

Dividing through by $2T$ and passing to the limit give

$$\overline{y^2} = \lim_{T\to\infty} \frac{1}{2T} \int_{-T}^{T} dt\, y^2(t) = \lim_{T\to\infty} \frac{1}{T} \int_0^{\infty} df\, |A_T(f)|^2. \quad (55)$$

If we now interchange the order of limits, inserting $G(f)$ for its equivalent, the proof of Eq. (51) is complete.

The above discussion of the spectral resolution of the function $y(t)$ has dealt with the power; as a consequence, all information concerning the phase relationships of y has been lost. It is well to remark on the difficulties encountered in attempting to deal more directly with the Fourier transform of y. The Fourier transform itself will exist only if $y(t)$ approaches zero as t becomes infinite. For functions such as those found in stationary random processes, $A_T(f)$ will, in general, either oscillate or grow without bound as T becomes infinite. Even a mean Fourier transform such as $\lim_{T\to\infty} (1/2T)A_T(f)$ or $\lim_{T\to\infty} [1/(2T)^{1/2}]A_T(f)$ will oscillate rather than approach a limit if y is, for example, a "periodic function" with a suitably varying phase.

Cross-spectral Density.—It is possible to define a cross-spectral density for two functions (u,v) as follows. Let

$$\left.\begin{aligned} A_T(f) &= \int_{-T}^{T} dt\, u(t)e^{-2\pi jft} \\ &\text{and} \\ B_T(f) &= \int_{-T}^{T} dt\, v(t)e^{-2\pi jft}. \end{aligned}\right\} \quad (56)$$

The *cross-spectral density* is then defined as

$$G_{uv}(f) = \lim_{T\to\infty} \frac{1}{T} A_T^*(f)B_T(f). \quad (57)$$

From the relations $A_T(f) = A_T^*(-f)$ and $B_T(f) = B_T^*(-f)$ one obtains

$$G_{uv}(f) = G_{uv}^*(-f) = G_{vu}(-f). \quad (58)$$

Hidden Periodicities.—The spectral density $G(f)$ may contain singular peaks of the type associated with the Dirac delta function.[1] This will

[1] The Dirac delta function has the following properties:

$$\int_0^{\epsilon} dy\, \delta(y) = \int_{-\epsilon}^{0} dy\, \delta(y) = \frac{1}{2} \qquad \text{for all } \epsilon > 0$$

and

$$\delta(y) = 0 \qquad \text{for } y \neq 0.$$

be the case if the mean value of y is not zero or if y contains hidden periodicities. The peaks occur at frequencies at which $(1/T)|A_T(f)|^2$ becomes infinite with T; the coefficient of the delta function at such a frequency is given by $\lim_{T\to\infty} (1/2T^2)|A_T(f)|^2$. We should therefore redefine $G(f)$ as follows:

$$\left.\begin{aligned} G(f) &= \left[\lim_{T\to\infty} \frac{1}{2T^2} |A_T(f_1)|^2\right] \delta(f - f_1) \quad &&\text{except where this is zero,} \\ G(f) &= \lim_{T\to\infty} \frac{1}{T} |A_T(f)|^2 &&\text{otherwise.} \end{aligned}\right\} \tag{59}$$

If the mean of $y(t)$ is not zero, then $G(f)$ will have a singularity at the origin:

$$G(f) = 2(\bar{y})^2\delta(f) + G_1(f). \tag{60}$$

For pure noise the peak at $f = 0$, corresponding to the d-c term, will usually be the only peak, and $G_1(f)$, defined by Eq. (60), will be a regular function representing the continuous spectrum. In this case it is sometimes convenient to introduce the *normalized spectral density:*

$$S(f) = \frac{G_1(f)}{\int_0^\infty df\, G_1(f)}. \tag{61}$$

This quantity has the dimension of time, since f has the dimension $(\text{time})^{-1}$. The denominator in Eq. (61) is simply the variance of y:

$$\overline{(y - \bar{y})^2} = \overline{y^2} - \bar{y}^2 = \int_0^\infty df\, G_1(f). \tag{62}$$

If $y(t)$ is a trigonometric polynomial

$$y(t) = A_0 + \sum A_k \sin(2\pi f_k t + \phi_k), \qquad f_k \neq 0, \tag{63}$$

then the spectral density is

$$G(f) = 2A_0^2\delta(f) + \sum \frac{A_k^2}{2} \delta(f - |f_k|). \tag{64}$$

In the general case of noise with hidden periodicities the spectral density will consist of a continuous part and a number of peaks at discrete frequencies.

Spectral Density of a Stationary Random Process.—The member functions of a stationary random process will (except for a choice of zero probability) have the same spectral density. This, then, may be called the "spectral density of the stationary random process." In computing it, one can deal with any typical function of the ensemble or, as desired, can carry out averages over the ensemble.

As a further example, let us obtain the spectral density of the stationary random process described by Eq. (1). Since the functions are given only in statistical terms, it will be necessary to obtain the ensemble average of the spectral density. Since, however, the process is stationary, this will be the spectral density for the individual functions except for a set of probability zero. Since s serves only to shift the time axis and since the spectral density is independent of phase, it is clear that we can suppose s to be zero. To simplify the calculations let us subtract out the mean at the very start. We have then

$$y(t) = a_n - \tfrac{1}{2} \qquad \text{for } n \leqq t < n + 1, \tag{65}$$

where the a_n's are independent random variables and take on the values 0 and 1 with equal likelihood. By Eq. (48),

$$\left.\begin{aligned} A_N(f) &= \sum_{n=-N}^{N-1} \left(a_n - \frac{1}{2}\right) \int_n^{n+1} dt\, e^{-2\pi i f t} \\ &= \frac{\sin \pi f}{\pi f} \sum_{n=-N}^{N-1} \left(a_n - \frac{1}{2}\right) e^{-2\pi i f\left(\frac{2n+1}{2}\right)}. \end{aligned}\right\} \tag{66}$$

Squaring the absolute value of $A_N(f)$ and dividing by N give

$$\frac{|A_N(f)|^2}{N} = \left(\frac{\sin \pi f}{\pi f}\right)^2 \frac{1}{N} \sum_{n,m=-N}^{N-1} \left(a_n - \frac{1}{2}\right)\left(a_m - \frac{1}{2}\right) e^{-2\pi i f\left(\frac{2n+1}{2} - \frac{2m+1}{2}\right)} \tag{67}$$

We now take the ensemble average of Eq. (67). Since

$$\left.\begin{aligned} \widetilde{(a_n - \tfrac{1}{2})(a_m - \tfrac{1}{2})} &= 0 \qquad \text{if } n \neq m, \\ &= \tfrac{1}{4} \qquad \text{if } n = m, \end{aligned}\right\} \tag{68}$$

it follows that

$$\frac{\widetilde{|A_n(f)|^2}}{N} = \left(\frac{\sin \pi f}{\pi f}\right)^2 \frac{1}{2}. \tag{69}$$

Taking the limit as N becomes infinite, we obtain the average spectral density:

$$\widetilde{G_1(f)} = \frac{1}{2}\left(\frac{\sin \pi f}{\pi f}\right)^2. \tag{70}$$

Spectral Density of a Random Series.—The spectral density for a stationary random series is defined in an analogous way. Given the time series y_n, consisting of data recorded at uniform intervals of length T_r,[1] we define, in analogy to Eq. (48),

$$A_N(f) = T_r \sum_{n=-N}^{N} y_n e^{-2\pi i f n T_r}. \tag{71}$$

[1] The quantity T_r is the same as the repetition period of Chap. 5.

This function is periodic in f with period $1/T_r$; it is completely determined by its values in the range $(-1/2T_r, 1/2T_r)$. Since the y_n are real, $A_N(f) = A_N^*(-f)$. We then define the spectral density of the time series, in analogy to Eqs. (59), as

$$G(f) = \left[\lim_{N\to\infty} \frac{1}{2(N+\frac{1}{2})^2 T_r^2} |A_N(f_1)|^2 \right] \delta(f - f_1),$$

except where the quantity in the bracket is zero, and as (72)

$$G(f) = \lim_{N\to\infty} \frac{1}{(N+\frac{1}{2})T_r} |A_N(f)|^2 \qquad \text{elsewhere.}$$

It follows from the periodicity of $A_N(f)$ and the orthogonality of the functions $e^{-2\pi i f n T_r}$ that

$$\sum_{-N}^{N} y_n^2 = \frac{1}{T_r} \int_{-1/2T_r}^{1/2T_r} df\, |A_N(f)|^2 = \frac{2}{T_r} \int_0^{1/2T_r} df\, |A_N(f)|^2. \tag{73}$$

Hence

$$\overline{y^2} = \lim_{N\to\infty} \frac{1}{2N+1} \sum_{-N}^{N} y_n^2 = \int_0^{1/2T_r} df\, G(f). \tag{74}$$

The spectral density of a stationary random series is, of course, defined as the spectral density of any typical series from that ensemble.

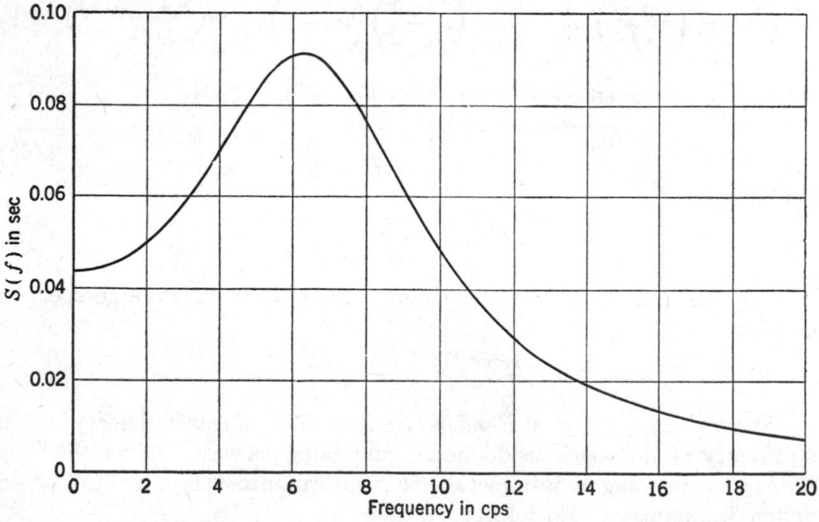

FIG. 6·3.—Normalized spectral density of fading record.

Spectral Density for Experimental Data.—There are several procedures whereby one can obtain the spectral density from experimental data. The best method is to calculate the spectral density as the Fourier transform of the autocorrelation function. This will be explained in detail in the following section. Figure 6·3 shows the spectral density obtained in this way for the radar fading record shown in Fig. 6·1.

It is, of course, possible to obtain the Fourier coefficients for a finite length T of data and then to compute $G(f)$ by means of Eq. (50), with the limit process omitted. Numerical-integration methods require that the data be discrete. From N pieces of data it is possible to obtain $N/2$ harmonics. This is, however, a very tedious task even when one takes advantage of short cuts.[1] Various machines have been devised to obtain the Fourier coefficients; one such is the Coradi harmonic analyzer, which performs the required integration, harmonic by harmonic, as the apparatus is driven so as to follow the curve representing the data. It is also possible to have a voltage follow the data and send the voltage through a wave analyzer.

6·8. The Relation between the Correlation Functions and the Spectral Density.—Both the autocorrelation function and the spectral density depend on the product of the function $y(t)$ by itself. Both functions likewise depend on the periodicities in the message but are independent of the relative phases of the Fourier components. It is therefore not surprising to find that they are Fourier transforms of each other.[2] In fact, as will be proved later

$$R(\tau) = \int_0^\infty df\, G(f) \cos 2\pi f\tau \tag{75}$$

and

$$G(f) = 4 \int_0^\infty d\tau\, R(\tau) \cos 2\pi f\tau. \tag{76a}$$

Similar relations hold for the normalized functions $\rho(\tau)$ and $S(f)$; for instance

$$S(f) = 4 \int_0^\infty d\tau\, \rho(\tau) \cos 2\pi f\tau. \tag{76b}$$

This intimate relationship between the spectral density and the autocorrelation function sheds more light on the interpretation of each. For example, a delta-function singularity in the spectral density at the frequency f_1 corresponds to a $\cos 2\pi f_1\tau$ term in the autocorrelation function. An exponential-decay autocorrelation function, such as is

[1] There exist short-cut methods for the cases $N = 12$ and $N = 24$. See, for instance, E. T. Whittaker and G. Robinson, *The Calculus of Observations*, Blackie, Glasgow, 1929, pp. 260–284.

[2] This relation is contained in a paper by N. Wiener, *Acta Math.* **55**, (1930). The reader will find in this reference a rigorous treatment of the subject matter of the present chapter, which, incidentally, avoids use of the delta function by working with the indefinite integral of the spectrum $G(f)$.

sometimes associated with noise,

$$R(\tau) = e^{-\beta|\tau|}, \tag{77}$$

has the spectral density

$$G(f) = \frac{4\beta}{\beta^2 + (2\pi f)^2}. \tag{78}$$

This function is bell-shaped, decreasing to half its zero-frequency amplitude at $f = \beta/2\pi$.

Aside from their theoretical importance, Eqs. (76) are extremely useful as an aid in the calculation of the spectral density. It is often simpler to compute the autocorrelation function first and then the spectral density by means of Eqs. (76) than to compute the spectral density directly. This is, for instance, the case with the stationary random process described in Eq. (1). The autocorrelation function [Eqs. (39) and (40)] is easily computed as an ensemble average. On subtraction of the contribution due to the square of the mean, this becomes

$$\left.\begin{aligned} R_1(\tau) &= \tfrac{1}{4}(1 - |\tau|) \qquad &&\text{for } |\tau| \leqq 1, \\ &= 0 &&\text{elsewhere.} \end{aligned}\right\} \tag{79}$$

Applying Eqs. (76), one obtains very simply the spectral density that was derived in Sec. 6·7 by a rather involved argument:

$$G_1(f) = \frac{1}{2}\left(\frac{\sin \pi f}{\pi f}\right)^2. \tag{70}$$

A second example is provided by the normalized spectral density (Fig. 6·3) of the radar fading record shown in Fig. 6·1. This was obtained by means of Eqs. (76) from an approximation to the normalized autocorrelation function of Fig. 6·2:

$$\rho(\tau) = e^{-24|\tau|} \cos 40\tau. \tag{80}$$

This function is plotted, along with the experimentally obtained autocorrelation function, in Fig. 6·4; it has all of the properties of an autocorrelation function. On comparing the spectral density and autocorrelation function, one sees that the peak in the spectral density occurs at the frequency of the damped oscillation of the autocorrelation function.

If the Fourier coefficients were to be obtained directly from Eqs. (76) by some method of numerical integration, use could be made of the fact that the autocorrelation function vanishes for all practical purposes for $\tau \geqq 0.2$ sec. On the other hand, in order to obtain the spectral density directly one would be forced to work with 20 sec of data. This is no easy matter when the frequencies of interest are as high as 30 cps. One could, however, argue that it is no easy matter to obtain the autocorrelation function. It is not difficult to calculate the number of computations involved in both methods. To obtain $N/2$ harmonics (sine and cosine) from N pieces of data, N^2 multiplications and N^2 additions are necessary. To compute $N/4$ values of the autocorrelation function from N pieces of data $\frac{7}{32}N^2$ multiplications and $\frac{7}{32}N^2$ additions are necessary. The work needed to obtain the spectral density from the autocorrelation depends upon the autocorrelation function. In general, for a random

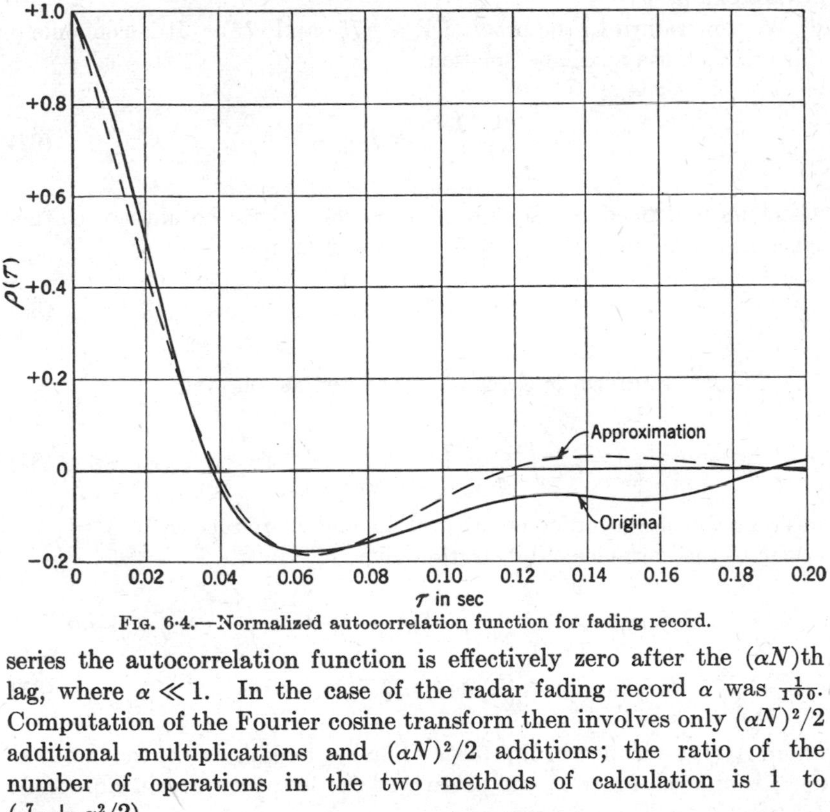

FIG. 6·4.—Normalized autocorrelation function for fading record.

series the autocorrelation function is effectively zero after the (αN)th lag, where $\alpha \ll 1$. In the case of the radar fading record α was $\frac{1}{100}$. Computation of the Fourier cosine transform then involves only $(\alpha N)^2/2$ additional multiplications and $(\alpha N)^2/2$ additions; the ratio of the number of operations in the two methods of calculation is 1 to $(\frac{7}{32} + \alpha^2/2)$.

Even when the autocorrelation function does not vanish for the larger values of τ, it is still of advantage to compute it first. Its usefulness lies in the fact that one can compute the indefinite integral of the normalized spectral density [see Eq. (61)] directly from the normalized autocorrelation function [see Eq. (30)]:

$$I(f_0) = \int_0^{f_0} df\, S(f) = \frac{2}{\pi} \int_0^\infty d\tau\, \frac{\rho(\tau)}{\tau} \sin 2\pi f_0 \tau. \tag{81}$$

[Equation (81) is obtained on integrating Eq. (76b) with respect to f.]

The integral equals the fractional power in the message below the frequency f_0, except for the d-c component. If $|I(f_2) - I(f_1)|$ is much less than 1 [note that $I(\infty) = 1$], then the values of $S(f)$ in the interval (f_1, f_2) are negligibly small and need not be computed. By computing $I(f)$ for several values of f one can therefore make a quick survey of the regions in which $S(f)$ is significantly different from zero. The advantage of knowing the important frequency regions of the spectrum needs no further emphasis.

We now return to the proof of Eqs. (75) and (76). It is convenient to work with the auxiliary function

$$C_T(\tau) = \frac{1}{2T}\int_{-\infty}^{\infty} dt\, y_T(t) y_T(t+\tau), \tag{82}$$

where y_T is defined by Eq. (47). It is clear that the autocorrelation function is the limit of $C_T(\tau)$ as T becomes infinite:

$$R(\tau) = \lim_{T\to\infty} C_T(\tau). \tag{83}$$

The Fourier transform of C_T can be rewritten as follows:

$$\int_{-\infty}^{\infty} d\tau\, C_T(\tau) e^{-2\pi i f\tau} = \frac{1}{2T}\int_{-\infty}^{\infty} d\tau \int_{-\infty}^{\infty} dt\, e^{-2\pi i f(t+\tau)} e^{2\pi i f t} y_T(t) y_T(t+\tau). \tag{84}$$

Interchange of the order of integration and introduction of $s = t + \tau$ as one of the variables of integration give

$$\begin{aligned}\int_{-\infty}^{\infty} d\tau\, C_T(\tau) e^{-2\pi i f\tau} &= \frac{1}{2T}\int_{-\infty}^{\infty} dt\, y_T(t) e^{-2\pi i f t}\int_{-\infty}^{\infty} ds\, y_T(s) e^{2\pi i f s} \\ &= \frac{1}{2T} A_T(f) A_T^*(f),\end{aligned} \tag{85}$$

where $A_T(f)$ is defined in Eq. (48). Finally, making use of the fact that $C_T(\tau)$ is an even function and passing to the limit, we obtain Eq. (76a):

$$\left.\begin{aligned}G(f) = \lim_{T\to\infty}\frac{1}{T}|A_T(f)|^2 &= \lim_{T\to\infty} 4\int_0^{\infty} d\tau\, C_T(\tau)\cos 2\pi f\tau \\ &= 4\int_0^{\infty} d\tau\, R(\tau)\cos 2\pi f\tau.\end{aligned}\right\} \tag{86}$$

Since the function $\lim_{T\to\infty} (1/T)|A_T(f)|^2$ is even, Eq. (75) can be obtained directly from Eq. (76a) by means of the Fourier integral theorem (see Chap. 2).

When $y(t)$ has a nonzero mean and contains periodic terms, its autocorrelation function has corresponding constant and cosine terms. In evaluating Eqs. (76) use must then be made of the following relations:[1]

$$\left.\begin{aligned} 4\int_0^\infty d\tau \cos 2\pi f\tau &= 2\delta(f), \\ 4\int_0^\infty d\tau \cos 2\pi f_0\tau \cos 2\pi f\tau &= \delta(f - |f_0|), \end{aligned}\right\} \tag{87}$$

where $f_0 \neq 0$. It is very easy to show that Eqs. (75) and (76) properly relate the autocorrelation function [Eq. (38)] and the spectral density [Eq. (64)] for a trigonometric polynomial.

Relations similar to Eqs. (75) and (76) exist between the cross-correlation function and the cross-spectral density. If y is a two-dimensional function (u,v), then the following theorem holds:

$$R_{uv}(\tau) = \overline{u(t)v(t+\tau)} = \frac{1}{2}\int_{-\infty}^{\infty} df\, G_{uv}(f)e^{2\pi jf\tau}, \tag{88}$$

$$G_{uv}(f) = 2\int_{-\infty}^{\infty} d\tau\, R_{uv}(\tau)e^{-2\pi jf\tau}, \tag{89}$$

where $G_{uv}(f)$ is defined as in Eq. (57).

In the case of discrete data taken at successive instants of time T_r sec apart, the analogues of Eqs. (75) and (76*a*) are

$$R(m) = \int_0^{1/2T_r} df\, G(f) \cos 2\pi f T_r m \tag{90}$$

and

$$G(f) = 4T_r\left[\frac{R(0)}{2} + \sum_{m=1}^{\infty} R(m) \cos 2\pi f T_r m\right]. \tag{91}$$

The proof of these results is similar to that for the continuous case. In evaluating Eq. (91) when y has a nonzero mean or contains periodic terms, use must be made of the following relations:

[1] If in the spectral density the entire frequency range were used instead of the $(0, \infty)$ interval, Eq. (87) could be rewritten as

$$\left.\begin{aligned} 4\int_0^\infty d\tau \cos 2\pi f\tau &= \delta(f) \\ 4\int_0^\infty d\tau \cos 2\pi f_0\tau \cos 2\pi f\tau &= \tfrac{1}{2}[\delta(f - f_0) + \delta(f + f_0)], \end{aligned}\right\}$$

in which case the second equation could be derived from the first.

$$\left.\begin{aligned} 4T_r\left(\frac{1}{2} + \sum_{m=1}^{\infty} \cos 2\pi f T_r m\right) &= 2\delta(f), \\ 4T_r\left[\frac{1}{2} + \sum_{m=1}^{\infty} (-1)^m \cos 2\pi f T_r m\right] &= 2\delta\left(f - \frac{1}{2T_r}\right), \\ 4T_r\left(\frac{1}{2} + \sum_{m=1}^{\infty} \cos 2\pi f_0 T_r m \cos 2\pi f T_r m\right) &= \delta(f - |f_0|). \end{aligned}\right\} \tag{92}$$

6·9. Spectral Density and Autocorrelation Function of the Filtered Signal.—The discussion up to this point has dealt with certain useful statistical properties of time-variable data in general. These ideas apply equally well to the input and the output of a servomechanism. It is the purpose of this section to study the response of a servomechanism to an input of which only certain statistical properties are known. We shall suppose that only the spectral density of the input (or its time equivalent, the autocorrelation function) is known. If the mechanism is linear and does not change with time, it is then easy to determine the spectral density of the output. Therein lies the principal usefulness of the spectral density.

The theorem is simply stated: If $Y(2\pi jf)$ is the transfer function of a linear time-invariant mechanism and $G_I(f)$ is the spectral density of the input, then the output spectral density $G_O(f)$ is

$$G_O(f) = |Y(2\pi jf)|^2 G_I(f). \tag{93}$$

One would certainly expect a theorem of this type to be true; but because of the way in which we have been forced to define the spectral density, the proof itself is not straightforward. The spectral density has been defined as a limit involving the Fourier transform $A_T(f)$ of y_T, which vanishes outside the interval $(-T,T)$. Although $Y(2\pi jf)A_T(f)$ is the Fourier transform of the output under these conditions, it is not the Fourier transform of a function that vanishes outside any finite interval. For this reason the proof of Eq. (93) which follows has its starting point in the time representation of the linear system.

It was shown in Chap. 2 that any stable linear time-invariant mechanism which acts only in the past[1] can be represented by a weighting function on the past of the input $y(t)$. Let the weighting function be written as $W(t)$. Then

[1] For the purposes of this discussion it is not necessary that the operator act only in the past.

and

$$\left.\begin{aligned} W(t) &= 0 \qquad \text{for } t < 0, \\ \int_{0-}^{\infty} dt\,|W(t)| &< \infty. \end{aligned}\right\} \tag{94}$$

The weighting function may contain Dirac delta functions. The output $z(t)$ is then

$$z(t) = \int_{0-}^{\infty} ds\, y(t-s)W(s) = \int_{-\infty}^{\infty} ds\, y(t-s)W(s). \tag{95}$$

The autocorrelation function of the output can be written in terms of the input as follows:

$$R_z(\tau) = \lim_{T\to\infty} \frac{1}{2T} \int_{-T}^{T} dt \left[\int_{-\infty}^{\infty} ds\, y(t-s)W(s) \times \int_{-\infty}^{\infty} dr\, y(t+\tau-r)W(r) \right]. \tag{96}$$

Interchanging the order of integration gives

$$R_z(\tau) = \lim_{T\to\infty} \int_{-\infty}^{\infty} ds \int_{-\infty}^{\infty} dr\, W(s) \times \left[\frac{1}{2T} \int_{-T}^{T} dt\, y(t-s)y(t+\tau-r) \right] \times W(r). \tag{97}$$

The limit, as T becomes infinite, of the quantity inside the brackets is

$$R_y(\tau + s - r) = \lim_{T\to\infty} \frac{1}{2T} \int_{-T}^{T} dt\, y(t)y(t+\tau+s-r). \tag{98}$$

Passing to the limit, therefore, gives

$$R_z(\tau) = \int_{-\infty}^{\infty} ds \int_{-\infty}^{\infty} dr\, W(s)R_y(\tau+s-r)W(r). \tag{99}$$

This is the time equivalent of Eq. (93). The mean-square value of the output $\overline{z^2}$, obtained from Eq. (99) by setting $\tau = 0$, is

$$\overline{z^2} = \int_{-\infty}^{\infty} ds \int_{-\infty}^{\infty} dr\, W(s)R_y(s-r)W(r). \tag{100}$$

Equation (93) can now be proved by taking the Fourier transform of Eq. (99). Thus

$$G_O(f) = 2\int_{-\infty}^{\infty} d\tau\, R_z(\tau)e^{-2\pi i f\tau} = 2\int_{-\infty}^{\infty} d\tau \int_{-\infty}^{\infty} ds \int_{-\infty}^{\infty} dr\, e^{-2\pi i f(\tau+s-r)} e^{2\pi i f s}e^{-2\pi i f r}R_y(\tau+s-r)W(s)W(r). \tag{101}$$

On change of the variable of integration τ to $(\tau + s - r)$, the volume integral breaks up into the product of three independent integrals:

$$G_O(f) = |Y(2\pi jf)|^2 G_I(f), \tag{93}$$

where

$$Y(2\pi jf) = \int_{-\infty}^{\infty} dt\, W(t) e^{-2\pi jft}, \tag{102}$$

as in Chap. 2.

We shall be interested in a case slightly more complicated than the problem just considered. Suppose that the input consists of two parts —signal and noise. To use the terminology of Sec. 6·2, the random process y, which describes the input, has two components (u,v), where u is the signal record and v the noise record. It frequently happens that the signal and noise enter the mechanism at different points or in different forms. In such a case, the mechanism will operate on these two component functions differently. Let the weighting function operating on u be W_1 and that operating on v be W_2, where both W_1 and W_2 satisfy the condition of Eq. (94). The output is then

$$z(t) = \int_{0-}^{\infty} ds\, u(t-s) W_1(s) + \int_{0-}^{\infty} ds\, v(t-s) W_2(s). \tag{103}$$

Applying the same reasoning as before, we obtain

$$\begin{aligned} R_z(\tau) = \int_{-\infty}^{\infty} ds \int_{-\infty}^{\infty} dr\, [W_1(s) R_u(\tau + s - r) W_1(r) \\ + W_2(s) R_v(\tau + s - r) W_2(r) + W_1(s) R_{uv}(\tau + s - r) W_2(r) \\ + W_1(r) R_{vu}(\tau + s - r) W_2(s)], \end{aligned} \tag{104}$$

where $R_{uv}(\tau) = \overline{u(t)v(t+\tau)}$. The Fourier transform of this equation is

$$\begin{aligned} G_O(f) = |Y_1(2\pi jf)|^2 G_u(f) + |Y_2(2\pi jf)|^2 G_v(f) \\ + Y_1^*(2\pi jf) G_{uv}(f) Y_2(2\pi jf) + Y_1(2\pi jf) G_{vu}(f) Y_2^*(2\pi jf), \end{aligned} \tag{105}$$

where $G_{uv}(f)$ is the cross-spectral density defined as in Eq. (57).

We shall conclude this section with a resumé of the analogous results for the case of a random series. If the filter is stable, linear, and time invariant, it can be represented as a weighting function w_m, where

$$\left.\begin{aligned} w_m = 0 \qquad \text{for } m < 0, \\ \sum_{m=0}^{\infty} |w_m| < \infty. \end{aligned}\right\} \tag{106}$$

For an input series $[y(m)]$, the output series is then

$$z(m) = \sum_{n=0}^{\infty} y(m-n) w_n. \tag{107}$$

The transfer function for w is

$$Y(2\pi jf) = \sum_{m=0}^{\infty} w_m e^{-2\pi jfT_r m}. \tag{108}$$

The output spectrum is again related to the input spectrum by Eq. (93), and the output autocorrelation formula is

$$R_z(m) = \sum_{n=0}^{\infty} \sum_{l=0}^{\infty} w_n R_y(m + n - l) w_l. \tag{109}$$

EXAMPLES

6·10. Radar Automatic-tracking Example.—It will be instructive to derive the error spectral density and autocorrelation function for a gyro-stabilized automatic-tracking radar mechanism on which a great deal of experimental data are available and to study the effect of fading in the reflected radar signal in causing tracking errors. In order to simplify the discussion it will be assumed that the aircraft being tracked is flying a radial course directly away from the tracking system. In this case the problem of following the maneuvers of the plane is trivial, and the only source of error will be the fading.

An abbreviated description of the tracking system will now be given. A measure of the difference between the direction to a target and the radar reflector axis is obtained by conically scanning a pulsed r-f beam. The received signal is first amplified and rectified. The resulting envelope is a modulated signal of the form

$$\sigma[1 + \epsilon(t) \sin (2\pi f_s t + \phi)], \tag{110}$$

where σ is proportional to reflection coefficient of the plane, $\epsilon(t)$ is proportional to the magnitude of the angular error in tracking, and f_s is the scan frequency (30 cps). The phase angle ϕ determines the direction of the error relative to the reflector axis; $\phi = 0$ corresponds to an error in traverse only.[1] Random variations of the reflection coefficient of the plane cause the signal envelope to be of the form

$$[1 + g(t)][1 + \epsilon(t) \sin (2\pi f_s t + \phi)]. \tag{111}$$

A typical record of $g(t)$ is that shown in Fig. 6·1.

The signal is then sent through a high-pass RC-coupling transformer which serves to take out the d-c term. The resulting signal is next

[1] The traverse angle is measured from the line of sight in a plane containing the line of sight and a horizontal line perpendicular to the line of sight. The error in azimuth is roughly equal to the error in traverse multiplied by the secant of the elevation angle.

commutated in order to determine the phase ϕ of the error proper. The commutator produces two signals, one equal to the input multiplied by $2 \sin 2\pi f_s t$, the second equal to the input multiplied by $2 \cos 2\pi f_s t$. [The normalizing factor 2 is introduced to make the peak value of the incoming signal $\epsilon(t) \sin (2\pi f_s t + \phi)$ equal the resultant of the mean values of the output signals $\epsilon(t) \cos \phi$ and $\epsilon(t) \sin \phi$.] The first of these signals, the traverse error signal, is then used as input to a servoamplifier that controls the azimuth of the antenna axis, whereas the second is used as input to another servoamplifier that controls the elevation of that axis. The traverse and elevation signals are thereafter handled similarly. The commutated signal is sent through a low-pass filter in order to eliminate the 60-cycle ripple. The resultant signal goes into a servoamplifier with equalizing circuit having a transfer function (see Chap. 2)

$$Y(p) = K_v \frac{T_1 p + 1}{T_2 p + 1}, \tag{112}$$

where p is the complex variable of the Laplace transform and

$$\left.\begin{aligned} T_1 &= 0.36 \text{ sec}, \\ T_2 &= 16 \text{ sec}, \\ K_v &= 80 \text{ sec}^{-1}. \end{aligned}\right\} \tag{113}$$

The equalizer was chosen to have a large velocity-error constant K_v and to cut off rapidly above frequencies common in tracking. In Chap. 4 this was called "proportional-plus-integral control."

A current proportional to the output voltages is used to excite the traverse and elevation torque motors, which, in turn, precess a free-floating line-of-sight gyro. The rate of precession is proportional to the currents through the torque motors. Finally, the reflector is slave to the gyro. The servo that performs this task is so much faster than the equalizing circuit that for purposes of this calculation it can be assumed perfect. The net effect is to drive the output θ_O, so that in terms of Laplace transforms (see Chap. 2)

$$\frac{\mathfrak{L}(\theta_O)}{\mathfrak{L}(\text{commutated error signal})} = \frac{K_v(T_1 p + 1)}{p(T_2 p + 1)}, \tag{114}$$

where all proportionality constants have been absorbed in K_v. When the system is in proper adjustment, there is no interaction between the elevation and traverse control systems. This permits us to limit the discussion to a single component of the error, the traverse component.

Let us begin our analysis with the received signal [Eq. (111)]. It is found in practice that $|\epsilon(t)|$ remains less than 0.05 and that the rms value of g is approximately 0.25. To a first approximation it is therefore possible to neglect the cross-product term; the received signal can be written as

$$s_1(t) = 1 + g(t) + \epsilon(t) \sin (2\pi f_s t + \phi). \tag{115}$$

In discussing the behavior of the azimuth servomechanism we can set $\phi = 0$, provided we allow $\epsilon(t)$ to assume positive and negative values; ϵ is then, strictly speaking, the difference between the traverse input θ_I and the traverse output θ_O. That is,

$$\epsilon = \theta_I - \theta_O. \tag{116}$$

The principal effect of the high-pass *RC*-coupling transformer on the signal $s_1(t)$ of Eq. (115) is to remove the d-c term; its output is essentially

$$s_2(t) = g(t) + (\theta_I - \theta_O) \sin 2\pi f_s t. \tag{117}$$

It is convenient at this point to convert g, θ_I, and θ_O to angular mils. The conversion factor is determined by and varies inversely with the fractional modulation in signal intensity caused by moving the reflector axis a given angle away from the target.

The signal $s_2(t)$ now goes through the commutator, which converts it to

$$\begin{aligned} s_3(t) &= [g(t) + (\theta_I - \theta_O) \sin 2\pi f_s t]\, 2 \sin 2\pi f_s t \\ &= 2g(t) \sin 2\pi f_s t + (\theta_I - \theta_O) - (\theta_I - \theta_O) \cos 4\pi f_s t. \end{aligned} \tag{118}$$

This commutated signal is then sent through a low-pass filter which eliminates the 60-cycle ripple term $(\theta_I - \theta_O) \cos 4\pi f_s t$. The low-pass filter has no effect on $(\theta_I - \theta_O)$, since most of the spectrum of $(\theta_I - \theta_O)$ lies below 2 cps. In the case of $2g(t) \sin 2\pi f_s t$ it serves to attenuate that part of the spectral density which lies above 10 cps. Let us designate by $\theta_N(t)$ that part of the filter output due to the input $2g(t) \sin 2\pi f_s t$. The net effect of the low-pass filter is then to change the commutated signal $s_3(t)$ into

$$s_4(t) = \theta_N + (\theta_I - \theta_O). \tag{119}$$

This signal is the input to the network with transfer function given by Eq. (114). Therefore

$$\mathfrak{L}(\theta_O) = \frac{K_v(T_1 p + 1)}{p(T_2 p + 1)} \mathfrak{L}(\theta_N + \theta_I - \theta_O). \tag{120}$$

Rearrangement of Eq. (120) gives

$$\mathfrak{L}(\epsilon) = \frac{\mathfrak{L}(\theta_I)}{1 + \dfrac{K_v(T_1 p + 1)}{p(T_2 p + 1)}} - \frac{\dfrac{K_v(T_1 p + 1)}{p(T_2 p + 1)} \mathfrak{L}(\theta_N)}{1 + \dfrac{K_v(T_1 p + 1)}{p(T_2 p + 1)}}. \tag{121}$$

We are now in a position to apply the theory developed in Sec. 6·9.

In terms of the quantities in Eq. (105), we have

$$\left.\begin{aligned} u &= \theta_I, \\ v &= \theta_N, \\ \text{Output} &= \epsilon, \end{aligned}\right\} \tag{122}$$

$$\left.\begin{aligned} Y_1(2\pi jf) &= \frac{(T_2 2\pi jf + 1)2\pi jf}{T_2(2\pi jf)^2 + (1 + K_v T_1)2\pi jf + K_v}, \\ Y_2(2\pi jf) &= \frac{K_v(T_1 2\pi jf + 1)}{T_2(2\pi jf)^2 + (1 + K_v T_1)2\pi jf + K_v}. \end{aligned}\right\} \tag{123}$$

Spectral Densities of the Input and Noise.—In general, the trajectory of the airplane has zero correlation with the fading, which is caused by fluctuations in the airplane reflection coefficient due to the erratic part of the plane's motion. For this reason the function $G_{uv}(f) = G_{vu}(-f)$ vanishes identically.

When consideration is limited, as it is here, to a plane flying a radial course, the only source of error is the fading itself. The input angle θ_I is a constant; we may take it to be unity, and

$$G_u(f) = 2\delta(f). \tag{124}$$

As $Y_1(2\pi jf)$ contains f as a factor, the quantity $|Y_1(2\pi jf)|^2 G_u(f)$ vanishes identically. The error spectrum $G_\epsilon(f)$ consequently reduces to

$$G_\epsilon(f) = |Y_2(2\pi jf)|^2 G_v(f). \tag{125}$$

There remains the determination of $G_v(f)$. Since $v = \theta_N(t)$ was obtained by sending the signal $2g(t) \sin 2\pi f_s t$ through the low-pass filter, we shall first obtain the autocorrelation function and then the spectral density for the function $2g(t) \sin 2\pi f_s t$. As we have seen

$$R(\tau) = \widetilde{4g(t)g(t + \tau) \sin 2\pi f_s t \sin 2\pi f_s(t + \tau)}. \tag{126}$$

Since the fading is independent of the position of the beam in a scan, a particular time series $g(t)$ is associated in the ensemble with all possible phases of the commutator. Hence all traverse error signals $2g(t) \sin 2\pi f_s t$, differing only by a translation in time of $g(t)$ or a translation in phase ϕ of the commutator, are equally likely. We therefore replace Eq. (126) by

$$R(\tau) = \widetilde{4g(t)g(t + \tau) \sin (2\pi f_s t + \phi) \sin [2\pi f_s(t + \tau) + \phi]}. \tag{127}$$

Averaging the sinusoidal factor over all possible commutator phases gives

$$\frac{1}{2\pi} \int_0^{2\pi} d\phi \sin (2\pi f_s t + \phi) \sin [2\pi f_s(t + \tau) + \phi] = \frac{1}{2} \cos 2\pi f_s \tau. \tag{128}$$

It follows that

$$R(\tau) = \widetilde{2 \cos 2\pi f_s \tau\, g(t)g(t + \tau)} = 2(\cos 2\pi f_s \tau) R_g(\tau). \tag{129}$$

The normalized autocorrelation function $\rho_g(\tau) = [R_g(\tau)]/[R_g(0)]$, computed from the fading record of Fig. 6·1, is shown in Fig. 6·2. Figure 6·3 gives the normalized spectral density $S_g(f)$ of $g(t)$, computed as the Fourier transform of $2\rho_g(\tau)$. It is a simple matter to go from the Fourier

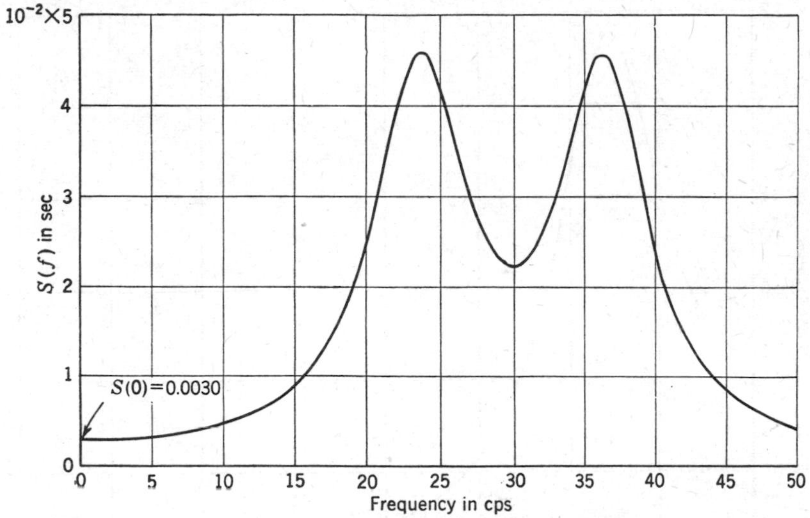

FIG. 6·5.—Normalized spectral density of the commutated fading record.

transform of $\rho_g(\tau)$ to that of $\rho_g(\tau)\cos 2\pi f_s\tau$, which is, of course, the normalized spectral density of $2g(t)\sin 2\pi f_s t$; this is easily shown to be

$$S(f) = \tfrac{1}{2}[S_g(f - f_s) + S_g(f + f_s)]. \tag{130}$$

The normalized spectral density of the commutated fading record is plotted in Fig. 6·5; it is quite flat out to about 10 cps, after which it rises to a double peak.

In order to obtain $G_v(f)$ we must multiply $S(f)$ by

$$R(0) = 2R_g(0) = 212 \qquad \text{mil}^2 \tag{131}$$

and by the square of the absolute value of the transfer function of the low-pass filter. The latter will not affect the low frequencies but will attenuate the higher frequencies, flattening out the peaks in Fig. 6·5. It will therefore be satisfactory to approximate $G_v(f)$ as a constant equal to $G_v(0)$ for frequencies up to 5 cps; beyond this it does not matter since the servoamplifier is insensitive to frequencies above about 5 cps. We therefore set

$$G_v(f) \equiv (0.0030)(212) = 0.636 \qquad \text{mil}^2\ \text{sec}. \tag{132}$$

The final equation for $G_\epsilon(f)$ is

$$G_\epsilon(f) = \left|\frac{K_v(T_1 2\pi jf + 1)}{T_2(2\pi jf)^2 + (1 + K_vT_1)2\pi jf + K_v}\right|^2 G_v(0). \tag{133}$$

The normalized error spectral density $S_\epsilon(f) = G_\epsilon(f)/\int_0^\infty G_\epsilon(f)\,df$ is plotted in Fig. 6·6 for special choice of constants given in Eq. (113).

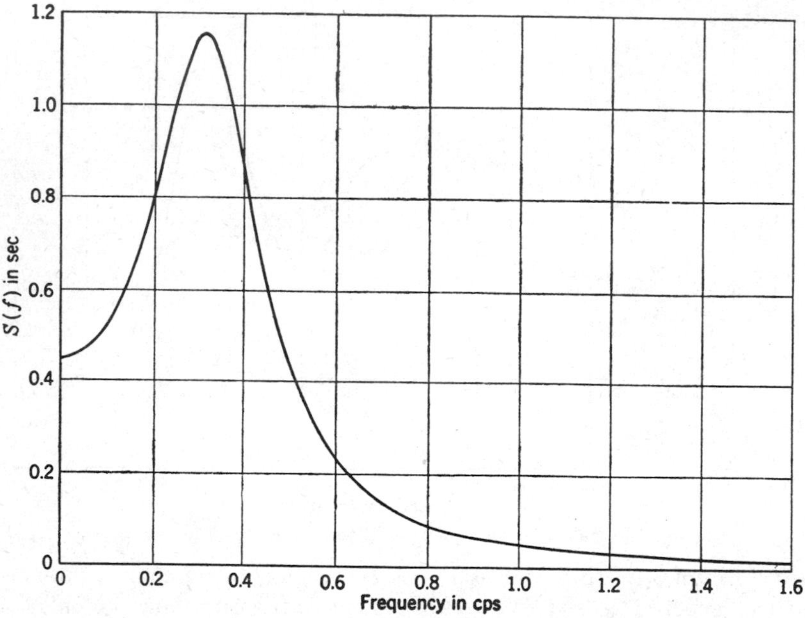

FIG. 6·6.—Theoretical normalized spectral density of the tracking error.

By means of the integration tables in the appendix (see Sec. 7·6), it is easy to show for these constant values that

$$\int_0^\infty df\, G_\epsilon(f) = 0.703 \qquad \text{mil}^2. \tag{134}$$

The normalized autocorrelation function can be computed from $S_\epsilon(f)$ by means of Eq. (75). The computed normalized function is, for the choice of constants given in Eq. (113),

$$\rho(\tau) = e^{-0.93|\tau|}\,(\cos 2\tau + 0.106 \sin 2|\tau|). \tag{135}$$

Equation (135), which is the final result of this theoretical argument, is plotted in Fig. 6·7 along with an experimentally obtained normalized autocorrelation function of the traverse tracking error for a receding plane. The experimental data from which the latter was obtained are shown in Fig. 6·8. The theoretical rms error was 0.84 mil, and the experimental value was 1.04 mil. The close correspondence between theory and experiment gives a good indication of the reliability of the method

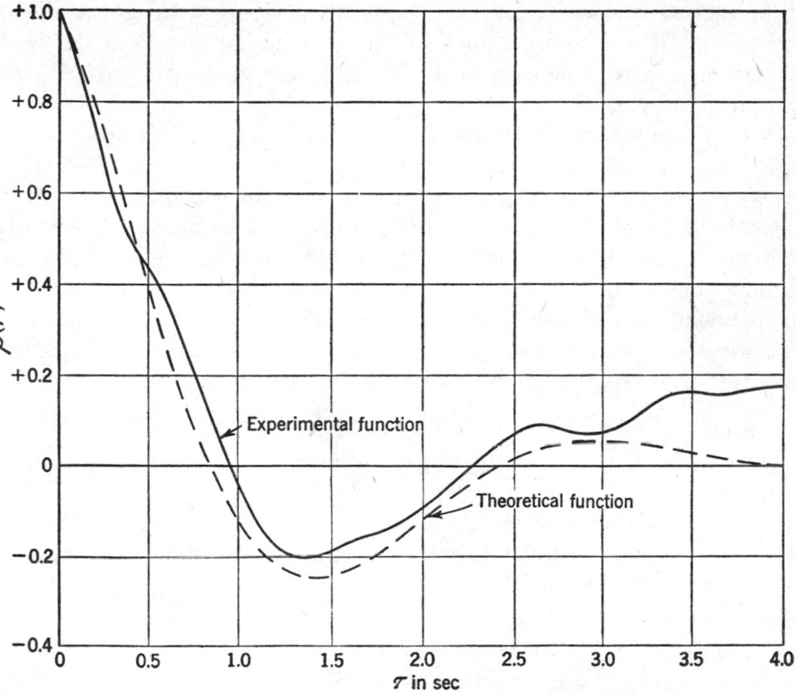

FIG. 6·7.—Theoretical and experimental normalized autocorrelation functions of traverse tracking error.

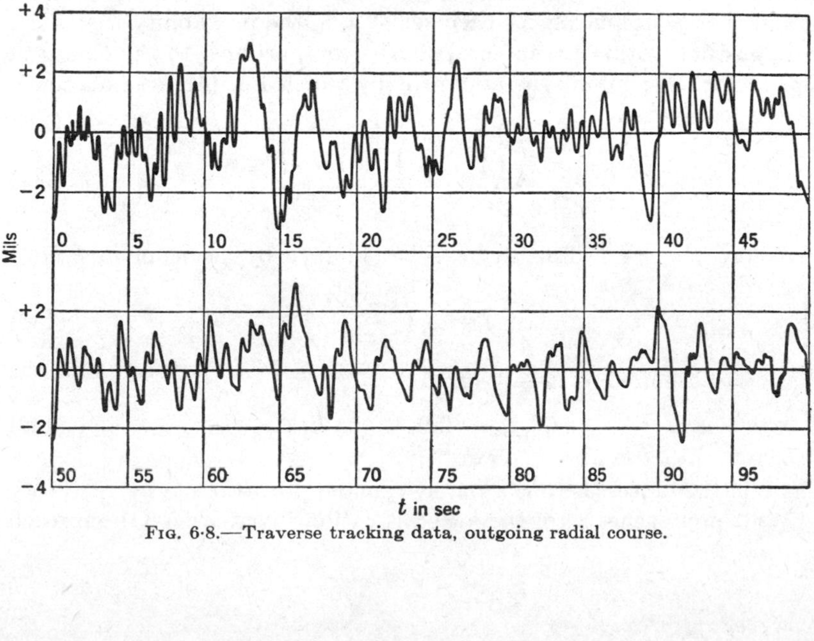

FIG. 6·8.—Traverse tracking data, outgoing radial course.

in predicting the behavior of a servomechanism with given design constants. It will be the purpose of the remaining chapters in this book to exploit these ideas further in developing design criteria for servomechanisms.

6·11. Purely Random Processes.—A stationary random process having a constant spectrum is called a *purely random process.* In finding the output of a servomechanism with a noise input it is often convenient to treat the noise as though it were a purely random process. This can be done because the noise usually has a flat spectrum that extends far beyond the cutoff frequency of the servomechanism; the change in amplitude at the high frequencies does not affect the output of the device. This was the case in the example treated in the last section. It is evident, however, that no such noise can ever be found in nature, since the average power of a purely random process $\int_0^\infty df\, G(f)$ is infinite. It will be instructive to determine some of the other properties of purely random processes.

A constant spectrum can be obtained as a limit from a variety of processes. A case in point is a modification of the stationary random process described by Eq. (1).
Let

$$y_s(t) = a_n, \qquad \left.\begin{aligned} &(n+s)\Delta \leqq t < (n+1+s)\Delta, \\ &n = 0, \pm 1, \pm 2, \cdots, \\ &\Delta > 0, \end{aligned}\right\} \tag{136}$$

where (1) $a_n = \pm\sqrt{N/2\Delta}$ with equal likelihood; (2) a_n is independent of a_m for $m \neq n$; and (3) for each set of a_n's, the probability that s lies in any region within the interval $(0,\Delta)$ is proportional to the length of that region. Following the argument by which Eq. (41) was obtained, one can easily derive

$$\left.\begin{aligned} R_\Delta(\tau) &= \frac{N}{2\Delta}\left(1 - \frac{|\tau|}{\Delta}\right) && \text{for } |\tau| \leqq \Delta, \\ &= 0 && \text{elsewhere.} \end{aligned}\right\} \tag{137}$$

As before, the spectral density can be obtained by means of Eqs. (76):

$$G_\Delta(f) = N\left(\frac{\sin \pi f\Delta}{\pi f\Delta}\right)^2. \tag{138}$$

Passing to the limit as $\Delta \to 0$, one has

$$G_0(f) = \lim_{\Delta\to 0} G_\Delta(f) \equiv N. \tag{139}$$

The limiting process is thus a purely random process.

As Δ approaches zero, the autocorrelation functions $R_\Delta(\tau)$ approach a delta function. Since the area under each curve $R_\Delta(\tau)$ is equal to $N/2$, this must be true of the limit curve. Thus

$$R(\tau) = \lim_{\Delta \to 0} R_\Delta(\tau) = \frac{N}{2}\,\delta(\tau). \tag{140}$$

If the relation in Eqs. (76) is to remain valid, this must certainly be the case.

Finally, the member functions of the process of Eq. (136) become increasingly wild as Δ approaches zero. In the limit the functions are made up of an infinitely dense sequence of independent delta functions; the values of the functions at any two different times are completely uncorrelated. Hence in the limit

$$P_2(y_1,y_2,\tau) = P_1(y_1)P_1(y_2) \quad \text{for } \tau \neq 0. \tag{141}$$

If purely random noise of constant spectral amplitude N is sent through a linear mechanism with transfer function $Y(2\pi jf)$, then the output spectrum will be, by Eq. (93),

$$G_O(f) = N|Y(2\pi jf)|^2. \tag{142}$$

If $W(t)$ is the weighting function corresponding to $Y(2\pi jf)$ [Eq. (102)], then by Eq. (99) the output autocorrelation function is

$$\begin{aligned} R_O(\tau) &= \frac{N}{2}\int_{-\infty}^{\infty} ds \int_{-\infty}^{\infty} dr\, W(s)\delta(\tau + s - r)W(r) \\ &= \frac{N}{2}\int_{-\infty}^{\infty} ds\, W(s)W(\tau + s). \end{aligned} \tag{143}$$

Consideration of this expression suggests another example of a purely random process. Since $W(t)$ is the response of the mechanism to a single impulse, one can easily show by direct calculation that Eq. (143) is the autocorrelation function of the output when the input consists of *any sequence of independent delta functions* having a zero average value, a mean-square value of $N/(2\beta)$, and a random distribution in time with density β. Furthermore, any stationary random-process input that gives an output with autocorrelation function that of Eq. (143), whatever the form of the weighting functions, must have a constant spectrum. Hence another example of a purely random process can be defined as follows:

$$y(t) = \sum a_n\delta(t - t_n), \tag{144}$$

where the a_n's are independent random variables all having the same distribution with zero mean and the intervals $(t_n - t_{n-1})$ are likewise independent random variables all having the same distribution with mean value $1/\beta$. If $\widetilde{a^2} = N/(2\beta)$, then the spectral density will have the constant value N. The corresponding output of a linear mechanism will be

$$z(t) = \sum a_n W(t - t_n). \tag{145}$$

A purely random series is defined analogously as a stationary random series having a constant spectrum. Any such series can be represented by

$$y_n = a_n, \qquad n = 0, \pm 1, \pm 2, \cdots, \tag{146}$$

where the n's are independent random variables all having the same distribution, with

$$\tilde{a} = 0, \qquad \widetilde{a^2} = \frac{N}{2T_r}, \tag{147}$$

T_r being the time between successive values of n (the repetition interval). It is clear that in this case

$$\left.\begin{aligned} R(m) &= \frac{N}{2T_r} \qquad \text{for } m = 0, \\ &= 0 \qquad \text{for } m \neq 0. \end{aligned}\right\} \tag{148}$$

The spectrum obtained by means of Eq. (91) is simply

$$G(f) = N. \tag{149}$$

The series produced by the coin flippers (Sec. 6·2) is an example of a purely random series.

6·12. A Typical Servomechanism Input.—This section will be devoted to an example of a servomechanism input that is appropriate for an automatic-tracking radar system. This example has been used in the following chapters. An automatic-tracking radar system is required to track all aircraft traveling through a hemisphere, say of radius 20,000 yd, about the system. As a first approximation, one may treat the angular rate of the airplane as constant through extended intervals, with abrupt changes from one value to another value independent of the first, etc. The angular displacement about the tracking system would then vary as indicated in Fig. 6·9*a*. The changes in angular velocity might correspond to the maneuvers of the aircraft. This type of input should not be confused with an input having a constant angular rate through extended intervals, with the *changes in rate* random and independent; in our example it is the rates themselves that are random and independent.

A better approximation than that of Fig. 6·9*a* to the trajectory of a maneuvering aircraft could be obtained by rounding off the corners so that within each interval the angular rate of the aircraft approaches a constant value asymptotically, with exponential decay of the difference. Such a trajectory is shown in Fig. 6·9b. If $y(t)$ is the first-mentioned trajectory, then the smoothed trajectory will be

$$z(t) = \nu \int_0^\infty ds\, y(t - s)e^{-\nu s}, \tag{150}$$

where ν is the reciprocal of the time constant for the exponential decay. The weighting function

$$W(t) = \nu e^{-\nu t} \tag{151}$$

has for its transfer function

$$Y(2\pi jf) = \frac{\nu}{\nu + 2\pi jf}. \tag{152}$$

If $G_y(f)$ is the spectral density of y, the spectral density of z will then be [Eq. (93)]

$$G_z(f) = \frac{\nu^2}{\nu^2 + (2\pi f)^2} G_y(f). \tag{153}$$

Our problem is therefore to determine the spectrum of y. Unfortunately, the function y wanders without bound in the course of its history and cannot be considered as a member of a stationary random process. On the other hand, in the applications to be made we shall be interested not so much in y as in its derivative. The derivative of y, which will be designated by x, does belong to a stationary process; it is plotted in Fig. 6·9c. The function $x(t)$ is of constant value over successive intervals, and its values over any two intervals are independent but have the same distribution. We shall proceed to determine the autocorrelation function and then the spectral density for x.

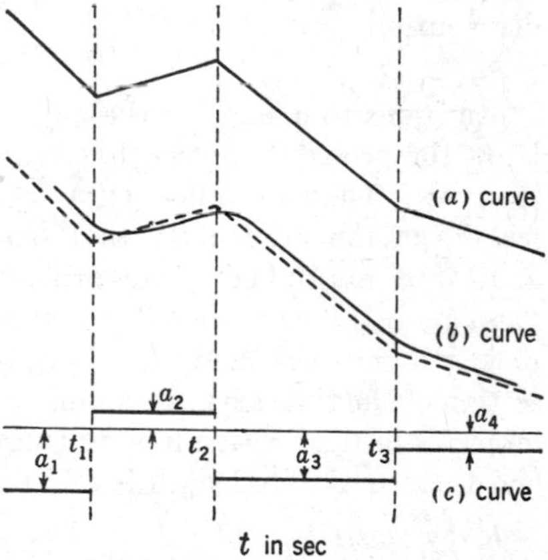

FIG. 6·9.—(a) Typical servo input; (b) exponentially smoothed input; (c) input velocity.

A precise definition of the stationary random process follows:

$$\left.\begin{aligned} x(t) = a_n, \qquad & \text{for } t_n \leqq t < t_{n+1}, \\ & n = 0, \pm 1, \pm 2, \cdots, \end{aligned}\right\} \tag{154}$$

where the a_n's are independent random variables having the same distribution and the interval lengths

$$(t_{n+1} - t_n) = l_n \tag{155}$$

are likewise independent random variables having the same probability distribution $H(l)$.

The times $\ldots, t_{-2}, t_{-1}, t_0, t_1, t_2, \ldots$, may, for example, have the Poisson distribution of shots on a line. In Poisson's problem each shot is independently placed on the line until the resultant set has a mean density of β shots per unit length t. The probability that any given interval of length Δ contains a shot of the set is approximately $\beta\Delta$; the probability that this interval does not contain a shot is $(1 - \beta\Delta)$. These expressions become exact as $\Delta \to 0$. To determine $H(l)$ in this case we start at an arbitrary shot and determine the probability that the closest shot lies within an interval Δ at a distance l to the right. Subdividing the interval of length l into subintervals of lengths Δ, it follows that the probability of no shot lying within any of the first $[(l/\Delta) - 1]$-subintervals is $(1 - \beta\Delta)^{(l/\Delta)-1}$, whereas the probability of a shot lying within the last subinterval is $\beta\Delta$. Hence the probability that both of these conditions are fulfilled is

$$H(l)\Delta \approx (1 - \beta\Delta)^{(l/\Delta)-1}\beta\Delta. \tag{156}$$

Passing to the limit as $\Delta = dl$ approaches zero, one obtains for the Poisson distribution

$$H(l)\,dl = \beta e^{-\beta l}\,dl. \tag{157}$$

In order to determine the autocorrelation function it is necessary to know the probability $Q(\tau)$ that $x(t)$ and $x(t + \tau)$ lie in the same defining interval. The probability $Q(\tau)$ is equal to the sum over intervals of all lengths of the probability that t is in an interval of length between l and $l + dl$ multiplied by the probability that this interval includes both t and $t + \tau$. The probability that an artibrary point t lies in an interval of length between l and $l + dl$ can be found as follows. Consider a long section of the time axis containing, say, K intervals. The total number of intervals in this section having lengths between l and $l + dl$ is $KH(l)\,dl$, and their aggregate length is $lKH(l)\,dl$. The total length of the section is $K \int_0^\infty dl\, lH(l)$. The desired probability is equal to that fraction of the section filled with intervals of length between l and $l + dl$:

$$\frac{l}{\bar{l}} H(l)\,dl, \tag{158}$$

where

$$\bar{l} = \int_0^\infty dl\, lH(l) \tag{159}$$

is the average interval length. The probability that an arbitrary interval of length l contains both t and $t + \tau$ is $(1 - \tau/l)$, if $\tau < l$. It follows that

$$Q(\tau) = \int_\tau^\infty dl\, \frac{l}{\bar{l}} H(l) \left(1 - \frac{\tau}{l}\right). \tag{160}$$

For the case of the Poisson distribution

$$\bar{l} = \frac{1}{\beta} \qquad \text{and} \qquad Q(\tau) = e^{-\beta|\tau|} \tag{161}$$

It is now an easy matter to determine the autocorrelation function for x. For a given function of the ensemble

$$x(t)x(t + \tau) = a_n^2 \text{ or } a_n a_{n+k}, \tag{162}$$

according as t and $t + \tau$ lie in the same interval or in two different intervals. For a given distribution of t_n's we first average over the a_n's. Because a_n is independent of a_{n+k}, we get $\widetilde{\widetilde{a^2}}$ or $\tilde{a}^2$ respectively for the above cases. Since the probability that t and $t + \tau$ lie in the same interval is just $Q(\tau)$, averaging over all distributions of the t_n's gives

$$\begin{aligned} R(\tau) &= \widetilde{\widetilde{x(t)x(t + \tau)}} \\ &= \widetilde{\widetilde{a^2}}Q(\tau) + a^2[1 - Q(\tau)]. \end{aligned} \tag{163}$$

The spectrum can now be computed by means of Eq. (76a):

$$G_x(f) = 4(\widetilde{\widetilde{a^2}} - \tilde{a}^2) \int_0^\infty d\tau\, Q(\tau) \cos 2\pi f\tau + 2\tilde{a}^2\delta(f). \tag{164}$$

If H rather than Q is given, the integral on the right of Eq. (164) can be expressed as

$$\begin{aligned} \int_0^\infty d\tau\, Q(\tau) \cos 2\pi f\tau &= \int_0^\infty d\tau \int_\tau^\infty dl\, \frac{(l - \tau)}{\bar{l}}\, H(l) \cos 2\pi f\tau, \\ &= \int_0^\infty dl \int_0^l d\tau\, \frac{(l - \tau)}{\bar{l}}\, H(l) \cos 2\pi f\tau, \\ &= \frac{1}{\bar{l}} \int_0^\infty dl\, H(l)\, \frac{(1 - \cos 2\pi fl)}{(2\pi f)^2}. \end{aligned} \tag{165}$$

Setting

$$\Omega(f) = \int_0^\infty dl\, H(l) \cos 2\pi fl, \tag{166}$$

this becomes

$$\int_0^\infty d\tau\, Q(\tau) \cos 2\pi f\tau = \frac{1 - \Omega(f)}{(2\pi f)^2\bar{l}}. \tag{167}$$

In the case of the Poisson distribution of points (t_n), with $\tilde{a} = 0$, we obtain

$$\Omega(f) = \frac{\beta^2}{\beta^2 + (2\pi f)^2}. \tag{168}$$

Substitution of this into Eqs. (164) and (167) gives

$$G_x(f) = \widetilde{\widetilde{a^2}}\, \frac{4\beta}{\beta^2 + (2\pi f)^2}, \tag{169}$$

in agreement with Eq. (78).

The stationary random process described by Eq. (1) is another special case of the process described by Eq. (154). In this case

$$H(l) = \delta(l - 1), \qquad \tilde{a} = \tfrac{1}{2}, \qquad \widetilde{a^2} = \tfrac{1}{2}. \tag{170}$$

The reader can readily verify that in this case the continuous part of Eq. (164) checks with Eq. (70).

In order to apply Eq. (169) in an aircraft example it will be necessary to have values for β and $\widetilde{a^2}$. Under present conditions β^{-1}, the average

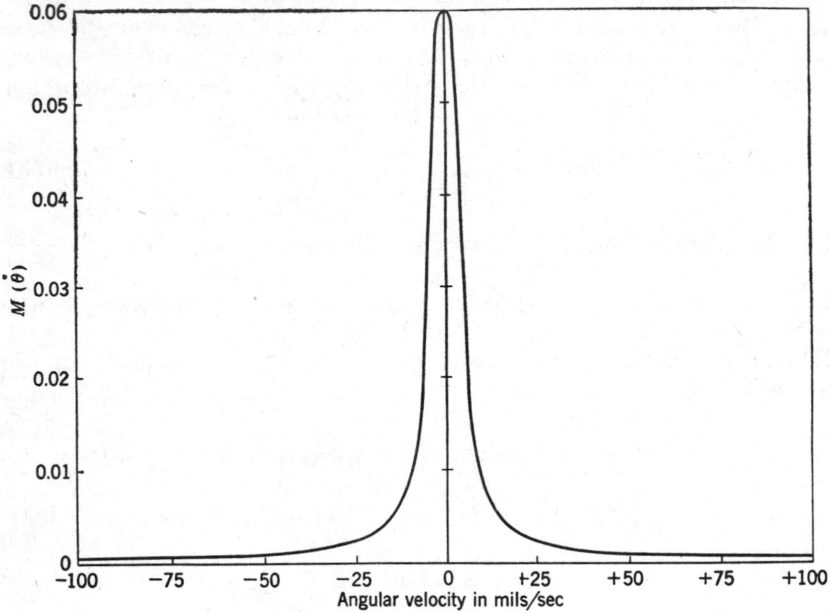

FIG. 6·10.—Probability distribution of angular velocity.

duration of a straight run by an attacking plane may range from 10 to 30 sec. An estimate of $\widetilde{a^2}$ has been made by considering the distribution of angular velocities for all straight-line paths in a plane traversed at 150 yd/sec. Only those paths were considered for which the minimum distance to the origin was less than 1500 yd; for these paths only that part from 9000 yd before crossover[1] to 9000 yd after crossover was used. Any part of a path in which the angular velocity exceeded $\frac{1}{2}$ radian/sec was omitted. Aside from these restrictions, portions of paths included in like areas in the plane were weighted equally. The resulting probability distribution $M(\dot{\theta})$ is plotted in Fig. 6·10. For this distribution the mean-square angular velocity $\widetilde{a^2}$ is 2.62×10^3 (mils/sec)^2; the rms angular velocity is 51 mils/sec.

[1] Crossover is that point on a straight-line path for which the distance to the origin is a minimum.

6·13. Potentiometer Noise.—It sometimes happens that the input to a servo is a voltage determined by a potentiometer setting; for instance, the automatic-tracking radar system output may drive a potentiometer, the output voltage of which is used as the input to a computer servomechanism. The transmitted voltage would be a faithful reproduction of the tracking-servo output if it were not for the finite granulation of the potentiometer, which introduces into a signal the type of noise that will be considered in this section.

We shall suppose that the input to the tracking servomechanism is the input discussed in the previous section and that the errors in following by the tracking servomechanism are negligible compared with the potentiometer resolution; the input to the potentiometer will then be precisely the original tracking-servomechanism input.

It will be convenient to make a few idealizations which will not appreciably affect the results. In the first place, since the input is unbounded, let us suppose that the potentiometer is an infinite helical potentiometer. Let us suppose further that the winding steps are uniformly Δ mils apart and that when the velocity of the input is a mils/sec, the potentiometer output differs from the input by a sinusoid of frequency a/Δ cps and amplitude $\Delta/2$ mils.

The potentiometer input has already been discussed in the previous section. Its velocity, given by Eq. (154), assumes independent constant values over a sequence of intervals. Let the probability distribution for these angular velocities be denoted by $M(a)$ and let

$$\widetilde{a} = 0. \tag{171}$$

The potentiometer output will be the original input plus sections of sinusoids, all of amplitude $\Delta/2$. In fact, if θ_I is the original input, then the noise term in the output will be precisely

$$z(t) = \frac{\Delta}{2} \sin 2\pi \frac{\theta_I}{\Delta}. \tag{172}$$

The functions $z(t)$ constitute a stationary random process. It is evident that the phases of adjacent segments of sinusoids are related, since z is continuous. For intervals long compared with the sinusoid period Δ/a, this correlation of phases will have little effect; therefore in obtaining the autocorrelation function we shall assume that the phases of adjoining sinusoidal segments are indepedent.

The autocorrelation function of the noise is the ensemble average of

$$z(t)z(t + \tau) = \frac{\Delta^2}{4} \sin (2\pi f_1 t + \phi_1) \sin [2\pi f_2(t + \tau) + \phi_2]. \tag{173}$$

Here $\phi_1 = \phi_2$ and $f_1 = f_2 = a/\Delta$ if t and $t + \tau$ are in the same segment, and f_1 is independent of f_2 and ϕ_1 is independent of ϕ_2 if t and $t + \tau$ lie in different segments. Cases for which t and $t + \tau$ lie in different segments do not contribute to the autocorrelation function as one sees by averaging ϕ_1 and ϕ_2 independently. When t and $t + \tau$ lie in the same segment, one can average over all phases ϕ for a given frequency $f = f_1 = f_2$ to get $(\Delta^2/8) \cos 2\pi f\tau$. Averaging over all frequencies then gives

$$(\Delta^3/8) \int_{-\infty}^{\infty} df\, M(\Delta f) \cos 2\pi f\tau.$$

To obtain the autocorrelation function this must now be multiplied by the probability that t and $t + \tau$ lie in the same interval:

$$R(\tau) = \frac{\Delta^3}{8} Q(\tau) \int_{-\infty}^{\infty} df\, M(\Delta f) \cos 2\pi f\tau, \tag{174}$$

where Q is defined as in Eq. (160).

We can now obtain the spectral density by applying Eqs. (76):

$$G_z(f) = 4 \int_0^{\infty} d\tau \cos 2\pi f\tau \left[\frac{\Delta^3}{8} Q(\tau) \int_{-\infty}^{\infty} df\, M(\Delta f) \cos 2\pi f\tau\right]. \tag{175}$$

This can be rewritten as

$$G_z(f) = \frac{\Delta^3}{4} \int_{-\infty}^{\infty} d\tau\, e^{-2\pi i f\tau} Q(\tau) \left[\int_{-\infty}^{\infty} df\, M(\Delta f) \cos 2\pi f\tau\right]. \tag{176}$$

The function $G_z(f)$ is the Fourier transform of the product of two functions and is therefore equal to the convolution of their transforms. The proof of this statement is similar to that of the convolution theorem for the Laplace transform given in Chap. 2. If we now assume $M(\Delta f)$ to be an even function, then

$$M(\Delta f) = \int_{-\infty}^{\infty} d\tau\, e^{-2\pi i f\tau} \int_{-\infty}^{\infty} df\, M(\Delta f) \cos 2\pi f\tau. \tag{177}$$

We thus find

$$G_z(f) = \frac{\Delta^3}{2} \int_{-\infty}^{\infty} ds\, K(s)\, M[\Delta(f - s)], \tag{178}$$

where

$$K(f) = \int_0^{\infty} d\tau\, Q(\tau) \cos 2\pi f\tau. \tag{179}$$

For purposes of illustration, let us suppose that (1) the potentiometer is wound in steps of $\Delta = 1$ mil, (2) the probability distribution of angular velocities $M(\dot{\theta})$ is the distribution plotted in Fig. 6·10, and (3) the set of points where a change in velocity of the input occurs is the Poisson distribution of shots on a line. As we have seen in the previous section, $Q(\tau) = e^{-\beta|\tau|}$, where β is the mean density of shots. It follows that

$$K(f) = \frac{\beta}{\beta^2 + (2\pi f)^2}. \tag{180}$$

Applying Eq. (178), we see that $G_z(f)$ is a weighted average of $M(\Delta f)$. The total weight for this averaging process is

$$\int_{-\infty}^{\infty} df\, K(f) = \frac{1}{2}, \tag{181}$$

If $\beta = 0.1 \text{ sec}^{-1}$, $K(f)$ attenuates very rapidly; in fact half of its area is in a frequency band of 0.032 cps about the origin. Hence its action as a weighting function on $M(\Delta f)$ is much like that of a delta function when Δ is less than 1 mil. For such Δ,

$$G_z(f) \approx \frac{\Delta^3}{4} M(\Delta f). \tag{182}$$

For $\Delta = 1$ mil, the distribution function $M(\Delta f)$ is sufficiently flat, for frequencies less than 5 cps, for $G_z(f)$ to be treated as a spectral density of a purely random process in servomechanism problems (see Sec. 6·11).

In order to complete this study of potentiometer noise it will be necessary to compute the cross-correlation function. In the usual servomechanism application the error depends on the noise and the derivative of the input signal. (See, for instance, the example of Sec. 6·10.) It will therefore be sufficient to find the cross-correlation function between the derivative of the input and the noise. This has the advantage of enabling us to work with stationary random processes.

The derivative of the input, $\dot{\theta}_I$, has been carefully defined in Eq. (154). For purposes of the present calculation we must be equally precise about θ_I itself. In order that $z(t)$ be a stationary random process it is necessary that all possible functions $z(t)$ be represented in the ensemble. This will be so if to a definite $\dot{\theta}_I$, defined by a given set of constants . . . , a_{-1}, a_0, a_1, a_2, . . . and a given sequence of times . . . , t_{-1}, t_0, t_1, t_2, . . . , there corresponds a set of inputs θ_I defined by

$$\theta_I(t) = \int_0^t ds\, \dot{\theta}_I(s) + \phi, \tag{183}$$

where the "phase angle" ϕ takes on all of the values in the interval $(0, \Delta)$ with equal likelihood.

The cross-correlation function is the ensemble average of the quantities

$$z(t)\dot{\theta}_I(t+\tau) = \frac{\Delta}{2}\left(\sin 2\pi \frac{\theta_I}{\Delta}\right) \dot{\theta}_I(t+\tau). \tag{184}$$

If one averages over all inputs θ_I that correspond to a definite $\dot{\theta}_I$, that is. over all phase angles ϕ, it is clear that the average will vanish. The ensemble average is then the average of this zero average over all possible $\dot{\theta}_I$; the cross-correlation function therefore vanishes identically.

CHAPTER 7

RMS-ERROR CRITERION IN SERVOMECHANISM DESIGN

By R. S. Phillips

7·1. Preliminary Discussion of the Method.—The servomechanism design procedure[1] developed in the present chapter may be considered as a quantitative extension of the steady-state methods of Chap. 4. The bases for the steady-state analysis have been the requirements of fidelity in the low-frequency response and of stability; a servo has been considered to be sufficiently stable if the transfer function for the entire system has an amplification of less than $1\frac{1}{2}$ or 2 at all frequencies. It is clear that such a criterion is qualitatively correct. If, however, certain frequencies are present only to a negligible extent in the servo input or noise sources, it will not be objectionable for the system to be underdamped at these frequencies; they will in any case seldom be excited. In general, it is desirable to weight the error transfer function at each frequency according to its probability of occurrence and then to minimize the total weighted error. In this way the design of a servo can be adapted to the requirements of its particular application more completely than is possible with steady-state methods. This is the basis of the rms-error approach.

The characteristics of a particular servomechanism should be determined by the actual input, the actual uncontrolled disturbances acting on the system, and the actual output requirements. It is clearly not sufficient to assume the input to be a step in displacement or velocity, nor is it sufficient to require only that the transient response be well damped and that the velocity lag be small. It is true, however, that an experienced servomechanist can arrive at many valid qualitative conclusions by examining these transient responses. It is equally true that one cannot by this method get beyond the conclusions of the steady-state analysis of Chap 4. In general, the actual input and noise as well as the output requirements need a statistical description of the kind discussed in Chap. 6. One can, of course, conceive of specialized servo problems in which the input is a displacement step and in which the requirements are based on the transient response; this situation, however, is the exception rather than the rule.

[1] Chapter 7 is a revision of a paper by the author entitled "Servomechanisms" which was published as RL Report No. 372, May 11, 1943.

We now come to the question of what kind of output is desirable for the servo. If it were not for the presence of uncontrolled disturbances in the input, our goal would be to make the output follow the input perfectly. In the presence of these disturbances, however, perfect following of the input involves at least good, if not perfect, following of the noise. It is apparent that *a compromise must be made between faithfully following the input signal and ignoring the noise.*

Since a compromise must be made, it is necessary that we have a criterion of goodness or figure of merit for any given design. In order to be of use, such a figure of merit must be in reasonable accord with practical requirements, it must be of general applicability, and it must not be difficult to apply. The wide variety of servo problems precludes a criterion of goodness that is universally applicable. Even when a criterion is not strictly applicable, design methods based upon it can often furnish useful information. A further requirement for the figure of merit is that it be unaffected by unlikely short-lived aberrations from the mean or shifts in the time axis; instead, it should be a measure of the average behavior of the servo. This is in accordance with the statistical nature of the actual input and of the noise. We shall here limit ourselves to a single figure of merit, the rms error in following. If θ_I is the input signal to be followed, if θ_O is the output, and if $\epsilon = \theta_I - \theta_O$ is the error in following, then the *rms error* is $\sqrt{\overline{\epsilon^2}}$, where

$$\overline{\epsilon^2} = \lim_{T\to\infty} \frac{1}{2T} \int_{-T}^{T} dt\, \epsilon^2(t). \tag{1}$$

We shall consider that servo best which minimizes the rms error.

The rms figure of merit has been used in many types of problem. Its use in this chapter was inspired by N. Wiener's work on the extrapolation, interpolation, and smoothing of stationary time series.[1] The idea of applying the integrated-square-error criterion to servo design has also been considered by A. C. Hall.[2] One of the reasons for the wide usage of the rms criterion stems from its mathematical convenience; there is a highly developed body of mathematical knowledge that has been built around the notion of a mean-square value—the harmonic analysis described in Chap. 6.

The rms-error criterion weights the undesirability of an error according to the square of its magnitude, as indicated in Fig. 7·1*a*, and this independently of the time at which the error occurs. In general such a weighting is adequate whenever the undesirability of an error grows

[1] N. Wiener, *The Extrapolation, Interpolation, and Smoothing of Stationary Time Series,* NDRC Report, Cambridge, Mass., 1942.

[2] A. C. Hall, *The Analysis and Synthesis of Linear Servomechanisms,* Massachusetts Institute of Technology Press, Cambridge, Mass., 1943, pp. 19–25.

with its magnitude. There are, however, cases where this weighting would not be suitable. If, for example, all sufficiently large errors were equally bad, it would be necessary to have a weighting similar to that shown in Fig. 7·1b. Nor is it always true that the undesirability of an error is independent of the time at which that error occurs. For instance, an error during a transition from one mode of operation to another may be more or less desirable than an error during a given mode of operation.[1]

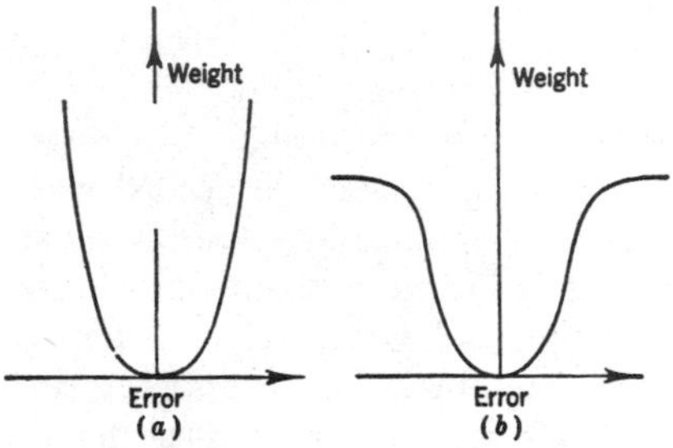

FIG. 7·1.—(a) Square-error weighting; (b) nonsquare-error weighting.

When applicable, a figure of merit such as the rms error is exceedingly useful. By means of it one can determine the "best" system possible under suitably restrictive conditions. Thus if the only limitation is that the system be a linear filter, one can find the best such filter by a method developed by Wiener.[2] Even if such a filter cannot be realized in the form of a servo, it will still be of great interest to know how well the rms error of the realized servo approximates the rms error of the ideally best filter.

As we have seen, the servo must compromise between following the signal and smoothing out the noise. Furthermore, the output is always powered by a source external to the input. It is reasonable to ask why these two operations, smoothing and following with increased power, could not be done in series. That is, why not first send the input through a filter that separates the signal from the noise? If the only source of noise is in the input signal, this is indeed feasible. If, however, the disturbances arise in the loading or at an interior point of the servomechanism, then the smoothing must be done in the servo itself. There is still another difficulty with filtering the signal first. In practice there is a limit to the accuracy with which a filter can be made. In particular, if the input range is excessive, the output of the filter will not be sufficiently accurate. Nevertheless, wherever possible, it is well to purify the input by first sending it through a filter. Since the servo will in any case act as a filter, its characteristics will have to be taken into account in the prefiltering.

The design procedure to be described in this chapter is basically simple and straightforward. In practice it is difficult to realize a given

[1] Transients can be treated in a manner similar to the procedure used for the mean-square error. In this case the integrated-square error in the transient is computed (see footnote on p. 314).

[2] See Wiener, *op. cit.*

weighting function as an electrical network, to say nothing of realizing it as a servomechanism. It is much more practical to start with a servo of a given type having certain adjustable parameters. The mean-square error can then be computed as the integral of the error spectral density directly from integral tables. This mean-square error will, of course, depend on the adjustable parameters of the servo; the best servo of the given type is then determined by finding the parameter values that minimize the mean-square error.

It is worth remarking that the *method proposed for finding the rms error does not involve solving for the roots of the characteristic equation* of the differential equation describing the servo. As a result, this method has a great advantage over the familiar transient analysis approach, which requires the use of a differential analyzer to handle effectively problems that have characteristic equations of degree five or higher. Most of the discussion is concerned with reducing the error spectral density to a form suitable for the use of the integral tables. The error spectral density is first expressed as a function of the error-signal transfer function, the error-noise transfer function, and the elements of the signal-noise spectral-density matrix. Since the servo is a stable lumped-constant system, the transfer functions are rational functions of the frequency. Now use of the integral tables requires that the error spectral density be expressed as the sum of squares of absolute values of rational functions. This, in turn, requires that the elements of the spectral-density matrix be approximated by rational functions. It is shown in Sec. 7·4 that the spectral-density matrix elements can always be so approximated.

The use of the integration tables is straightforward, and there are standard procedures for minimizing the resulting expression with respect to the servo parameters. The method is illustrated by two servomechanisms, one of which was independently designed by experimental methods. The results of the theoretical and experimental procedures are in good agreement. A final section of the chapter is devoted to the method used in deriving the table of integrals.

Although the present discussion deals only with servomechanisms with a continuous flow of data, it will be evident to the reader that servomechanisms with pulsed data can be treated similarly. The necessary machinery for the discussion of pulsed servos has already been developed in Chaps. 5 and 6.[1]

It is well to add a word about the disadvantages of the method proposed in this chapter. In the first place, it is assumed that the mathematical representations of the different parts of the servo system are

[1] In applying the rms-error criterion to the pulsed servo it is convenient to work with the complex variable $z = e^{2\pi i f T_r}$ on the unit circle rather than with the real variable f in the interval $(-1/2T_r, 1/2T_r)$.

known. In practice it may be difficult to determine the constants required for such a representation. The steady-state analysis of Chap. 4 does not require a knowledge of these values, requiring instead only that measurements be made on the steady-state response of the system. Another difficulty lies in the fact that it is necessary to start with a proper type of equalizer. The steady-state design principles of Chap. 4 can be employed in the choice of a good type of equalizer; the rms-error analysis can then be used to make the final adjustments of the constants. Lastly, one might complain that this procedure works only with the rms error and furnishes no insight into what goes on in the mechanism when the equalizer and input parameters are varied. On the other hand there is nothing to prevent one from studying the decibel–log-frequency diagrams as a function of these parameters; this, in fact, has been done for two common servo types in Chap. 8.

7·2. Mathematical Formulation of the RMS Error.—In this section we shall obtain an expression for the rms error in terms of the transfer functions characterizing the servomechanism and the spectral densities characterizing the input signal and noise. We shall start with the assumption that the servomechanism is a linear filter and that the error can be represented as the sum of a linear operator acting on the input signal plus a linear operator acting on the noise. In symbols, this assumption takes the form

$$\epsilon(t) = \int_{0-}^{\infty} ds\, \theta_I(t - s) W_1(s) + \int_{0-}^{\infty} ds\, \theta_N(t - s) W_2(s), \tag{2}$$

where $\theta_N(t)$ is the noise record and, as in Chap. 2, the $W_i(t)$ $(i = 1, 2)$ are stable weighting functions satisfying the conditions.

$$\left.\begin{aligned} W_i(t) &= 0 \qquad \text{for } t < 0, \\ \int_{0-}^{\infty} dt\, &|W_i(t)| < \infty, \end{aligned}\right\} \qquad (i = 1, 2). \tag{3}$$

This is the usual linear assumption; it will be valid provided that such nonlinear effects as saturation, backlash, and stiction are negligible, and provided that there is no interaction between input and noise.

The two weighting functions W_1 and W_2 will generally be different and will depend on the way in which the input and noise enter the system. If the input and noise enter the system at the same point, then the output depends in the same way on both. In this case if $W(t)$ is the weighting function for the over-all system, then

$$\theta_O(t) = \int_{0-}^{\infty} ds\, [\theta_I(t - s) + \theta_N(t - s)] W(s). \tag{4}$$

It follows that

$$\epsilon(t) = \theta_I(t) - \int_{0-}^{\infty} ds\, \theta_I(t - s)W(s) - \int_{0-}^{\infty} ds\, \theta_N(t - s)W(s). \tag{5}$$

Hence, in this case,

$$\left.\begin{aligned} W_1(t) &= \delta(t) - W(t), \\ W_2(t) &= -W(t). \end{aligned}\right\} \tag{6}$$

If the servo is subject to a random load disturbance, then still a different relation will exist between W_1 and W_2.

We shall now make use of the harmonic analysis developed in Chap. 6. We set

$$A_T(f) = \int_{-T}^{T} dt\, \epsilon(t)e^{-2\pi ift} \tag{7}$$

and similarly define $B_T(f)$ and $C_T(f)$ to be the Fourier transforms of $\theta_I(t)$ and $\theta_N(t)$, respectively, over the limited range $(-T,T)$. Then, as in Sec. 6·7, the spectral density of ϵ is defined as

$$G_\epsilon(f) = \lim_{T\to\infty} \frac{1}{T} |A_T(f)|^2. \tag{8}$$

Similar definitions hold for $G_I(f)$ and $G_N(f)$, the spectral densities of θ_I and θ_N, respectively. The cross-spectral density is defined as

$$G_{IN}(f) = \lim_{T\to\infty} \frac{1}{T} B_T^*(f)C_T(f), \tag{9}$$

from which it follows that

$$G_{IN}(f) = G_{NI}^*(f) = G_{IN}^*(-f). \tag{10}$$

Finally the input-noise spectral-density matrix is defined as

$$\mathsf{G}(f) = \begin{pmatrix} G_I(f) & G_{IN}(f) \\ G_{NI}(f) & G_N(f) \end{pmatrix}. \tag{11}$$

It is evident that[1]

$$\mathsf{G}(f) = \tilde{\mathsf{G}}^*(f) = \mathsf{G}^*(-f). \tag{12}$$

It was shown in Sec. 6·7 that the mean-square value of the error can be computed as the integral of its spectral density over all nonnegative frequencies. Since the spectral density is an even function of frequency, we may write

$$\overline{\epsilon^2} = \tfrac{1}{2} \int_{-\infty}^{\infty} df\, G_\epsilon(f). \tag{13}$$

Thus our problem is reduced to that of obtaining a suitable expression for the error spectral density.

[1] The symbol $\tilde{\mathsf{G}}$ denotes the transpose of the matrix G.

Taking the Fourier transform of both sides of Eq. (2) with functions θ_I and θ_N, which vanish outside the interval $(-T, T)$, we obtain, approximately,

$$A_T(f) \approx Y_1(2\pi jf)B_T(f) + Y_2(2\pi jf)C_T(f). \tag{14}$$

Here the transfer functions Y_i are, of course, the Fourier transforms of the weighting functions W_i:

$$Y_i(2\pi jf) = \int_{0-}^{\infty} dt\, W_i(t)e^{-2\pi jft}, \qquad (i = 1, 2). \tag{15}$$

To obtain the error spectral density we need only take $1/T$ times the absolute value squared of $A_T(f)$, given in Eq. (14):

$$G_\epsilon(f) = \lim_{T\to\infty} \frac{1}{T} |Y_1(2\pi jf)B_T(f) + Y_2(2\pi jf)C_T(f)|^2. \tag{16}$$

This equation can be rewritten in terms of the elements of the spectral-density matrix as follows:

$$G_\epsilon(f) = |Y_1(2\pi jf)|^2G_I(f) + |Y_2(2\pi jf)|^2G_N(f) \\ + Y_1^*(2\pi jf)G_{IN}(f)Y_2(2\pi jf) + Y_1(2\pi jf)G_{NI}(f)Y_2^*(2\pi jf). \tag{17}$$

As shown in Sec. 6·9, this result can be derived by a more rigorous argument. It is worth remarking that for sufficiently large T the expression on the right-hand side of Eq. (16) approximates closely to $G_\epsilon(f)$. Hence, Eq. (16) without the limit symbol can be used to compute $G_\epsilon(f)$ when θ_I and θ_N are obtained experimentally.

Combining Eqs. (13) and (17), we now have an expression for the mean-square error in terms of the transfer functions, characterizing the servo system, and the elements of the input-noise spectral-density matrix, characterizing the inputs.[1] The transfer functions will usually be related. For instance, $Y_1 = 1 + Y_2$, in accordance with Eq. (6), when the signal and the noise enter the system at the same point. Our next problem is to find the transfer functions that minimize the mean-square error, allowing, of course, for the interdependence of the Y's.

It is interesting to see the physical significance of this minimization problem. The quantity on the right of Eq. (17), the integral of which we wish to minimize, weights the frequency-transfer functions at a given

[1] The integrated-square error can be given in a form similar to the mean-square error. Suppose, for instance, that the input and noise vanish for $t < 0$ and that their Laplace transforms are $\Theta_I(p)$ and $\Theta_N(p)$, respectively. Then

$$\int_0^\infty dt\,[\epsilon(t)]^2 = \int_{-\infty}^{\infty} df\,|Y_1(2\pi jf)\Theta_I(2\pi jf) + Y_2(2\pi jf)\Theta_N(2\pi jf)|^2.$$

The integrated-square error is a measure of the transient response if the input is, for example, a step function and noise is not present.

frequency according to the relative importance of that frequency in the signal and noise. This is precisely the kind of relation which is needed for a quantitative extension of the steady-state design methods of Chap. 4. Furthermore we have an experimental check on the reliability of Eq. (17), for in the example of Sec. 6·10 we were able to compare an experimentally obtained autocorrelation function with one determined by Eq. (17).

7·3. Nature of the Transfer Function.—In minimizing the rms error it is, of course, possible to seek the ideal transfer functions. This involves a rather long computation; even when one has determined the ideal transfer functions, there remains the difficult task of realizing them. In practice it is more convenient to choose a suitable type of filter with certain adjustable elements and then to determine the best possible adjustment of these elements. We shall therefore start with a given family of transfer functions and find that transfer function of this set which minimizes the mean-square error.

This filter will consist of a network of lumped elements, some of which are adjustable. Such a filter can always be represented by a differential equation of the form

$$\begin{aligned} A_0\epsilon^{(n)} + A_1\epsilon^{(n-1)} + \cdots + A_n\epsilon = B_0\theta_I^{(m)} + B_1\theta_I^{(m-1)} + \cdots + B_m\theta_I \\ + C_0\theta_N^{(l)} + C_1\theta_N^{(l-1)} + \cdots + C_l\theta_N, \end{aligned} \tag{18}$$

where $m, l \leqq n$; $y^{(k)}$ denotes the kth derivative of y with respect to time t. The numerical coefficients A, B, C are all real and depend on the adjustable parameters. For any given servomechanism, each of the components can be represented by a differential equation with certain driving functions. By combining these equations one can eliminate all functions except ϵ, θ_I, and θ_N. The resulting differential equation will be of the form of Eq. (18). As shown in Chap. 2, the transfer functions for the weighting functions W_1 and W_2, described in the previous section, are

$$\left.\begin{aligned} Y_1(2\pi jf) &= \frac{\sum_{i=0}^{m} B_i(2\pi jf)^{m-i}}{\sum_{i=0}^{n} A_i(2\pi jf)^{n-i}}, \\ Y_2(2\pi jf) &= \frac{\sum_{i=0}^{l} C_i(2\pi jf)^{l-i}}{\sum_{i=0}^{n} A_i(2\pi jf)^{n-i}}. \end{aligned}\right\} \tag{19}$$

If the performance of a filter is to be at all satisfactory, it must be stable. This, of course, is assured if the filter contains only passive elements. The servo, on the other hand, is a special kind of filter, containing active elements and a feedback; it is therefore possible for a servo system to become unstable and oscillate. Whether or not the system is unstable will usually depend on the adjustment of certain quantities in the equalizer, such as the amplifier gain, and the magnitudes of certain of the resistances and capacitances. For some values of these parameters the system will oscillate, but for others it will not oscillate. The set of all values of the parameters for which the system does not oscillate will be called the *region of stability.*

As was shown in Chap. 2, the system will be stable if, and only if, the roots of the polynomial

$$H(f) = \sum_{i=0}^{n} A_i(2\pi jf)^{n-i} \tag{20}$$

lie in the upper half plane. Now the roots are continuous functions of the coefficients A_k of $H(f)$. Hence, as the coefficients are continuously varied, the system can go from a stable to an unstable state if, and only if, at least one root assumes a value on the real axis. Since the coefficients are continuous functions of the parameters, the above statement is likewise true of these parameters. It follows that in the space of parameters the region of stability will be bounded by those values of the parameters for which the roots of the polynomial $H(f)$ lie on the real axis.

In the polynomial $H(f)$, A_k, the coefficient of $(2\pi jf)^{n-k}$, is real. Consequently the roots of $H(f) = 0$ are symmetrically situated about the imaginary axis. That is, they are either pure imaginaries or occur in conjugate pairs of the type $(jv \pm u)$, where v and u are real. If a root r_k lies on the real axis, there are two possibilities: Either $r_k = 0$, or there is a second real root r_i such that $r_i = -r_k$. If $r_k = 0$, then the product of all roots will vanish and we will have $A_n = 0$. If r_k is real and nonzero, then the product of sums of all pairs of roots, $\prod_{i<k} (r_i + r_k)$, will vanish. It follows that the boundary of the region of stability is contained in the surface defined by

$$A_n \prod_{i<k} (r_i + r_k) = 0. \tag{21}$$

An explicit expression for this surface in terms of the coefficients of $H(f)$ can be found by the methods of Sec. 7·9 [see Eqs. (104) and (105)].

Not all points on this surface are boundary points of the region of stability, since $(r_i + r_k)$ can vanish without r_i being real. It remains to be determined which of the bounded regions are actually regions of stability. It is clear that either all points in each such bounded domain correspond to stable states of the system or all points correspond to unstable states. The stability of each domain is therefore determined by the stability of a single point in that domain. Each domain can thus be tested at a single point by means of the Routh criterion or the Nyquist criterion (see Chap. 2).

7·4. Reduction of the Error Spectral Density to a Convenient Form.—As we have seen, the mean-square error can be expressed as the integral of the error spectral density. Our next step is to put $G_\epsilon(f)$ into a form amenable to computation. We shall make use of Eq. (17), in which $G_\epsilon(f)$ is given in terms of the transfer functions and the elements of the input-noise spectral-density matrix. Since we have limited ourselves to filters of lumped elements, the transfer functions will be of the form shown in Eq. (19); each Y is a rational function with poles in the upper half plane, symmetrically placed about the imaginary axis.[1] It is therefore convenient and natural to attempt to express $G_\epsilon(f)$ as the square of the absolute value of such a rational function in f or as the sum of such expressions. It will be shown in Sec. 7·6 that this is, in fact, a convenient form for the integration.

In many problems the elements of the spectral-density matrix will be known rational functions. In such cases it is relatively easy to bring G_ϵ into the desired form. When, however, the matrix elements are not rational functions or are known only experimentally, approximations will be required in the treatment. We shall now discuss each of these cases in detail.

Reduction when the Elements of G *Are Rational Functions.*—Suppose first that the elements of the spectral-density matrix are rational functions. We shall show how to express G_ϵ as a sum of terms, each of which is the absolute value squared of a rational function with all poles in the upper half plane, symmetrically placed about the imaginary axis.

Since $G_I(f)$ is rational, it can be expressed as the product of two rational factors $X_{11}(f)$ and $Z_{11}(f)$ such that X_{11} has for its zeros and poles those of G_I in the upper half plane and Z_{11} has for its zeros and poles those of G_I in the lower half plane.

$$G_I(f) = X_{11}(f)Z_{11}(f). \tag{22}$$

Since $G_I(f)$ is real valued for real f, both its zeros and poles must be symmetric in pairs with respect to the real axis; since it is an even function of f, both its zeros and poles must be symmetrically placed about the imaginary axis. The zeros and poles of X_{11} will also be symmetrically placed about the imaginary axis. Furthermore, by properly choosing

[1] The poles of Y will be symmetrically placed about the imaginary axis if, and only if, the coefficients A_k of $H(f)$ [see Eq. (20)] are real valued.

constant factors one can write

$$X_{11}(f) = Z_{11}^*(f) = X_{11}^*(-f) \tag{23}$$

for real values of f. Then

$$G_I(f) = |X_{11}(f)|^2. \tag{24}$$

Thus the first term of G_ϵ, namely, $|Y_1(2\pi jf)|^2 G_I(f)$, has the desired form. Similarly, one can write

$$G_N(f) = |X_{22}(f)|^2, \tag{25}$$

with the zeros and poles of X_{22} in the upper half plane, symmetrically placed about the imaginary axis.

It remains to show that the last two terms of G_ϵ, namely,

$$Y_1^*(2\pi jf)G_{IN}(f)Y_2(2\pi jf) + Y_1(2\pi jf)G_{NI}(f)Y_2^*(2\pi jf),$$

can be brought into the desired form. We shall treat these cross-spectral terms together. In the first place, it is evident from Eq. (6·89) that $G_{IN}(f)$ is the Fourier transform of a real-valued function, the cross-correlation function $R_{IN}(\tau)$. It follows that both the zeros and the poles of $G_{IN}(f)$ are symmetrically placed about the imaginary axis. Let us now factor $G_{IN}(f)$ into two rational factors $X_{12}(f)$ and $Z_{12}(f)$ such that X_{12} has for its zeros and poles those of G_{IN} in the upper half plane, and Z_{12} has for its zeros and poles those of G_{IN} in the lower half plane:

$$G_{IN}(f) = X_{12}(f)Z_{12}(f). \tag{26}$$

For each factor, both the zeros and the poles will likewise be symmetrically placed about the imaginary axis. We can similarly define the rational factors X_{21} and Z_{21} of G_{NI}:

$$G_{NI}(f) = X_{21}(f)Z_{21}(f). \tag{27}$$

From Eq. (6·44)

$$R_{IN}(\tau) = R_{NI}(-\tau); \tag{28}$$

it follows that

$$\begin{aligned} G_{IN}(u + jv) &= 2\int_{-\infty}^{\infty} d\tau\, R_{IN}(\tau)e^{-2\pi j(u+jv)} \\ &= 2\int_{-\infty}^{\infty} d\tau\, R_{NI}(\tau)e^{2\pi j(u+jv)\tau} \\ &= G_{NI}^*(u - jv). \end{aligned} \tag{29}$$

Hence the zeros and the poles of $G_{IN}(f)$ are the complex conjugates of the zeros and the poles of $G_{NI}(f)$. Furthermore we can therefore conclude from Eq. (29) that

$$X_{12}(u + jv) = Z_{21}^*(u - jv) \tag{30a}$$

and

$$Z_{12}(u + jv) = X_{21}^{*}(u - jv). \tag{30b}$$

Hence, for real values of f,

$$G_{IN}(f) = X_{12}(f)X_{21}^{*}(f) = G_{NI}^{*}(f). \tag{31}$$

Finally, we note that the poles for each expression $Y_1(2\pi jf)X_{12}(f)$ and $Y_2(2\pi jf)X_{21}(f)$ lie in the upper half plane and are symmetrically placed about the imaginary axis. We can therefore express $G_\epsilon(f)$ in the desired form as

$$G_\epsilon(f) = |Y_1X_{11}|^2 + |Y_2X_{22}|^2 + \tfrac{1}{2}|Y_1X_{12} + Y_2X_{21}|^2 - \tfrac{1}{2}|Y_1X_{12} - Y_2X_{21}|^2. \tag{32}$$

Reduction when G *Is Given by Experimental Data.*—A reasonably simple method is available for reducing the error spectral density to the desired form when the spectral densities are obtained from experimental data. As is mentioned in Sec. 7·2, in this case the error spectral density can be written as

$$G_\epsilon(f) = \frac{1}{T}|Y_1(2\pi jf)B_T(f) + Y_2(2\pi jf)C_T(f)|^2. \tag{3}$$

To suit the needs of the following method of approximation, let us suppose that $\theta_I(t)$ and $\theta_N(t)$ have been determined for the time range $(0,2T)$ and that the limits of the integrals defining B_T and C_T [Eq. (7)] are 0 and $2T$. It will be our purpose to obtain rational-function approximations for B_T and C_T, with poles all in the upper half plane and symmetrically placed about the imaginary axis. It is clear that by substituting these approximations into Eq. (33) we will bring G_ϵ into the desired form.

The usual technique in making such an approximation is to approximate the function by a finite partial expansion in terms of a complete orthonormal set of functions. The Fourier transforms of the Laguerre functions[1] is a suitable set of orthonormal functions. The kth Laguerre function can be written as

$$L_k(t) = e^{-t}\left\{\frac{2^{k+\frac{1}{2}}t^k}{k!} - \frac{k\,2^{k-\frac{1}{2}}t^{k-1}}{(k-1)!} + \cdots + \frac{k!\,2^{k-i+\frac{1}{2}}t^{k-i}}{[(k-i)!]^2\,i!}(-1)^i \cdots + 2^{\frac{1}{2}}(-1)^k\right\}. \tag{34}$$

The Fourier transform of L_k is simply

$$l_k(f) = \sqrt{2}\,\frac{(1 - 2\pi jf)^k}{(1 + 2\pi jf)^{k+1}}. \tag{35}$$

This function has its only pole in the upper half plane and on the imaginary axis; it is thus satisfactory for our purposes. Furthermore, since the Laguerre functions form a complete orthonormal set for functions that vanish for $t < 0$, it follows that their transforms can approximate

[1] N. Wiener, *op. cit.*

to any desired accuracy the transforms of such functions. Hence we can approximate $B_T(f)$ by

$$\mathcal{B}_T(f) = \sum_{k=0}^{N} c_k l_k(f), \tag{36}$$

where

$$c_k = \int_{-\infty}^{\infty} df\, B_T(f) l_k^*(f). \tag{37}$$

A similar approximation may be used for $C_T(f)$. Another, and perhaps a more convenient, way of obtaining the coefficients c_k follows from the fact that the bilinear form of Eq. (37) does not change its value if the functions are replaced by their Fourier transforms. Hence

$$c_k = \int_0^{2T} dt\, \theta_I(t) L_k(t). \tag{38}$$

It is evident that the series of Eq. (36) will not converge rapidly unless the time scale is so adjusted that T is of the order of 1; even then the convergence may be slow.

General Reduction of G.—If the elements of the spectral-density matrix are not rational functions, one tries to obtain a suitable rational-function approximation for these elements and thus reduce the general case to the rational-function case already considered. For instance, when the elements are analytic except for poles, one can frequently get such an approximation by taking the sum of the principal parts of each matrix element at a finite set of poles symmetrically placed about the imaginary axis.

Another method for accomplishing this end involves factoring the spectal-density matrix G into two factors X and Z:

$$\mathsf{G} = \mathsf{XZ}. \tag{39}$$

The elements of X are analytic and bounded in the lower half plane, whereas those of Z are analytic and bounded in the upper half plane. In addition, for real values of f

$$\mathsf{X}(f) = X^*(-f) \tag{40}$$

and

$$\mathsf{X}(f) = \tilde{\mathsf{Z}}^*(f). \tag{41}$$

By Eq. (41)

$$\mathsf{G} = \mathsf{X}\tilde{\mathsf{X}}^* \tag{42}$$

for real values of f. It is sufficient, therefore, to obtain suitable rational-function approximations for the elements of X. Because the elements of X are analytic and bounded in the lower half plane and because of the condition expressed by Eq. (40), it is possible to make these approximations.

Factoring the spectral-density matrix is unfortunately a very tedious and, for most engineering applications, an impractical task. For details of this factoring process the reader is referred to the previously cited memoir by Wiener.

7·5. A Simple Servo Problem.—It will be instructive to apply these ideas to a simple servomechanism to be used in driving a heavy gun mount in train. We shall suppose that the targets are essentially stationary but that the gun is required to slew rapidly from one target to the next closest. The input will be a series of step displacements through random angles, occurring in some random fashion in time. The input can then be expressed as

$$\theta_I(t) = \sum_k c_k u(t - t_k), \tag{43}$$

where $u(t)$ is a unit-step function:

$$\left.\begin{aligned} u(t) &= 0 \qquad \text{for } t < 0, \\ &= 1 \qquad \text{for } t \geqq 0. \end{aligned}\right\} \tag{44}$$

The intervals $(t_k - t_{k-1})$ are independent random variables all having the same distribution, and the c's are likewise independent random variables all having the same distribution.

It is clear that θ_I defines a random process. Its derivative is, in fact, one of the purely random stationary processes discussed in Sec. 6·11 and was shown there to have the spectral density

$$G_I(f) = 2\beta\sigma, \tag{45}$$

where β is the mean density of the t's and σ is the mean-square value of the c's. (We here assume that the mean value of the c's is zero.) We shall see in the present problem that we need to know the spectral density for the input derivative [Eq. (45)], rather than the spectral density of the input itself. The subscript I denotes the input derivative in this section.

Let us now suppose that there is a noise source within the error-measuring device, such that the output of the differential is $(\theta_I - \theta_O + \theta_N)$, where θ_N is the noise function. For purposes of simplicity we shall assume that θ_N is a purely random stationary process having a spectral density

$$G_N(f) = N. \tag{46}$$

Finally, we shall assume that the noise and the derivative of the signal are uncorrelated:

$$G_{IN}(f) = 0. \tag{47}$$

In the design of this servomechanism we shall limit ourselves to an equalizer with a fixed time delay T_1 and an adjustable gain K_1. The output voltage V of the equalizer is then determined by

$$T_1 \frac{dV}{dt} + V = K_1(\epsilon + \theta_N). \tag{48}$$

As was shown in Chap. 3, the equation of motion of the motor is

$$J \frac{d^2\theta_O}{dt^2} + K_2 \frac{d\theta_O}{dt} = K_3 V, \tag{49}$$

where J is the rotor-plus-output inertia, K_2 is the back-emf and viscous-damping factor, and K_3 is the output torque per volt input. If we now set $T_2 = J/K_2$ and combine Eqs. (48) and (49), we obtain

$$\begin{aligned} T_1T_2 \frac{d^3\epsilon}{dt^3} &+ (T_1 + T_2) \frac{d^2\epsilon}{dt^2} + \frac{d\epsilon}{dt} + \frac{K_1K_3}{K_2}\epsilon \\ &= T_1T_2 \frac{d^3\theta_I}{dt^3} + (T_1 + T_2) \frac{d^2\theta_I}{dt^2} + \frac{d\theta_I}{dt} - \frac{K_1K_3}{K_2}\theta_N. \end{aligned} \tag{50}$$

This, then, is the differential equation of the servo. The only adjustable parameter is K_1.

It will be noted that the servo differential equation depends only upon the noise and the *derivative* of the input. Hence the spectral density of the input derivative and the associated transfer function take the place in our analysis of the usual input spectral density and its transfer function. Equation (17) can then be written as

$$G_\epsilon(f) = |Y_1(2\pi jf)|^2 G_1(f) + |Y_2(2\pi jf)|^2 G_N(f), \tag{51}$$

where

$$\left.\begin{aligned} Y_1(2\pi jf) &= \frac{T_1T_2(2\pi jf)^2 + (T_1 + T_2)(2\pi jf) + 1}{T_1T_2(2\pi jf)^3 + (T_1 + T_2)(2\pi jf)^2 + (2\pi jf) + \dfrac{K_1K_3}{K_2}} \\ &\text{and} \\ Y_2(2\pi jf) &= \frac{-\dfrac{K_1K_3}{K_2}}{T_1T_2(2\pi jf)^3 + (T_1 + T_2)(2\pi jf)^2 + (2\pi jf) + \dfrac{K_1K_3}{K_2}}. \end{aligned}\right\} \tag{52}$$

Thus $G_\epsilon(f)$ is already in the desired form, being the sum of two expressions, each of which is the absolute value squared of a rational function with all poles in the upper half plane, symmetrically placed about the imaginary axis.

The transfer functions can be put into a more convenient form by a change of variable. Let

$$\left.\begin{aligned} T &= T_1 + T_2, \\ x &= 2\pi f T, \\ \alpha &= T\frac{K_1K_3}{K_2}, \\ A &= \frac{T_1T_2}{T^2}. \end{aligned}\right\} \tag{53}$$

The value of A is fixed and less than or equal to $\frac{1}{4}$ for all positive T_1, T_2; α represents the adjustable gain. It then follows from Eq. (13) that the mean-square error is

$$\begin{aligned} \overline{\epsilon^2} = \frac{1}{2\pi}\int_{-\infty}^{\infty} dx\, \frac{A^2x^4 + (1-2A)x^2 + 1}{|A(jx)^3 + (jx)^2 + jx + \alpha|^2}\,\beta\sigma T \\ + \frac{1}{2\pi}\int_{-\infty}^{\infty} dx\, \frac{\alpha^2}{|A(jx)^3 + (jx)^2 + jx + \alpha|^2}\,\frac{N}{2T}. \end{aligned} \tag{54}$$

7·6. Integration of the Error Spectral Density.—We have shown that the mean-square error can be expressed as the integral of the error spectral density and that G_ϵ can be expressed as the square of the absolute value of a rational function, or the sum of such terms, with poles all in the upper half plane, symmetrically placed about the imaginary axis. We shall now see how to obtain a numerical value for the mean-square error by means of the table of integrals given in the appendix.

Any rational function can be written as the quotient of two polynomials: $N(f)/D(f)$. The above condition on the poles of the rational function is equivalent to the condition that the roots of $D(f)$ all lie in the upper half plane and be symmetrically placed about the imaginary axis. We can therefore express $D(f)$ in factored form as follows:

$$D(f) = a_0 \prod_k (f - u_k - jv_k) \prod_k (f + u_k - jv_k) \prod_l (f - jv_l), \tag{55}$$

where a_0, the coefficient of the highest power in f, can be assumed to be a real number. The u's and the v's are likewise real numbers. If $D(f)$ is of degree n, then for real values of f

$$\begin{aligned} D(-f) &= (-1)^n a_0 \prod_k (f + u_k + jv_k) \prod_k (f - u_k + jv_k) \prod_l (f + jv_l) \\ &= (-1)^n D^*(f). \end{aligned} \tag{56}$$

We can therefore write the square of the absolute value of our rational function as

$$\left|\frac{N(f)}{D(f)}\right|^2 = \frac{(-1)^n |N(f)|^2}{D(f)D(-f)}, \tag{57}$$

for any real f.

We have in this fashion reduced the problem of computing the mean-square error to that of obtaining the integral of Eq. (57) over all frequencies. The numerator $(-1)^n|N(f)|^2$ is, of course, a polynomial in f. The contribution of any odd-power term in the numerator to this integral is zero, since the denominator is an even function of f. We need therefore consider only the even powers in the numerator. Finally, if the mean-square error is finite, the degree of the numerator $N(f)$ must be less than the degree of the denominator $D(f)$. It follows that our problem is solved if we can evaluate integrals of the form

$$I_n = \frac{1}{2\pi j}\int_{-\infty}^{\infty} df \frac{g_n(f)}{h_n(f)h_n(-f)}, \tag{58}$$

where

$$\begin{aligned} h_n(f) &= a_0f^n + a_1f^{n-1} + \cdots + a_n, \\ g_n(f) &= b_0f^{2n-2} + b_1f^{2n-4} + \cdots + b_{n-1}, \end{aligned}$$

and the *roots of* $h_n(f)$ *all lie in the upper half plane.* Explicit formulas for all integrals of this type for which h_n is of degree seven or less are given in the appendix. The method by which these integrals were evaluated is presented in Sec. 7·9.

For purposes of illustration, let us now evaluate the mean-square error for the servo used as an example in the previous section. As can be seen in Eq. (54), this involves two integrals of the type shown in Eq. (58). The denominator polynomial is in each case

$$h(x) = -Ajx^3 - x^2 + jx + \alpha, \tag{59}$$

the denominator of the transfer functions.

Let us first determine under what conditions the roots of $h(x)$ lie in the upper half plane. The roots are clearly of the form

$$\left.\begin{aligned} r_1 &= js, \\ r_2 &= jv + u, \\ r_3 &= jv - u, \end{aligned}\right\} \tag{60}$$

where s, v, and u are real numbers. Since

$$\frac{\alpha}{Aj} = \prod r_k = -js(v^2 + u^2), \tag{61}$$

it follows that if r_1 is to lie in the upper half plane (that is, if $s > 0$), then $\alpha/A > 0$ and hence $\alpha > 0$. On the other hand, by Eq. (104)

$$-2jv[(s + v)^2 + u^2] = \prod_{k<l} (r_k + r_l) = \frac{-j(1 - \alpha A)}{A^2}. \tag{62}$$

Consequently if r_2 and r_3 are to lie in the upper half plane (that is, if

$v > 0$), it is necessary that $\alpha < 1/A$. The region of stability for this servo is therefore

$$0 < \alpha < \frac{1}{A}. \tag{63}$$

Only when α is within this region of stability can one make use of the table in the appendix to determine the mean-square error; when α is outside the region of stability, the mean-square error is infinite.

The integral table is very easy to use. For instance, in evaluating the first of the integrals in Eq. (54), one substitutes in the formula for I_3, setting

$$\left.\begin{aligned} a_0 &= -Aj, & b_0 &= A^2, \\ a_1 &= -1, & b_1 &= 1 - 2A, \\ a_2 &= j, & b_2 &= 1, \\ a_3 &= \alpha. & & \end{aligned}\right\} \tag{64}$$

One finds that

$$\overline{\epsilon_I^2} = \beta\sigma T \frac{1 + \alpha(1 - A)}{2\alpha(1 - A\alpha)}. \tag{65}$$

This would be the mean-square error in following the input signal in the absence of noise. It is evident that $\overline{\epsilon_I^2}$ becomes infinite on the boundaries of the region of stability. In a similar fashion the second integral can be evaluated; the contribution of the noise to the mean-square error is

$$\overline{\epsilon_N^2} = \frac{N}{2T}\frac{\alpha}{2(1 - A\alpha)}. \tag{66}$$

The mean-square error itself is the sum of these two components:

$$\overline{\epsilon^2} = \beta\sigma T \frac{1 + \alpha(1 - A) + L\alpha^2}{2\alpha(1 - A\alpha)}, \tag{67}$$

where

$$L = \frac{N}{2\beta\sigma T^2}. \tag{68}$$

In general the polynominal $h_n(f)$ will be the product of two polynomials, one from the signal or noise spectra and the other from the transfer function. The signal or noise polynomial is fixed once for all; its roots lie in the upper half plane. On the other hand, the transfer-function polynomial varies as we vary the equalizer parameters. Its roots will lie in the upper half plane if, and only if, these parameters lie in the region of stability.

7·7. Minimizing the Mean-square Error.—We have now obtained an explicit formula for the mean-square error as a rational function of the equalizer parameters for values of these parameters inside the region of stability. The next step is, of course, to obtain the values of the equalizer parameters that minimize the mean-square error. These "best" values can be determined by setting equal to zero the partial derivatives of the mean-square error with respect to the parameters and solving for the values of the parameters. Sometimes this process becomes very involved; in such cases it is simpler to locate the minimum by direct exploratory calculations of mean-square-error values. We are also in a position to study various other properties of the servo. We can, for instance, determine how sensitive the mean-square error is to small deviations of the equalizer parameters from their best values. Since it is often possible to eliminate some of the noise at its source by sufficiently elaborate filters, it is of interest to see how the minimal mean-square error varies with the noise level. We can also draw any desired decibel–log-frequency diagram; this will be of help to the experimentalist whose principal method of adjustment makes use of the servo steady-state response.

It will be instructive to apply some of these ideas to the example discussed in Secs. 7·5 and 7·6. In the previous section we obtained an expression [Eq. (67)] for the mean-square error:

$$\overline{\epsilon^2} = \beta\sigma T \frac{1 + \alpha(1 - A) + L\alpha^2}{2\alpha(1 - A\alpha)}. \tag{67}$$

In order to find the minimum mean-square error, we differentiate $\overline{\epsilon^2}$ with respect to the gain parameter α and set the derivative equal to zero. The resulting equation is quadratic in α. Only one of its two roots,

$$\alpha_m = \frac{1}{A + \sqrt{A + L}}, \tag{69}$$

lies in the region of stability. Substituting α_m into Eq. (67), one obtains the minimal mean-square error,

$$\overline{\epsilon_m^2} = \frac{\beta\sigma T}{2} (A + 2\sqrt{A + L} + 1). \tag{70}$$

Figure 7·2 shows plots of α_m and $\overline{\epsilon_m^2}/\beta\sigma T$, as functions of L, for $A = \frac{1}{4}$ (that is, for $T_1 = T_2$). As was to be expected, the "best" gain value decreases as the noise level increases. For no noise whatever (that is, $L = 0$) and $A = \frac{1}{4}$ the best value of the gain is $\frac{4}{3}$. For this minimal condition, the roots of the characteristic equation are

$$\left(\frac{-3.276}{T}, \frac{-0.362 \pm 1.224j}{T}\right). \tag{71}$$

The logarithmic decrement for the complex roots is $\delta_m = 1.85$. A graph of the error response to a unit-step function is shown in Fig. 7·3. According to the usual standards, one would say that the system is a bit underdamped. It must be remembered, however, that in this case $L = 0$. As L increases (A remaining equal to $\frac{1}{4}$), the roots of the optimal-condi-

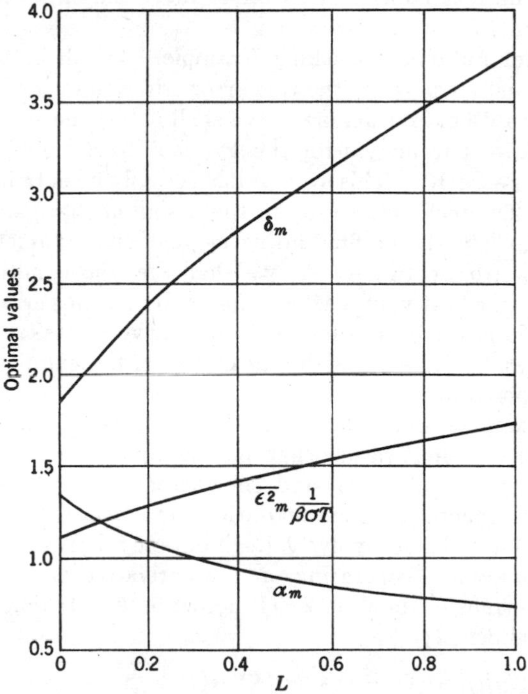

FIG. 7·2.—Optimal values of mean-square error, gain, and logarithmic decrement. $A = \frac{1}{4}$.

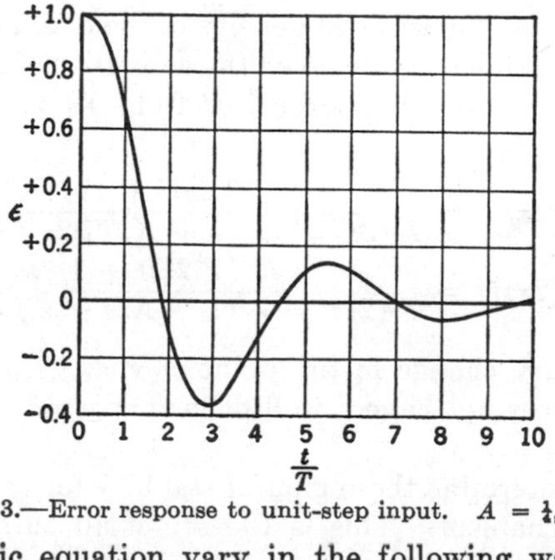

FIG. 7·3.—Error response to unit-step input. $A = \frac{1}{4}, L = 0$.

tion characteristic equation vary in the following way: The real root decreases slightly in magnitude until for $L = 1$ it is $-(2.99/T)$; the real part of the complex roots increases slightly while the imaginary part decreases until for $L = 1$ the complex roots are $(-0.50 \pm 0.85j)/T$. Thus as L increases, the system becomes more damped. A graph of the logarithmic decrement as a function of L for the optimal conditions is shown in Fig. 7·2.

7·8. Radar Automatic-tracking Example.—It will be the purpose of the present section to apply the rms-error criterion to the practical problem of radar automatic tracking. We shall determine the "best" values of the equalizer parameters for the gyrostabilized tracking mechanism described in Sec. 6·10. This system has actually been built and put into operation. The techniques used in the design of the system were those described in Chap. 4; the final adjustment of the parameters was made by trial-and-error methods. As we shall see, the resulting values are very close to the best values as determined by the rms criterion if certain restrictions imposed by the mount power drive are taken into account. This, in effect, furnishes us with an example of the validity of the design method proposed in this chapter.

In this example, as in that of Sec. 7·5, we may focus attention on the derivative of the input rather than on the input itself. In Eqs. (6·122) and (6·123), the input is θ_I, and the factor $2\pi jf$ appears in Y_1. The presence of this factor calls our attention to the fact that the servo differential equation does not involve θ_I itself but only derivatives of θ_I. Now, a transfer function Y operating on the derivative of θ_I gives the same result as the transfer function $2\pi jfY$ acting on θ_I. It follows that in the error spectral density

$$G_\epsilon(f) = |Y_1(2\pi jf)|^2G_I(f) + |Y_2(2\pi jf)|^2G_N(f) + Y_1^*(2\pi jf)G_{IN}(f)Y_2(2\pi jf) + Y_1(2\pi jf)G_{NI}(f)Y_2^*(2\pi jf), \quad (17)$$

we can take $G_I(f)$ as the spectral density of the derivative of θ_I and $G_{IN}(f)$ as the cross-spectral density between the derivative of θ_I and the noise if at the same time we drop the factor $2\pi jf$ from Y_1 as previously defined, writing

$$Y_1(2\pi jf) = \frac{(T_2 2\pi jf + 1)}{T_2(2\pi jf)^2 + (1 + K_vT_1)2\pi jf + K_v}, \quad (72a)$$

$$Y_2(2\pi jf) = \frac{K_v(T_1 2\pi jf + 1)}{T_2(2\pi jf)^2 + (1 + K_vT_1)2\pi jf + K_v}. \quad (72b)$$

This is a necessary change in the point of view because the θ_I that we propose to use does not have a well-defined spectral density whereas its derivative does.

Let us first determine the region of stability for the transfer function of this servomechanism. This is the set of all parameter values (T_1, T_2, K_v) for which the roots of

$$H(f) = T_2(2\pi jf)^2 + (1 + K_vT_1)(2\pi jf) + K_v \quad (73)$$

lie in the upper half plane. It will be found that the region of stability is defined by the inequalities

$$\left.\begin{aligned} K_v &> 0, \\ 1 + K_v T_1 &> 0, \\ T_2 &> 0. \end{aligned}\right\} \tag{74}$$

Although the region defined by reversing all these inequalities would also lead to roots of $H(f)$ in the upper half plane, such a region is ruled out of consideration by the physical nature of the parameters. We see then that the system will be stable for all of the inherently positive values of the parameters. Furthermore, the system does not tend to become unstable as the gain K_v is increased. (In any actual system, however, one finds that as the gain is increased, this second-order idealization of the servo breaks down because of nonlinear effects and time lags that are no longer negligible.)

The principal source of noise in radar tracking is fading. It was shown in Sec. 6·10 that one can approximate the noise spectral density by a constant,

$$G_N(f) = N, \tag{75}$$

where, as in Eq. (6·132),

$$N = 0.636 \qquad \text{mil}^2\ \text{sec}. \tag{76}$$

The trajectory of the airplane will, in general, have zero correlation with the fading. Hence we shall assume that $G_{IN}(f)$ and $G_{NI}(f)$ vanish identically.

Finally, for the servo input we shall use an input of the type studied in Sec. 6·12 and pictured in Fig. 6·9*b*. We shall suppose that the time axis is divided into intervals with end points . . . , $t_{-2}, t_{-1}, t_0, t_1, t_2,$ . . . , that satisfy the conditions for a Poisson distribution with mean density β. Within each interval the angular velocity approaches a new value exponentially, with time constant $1/\nu$. The values approached do not depend on any of the previous or subsequent interval values and have a zero mean and a mean-square value equal to $\widetilde{a^2}$. Combining Eqs. (6·153) and (6·169), we see that

$$G_I(f) = \frac{\nu^2}{\nu^2 + (2\pi f)^2} \frac{4\beta\widetilde{a^2}}{\beta^2 + (2\pi f)^2}. \tag{77}$$

We shall take

$$\left.\begin{aligned} \beta &= 0.04\ \text{sec}^{-1} \\ \nu &= 0.10\ \text{sec}^{-1} \\ \widetilde{a^2} &= 2.62 \times 10^3\ (\text{mils/sec})^2 \end{aligned}\right\} \tag{78}$$

for reasons discussed at the end of Sec. 6·12.

In this case the spectral-density matrix consists only of diagonal terms. The spectral density G_N, being a constant, is already in the form required by Sec. 7·4. It is also an easy matter to factor G_I, for, as can be seen by inspection,

$$G_I(f) = |X_{11}(f)|^2, \tag{79}$$

where

$$X_{11}(f) = \frac{2\nu\sqrt{\beta\widetilde{a^2}}}{(\nu + 2\pi jf)(\beta + 2\pi jf)}. \tag{80}$$

The poles of X_{11} lie in the upper half plane on the imaginary axis.

We are now in a position to compute the mean-square error. Since the cross-spectral density vanishes identically, the mean-square-error integral becomes the sum of two integrals—one part due to the signal, $\overline{\epsilon_I^2}$, and another part due to the noise, $\overline{\epsilon_N^2}$. The component integrals can be written as follows:

$$\begin{aligned}\overline{\epsilon_I^2} &= \frac{1}{2}\int_{-\infty}^{\infty} df|Y_1(2\pi jf)|^2G_I(f)\\ &= \frac{1}{4\pi}\int_{-\infty}^{\infty} dx\,\frac{T_2^2x^2+1}{H\left(\frac{x}{2\pi}\right)H\left(-\frac{x}{2\pi}\right)}\,\frac{4\beta\nu^2\widetilde{a^2}}{|(\nu+xj)(\beta+xj)|^2},\end{aligned} \tag{81}$$

where we have introduced the variable $x = 2\pi f$; and

$$\begin{aligned}\overline{\epsilon_N^2} &= \frac{1}{2}\int_{-\infty}^{\infty} df\,|Y_2(2\pi jf)|^2G_N(f)\\ &= \frac{1}{4\pi}\int_{-\infty}^{\infty} dx\,\frac{K_v^2(T_1^2x^2+1)}{H\left(\frac{x}{2\pi}\right)H\left(-\frac{x}{2\pi}\right)}\,N.\end{aligned} \tag{82}$$

The integral in Eq. (81) can be brought into the form of Eq. (58) by taking

$$\begin{aligned}h(x) &= [-T_2x^2 + (1 + K_vT_1)jx + K_v][(jx+\nu)(jx+\beta)]\\ &= T_2x^4 - j(\alpha + T_2S)x^3 - (K_v + \alpha S + T_2P)x^2\\ &\qquad + j(K_vS + \alpha P)x + K_vP,\end{aligned} \tag{83}$$

where

$$\left.\begin{aligned}\alpha &= 1 + K_vT_1,\\ S &= \beta + \nu,\\ P &= \beta\nu.\end{aligned}\right\} \tag{84}$$

The evaluation of the integrals [Eqs. (81) and (82)] by means of the appendix table is then straightforward and leads to the result

$$\left.\begin{aligned}\overline{\epsilon_1^2} &= \frac{\widetilde{a^2}P\nu}{\alpha S}\,\frac{\alpha T_2^2 + T_2^3S + \frac{1}{K_vP}(\alpha K_v + \alpha^2S + \alpha T_2S^2 + T_2^2SP)}{[(K_v - T_2P)^2 + (\alpha + T_2S)(K_vS + \alpha P)]},\\ \overline{\epsilon_N^2} &= \frac{N}{2T_2}\,\frac{(\alpha-1)^2 + T_2K_v}{2\alpha}.\end{aligned}\right\} \tag{85}$$

As before

$$\overline{\epsilon^2} = \overline{\epsilon_I^2} + \overline{\epsilon_N^2}. \tag{86}$$

There remains the formidable problem of finding positive values of (α, T_2, K_v) that minimize the mean-square error. Since a direct analytic solution of the equations obtained by setting the derivatives of $\overline{\epsilon^2}$ equal to zero is impracticable in this case, one is forced to invent another approach.

We can gain some insight into the nature of $\overline{\epsilon^2}$ by studying the asymptotic behavior as the parameters become infinite. If we set

$$\left.\begin{aligned} \alpha &= \alpha_1 x, \\ K_v &= K_1 x, \\ T_2 &= x, \end{aligned}\right\} \tag{87}$$

and take the limit as x becomes infinite, we obtain a much simpler expression for $\overline{\epsilon^2}$:

$$\overline{\epsilon_\infty^2} = \frac{\widetilde{a^2}P\nu}{\alpha_1 S} \frac{\alpha_1 + S}{(K_1 - P)^2 + (\alpha_1 + S)(K_1 S + \alpha_1 P)} + \frac{N}{4}\frac{\alpha_1^2 + K_1}{\alpha_1}. \tag{88}$$

It is not difficult to obtain the minimum of $\overline{\epsilon_\infty^2}$ by semiempirical methods. Table 7·1 gives the optimal values of (α_1, K_1), together with deviations from these values which cause a 10 per cent increase in $\overline{\epsilon_\infty^2}$. As can be

TABLE 7·1.—ASYMPTOTIC BEHAVIOR OF $\overline{\epsilon^2}$

	α_1	K_1	$\overline{\epsilon_{I\infty}^2}$	$\overline{\epsilon_{N\infty}^2}$	$\overline{\epsilon_\infty^2}$
Optimal values........	2.54	6.10	0.199	0.786	0.985
Nonoptimal values......	1.50	6.10	0.218	0.875	1.093
	4.20	6.10	0.194	0.896	1.090
	2.54	4.05	0.438	0.652	1.090
	2.54	9.75	0.080	1.012	1.092

seen, the values of $\overline{\epsilon_\infty^2}$ are not very sensitive to variations in (α_1, K_1) about their optimal values.

We shall now determine how $\overline{\epsilon^2}$ varies with x, for $\alpha_1 = 2.54$ and $K_1 = 6.10$. This is easy, as $\overline{\epsilon^2}$ is of second degree in $(1/x)$; in fact

$$\overline{\epsilon^2} = \overline{\epsilon_\infty^2} - \frac{N}{2}\frac{1}{x} + \left[\frac{\widetilde{a^2}\nu}{\alpha_1 K_1 S} \frac{\alpha_1 K_1 + \alpha_1^2 S + \alpha_1 S^2 + SP}{(K_1 - P)^2 + (\alpha_1 + S)(K_1 S + \alpha_1 P)} + \frac{N}{4\alpha_1}\right]\left(\frac{1}{x}\right)^2. \tag{89}$$

A graph of $\overline{\epsilon^2}$ as a function of x is shown in Fig. 7·4. There is a very shallow minimum which occurs at

$$x_m = 314.5\ (\alpha = 800,\ K_v = 1918,\ T_2 = 314.5).$$

At this point

$$\overline{\epsilon^2} = 0.1991 + 0.7846 = 0.9837 \text{ mil}^2. \tag{90}$$

The graph rises rapidly as x decreases past 50.

For $x = x_m$, the $(1/x)^2$-term in Eq. (89) is only 0.05 per cent of $\overline{\epsilon^2}$. It is evident that this term does not vary rapidly with α_1 or K_1; we must therefore expect the absolute minimum of $\overline{\epsilon^2}$ to be close to its minimum along the line ($\alpha_1 = 2.54x$, $K_1 = 6.10x$, $T_2 = x$). This, in fact, is the case, and for all practical purposes the absolute minimum can be considered to be at the above determined point. To obtain an estimate of the variation

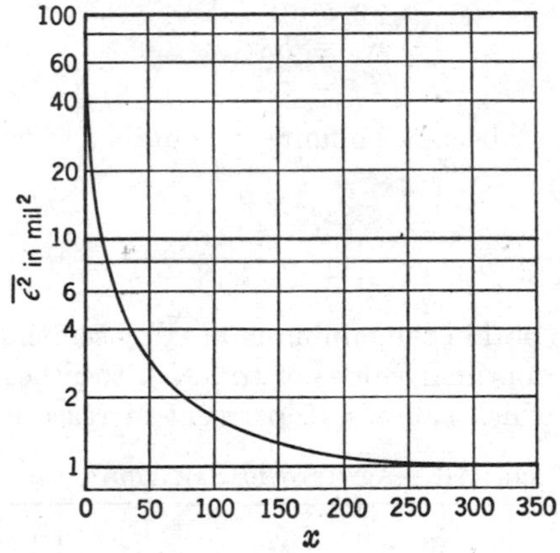

FIG. 7·4.—Variation of $\overline{\epsilon^2}$ along the line ($\alpha = 2.54x$, $K_v = 6.1x$, $T_2 = x$).

of $\overline{\epsilon^2}$ with α and K_v, one need only substitute $\alpha = 314.5\ \alpha_1$ for α_1, and $K_v = 314.5\ K_1$ for K_1 in Table 7·1.

TABLE 7·2.—$\overline{\epsilon^2}$ FOR $K_v = 80$ sec^{-1}

	K_v	T_2	α	$\overline{\epsilon_I^2}$	$\overline{\epsilon_N^2}$	$\overline{\epsilon^2}$
Optimal values........	80	13	33.0	0.486	0.765	1.251
Experimental values...	80	16	29.8	0.593	0.703	1.296
Nonoptimal values....	80	13	49.0	0.477	0.835	1.312
	80	13	22.0	0.495	0.823	1.318
	80	17	33.0	0.629	0.676	1.305
	80	9	33.0	0.382	0.934	1.316

In the actual tracking system it was found that if K_v was increased beyond the value 80 sec^{-1}, one could no longer ignore the effect of the mount power servo and the system performance rapidly deteriorated. With this limitation in mind, the best parameter values for α and T_2 were determined for $K_v = 80$ sec^{-1}. Listed in Table 7·2 are the mean-square errors for these optimal values, for the actual experimental values [see Eq. (6.113)], and finally for values that give a 6 per cent increase in the mean-square error. We see from Table 7·2 that limiting K_v to 80 $\sec^{-1}$ increases the mean-square error only 25 per cent above its absolute minimum. This results in a 12 per cent increase in the rms error, which is quite acceptable. The experimentally determined parameter values give a mean-square error extremely close to the restricted minimum value and, in a sense, confirm the arguments of this chapter.

7·9. Evaluation of the Integrals.—It remains to show how the integrals in the appendix have been evaluated. These integrals are of the form

$$I_n = \frac{1}{2\pi j}\int_{-\infty}^{\infty} dx\,\frac{g_n(x)}{h_n(x)h_n(-x)}, \tag{91}$$

where

$$\begin{aligned} h_n(x) &= a_0x^n + a_1x^{n-1} + \cdots + a_n, \\ g_n(x) &= b_0x^{2n-2} + b_1x^{2n-4} + \cdots + b_{n-1}, \end{aligned}$$

and the *roots of* $h_n(x)$ *all lie in the upper half plane.* No greater generality would be achieved by allowing g to contain odd powers of x, since the contribution of such terms to the integral would be zero.

We now apply the method of residues[1] to the integral in Eq. (91). In the present application this method requires that the value of the integral taken along a semicircle C_R of radius R, which has its center at the origin and lies in the upper half plane (see Fig. 7·5), approach zero as R becomes infinite. This condition is clearly satisfied, since for sufficiently large R the integrand is less in absolute value than M/R^2, for some positive constant M. It follows that

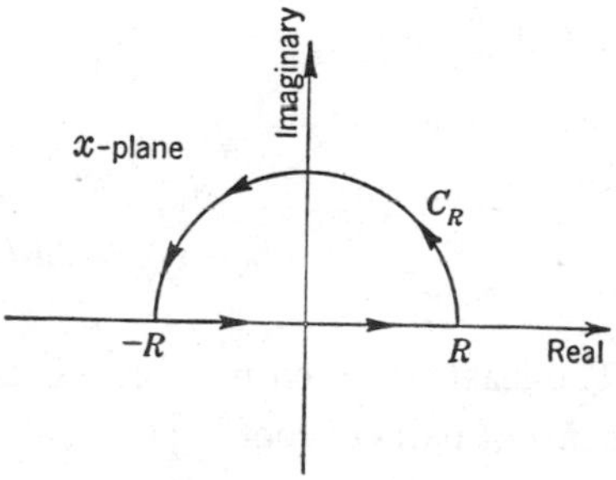

FIG. 7·5.—Path of integration.

$$I_n = \lim_{R\to\infty} \frac{1}{2\pi j}\left(\int_{-R}^{R} + \int_{C_R}\right) dx\,\frac{g_n(x)}{h_n(x)h_n(-x)}. \tag{92}$$

The integral about the closed path $[(-R, R) + C_R]$ is independent of R for sufficiently large R's and is, in fact, equal to the sum of the residues at the poles of the integrand contained within this closed path.

In the further developments, the n may be omitted as a subscript where this cannot lead to confusion.

Since the roots of $h(x)$ all lie in the upper half plane, the roots of $h(-x)$ lie in the lower half plane. Consequently for sufficiently large R the poles

[1] See E. C. Titchmarsh, *The Theory of Functions*, Oxford, New York, 1932.

of the integrand contained in the closed path of integration $[(-R, R) + C_R]$ will be precisely the roots of $h(x)$. Therefore I is equal to the sum of the residues taken at the roots of $h(x)$. It will be assumed for the moment that these roots are all simple; it will be shown later that the stated result holds even when some of the roots are multiple roots.

Since each residue is a rational function of a root of $h(x)$ and since all roots are treated alike, the integral is a symmetric rational function of the roots of $h(x)$. It follows that *I can be expressed rationally in terms of the coefficients of h and g.*[1] It will be the purpose of this section to derive such an expression.

Let $x_1, x_2, \ldots, x_n$ be the roots of $h(x)$, assumed distinct. Writing I as the sum of residues in the upper half plane, one has

$$I = \sum_{k=1}^{n} \frac{g(x_k)}{h'(x_k)h(-x_k)}, \tag{93}$$

where $h'(x)$ is the derivative of $h(x)$ with respect to x.

By the factor theorem,

$$h(x) = a_0 \prod_{i=1}^{n} (x - x_i). \tag{94}$$

Hence

$$h(-x_k) = 2a_0(-1)^n x_k \prod_{i \neq k} (x_k + x_i). \tag{95}$$

The least common multiple of the factors $(x_k + x_i)$ is the product of all sums of pairs of roots, $\prod\limits_{l<m} (x_m + x_l)$. Equation (93) can now be written as

$$I = \frac{(-1)^n}{2a_0 \prod\limits_{l<m} (x_m + x_l)} \sum_{k=1}^{n} \frac{g(x_k)}{x_k h'(x_k)} \prod_{j<i}^{i,j \neq k} (x_i + x_j). \tag{96}$$

The evaluation of Eq. (96) for $n = 2$ is simple enough, but a systematized approach is required when $n > 2$. The following procedure consists of two parts. First an expression is obtained for the product of all sums of pairs of roots of a polynomial in terms of its coefficients. This is clearly necessary for the term $\prod\limits_{l<m} (x_m + x_l)$ and will also be useful in evaluating the expression $\prod\limits_{j<i}^{i,j \neq k} (x_i + x_j)$, which is the product of all pairs

[1] See L. E. Dickson, *First Course in the Theory of Equations*, Wiley, New York, 1922, Chap. 9.

of roots of the polynomial

$$f_k(x) = \frac{h(x)}{x - x_k} = a_0x^{n-1} + (a_0x_k + a_1)x^{n-2}$$
$$+ (a_0x_k^2 + a_1x_k + a_2)x^{n-3} \cdot \cdot \cdot + (a_0x_k^{n-1} + \cdot \cdot \cdot + a_{n-1}). \quad (97)$$

The resulting expression is, in this case, a polynomial in x_k with coefficients that are algebraic functions of the coefficients of $h(x)$. The problem will then be reduced to evaluating symmetric functions of the form

$$\sum_{k=1}^{n} \frac{x_k^l}{h'(x_k)}, \qquad (l = -1, 0, 1, 2, \cdot \cdot \cdot). \quad (98)$$

This will be accomplished in the second part.

Let us now obtain an expression for the product of all sums of pairs of roots of an arbitrary polynomial,

$$Q(z) = \sum_{j=0}^{N} A_j z^{N-j}. \quad (99)$$

Suppose $Q(z)$ has the roots $z_1, z_2, \ . \ . \ . \ , z_N$, all distinct. Then, given the two roots z_k and z_l, let

$$\alpha = \frac{z_l + z_k}{2}. \quad (100)$$

It will be noted that $Q(\alpha - y)$ and $Q(\alpha + y)$, considered as polynomials in the variable y, have a common root $y = (z_l - z_k)/2$, since

$$\left.\begin{aligned} \alpha - \left(\frac{z_l - z_k}{2}\right) = z_k, \qquad \alpha + \left(\frac{z_l - z_k}{2}\right) = z_l, \\ \text{and} \qquad Q(z_k) = 0 = Q(z_l). \end{aligned}\right\} \quad (101)$$

Adding and subtracting the equations

$$\begin{aligned} Q(\alpha - y) &= 0, \\ Q(\alpha + y) &= 0, \end{aligned} \quad (102)$$

one obtains two equations in y^2 which have the common root $(z_l - z_k)/2$. The resultant[1] found by eliminating y^2 from these two equations must therefore vanish for α given by Eq. (100). On setting the resultant equal to zero, one gets an equation of degree $[N(N - 1)]/2$ in α. It is clear that all sums of the type $(z_l + z_k)/2$ will satisfy this equation. Since there are precisely $[N(N - 1)]/2$ such sums, all roots are of this type; that is, there is a one-to-one correspondence between the roots of this equation and the terms $(z_l + z_k)/2$ for all possible choices of l and k. It follows that the constant term of this equation, divided by the coefficient of highest power in α, is precisely

[1] See for instance L. E. Dickson, *op. cit.*, Chap. 10.

$$\frac{1}{(-2)^{[N(N-1)]/2}} \prod_{l<k} (z_k + z_l). \tag{103}$$

The actual computation of this ratio is tedious but none the less straightforward. The result is that for

N odd,

$$\prod_{l<k} (z_k + z_l) = \frac{(-1)^{[(N-1)(N-3)]/8}}{A_0^{N-1}} \left| \begin{array}{cccccccc} A_0 & A_2 & A_4 & - & A_{N-1} & 0 & - & 0 \\ 0 & A_0 & A_2 & - & A_{N-3} & A_{N-1} & - & 0 \\ - & - & - & - & - & - & - & - \\ - & - & - & - & - & - & - & - \\ A_1 & A_3 & A_5 & - & A_N & 0 & - & 0 \\ 0 & A_1 & A_3 & - & A_{N-2} & A_N & - & 0 \\ - & - & - & - & - & - & - & - \\ - & - & - & - & - & - & - & - \end{array} \right| \begin{array}{l} \left.\begin{array}{l} \\ \\ \\ \\ \end{array}\right\} \frac{N-1}{2} \text{ rows} \\ \left.\begin{array}{l} \\ \\ \\ \\ \end{array}\right\} \frac{N-1}{2} \text{ rows} \end{array} \tag{104}$$

N even,

$$\prod_{l<k} (z_k + z_l) = \frac{(-1)^{(N^2+2N)/8}}{A_0^{N-1}} \left| \begin{array}{ccccccccc} A_0 & A_2 & A_4 & - & A_{N-2} & A_N & 0 & - & 0 \\ 0 & A_0 & A_2 & - & A_{N-4} & A_{N-2} & A_N & - & 0 \\ - & - & - & - & - & - & - & - & - \\ - & - & - & - & - & - & - & - & - \\ A_1 & A_3 & A_5 & - & A_{N-1} & 0 & 0 & - & 0 \\ 0 & A_1 & A_3 & - & A_{N-3} & A_{N-1} & 0 & - & 0 \\ - & - & - & - & - & - & - & - & - \\ - & - & - & - & - & - & - & - & - \end{array} \right| \begin{array}{l} \left.\begin{array}{l} \\ \\ \\ \\ \end{array}\right\} \frac{N}{2} - 1 \text{ rows} \\ \left.\begin{array}{l} \\ \\ \\ \\ \end{array}\right\} \frac{N}{2} \text{ rows} \end{array} \tag{105}$$

As one might expect, these determinants appear in Routh's criterion.

As has already been mentioned, this result is used in two ways in the evaluation of the expression in Eq. (96). In order to obtain

$$\prod_{l<m} (x_m + x_l),$$

one merely replaces $Q(z)$ by $h(x)$; A_r is then replaced by a_r, and N is replaced by n. On the other hand, in order to obtain $\prod_{\substack{j<i \\ i,j\neq k}} (x_i + x_j)$, one replaces $Q(z)$ by the polynomial $f_k(x)$ of Eq. (97); A_r is replaced by

$$(a_0x_k^r + a_1x_k^{r-1} + \cdots + a_r),$$

and N by $(n - 1)$. In the latter case it is evident that the determinants become polynomials in x_k, say $\Delta(x_k)$, with coefficients that are rational functions of the coefficients of h. Equation (96) therefore assumes the form

$$I = \frac{(-1)^n}{2a_0 \prod\limits_{l<m} (x_m + x_l)} \sum_{k=1}^{n} \frac{g(x_k)\Delta(x_k)}{x_k h'(x_k)}. \tag{106}$$

The product $g(x_k)\Delta(x_k)$ is again a polynomial in x_k. Since each term of this polynomial can be evaluated separately, it remains only to calculate expressions of the type

$$\sum_{k=1}^{n} \frac{x_k^l}{h'(x_k)}, \qquad (l = -1, 0, 1, 2, \cdots). \tag{98}$$

This is the sum of all residues in the plane[1] of the function $x^l/[h(x)]$. When the degree of the numerator is at least two less than the degree of the denominator, the sum of the residues in the plane vanishes. It follows that

$$\sum_{k=1}^{n} \frac{1}{x_k h'(x_k)} = -\frac{1}{h(0)}, \tag{107a}$$

$$\sum_{k=1}^{n} \frac{x_k^l}{h'(x_k)} = 0 \qquad \text{for } 0 \leqq l \leqq n - 2. \tag{107b}$$

In order to obtain the result for larger values of l, it is convenient to write

$$\frac{a_0 x^n}{h(x)} = \frac{x^n}{\prod (x - x_k)} = \frac{1}{\prod \left(1 - \frac{x_k}{x}\right)} = \prod \left(1 + \frac{x_k}{x} + \frac{x_k^2}{x^2} + \cdots \right)$$

$$= \sum_{r=0}^{\infty} \frac{\Gamma_r}{x^r} \qquad \text{for } |x| > \max|x_k|, \tag{108}$$

where Γ_r is the sum of all symmetric functions of weight r:

$$\left.\begin{aligned}
\Gamma_0 &= 1, \\
\Gamma_1 &= \sum x_k = -\frac{a_1}{a_0}, \\
\Gamma_2 &= \sum x_k^2 + \sum_{k<l} x_k x_l = \left(\frac{a_1}{a_0}\right)^2 - \frac{a_2}{a_0}, \\
\Gamma_3 &= \sum x_k^3 + \sum_{k \neq l} x_k^2 x_l + \sum_{k<l<m} x_k x_l x_m \\
&\qquad = -\left(\frac{a_1}{a_0}\right)^3 + 2\frac{a_1 a_2}{a_0^2} - \frac{a_3}{a_0}, \\
\Gamma_4 &= \text{etc.}
\end{aligned}\right\} \tag{109}$$

[1] For a more complete development of this argument we refer the reader to W. S. Burnside and A. W. Panton, *Theory of Equations*, 9th ed., Vol. I, Longmans, London, 1928, pp. 171–179.

Returning to Eq. (108), we multiply through by x^{l-n} and obtain for the sum of the residues in the plane

$$\sum_{k=1}^{n} \frac{x_k^l}{h'(x_k)} = \frac{\Gamma_{l-n+1}}{a_0} \qquad \text{for } l \geqq n-1. \tag{107c}$$

It is possible to derive a recurrence formula for the Γ's by making use of Eq. (108) in the following way:

$$\begin{aligned} a_0 &= \frac{h(x)}{x^n}\left(\sum_{r=0}^{\infty} \frac{\Gamma_r}{x^r}\right) \\ &= \left(a_0 + a_1\frac{1}{x} + a_2\frac{1}{x^2} + \cdots + a_n\frac{1}{x^n}\right)\left(\sum_{r=0}^{\infty}\frac{\Gamma_r}{x^r}\right). \end{aligned} \tag{110}$$

Comparing like powers of x on both sides of Eq. (110) gives

$$a_0\Gamma_m + a_1\Gamma_{m-1} + \cdots + a_m\Gamma_0 = 0. \tag{111}$$

Here $a_m = 0$ for $m > n$. One can avoid the use of the Γ's by successively reducing the degree of the numerator of Eq. (106) to $n - 1$, by means of the formula

$$-a_0x_k^l = a_1x_k^{l-1} + a_2x_k^{l-2} + \cdots + a_nx_k^{l-n} \qquad \text{for } (l \geqq n). \tag{112}$$

Since Eq. (112) is merely the statement that $h(x_k) = 0$, this substitution can be made at any stage of the calculation.

When the computation is carried through as outlined above, one obtains I_n as a rational function of the coefficients of $g_n(x)$ and $h_n(x)$. This expression has been shown to hold for the roots of $h_n(x)$ distinct and in the upper half plane. Furthermore, since the coefficients of $h_n(x)$ are continuous functions of the roots, both the computed expression for I_n and its integrand are continuous functions of the roots. The expression for I_n equals the integral as the roots approach a multiple state; it follows that it is equal to the integral in the limit.

It will be instructive to carry through the above process for I_3. In this case

$$\left.\begin{aligned} h(x) &= a_0x^3 + a_1x^2 + a_2x + a_3, \\ g(x) &= b_0x^4 + b_1x^2 + b_2, \end{aligned}\right\} \tag{113}$$

and the roots of $h(x)$ are assumed to lie in the upper half plane. It follows from Eq. (104) that

$$\prod_{l<m} (x_m + x_l) = \frac{1}{a_0^2}\begin{vmatrix} a_0 & a_2 \\ a_1 & a_3 \end{vmatrix} = \frac{a_0a_3 - a_1a_2}{a_0^2}. \tag{114}$$

In this case Eq. (97) becomes

$$f_k(x) = a_0x^2 + (a_0x_k + a_1)x + (a_0x_k^2 + a_1x_k + a_2); \tag{115}$$

then, by Eq. (105),

$$\prod_{j<i}^{i,j\neq k} (x_i + x_j) = \frac{-1}{a_0}(a_0x_k + a_1). \tag{116}$$

Equation (106) can now be written as

$$I_3 = \frac{-1}{2a_0\left(\dfrac{a_0a_3 - a_1a_2}{a_0^2}\right)} \sum_{k=1}^{3} \frac{(b_0x_k^4 + b_1x_k^2 + b_2)}{x_kh'(x_k)} \frac{(-a_0x_k - a_1)}{a_0}$$

$$= \frac{1}{2(a_0a_3 - a_1a_2)}$$

$$\times \sum_{k=1}^{3} \frac{a_0b_0x_k^5 + a_1b_0x_k^4 + a_0b_1x_k^3 + a_1b_1x_k^2 + a_0b_2x_k + a_1b_2}{x_kh'(x_k)}. \tag{117}$$

By Eqs. (107),

$$\left.\begin{aligned}
&\sum \frac{1}{x_kh'(x_k)} = -\frac{1}{h(0)} = \frac{-1}{a_3},\\
&\sum \frac{x_k^l}{h'(x_k)} = 0 \qquad \text{for } 0 \leqq l \leqq 3 - 2 = 1,\\
&\sum \frac{x_k^2}{h'(x_k)} = \frac{\Gamma_0}{a_0} = \frac{1}{a_0},\\
&\sum \frac{x_k^3}{h'(x_k)} = \frac{\Gamma_1}{a_0} = -\frac{a_1}{a_0^2},\\
&\sum \frac{x_k^4}{h'(x_k)} = \frac{\Gamma_2}{a_0} = \frac{1}{a_0}\left[\left(\frac{a_1}{a_0}\right)^2 - \frac{a_2}{a_0}\right].
\end{aligned}\right\} \tag{118}$$

Combining these results with Eq. (117), one obtains

$$I_3 = \frac{1}{2(a_0a_3 - a_1a_2)} \left\{\frac{a_0b_0}{a_0}\left[\left(\frac{a_1}{a_0}\right)^2 - \frac{a_2}{a_0}\right] + a_1b_0\left(-\frac{a_1}{a_0^2}\right) + a_0b_1\left(\frac{1}{a_0}\right) + a_1b_1(0) + a_0b_2(0) + a_1b_2\left(\frac{-1}{a_3}\right)\right\}. \tag{119}$$

This can be arranged so as to give

$$I_3 = \frac{-a_2b_0 + a_0b_1 - \dfrac{a_0a_1}{a_3}b_2}{2a_0(a_0a_3 - a_1a_2)}, \tag{120}$$

which checks with I_3 as given in the appendix.

CHAPTER 8

APPLICATIONS OF THE NEW DESIGN METHOD

By C. H. Dowker and R. S. Phillips[1]

In the preceding chapter a method was developed by which one may choose the best design for a servomechanism of a given type. In order to make this choice, the type of servo must be decided upon in advance and the statistical properties of the input signal and the noise disturbances must be known. The best servomechanism performance is taken to be that which minimizes the rms error in the output.

The usefulness of this method of servo design would be greatly enhanced if the optimal designs for general types of input signals and noise were determined once and for all. In that case one would not have to go through the detailed calculations for each particular application; instead, after computing the correlation functions for the input signal and noise, one could then look up the specifications for the best servomechanism. One would, in addition, be able to relate these results to those of the steady-state analysis by translating the characteristics of the best servos into the language of the decibel–log-frequency diagram.

It is the purpose of the first part of the present chapter to make a modest beginning on such a program. The optimal servo parameters for two simple servomechanisms of standard type are found for a variety of inputs. These results are presented by means of graphs, Nyquist diagrams, and decibel–log-frequency diagrams.

In the second part of this chapter the rms-error criterion is applied to manual tracking of a type that has, for instance, important military applications. The tracking apparatus plus the human operator forms a servo system; the novel feature of such a system lies in the biomechanical link. The best time constant for the given tracking unit is determined.

8·1. Input Signal and Noise.—We shall assume in this discussion spectral densities of input signal and noise that depend on three parameters. This dependence is so flexible that many actual input spectral densities can be approximated by a suitable choice of these parameters; yet the dependence is simple enough to allow at least approximate solution for the best servo parameters in terms of the input parameters.

We shall assume that the input to the servo is $\theta_I + \theta_N$, where θ_I is

[1] Sections 8·1 through 8·9 by C. H. Dowker; Secs. 8·10 through 8·12 by R. S. Phillips.

the true input signal and θ_N is the noise. We shall take as our typical servo input the one described in Sec. 6·12. For this input the velocity is constant throughout extended intervals of time, changing abruptly at the beginning of each interval to a new value independent of any other; the end points of the time intervals have a Poisson distribution. The mean length of the time intervals is denoted by $1/\beta$. If $\widetilde{a^2}$ is the mean-square value of the velocity, then the spectral density of the derivative of the input is [see Eq. (6·169)]

$$G_I(f) = \frac{4\beta\widetilde{a^2}}{\omega^2 + \beta^2}, \tag{1}$$

where $\omega = 2\pi f$.

The spectral density given in Eq. (1) represents at least approximately the spectral density for many other servomechanism inputs. As long as the power of the input derivative is concentrated at the low frequencies, Eq. (1) is an adequate representation; $\beta/2\pi$ can be thought of as the cutoff frequency of the input derivative.

The spectral density of θ_N is assumed to be of the form

$$G_N(f) = N, \tag{2}$$

where N is a constant. In the terminology of Sec. 6·11, the noise input is assumed to be a purely random process. Such a spectral density can be considered to approximate a spectral density that is essentially constant for all frequencies low enough to pass through the servo without serious attenuation. In Sec. 6·10 this approximation was found to give a satisfactory representation for radar fading in the automatic-tracking servo system.

We shall further assume that the cross-spectral density vanishes identically:

$$G_{IN}(f) \equiv 0. \tag{3}$$

This will, in general, be the case whenever the sources for the input signal and the noise are independent.

In the particular examples of servo inputs that we shall consider the rms input speed $\sqrt{\widetilde{a^2}}$ is about 50 mils/sec and $1/\beta$ is about 10 sec (see Sec. 6·12). Thus $G_I(0) = 4\widetilde{a^2}/\beta \approx 10^5$ mils²/sec. In addition,

$$G_N(f) = N \approx 1 \text{ mil}^2 \text{ sec}$$

as in Eq. (6·132). These comparative magnitudes will form the basis for approximations made in the course of the following discussion.

When the cross-spectral density vanishes, the spectral density for the error (Sec. 7·2) is given by

$$G_\epsilon(f) = |Y_1(2\pi jf)|^2 G_I(f) + |Y_2(2\pi jf)|^2 G_N(f), \tag{4}$$

where Y_1 is the transfer function for the input-signal derivative and Y_2

is the transfer function for the noise input. The mean-square error can then be found as in Chap. 7 from the expression

$$\overline{\epsilon^2} = \int_0^\infty df\, G_\epsilon(f). \tag{5}$$

SERVO WITH PROPORTIONAL CONTROL

8·2. Best Control Parameter.—We begin with the simplest and best-known type of servomechanism—a servo with proportional control. This type of servo is of considerable interest in itself; it is, in addition, suitable for exhibiting the complete analysis of a simple problem. The minimum mean-square error for the proportional-control servo will also furnish a standard with which to compare the performance of more complicated types of servomechanisms.

It will be convenient in what follows to omit the symbol $\mathcal{L}(\ )$, denoting the Laplace transform of the function within the parentheses. The reader should have no difficulty in differentiating between the function of time and its Laplace transform by the context.

The output θ_O of the servo with proportional control is related to the input by the equation [see Eq. (4·5)]

$$(T_m p + 1)p\theta_O = K_v(\theta_I + \theta_N - \theta_O), \tag{6}$$

where K_v is the velocity-error constant and T_m is the motor time constant. Here K_v is a true parameter, variable over a wide range, whereas T_m can be changed only by replacing the motor or changing the load inertia.

We shall show that if the motor time constant T_m is too large for the particular servo application, the minimum mean-square error depends strongly on T_m. If T_m is less than a certain critical value, the minimum mean-square error and the optimal value of K_v are practically independent of T_m. If T_m has this critical value, the peak amplifications are larger for the optimal servos than might be expected on the basis of the steady-state analysis of Chap. 4; but if T_m is well below this critical value, the usual peak amplifications are obtained. The decisive factor in the design of the proportional-control servo is the noise-to-signal ratio $N/\widetilde{a^2}$. When this ratio is small, the minimum mean-square error is proportional to $(\widetilde{a^2}N^2)^{1/3}$ and the optimal K_v is proportional to $(\widetilde{a^2}/N)^{1/3}$.

Equation (6) of the servo can be solved for θ_O as follows:

$$\theta_O = \theta_I - \frac{T_m p + 1}{K_v + (T_m p + 1)p}\, p\theta_I + \frac{K_v}{K_v + (T_m p + 1)p}\, \theta_N. \tag{7}$$

Thus θ_O differs from θ_I by an error ϵ consisting of two parts—the error due to the failure of the servo to follow the input signal and the error resulting from the noise. Since the spectral density of $p\theta_I$ is $4\beta\widetilde{a^2}/(\omega^2 + \beta^2)$, the mean-square error in following the input is

$$\overline{\epsilon_I^2} = \frac{1}{2\pi}\int_0^\infty d\omega \frac{T_m^2\omega^2 + 1}{|K_v + j\omega - T_m\omega^2|^2}\frac{4\beta\widetilde{\widetilde{a^2}}}{\omega^2 + \beta^2}. \tag{8}$$

On integrating this expression by the method of Sec. 7·6 and simplifying the result, one obtains

$$\overline{\epsilon_I^2} = \frac{\widetilde{\widetilde{a^2}}}{K_v}\frac{1 + K_v\beta T_m^2 + \beta T_m}{K_v + \beta + \beta^2 T_m}. \tag{9}$$

Similarly, since $G_N(f) = N$, the mean-square error resulting from the noise is

$$\overline{\epsilon_N^2} = \frac{1}{2\pi}\int_0^\infty d\omega \frac{K_v^2}{|K_v + j\omega - T_m\omega^2|^2} N, \tag{10}$$

which, when integrated, becomes

$$\overline{\epsilon_N^2} = \frac{NK_v}{4}. \tag{11}$$

The mean-square error in following is then

$$\overline{\epsilon^2} = \overline{\epsilon_I^2} + \overline{\epsilon_N^2} = \frac{\widetilde{\widetilde{a^2}}}{K_v}\frac{1 + K_v\beta T_m^2 + \beta T_m}{K_v + \beta + \beta^2 T_m} + \frac{NK_v}{4}. \tag{12}$$

At this point it is convenient to make certain approximations which will normally be justified. The number β, that is, the cutoff frequency of the input signal, is usually small; for instance, β^{-1} is between 10 and 30 sec in the input discussed in Sec. 6·12. The motor time constant T_m is usually between 0.5 and 0.05 sec. Hence βT_m is likely to be small compared with unity. If also β/K_v is small compared with 1, we may approximate to $\overline{\epsilon^2}$ by the formula

$$\overline{\epsilon^2} \approx \frac{\widetilde{\widetilde{a^2}}}{K_v^2}(1 + K_v\beta T_m^2) + \frac{NK_v}{4}. \tag{13}$$

The computations will be simplified if we substitute for K_v in terms of the dimensionless parameter

$$y = \frac{K_v}{2}\left(\frac{N}{\widetilde{\widetilde{a^2}}}\right)^{1/3}. \tag{14}$$

The form of the mean-square error that we obtain is

$$\overline{\epsilon^2} \approx (\widetilde{\widetilde{a^2}}N^2)^{1/3}\left[\frac{1}{4y^2} + \left(\frac{\widetilde{\widetilde{a^2}}}{N}\right)^{1/3}\frac{\beta T_m^2}{2y} + \frac{y}{2}\right]. \tag{15}$$

We are now in a position to find the best value of K_v—the value of K_v and hence y that minimizes the mean-square error. To this end, we differentiate $\overline{\epsilon^2}$ with respect to y and equate the result to zero:

$$\frac{d}{dy}\frac{\overline{\epsilon^2}}{(\widetilde{a^2}N^2)^{1/3}} = -\frac{1}{2y^3} - \left(\frac{\widetilde{a^2}\beta^3}{N}\right)^{1/3}\frac{T_m^2}{2y^2} + \frac{1}{2} = 0. \tag{16}$$

Hence

$$\sqrt{y^2 - \frac{1}{y}} = \left(\frac{\widetilde{a^2}\beta^3}{N}\right)^{1/6} T_m. \tag{17}$$

Substituting the optimal value of y into Eq. (15), we find the minimum mean-square error

$$\overline{\epsilon_m^2} = (\widetilde{a^2}N^2)^{1/3}\left(y - \frac{1}{4y^2}\right). \tag{18}$$

For each value of $y \geqq 1$[1] Eqs. (17), (18), and (14) give respectively a value of T_m and, corresponding to this T_m, the minimum $\overline{\epsilon^2}$ and the optimal value of K_v. Figure 8·1 shows how the minimum $\overline{\epsilon^2}$ and the optimal

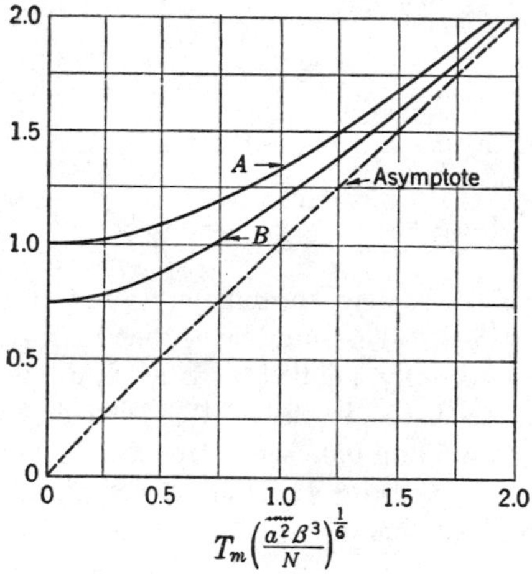

FIG. 8·1.—Best velocity-error constant and mean-square error of servo with proportional control as a function of motor time constant. Curve A, $y = (K_v/2)(N/\widetilde{a^2})^{1/3}$; Curve B, $\overline{\epsilon_m{}^2}/(\widetilde{a^2}N^2)^{1/3}$.

K_v vary with T_m. One sees that for large T_m, $\overline{\epsilon_m^2}$ is proportional to T_m. On the other hand, if T_m is small, $\overline{\epsilon_m^2}$ is largely independent of T_m; the best value of K_v is then approximately 2 $[(\widetilde{a^2}/N)^{1/3}]$.

If

$$K_v = 2\left(\frac{\widetilde{a^2}}{N}\right)^{1/3}, \tag{19}$$

then $y = 1$ and, by Eq. (15),

$$\frac{\overline{\epsilon^2}}{(\widetilde{a^2}N^2)^{1/3}} = \frac{3}{4} + \frac{1}{2}\left(\frac{\widetilde{a^2}\beta^3}{N}\right)^{1/3} T_m^2. \tag{20}$$

[1] $y \geqq 1$ corresponds to the real range of T_m.

Consequently, if

$$T_m < 0.4\left(\frac{N}{\widetilde{a^2}\beta^3}\right)^{1/6}, \tag{21}$$

then $\overline{\epsilon^2}$ is less than 11 per cent above its absolute minimum value, which is approached as $T_m \to 0$. If we now separate the error in following the signal from the error due to noise, we see that

$$\frac{\overline{\epsilon_I^2}}{(\widetilde{a^2}N^2)^{1/3}} = \frac{1}{4} + \frac{1}{2}\left(\frac{\widetilde{a^2}\beta^3}{N}\right)^{1/3} T_m^2 \tag{22a}$$

$$\frac{\overline{\epsilon_N^2}}{(\widetilde{a^2}N^2)^{1/3}} = \frac{1}{2} \tag{22b}$$

As $T_m \to 0$, the mean-square error in following the signal becomes half of the mean-square error due to noise. For $T_m < 0.4\,(N/\widetilde{a^2}\beta^3)^{1/6}$, the component mean-square errors are related by

$$0.50\overline{\epsilon_N^2} < \overline{\epsilon_I^2} < 0.66\overline{\epsilon_N^2}. \tag{23}$$

These computations and the approximation [Eq. (13)] on which they are based are valid only if for K_v near its optimal value, β/K_v is small compared with unity. But $\widetilde{a^2}$ is normally very large compared with N, and thus $K_v = 2(\widetilde{a^2}/N)^{1/3}$ is large. In the example below [Eq. (33b)] $K_v > 30\ \text{sec}^{-1}$. Hence, since β is usually small compared with $1\ \text{sec}^{-1}$, β/K_v is likely to be very small.

8·3. Properties of the Best Servo with Proportional Control.—Let us now examine the properties of a servo with proportional control, when the best choice is made of the parameter K_v.

From Eq. (6) one sees that

$$\theta_O = \frac{K_v}{(T_m p + 1)p}\,\epsilon, \tag{24}$$

where $\epsilon = \theta_I + \theta_N - \theta_O$ is the error signal (not the error $\theta_I - \theta_O$ in following the intended input). Hence

$$\left|\frac{\theta_O}{\epsilon}\right| = \left|\frac{K_v}{(T_m j\omega + 1)j\omega}\right|. \tag{25}$$

Thus we have the limiting relations

$$\left|\frac{\theta_O}{\epsilon}\right| \approx \frac{K_v}{\omega}, \qquad \omega \ll \frac{1}{T_m}, \tag{26a}$$

$$\left|\frac{\theta_O}{\epsilon}\right| \approx \frac{K_v}{T_m\omega^2}, \qquad \omega \gg \frac{1}{T_m}. \tag{26b}$$

If T_m is small enough, that is, if $T_m < 0.4\,[N/(\widetilde{a^2}\beta^3)]^{1/6}$, then, by Fig. 8·1, K_v can be chosen equal to $2(\widetilde{a^2}/N)^{1/3}$ independently of T_m. For small values of ω the loop gain will then be equal to

$$\left|\frac{\theta_O}{\epsilon}\right| \approx \frac{K_v}{\omega} = \frac{2}{\omega}\left(\frac{\widetilde{a^2}}{N}\right)^{1/3}. \tag{27}$$

Thus two decibel–log-frequency diagrams, for different small values of T_m, will have the same asymptote at low frequencies (Fig. 8·2).

If the feedback cutoff frequency (the frequency f_c at which the loop gain is unity) is much greater than $1/(2\pi T_m)$, we have

$$K_v \approx T_m\omega_c^2, \tag{28a}$$

$$f_c = \frac{1}{2\pi}\,\omega_c \approx \frac{1}{2\pi}\left(\frac{K_v}{T_m}\right)^{1/2}, \quad \left(\omega_c \gg \frac{1}{T_m}\right). \tag{28b}$$

It follows from Eq. (6), with neglect of θ_N relative to θ_I, that the over-all amplifications of the servo is

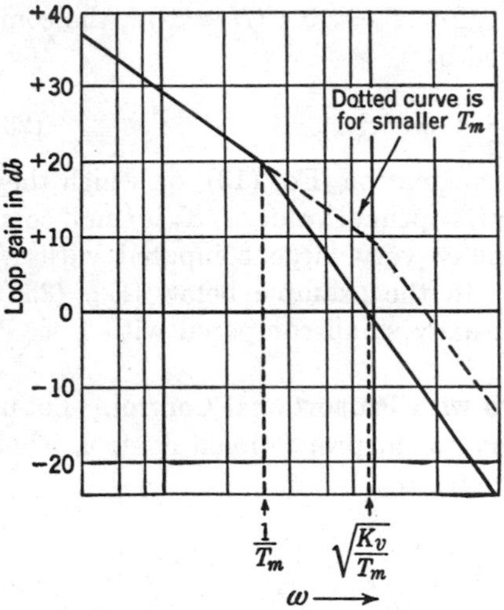

FIG. 8·2.—Decibel–log-frequency diagram for servo with proportional control.

$$\left|\frac{\theta_O}{\theta_I}\right| \approx \left|\frac{K_v}{K_v + j\omega - T_m\omega^2}\right|. \tag{29}$$

The peak over-all amplification is approximately the amplification at the cutoff frequency if K_vT_m is sufficiently large; for instance, if $K_vT_m > 2.5$, then a 5 per cent error is made by the approximation

$$\left|\frac{\theta_O}{\theta_I}\right|_{\max} \approx \left|\frac{K_v}{K_v + j\omega_c - T_m\omega_c^2}\right| = \left|\frac{K_v}{\omega_c}\right| \approx \sqrt{K_vT_m}. \tag{30}$$

If the approximations of the three preceding paragraphs are all valid, the cutoff frequency is, by Eqs. (19), (21), and (28),

$$f_c = \frac{1}{2\pi}\sqrt{\frac{K_v}{T_m}} > 0.356\left(\frac{\widetilde{a^2}\beta}{N}\right)^{1/4}. \tag{31}$$

Similarly, the peak amplification is

$$\left|\frac{\theta_O}{\theta_I}\right|_{\max} = \sqrt{K_vT_m} < 0.894\left(\frac{\widetilde{a^2}}{N\beta^3}\right)^{1/12}. \tag{32}$$

It should be noted that although $\widetilde{a^2}/N\beta^3$ is usually a very large number, its twelfth root is not large.

In the case of the radar automatic-tracking example in Secs. 6·10 and 6·12, we have $\widetilde{a^2} = 2620$ mils²/sec², $N = 0.636$ mil² sec, $\beta = 0.1$ sec⁻¹.

If

$$T_m < 0.4 \left(\frac{N}{\widetilde{a^2}\beta^3}\right)^{1/6} = 0.316 \qquad \text{sec} \tag{33a}$$

and

$$K_v = 2 \left(\frac{\widetilde{a^2}}{N}\right)^{1/3} = 32.1 \qquad \text{sec}^{-1}, \tag{33b}$$

then, by Eq. (20),

$$\left.\begin{aligned} \overline{\epsilon^2} &< 0.83(\widetilde{a^2}N^2)^{1/3} = 8.46 \qquad \text{mil}^2, \\ \sqrt{\overline{\epsilon^2}} &< 2.91 \qquad \text{mil}. \end{aligned}\right\} \tag{33c}$$

The cutoff frequency is

$$f_c > 0.356 \left(\frac{\widetilde{a^2}\beta}{N}\right)^{1/4} = 1.60 \qquad \text{cps}, \tag{33d}$$

and the peak amplification is

$$\left|\frac{\theta_O}{\theta_I}\right|_{\max} < 0.894 \left(\frac{\widetilde{a^2}}{N\beta^3}\right)^{1/12} = 3.18. \tag{33e}$$

It may be pointed out that in practice, T_m is frequently chosen smaller than is required by Eq. (21). This gives a smaller error and a smaller peak amplification. If in the previous example we choose

$$T_m = 0.1 \qquad \text{sec}, \tag{34}$$

we find that

$$\left.\begin{aligned} \sqrt{\overline{\epsilon^2}} &= 2.75 \qquad \text{mils}, \\ f_c &= 2.85 \qquad \text{cps}, \\ \left|\frac{\theta_O}{\theta_I}\right|_{\max} &= 1.79. \end{aligned}\right\} \tag{35}$$

8·4. Servo with Proportional Control, $T_m = 0$.—We have thus far been using the approximate formula of Eq. (13) for $\overline{\epsilon^2}$. If T_m is negligible, however, a better approximation to Eq. (12) is

$$\overline{\epsilon^2} = \frac{\widetilde{a^2}}{K_v} \frac{1}{K_v + \beta} + \frac{NK_v}{4}. \tag{36}$$

Assuming T_m to be negligible, we shall now study the effect of noise on the performance of the servomechanism. The relative magnitude of the noise can be expressed in terms of the noise-to-signal ratio $N/\widetilde{a^2}$. This ratio (in sec^3) is usually a very small number, and its dimensionless product by β^3 is a still smaller number. Hence it is convenient to introduce instead of the noise-to-signal ratio, the number [*cf.* Eq. (32)]

$$r = \left(\frac{N\beta^3}{\widetilde{a^2}}\right)^{1/12}. \tag{37}$$

Equation (36) then becomes

$$\frac{\overline{\epsilon^2}}{(\widetilde{a^2}N^2)^{1/3}} = \frac{1}{2y(2y + r^4)} + \frac{y}{2}. \tag{38}$$

Now if K_v and hence y are chosen so as to minimize $\overline{\epsilon^2}$, then

$$2\frac{d}{dy}\frac{\overline{\epsilon^2}}{(\widetilde{a^2}N^2)^{1/3}} = -\frac{4y + r^4}{y^2(2y + r^4)^2} + 1 = 0. \tag{39}$$

Therefore, for optimal performance

$$y^2(y + \tfrac{1}{2}r^4)^2 = y + \tfrac{1}{4}r^4. \tag{40}$$

Solving for y and substituting back in Eqs. (14) and (38), one obtains the best K_v and its corresponding $\overline{\epsilon_m^2}$ for each value of r.

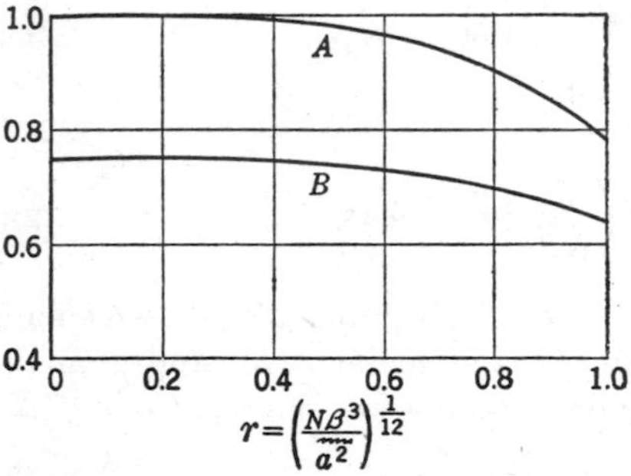

FIG. 8·3.—Best K_v and $\overline{\epsilon_m^2}$ of servo with proportional control and small motor time constant, plotted against noise-to-signal parameter r. Curve A, $(K_v/2)(N/\widetilde{a^2})^{1/3}$; Curve B, $\overline{\epsilon_m^2}/[(\widetilde{a^2}N^2)^{1/3}]$.

If r is small, we can solve Eq. (40) as a power series in r,

$$y = 1 - \tfrac{1}{4}r^4 + \tfrac{1}{24}r^8 - \tfrac{1}{768}r^{16} + \cdots. \tag{41}$$

Substituting back in Eq. (38), we get

$$\overline{\epsilon_m^2} = \tfrac{3}{4}(\widetilde{a^2}N^2)^{1/3}(1 - \tfrac{1}{6}r^4 + \tfrac{1}{48}r^8 - \tfrac{1}{2304}r^{16} + \cdots). \tag{42}$$

The optimal $(K_v/2)(N/\widetilde{a^2})^{1/3}$ and $\overline{\epsilon_m^2}/[(\widetilde{a^2}N^2)^{1/3}]$ are plotted against r in Fig. 8·3. It is seen that for small values of r, $\overline{\epsilon_m^2}$ is proportional to $(\widetilde{a^2}N^2)^{1/3}$ and the optimal K_v is proportional to $(\widetilde{a^2}/N)^{1/3}$.

TACHOMETER FEEDBACK CONTROL

8·5. Mean-square Error of Output.—By adding a tachometer-feedback loop (see Fig. 8·4) to the servo with proportional control, one can reduce still further the dependence of the mean-square error on the motor time constant T_m. One thereby makes possible an increase in K_v and a consequent decrease in the error for a constant-velocity input.

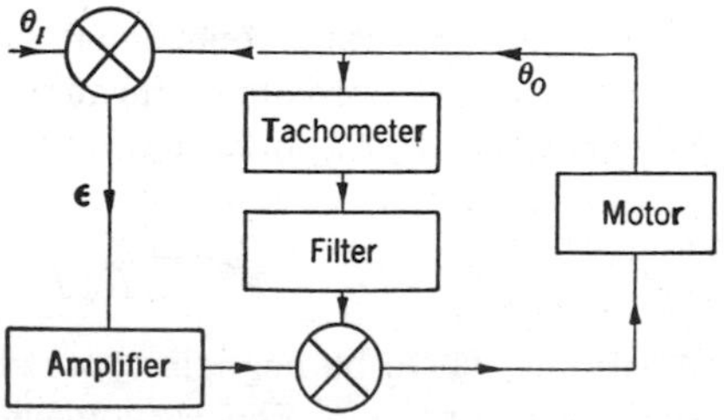

FIG. 8·4.—Servo with tachometer-feedback loop.

The equation of the servo with tachometer-feedback loop is

$$(T_mp + 1)p\theta_O = K_v(\theta_I + \theta_N - \theta_O) - A\frac{T_ap}{T_ap + 1}p\theta_O. \tag{43}$$

There are now three servo parameters—the velocity-error constant K_v, the tachometer-loop gain A, and the tachometer-filter time constant T_a—in addition to the limited parameter T_m.

Solving Eq. (43) for θ_O gives

$$\theta_O = \theta_I - \frac{(T_ap + 1)(T_mp + 1) + AT_ap}{K_v(T_ap + 1) + (T_ap + 1)(T_mp + 1)p + AT_ap^2}\, p\theta_I + \frac{K_v(T_ap + 1)}{K_v(T_ap + 1) + (T_ap + 1)(T_mp + 1)p + AT_ap^2}\, \theta_N. \qquad (44)$$

Since the spectral density of $p\theta_I$ is $(4\beta\widetilde{a^2})/(\omega^2 + \beta^2)$ [see Eq. (1)], the mean-square error in following the input is

$$\overline{\epsilon_I^2} = \frac{1}{2\pi}\int_0^\infty d\omega \frac{1 + [(T_a + T_m + AT_a)^2 - 2T_aT_m]\omega^2 + T_a^2T_m^2\omega^4}{|K_v + (K_vT_a + 1)j\omega - (T_a + T_m + AT_a)\omega^2 - T_aT_mj\omega^3|^2}\,\frac{4\beta\widetilde{a^2}}{\omega^2 + \beta^2}, \qquad (45)$$

which on integration becomes

$$\begin{aligned}\overline{\epsilon_I^2} = \frac{\widetilde{a^2}}{K_v}&[(K_vT_a + 1)(T_a + T_m + AT_a) - K_vT_aT_m]^{-1}\\ &\times [K_v + (K_vT_a + 1)\beta + (T_a + T_m + AT_a)\beta^2 + T_aT_m\beta^3]^{-1}\\ &\times \{(K_vT_a + 1)(T_a + T_m + AT_a) - K_vT_aT_m + (T_a + T_m + AT_a)^2\beta\\ &+ (T_a + T_m + AT_a)T_aT_m\beta^2 + K_v[(T_a + T_m + AT_a)^2 - 2T_aT_m]\\ &\times [(T_a + T_m + AT_a)\beta + T_aT_m\beta^2]\\ &+ K_vT_a^2T_m^2[K_v\beta + (K_vT_a + 1)\beta^2]\}. \qquad (46)\end{aligned}$$

The spectral density of the noise is $G_N(f) = N$ [see Eq. (2)]; the mean-square error due to noise is therefore

$$\overline{\epsilon_N^2} = \frac{1}{2\pi}\int_0^\infty d\omega \frac{K_v^2(1 + T_a^2\omega^2)}{|K_v + (K_vT_a + 1)j\omega - (T_a + T_m + AT_a)\omega^2 - T_aT_mj\omega^3|^2}\, N, \qquad (47)$$

which, when integrated and simplified, becomes

$$\overline{\epsilon_N^2} = \frac{NK_v}{4}\,\frac{1}{1 + \dfrac{AK_vT_a^2}{T_a + T_m + AT_a + K_vT_a^2}}. \qquad (48)$$

The mean-square error of the output is, of course,

$$\overline{\epsilon^2} = \overline{\epsilon_I^2} + \overline{\epsilon_N^2}. \qquad (49)$$

8·6. Ideal Case of Infinite Gain.—We shall see that if the tachometer-loop gain A is large enough, a servo with tachometer feedback can be made to have a smaller mean-square error than a proportional-control servo even if the former has a large T_m and the latter a small T_m.

With this end in view, let us take the limiting case where $K_v = CA$ and $A \to \infty$. In this limit, Eqs. (46) and (48) become

$$\overline{\epsilon_I^2} = \frac{\widetilde{a^2}\beta T_a}{C(C + CT_a\beta + T_a\beta^2)} \tag{50}$$

and

$$\overline{\epsilon_N^2} = \frac{N}{4}\left(\frac{1}{T_a} + C\right); \tag{51}$$

and hence

$$\overline{\epsilon^2} = \frac{\widetilde{a^2}\beta T_a}{C(C + CT_a\beta + T_a\beta^2)} + \frac{N}{4}\frac{1}{T_a} + \frac{N}{4}C. \tag{52}$$

It will be noted that in this limiting case $\overline{\epsilon^2}$ is independent of T_m.

We now choose the parameters C and T_a so as to minimize $\overline{\epsilon^2}$. Then

$$\frac{\partial\overline{\epsilon^2}}{\partial C} = -\frac{\widetilde{a^2}\beta T_a(2C + 2CT_a\beta + T_a\beta^2)}{C^2(C + CT_a\beta + T_a\beta^2)^2} + \frac{N}{4} = 0, \tag{53}$$

$$\frac{\partial\overline{\epsilon^2}}{\partial T_a} = \frac{\widetilde{a^2}\beta}{(C + CT_a\beta + T_a\beta^2)^2} - \frac{N}{4T_a^2} = 0. \tag{54}$$

Equations (53) and (54) may be solved for C and T_a as follows. Elimination of $\widetilde{a^2}$ between Eqs. (53) and (54) yields

$$C + CT_a\beta + T_a\beta^2 = \frac{(C^2 + \beta^2)T_a}{2}. \tag{55}$$

Substitution of this expression into Eq. (54) now gives

$$\frac{4\widetilde{a^2}\beta}{(C^2 + \beta^2)^2T_a^2} - \frac{N}{4T_a^2} = 0 \tag{56}$$

or

$$C^2 + \beta^2 = 4\left(\frac{\widetilde{a^2}\beta}{N}\right)^{1/2} = 4\beta^2r^{-6}, \tag{57}$$

where r is the parameter defined in Eq. (37). Solution for C yields

$$C = \beta\sqrt{4r^{-6} - 1}. \tag{58}$$

Equation (55) can now be solved for T_a,

$$T_a = \frac{2C}{C^2 - 2C\beta - \beta^2}, \tag{59}$$

or, by Eq. (58),

$$T_a = \frac{1}{\beta}\frac{\sqrt{4r^{-6} - 1}}{2r^{-6} - 1 - \sqrt{4r^{-6} - 1}}. \tag{60}$$

The above procedure is valid only if it leads to real positive finite values of the parameters. In particular, $\overline{\epsilon^2}$ is a minimum for finite T_a only if the denominator in Eq. (60) is positive, that is, only if

$$r < (2 - \sqrt{2})^{1/6} = 0.915. \tag{61}$$

If r satisfies this condition, both C and T_a will be real and positive.

Now, having found the optimal values of C and T_a in terms of the parameter r, we can substitute back in Eq. (52) to get the minimum value of $\overline{\epsilon^2}$. Combining Eqs. (52) and (54), we obtain

$$\begin{aligned} \overline{\epsilon_m^2} &= \frac{T_a}{C} \frac{N}{4T_a^2} (C + CT_a\beta + T_a\beta^2) + \frac{N}{4}\left(\frac{1}{T_a} + C\right) \\ &= \frac{N}{4CT_a} (2C + 2CT_a\beta + T_a\beta^2 - CT_a\beta + C^2T_a), \end{aligned} \tag{62}$$

which, together with Eq. (55), gives

$$\overline{\epsilon_m^2} = \frac{N}{4CT_a} (C^2T_a - CT_a\beta + C^2T_a) = \frac{N}{4} (2C - \beta). \tag{63}$$

If we now express C in terms of r, using Eq. (58), we get

$$\overline{\epsilon_m^2} = \frac{N\beta}{r^3}\left(\sqrt{1 - \frac{1}{4} r^6} - \frac{1}{4} r^3\right). \tag{64}$$

From the definition of r it fol' ws that

$$\frac{N\beta}{r^3} = (\widetilde{a^2}\beta N^3)^{1/4}. \tag{65}$$

Our final expression for $\overline{\epsilon_m^2}$ is then

$$\overline{\epsilon_m^2} = (\widetilde{a^2}\beta N^3)^{1/4} (\sqrt{1 - \tfrac{1}{4}r^6} - \tfrac{1}{4}r^3). \tag{66}$$

As we have already remarked, $\overline{\epsilon^2}$ and hence $\overline{\epsilon_m^2}$ are independent of T_m when there is high-gain tachometer feedback in addition to proportional control. In the case of a servo with proportional control only, the minimum mean-square error is dependent on T_m; its smallest value, when $T_m \to 0$, is given by Eq. (42). The ratio of the minimum mean-square error of a servo with tachometer loop and arbitrary T_m (but infinite A and K_v) to the minimum mean-square error of a servo with proportional control and negligible T_m is

$$\frac{\overline{\epsilon_m^2} \text{ with tachometer}}{\overline{\epsilon_m^2} \text{ without tachometer}} = \frac{4}{3} r \frac{\sqrt{1 - \frac{1}{4}r^6} - \frac{1}{4}r^3}{1 - \frac{1}{6}r^4 + \frac{1}{48}r^8 - \frac{1}{2304}r^{16} + \cdots +}. \tag{67}$$

This ratio is shown plotted against r in Fig. 8·5. It is seen that for all reasonable values of r the tachometer-feedback servo performs better than the proportional-control servo even if in the latter case $T_m = 0$.

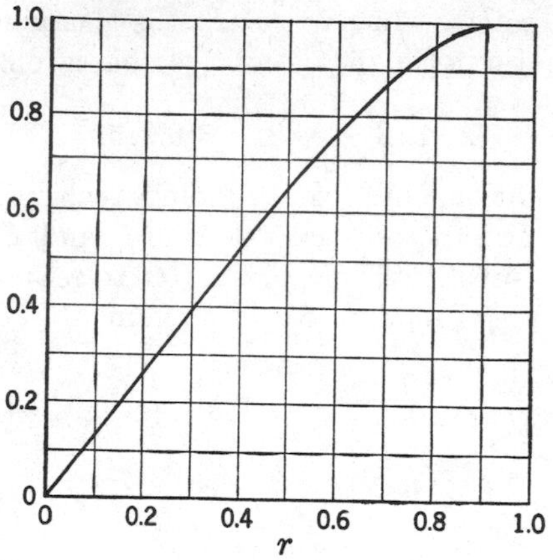

FIG. 8·5.—Ratio of minimum mean-square errors of servos with tachometer loop to minimum mean-square error of servo without tachometer loop plotted against $r = (N\beta^3/\widetilde{a^2})^{1/12}$.

8·7. Best Control Parameters for Finite Amplifications.—In actual practice, A and K_v cannot be made arbitrarily large; the preceding treatment is therefore an analysis of a somewhat idealized situation. We shall now modify this analysis and seek an approximation to the optimal values of the parameters K_v and T_a for the case of a finite A.

We first make some approximations to Eqs. (46) and (48). We assume that K_v is large compared with each of the following: $1/T_a$, $1/T_m$, T_m/T_a^2, β, $\beta^2 T_m$, βA. The last assumption is justified because (1) if A is large and r is less than $\frac{1}{2}$, then by Eq. (58), $K_v/\beta A \approx 2/r^3$, which is large relative to unity, whereas (2) if A is small it is obvious that $K_v \gg \beta A$. Using these approximations, Eqs. (46) and (48) become

$$\left.\begin{aligned} \overline{\epsilon_I^2} &\approx \frac{\widetilde{a^2}}{K_v^2}\left[1 + \beta A^2 T_a \frac{1 + \dfrac{1}{A}\left(2 + 3\dfrac{T_m}{T_a} + \beta T_m\right)}{1 + \beta T_a} + \frac{K_v \beta T_m^2}{1 + A}\right], \\ \overline{\epsilon_N^2} &\approx \frac{N}{4(1 + A)}\left(K_v + \frac{A}{T_a}\right). \end{aligned}\right\} \tag{68}$$

We now make the further assumption that β is so small that $\beta T_a \ll 1$ and $\beta T_m \ll 1$. (In the examples below, these relations and approximations are valid; if β is not small, the formulas below must be used with caution.) The formula for the mean-square error then becomes

$$\begin{aligned} \overline{\epsilon^2} \approx \frac{\widetilde{a^2}}{K_v^2}\left(1 + 3\beta A T_m + \beta A(2 + A)T_a + \frac{K_v \beta T_m^2}{1 + A}\right) \\ + \frac{N}{4(1 + A)}\left(K_v + \frac{A}{T_a}\right). \end{aligned} \tag{69}$$

Given A and T_m, we now choose K_v and T_a so as to minimize $\overline{\epsilon^2}$. Then

$$\frac{\partial\overline{\epsilon^2}}{\partial K_v} = -\frac{\widetilde{a^2}}{K_v^3}\left[2 + 6\beta A T_m + 2\beta A(2 + A)T_a + \frac{K_v\beta T_m^2}{1 + A}\right] + \frac{N}{4(1 + A)} = 0, \quad (70a)$$

$$\frac{\partial\overline{\epsilon^2}}{\partial T_a} = \frac{\widetilde{a^2}\beta A(2 + A)}{K_v^2} - \frac{NA}{4(1 + A)T_a^2} = 0. \quad (70b)$$

We solve Eqs. (70) for K_v and T_a as follows. Solution of Eq. (70b) for K_v^2 gives

$$K_v^2 = 4\frac{\widetilde{a^2}}{N\beta^3}\beta^4(1 + A)(2 + A)T_a^2. \quad (71)$$

Elimination of $\widetilde{a^2}$ by means of Eq. (37) yields K_v in terms of T_a,

$$K_v = \frac{2\sqrt{(1 + A)(2 + A)}\,\beta^2 T_a}{r^6}. \quad (72)$$

Also, substitution of Eq. (70b) into Eq. (70a) gives

$$1 + 3\beta A T_m + \beta A(2 + A)T_a + \frac{1}{2}\frac{K_v\beta T_m^2}{1 + A} = \frac{1}{2}K_v\beta(2 + A)T_a^2. \quad (73)$$

If we now make use of Eq. (72), we obtain

$$1 + 3\beta A T_m + \beta A(2 + A)T_a + \frac{\sqrt{2 + A}\,\beta^3 T_a T_m^2}{\sqrt{1 + A}\,r^6} = \frac{(2 + A)^{3/2}\sqrt{1 + A}\,\beta^3 T_a^3}{r^6}. \quad (74)$$

On substitution for T_m of the dimensionless parameter z, defined by

$$z^2 = \frac{1}{A\sqrt{2 + A}\sqrt{1 + A}}\frac{\beta^2 T_m^2}{r^6}, \quad (75)$$

this becomes

$$1 + 3\beta A T_m + \beta A(2 + A)T_a(1 + z^2) = \frac{(2 + A)^{3/2}\sqrt{1 + A}\,\beta^3 T_a^3}{r^6}. \quad (76)$$

In order to simplify this equation we introduce another parameter,

$$x = \left[\frac{(1 + A)(2 + A)}{A^2}\right]^{1/4}\frac{\beta T_a}{r^3(1 + z^2)^{1/2}}; \quad (77)$$

eliminating T_a, we obtain

$$1 + 3\beta A T_m + \left[\frac{A^6(2 + A)^3}{1 + A}\right]^{1/4} r^3(1 + z^2)^{3/2}x = \left[\frac{A^6(2 + A)^3}{1 + A}\right]^{1/4} r^3(1 + z^2)^{3/2}x^3, \quad (78a)$$

which may also be written as

$$x^3 - x = (1 + 3\beta A T_m) \left[\frac{1 + A}{A^6(2 + A)^3}\right]^{1/4} \frac{1}{r^3(1 + z^2)^{3/2}}. \tag{78b}$$

This equation can now be solved for x. Finally, solving Eqs. (72) and (77) for K_v and T_a in terms of x, we have

$$K_v = \frac{2\beta[A^2(1 + A)(2 + A)]^{1/4}(1 + z^2)^{1/2}x}{r^3}, \tag{79}$$

$$T_a = \left[\frac{A^2}{(1 + A)(2 + A)}\right]^{1/4} \frac{r^3(1 + z^2)^{1/2}x}{\beta}. \tag{80}$$

Equations (78b), (79), and (80) give us the optimal values of K_v and T_a for each set of values of A, T_m, and the input parameters.

We now may substitute into Eq. (69) to find the minimum value of $\overline{\epsilon^2}$. First, use of Eq. (70b) gives

$$\overline{\epsilon_m^2} = \frac{N}{4\beta(2 + A)(1 + A)T_a^2}\left(1 + 3\beta A T_m + \beta A(2 + A)T_a + \frac{K_v \beta T_m^2}{1 + A}\right) + \frac{N}{4(1 + A)}\left(K_v + \frac{A}{T_a}\right).$$

Use of Eq. (73) then gives

$$\overline{\epsilon_m^2} = \frac{N}{4(1 + A)} \left\{\frac{3}{2}K_v + \frac{A}{T_a}\left[1 + \frac{K_v T_m^2}{2A(1 + A)(2 + A)T_a}\right]\right\}. \tag{81}$$

But, by Eq. (72),

$$\frac{K_v T_m^2}{2A(1 + A)(2 + A)T_a} = \frac{T_m^2}{2A(1 + A)(2 + A)} \frac{2(1 + A)^{1/2}(2 + A)^{1/2}\beta^2}{r^6}, \tag{82}$$

and hence, by Eq. (75),

$$\frac{K_v T_m^2}{2A(1 + A)(2 + A)T_a} = z^2. \tag{83}$$

Therefore

$$\overline{\epsilon_m^2} = \frac{N}{4(1 + A)}\left[\frac{3}{2}K_v + \frac{A}{T_a}(1 + z^2)\right].$$

Substituting for K_v and T_a from Eqs. (79) and (80), we have

$$\overline{\epsilon_m^2} = \frac{1}{4}\frac{N\beta}{r^3}\left[\frac{A^2(2 + A)}{(1 + A)^3}\right]^{1/4}(1 + z^2)^{1/2}\left(3x + \frac{1}{x}\right). \tag{84}$$

Finally, by Eq. (65),

$$\frac{\overline{\epsilon_m^2}}{(\widetilde{a^2}\beta N^3)^{1/4}} = \frac{1}{4}\left[\frac{A^2(2 + A)}{(1 + A)^3}\right]^{1/4}(1 + z^2)^{1/2}\left(3x + \frac{1}{x}\right). \tag{85}$$

In Fig. 8·6, $\overline{\epsilon_m^2}$ is plotted against $A/(10 + A)$ for $T_m = z = 0$ and for three different values of r: $r = 0.215$, 0.368, and 0.585, or $r^3 = 0.01$, 0.05, and 0.20. It can be seen that for this range of values of r, if

$$A > \frac{1}{r^2}, \tag{86}$$

then the mean-square error is less than 5 per cent above its limiting value when $A \to \infty$.

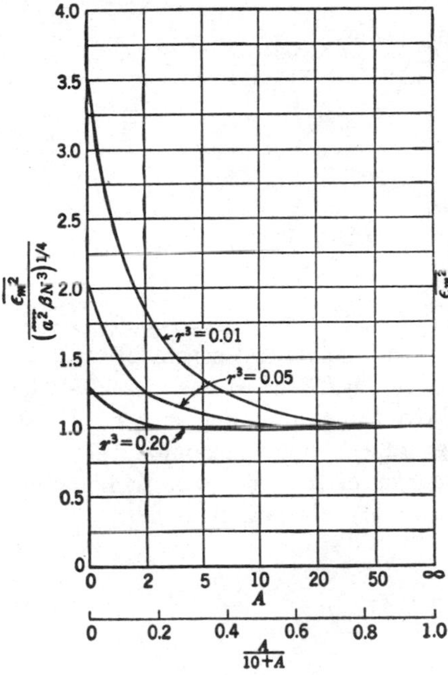

FIG. 8·6.

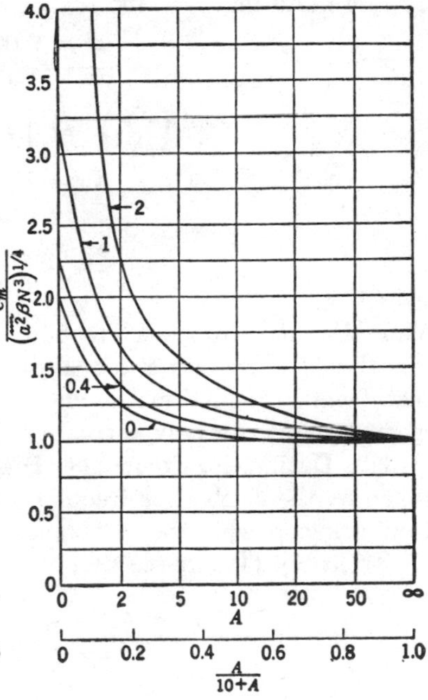

FIG. 8·7.

FIG. 8·6.—Minimum mean-square error of servo with tachometer-feedback loop as a function of tachometer-loop gain A, when $T_m = 0$.

FIG. 8·7.—Minimum mean-square error of servo with tachometer-feedback loop as a function of tachometer-loop gain A, when $r^3 = 0.05$. Numbers on curves are values of $T_m(\widetilde{a^2}\beta^2/N)^{1/6}$.

Figure 8·7 shows how the minimum ϵ^2 depends on T_m. The curves are plotted for four different values of T_m when $r^3 = 0.05$, that is, when $r = 0.368$. The dependence on T_m becomes important only for values of A less than 2.

Example.—We return to the example of Sec. 8·3 and assume that

$$\left.\begin{aligned} \widetilde{a^2} &= 2620 && \text{mil}^2\ \text{sec}^{-2}, \\ N &= 0.636 && \text{mil}^2\ \text{sec}, \\ \beta &= 0.1 && \text{sec}^{-1}, \\ T_m &= 0.316 && \text{sec}. \end{aligned}\right\} \tag{87}$$

Then

$$\left.\begin{aligned} r &= 0.281, \\ \frac{1}{r^2} &= 12.7. \end{aligned}\right\} \tag{88}$$

Taking $A > 1/r^2$ [see Eq. (86)], we choose

$$A = 14. \tag{89}$$

Then we find that

$$\left.\begin{aligned} z^2 &= 0.009, \\ x &= 1.187, \\ T_m\left(\frac{\widetilde{a^2}\beta}{N}\right)^{1/6} &= 0.4, \\ K_v &= 158 \quad \text{sec}^{-1}, \\ T_a &= 0.252 \quad \text{sec}, \\ \overline{\epsilon_m^2} &= 3.11 \quad \text{mils}^2, \\ \sqrt{\overline{\epsilon_m^2}} &= 1.76 \quad \text{mils}. \end{aligned}\right\} \tag{90}$$

Thus the rms error for the tachometer-feedback-loop servo is 35 per cent less than the rms error for the proportional-control servo. It will be seen from Fig. 8·7 that the choice of $T_m = 0.316$ sec has increased the mean-square error only negligibly above the minimum given by $T_m = 0$.

8·8. Decibel–log-frequency Diagram.—We now examine the form taken by the decibel–log-frequency curve for the servo with tachometer-feedback loop, when the best choice is made of the parameters.

From Eq. (43) we see that

$$\theta_O = \frac{K_v}{(T_m p + 1)p + A \dfrac{T_a p}{T_a p + 1} p}\, \epsilon. \tag{91}$$

This may also be written as

$$\frac{\theta_O}{\epsilon} = \frac{K_v(T_a j\omega + 1)}{-A T_a \omega^2} \, \frac{\dfrac{A T_a j\omega}{(T_m j\omega + 1)(T_a j\omega + 1)}}{1 + \dfrac{A T_a j\omega}{(T_m j\omega + 1)(T_a j\omega + 1)}}. \tag{92}$$

Now

$$\left.\begin{aligned} \frac{A T_a j\omega}{(T_m j\omega + 1)(T_a j\omega + 1)} &\approx A T_a j\omega, \qquad \text{if } \omega \text{ is small}, \\ &\approx \frac{A}{T_m j\omega}, \qquad \text{if } \omega \text{ is large}. \end{aligned}\right\} \tag{93}$$

Therefore, if A is large, $A T_a j\omega/[(T_m j\omega + 1)(T_a j\omega + 1)]$ is the dominant term in the denominator of Eq. (92) provided that $1/A T_a < \omega < A/T_m$. Thus, if A is large,

$$\frac{\theta_O}{\epsilon} \approx -j\frac{K_v}{\omega}, \qquad \text{if } \omega < \frac{1}{AT_a}, \tag{94a}$$

$$\approx -\frac{K_v}{AT_a\omega^2}, \qquad \text{if } \frac{1}{AT_a} < \omega < \frac{1}{T_a}, \tag{94b}$$

$$\approx -\frac{jK_v}{A\omega}, \qquad \text{if } \frac{1}{T_a} < \omega < \frac{A}{T_m}, \tag{94c}$$

$$\approx -\frac{K_v}{T_m\omega^2}, \qquad \text{if } \omega > \frac{A}{T_m}. \tag{94d}$$

The central segments of the segmented approximate decibel–log-frequency diagram meet at a point where $\omega = 1/T_a$ and $|\theta_O/\epsilon| \approx (K_vT_a)/A$. This completes the general characterization to the transfer locus, it being assumed only that A is large. We have now to consider the effect of the best choice of constants, according to the theory developed above.

If A is sufficiently large, it follows from Eq. (75) that $z \approx 0$ and from Eq. (78b) that $x \approx 1$. By Eqs. (79) and (80), the best choice of constants makes

$$\frac{K_vT_a}{A} = 2(1 + z^2)x^2 \approx 2. \tag{95}$$

Thus one should have $|\theta_O/\epsilon| \approx 2$ where the central segments of the decibel–log-frequency diagram intersect; in other words, the velocity-error constant K_v should be so chosen that the intersection of the segments of the decibel–log-frequency diagram at $\omega = 1/T_a$ will be about 6 db above feedback cutoff. The loop gain $|\theta_O/\epsilon|$ becomes zero db in the 6-db-per-octave segment, 6 db from the above-mentioned intersection; by Eq. (94c) this occurs for

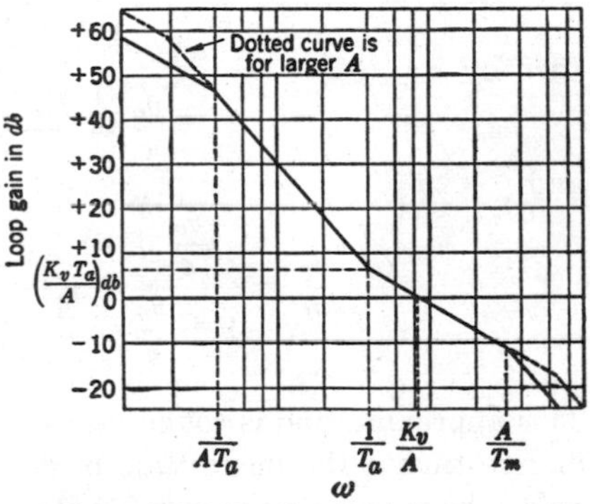

FIG. 8·8.—Decibel–log-frequency diagram for servo with tachometer-feedback loop.

$$\omega_c \approx \frac{K_v}{A}, \tag{96}$$

$$f_c \approx \frac{1}{2\pi}\frac{K_v}{A} \approx \frac{1}{\pi T_a}. \tag{97}$$

The theory, as illustrated by Fig. 8·7, has shown that the exact value of A does not much matter if it is only great enough. Change in A will not materially change the central part of the decibel–log-frequency diagram but only the length of the central segments; all that is required is that these shall be sufficiently long. [From the steady-state point of view it is clear that the length of the $(1/T_a, A/T_m)$-segment controls the stability of the servo.] The best filter time constant T_a is determined by Eq. (80) or, if A is large enough, by

$$T_a \approx \frac{r^3}{\beta}. \tag{98}$$

This theoretically derived decibel–log-frequency diagram is similar to that commonly believed desirable, except that the velocity-error constant is smaller than might have been expected; usually K_v is assumed to be so chosen that 0 db is at or below the *middle* of the 6-db-per-octave middle segment. In practice, however, the amplifier gain is frequently turned down considerably below that assumed in the steady-state design of the servo. Thus we can claim substantial agreement with the usual design practice, if not with its theory.

The approximate peak amplification is found as follows: If A is sufficiently large and if

$$\frac{1}{AT_a} < \omega < \frac{A}{T_m}, \tag{99}$$

then by Eq. (92)

$$\frac{\theta_O}{\epsilon} \approx \frac{K_v(T_a j\omega + 1)}{-AT_a\omega^2} \tag{100}$$

and

$$\frac{\theta_O}{\theta_I} = \frac{\dfrac{\theta_O}{\epsilon}}{1 + \dfrac{\theta_O}{\epsilon}} \approx \frac{-K_v(T_a j\omega + 1)}{AT_a\omega^2 - K_v(T_a j\omega + 1)}. \tag{101}$$

This approximation is rough unless A is very large; otherwise it tends to underestimate the magnitude of θ_O/θ_I. However, if we so approximate θ_O/θ_I, the square of the amplification is

$$\left|\frac{\theta_O}{\theta_I}\right|^2 = \frac{K_v^2(T_a^2\omega^2 + 1)}{A^2T_a^2\omega^4 - 2K_vAT_a\omega^2 + K_v^2 + K_v^2T_a^2\omega^2}. \tag{102}$$

To simplify the computation we substitute the dimensionless parameters

$$\left.\begin{aligned} q &= \frac{K_vT_a}{A}, \\ x &= T_a^2\omega^2, \end{aligned}\right\} \tag{103}$$

and obtain

$$\left|\frac{\theta_O}{\theta_I}\right|^2 = q^2\frac{1 + x}{x^2 - 2qx + q^2 + q^2x}. \tag{104}$$

The peak amplification occurs for the value of x at which $|\theta_O/\theta_I|^2$ is maximum—the value of x for which

$$q^2\left|\frac{\theta_I}{\theta_O}\right|^2 = \frac{x^2 - 2qx}{1 + x} + q^2 \tag{105}$$

is a minimum. This value of x is determined by

$$\frac{d}{dx}\left(\frac{x^2 - 2qx}{1 + x} + q^2\right) = \frac{(1 + x)(2x - 2q) - (x^2 - 2qx)}{(1 + x)^2} = 0 \quad (106a)$$

or

$$x^2 + 2x - 2q = 0; \quad (106b)$$

solving this, we obtain

$$x = -1 + \sqrt{1 + 2q} \quad (107a)$$

or

$$\omega^2 = \frac{1}{T_a^2}\left(\sqrt{1 + 2\frac{K_v T_a}{A}} - 1\right). \quad (107b)$$

Substituting Eq. (107*a*) back into Eq. (104), we find that the peak amplification is

$$\left|\frac{\theta_O}{\theta_I}\right|_{\max} = \sqrt{\frac{q^2\sqrt{1 + 2q}}{2 + 4q + (q^2 - 2q - 2)\sqrt{1 + 2q}}}. \quad (108)$$

In Fig. 8·9 the peak amplification is shown plotted against q. This graph is to be used with caution, since, as mentioned above, for reasonable values of A the peak amplification is underestimated. If A is very large, $q \approx 2$ [see Eq. (95)]; the peak amplification is then

$$\left|\frac{\theta_O}{\theta_I}\right|_{\max} \approx 1.27. \quad (109)$$

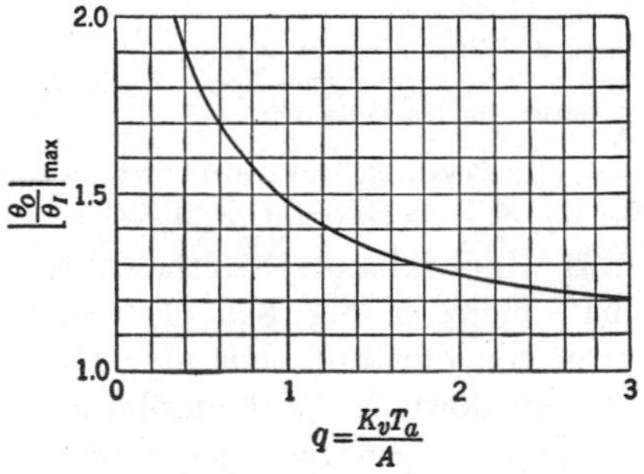

FIG. 8·9.—Peak amplification of servo with tachometer-feedback loop when tachometer-loop gain is large.

8·9. Nyquist Diagram.—The form of the Nyquist diagram of the servo with tachometer-feedback loop can be inferred from the form of the decibel–log-frequency diagram. However, since the Nyquist diagram is much used in servo design, it may be worth while to give an example of a Nyquist diagram of a servo designed in accordance with the rms-error criterion.

Let us assume the same input signal as in the example of Sec. 8·3 or 6·12 and assume that the noise arises only from a potentiometer wound with $\frac{2}{3}$ turn per mil (see Sec. 6·13). The spectral density of the noise is then fairly flat out to 3 cps; we assume that it can be fairly represented by $G_N(f) = 0.05$ mil² sec [see Eq. (6·182)]. We choose then

$$\left.\begin{aligned} \widetilde{a^2} &= 2620 \quad \text{mils}^2/\text{sec}^2, \\ N &= 0.05 \quad \text{mil}^2\ \text{sec}, \\ \beta &= 0.1 \quad \text{sec}^{-1}, \end{aligned}\right\} \quad (110)$$

and hence

$$r = 0.227. \tag{111}$$

If A were zero, we should wish to take $T_m < 0.4r^{-2}$ [Eq. (21)]—in this case $T_m < 0.207$. Since A is not to be taken as zero, we choose

$$T_m = 0.3 \quad \text{sec.} \tag{112}$$

Now

$$\frac{1}{r^2} = 19.4, \tag{113}$$

and we wish to choose A enough larger than this to allow for the effect of the larger T_m. We therefore take

$$A = 25. \tag{114}$$

Then

$$\left.\begin{aligned} z^2 &= 0.009, \\ x &= 1.162, \\ q &= 2.72, \\ K_v &= 511 \quad \text{sec}^{-1}, \\ T_a &= 0.133 \quad \text{sec}, \\ \sqrt{\overline{\epsilon_m^2}} &= 0.68 \quad \text{mil}, \\ f_c &= 3.13 \quad \text{cps}. \end{aligned}\right\} \tag{115}$$

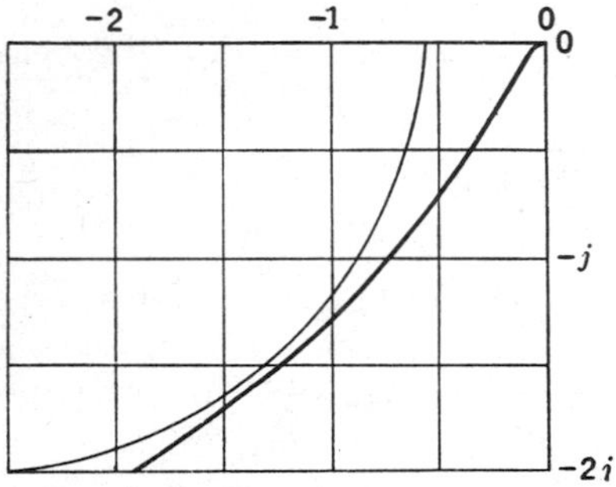

FIG. 8·10.—Nyquist diagram of servo with tachometer-feedback loop. The circle is drawn for $|\theta_O/\theta_I| = 1.28$.

The Nyquist diagram for this servo is shown in Fig. 8·10. The circle in Fig. 8·10 is the plot of $|\theta_O/\theta_I| = 1.28$. The peak amplification is nearly 1.28, which is larger than the value 1.22 that can be read from the approximate curve of Fig. 8·9. It is noteworthy that doubling the velocity-error constant and thus magnifying this Nyquist plot in the ratio 2/1 will cut down the peak amplification and thus improve stability.

Thus we see again (*cf.* Sec. 8·8) that the rms-error criterion calls for a lower gain than a naive examination of the Nyquist diagram would indicate. In actual practice a servo to be used in the presence of potentiometer noise is designed with the help of a Nyquist diagram, and the gain is thereafter arbitrarily reduced. Our theory is thus in accord with existing practice.

MANUAL TRACKING

8·10. Introduction.—In manual tracking the human operator can be considered as part of a servo loop, in which he performs the functions of a power element and a servomotor (Fig. 8·11). The operator observes the misalignment between the telescope and the target and turns a handwheel in the direction that tends to reduce this misalignment. The handwheel drives the tracking unit, which, in turn, positions the telescope, thus closing the feedback loop.

In the simplest type of manual-tracking system the human operator is the only power source in the closed loop. In more complex systems, where torque amplification requires the use of a driving motor, the human operator is a secondary servomotor. Limitations on the speed and torque available apply to both the power motor and the human operator; in addition, the performance of the human operator is governed by conditions of fatigue and mental and physical comfort. It is characteristic of the human operator that there is a time lag between the instant when an error is observed and the instant when corrective action on the part of the operator is started.

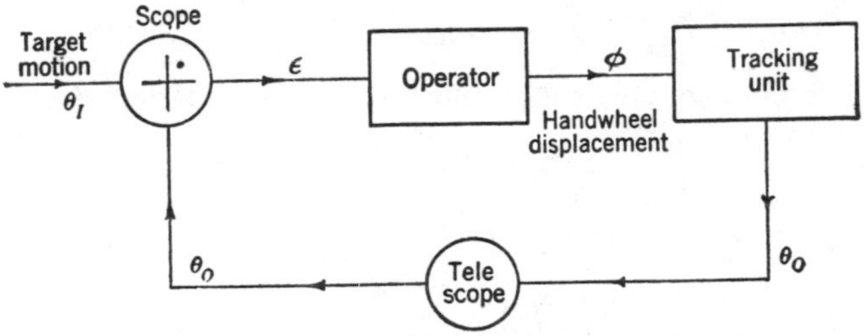

FIG. 8·11.—Manual-tracking loop.

As in any servo system, in order to obtain good performance the loop must have high gain and stability. The equalization is achieved by the judicious choice of the available parameters: the handwheel ratio, the optical magnification, and the tracking time constants. The present chapter includes a theoretical discussion of a tracking system based on the assumption that the human operator behaves like a linear mechanism. The rms-error criterion is applied to obtain the best tracking time constant. The theoretical results compare favorably with those found by experiment. The entire discussion is limited to an aided-tracking system with a handwheel input.

8·11. The Aided-tracking Unit.—Aided tracking is a combination of displacement and rate tracking. In pure displacement tracking the operator has a direct connection, either mechanically or electrically, with the controlled member. In tracking a target moving at constant angular rate, the operator must turn his handwheel at a constant rate. If he is lagging the target, he will turn faster until the error is corrected; if he is leading the target, he will turn more slowly.

In pure rate tracking it is the speed of the output that is determined by the position of the input handwheel; in tracking a target moving at a constant rate the handwheel need not be turned after the proper adjustment has been made.

When these two types of tracking are combined, an error in rate and the resulting displacement error are corrected simultaneously; a change in the handwheel position changes the rate of motion of the output at the same time that the displacement error is corrected. This is aided tracking.

A basic design for the aided-tracking unit is shown in Fig. 8·12. The output of the differential θ_O is a linear combination of the handwheel displacement ϕ and the displacement of the variable-speed-drive output Ω;

$$\theta_O = K_1\phi + K_2\Omega, \tag{116}$$

where K_1 and K_2 are gear ratios. The speed of the variable-speed drive is proportional to the handwheel displacement;

$$\phi = K_3\Omega'. \tag{117}$$

The two foregoing equations combine to give the equation of the aided-tracking unit;

$$\theta_O' = K_1\left(\phi' + \frac{1}{T_a}\phi\right), \tag{118}$$

where

$$T_a = \frac{K_1K_3}{K_2} \tag{119}$$

is the aided-tracking time constant. The aided-tracking time constant has the following physical interpretation: If a given change in the position of the handwheel results in changes in position and velocity of the output by $\Delta\theta_O$ and $\Delta\theta_O'$, respectively, then

$$T_a = \frac{\Delta\theta_O}{\Delta\theta_O'}. \tag{120}$$

In the aided-tracking unit shown in Fig. 8·12, the operator's handwheel is connected through gearing directly to the load, as well as to the movable member of the variable-speed drive. Such an arrangement is satisfactory only when the speed and torque requirements at the load can be met without the application of high torques at the handwheel and it is mechanically convenient to gear directly from the handwheel input to the load. Frequently, however, the operator's position is remote from the load to be controlled, or the output torque required is high; in either case, some form of electrical power drive must be used. A tracking unit suitable for this purpose is shown in Fig. 8·13.

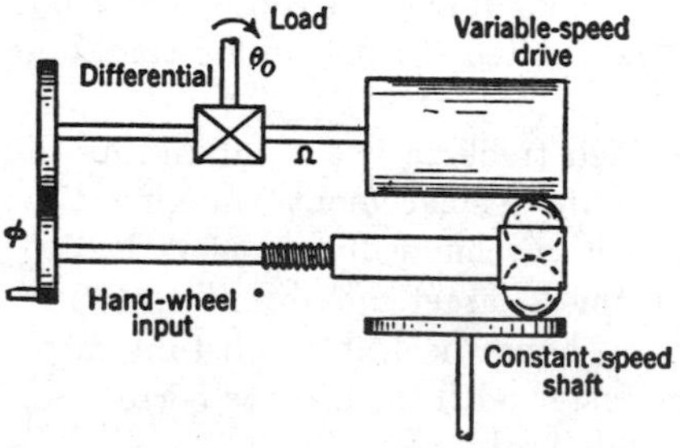

FIG. 8·12.—Basic mechanical design of an aided-tracking unit.

There are several common types of manual-tracking controls, (1) a handwheel, (2) a handle bar or some modification of a handle bar, (3) a joy stick. The choice of input control depends largely on the type of tracking to be performed, that is, whether it is tracking in one or two coordinates and whether the tracking is done by one or more operators. The choice depends also on whether the operator is in motion or is stationary, on whether he can use one or both hands for tracking, and on the space available for the operator and the tracking controls.

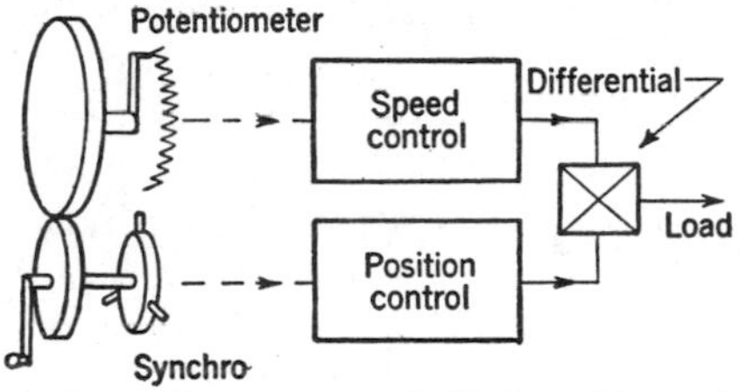

FIG. 8·13.—Remote-control aided-tracking unit.

If the operator is seated at a console and tracks in only one coordinate, the handwheel type of input seems to be preferred. The relationship between handwheel speed and output should be such that the operator is not required to turn much more slowly than 10 rpm nor much faster than 200 rpm. The handwheel should have sufficient inertia and be large enough to permit smoothness in turning but should be as free of frictional drag as possible to prevent tiring of the operator by long periods of tracking.

The time required for an error in tracking to become perceptible, if the tracking is done through a telescope, can be reduced by increasing the magnifying power of the telescope. The optical magnification that can be used is limited, however, by the size of field. If the field of view is too small, it is very difficult to get on target; in addition, the apparent velocity of the target in the field of view is so great as to make tracking arduous.

8·12. Application of the Rms-error Criterion in Determining the Best Aided-tracking Time Constant.—It will be the purpose of the present section[1] to give a quantitative treatment of the aided-tracking system with handwheel control. We shall determine the values of the aided-tracking time constant for which the system is stable, as well as the best value in the rms sense.

For the purpose of this investigation it is assumed that the human operator behaves like a linear mechanism. More precisely, it is thought reasonable (on the basis of admittedly crude experiments) to assume that

[1] Section 8·12 is a revision of a paper by R. S. Phillips entitled "Aided Tracking, Part II," which was published as RL Report No. 453, Nov. 3, 1943.

at all times the operator turns the handwheel at a rate proportional to the magnitude of the tracking error. It is well known that there is a time lag between the stimulus and the operator's reaction. In fact, it seems to be reasonable to assume that at any time t he turns the handwheel at a rate proportional to the tracking error which existed at the time $(t - L)$, where L is the magnitude of the time lag. The rate of turning can then be expressed as $\phi'(t) = \nu_1\epsilon(t - L)$. A reasonable value for the time delay L was found to be 0.5 sec.

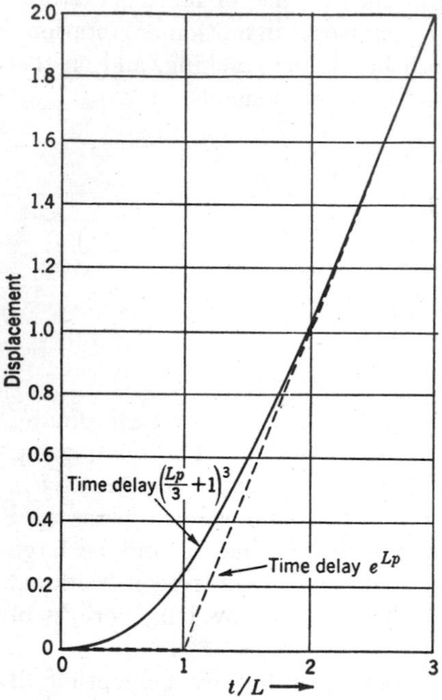

FIG. 8·14.—Delayed response to a unit-step function ϵ-input.

An experienced operator might also anticipate the error by taking into account the rate of change of error. This would add a derivative term to the above equation, which then becomes

$$\phi'(t) = \nu_1\epsilon(t - L) + \nu_2\epsilon'(t - L), \qquad (121)$$

where ν_1 is the proportional-control constant in $(\text{sec})^{-1}$ and ν_2 is the derivative-control constant (dimensionless). The equivalent expression for $\phi'(t)$ in the Laplace-transform terminology[1] is

$$p\phi = \frac{\nu_1\epsilon + \nu_2 p\epsilon}{e^{Lp}}. \qquad (122)$$

For mathematical convenience, the term e^{Lp} has been replaced by the expression $[(Lp/3) + 1]^3$. An idea of the goodness of this approximation can be gained from Fig. 8·14, where there is plotted the response of an operator with $\nu_2 = 0$ to a unit-step function ϵ-input, for the two conditions of time lag e^{Lp} and $[(Lp/3) + 1]^3$. The full curve gives the response for a reaction lag of the form $[(Lp/3 + 1]^3$; this is

$$y(t) = \frac{t}{L} - 1 + e^{-3t/L}\left[1 + 2\frac{t}{L} + \frac{3}{2}\left(\frac{t}{L}\right)^2\right]. \qquad (123)$$

The dashed curve illustrates the type of response to be expected on the assumption that the operator does nothing until a time L after his stimulus and then turns at a rate proportional to the error.

[1] See Chap. 2 of this volume.

The equation of the aided-tracking unit [Eq. (118)] can be rewritten as

$$p\theta_O = K_1\left(p + \frac{1}{T_a}\right)\phi. \tag{124}$$

The approximation to Eq. (122) that we shall use is

$$\left(\frac{Lp}{3} + 1\right)^3 p\phi = (\nu_1 + \nu_2 p)\epsilon. \tag{125}$$

Combining Eqs. (124) and (125) then gives

$$\left(\frac{Lp}{3} + 1\right)^3 p^2\theta_O = \left[\nu_2 p^2 + \left(\nu_1 + \frac{\nu_2}{T_a}\right) p + \frac{\nu_1}{T_a}\right]\epsilon. \tag{126}$$

Here we have replaced $K_1\nu_1$ by ν_1 and $K_1\nu_2$ by ν_2. This does not restrict the generality in any way, since we can only obtain conditions on the ratio ν_1/ν_2 by a linear type of theory. Finally, making use of the relation $\theta_O = \theta_I - \epsilon$, we obtain an equation relating the error and the input,

$$\left[\left(\frac{Lp}{3} + 1\right)^3 p^2 + \nu_2 p^2 + \left(\nu_1 + \frac{\nu_2}{T_a}\right)p + \frac{\nu_1}{T_a}\right]\epsilon = \left(\frac{Lp}{3} + 1\right)^3 p^2\theta_I. \tag{127}$$

The above chain of physical considerations has thus brought us to the aided-tracking equation. There remains the problem of determining the best value of the tracking constant T_a and the operator parameters (ν_1,ν_2). In order to accomplish this, the rms error will first be computed and then minimized; this procedure follows the method developed in Chap. 7.

The input θ_I to be assumed is one of constant velocity over a sequence of intervals, with abrupt changes in velocity at the end of each interval. These changes are all independent, because in aided tracking it is the change in velocity, and not the angular positions, that is significant. Let $x(t)$ be a unit-ramp function,

$$\left.\begin{aligned} x(t) &= 0, \qquad (t \leqq 0), \\ x(t) &= t, \qquad (t > 0), \end{aligned}\right\} \tag{128}$$

and let the a_n be independent random variables with zero means. Then θ_I is defined as

$$\theta_I = \sum_n a_n x(t - t_n), \tag{129}$$

where the t_n are distributed in some random fashion with density σ. A sample of θ_I is shown in Fig. 8·15. This type of input was chosen because it represents, at least roughly, the typical input in an aided-tracking system, in which the operator corrects mainly for changes in the angular velocity of the target.

Although θ_I is not a stationary random process, its second derivative is a sequence of independent delta functions of the type described in Sec. 6·11. The spectral density of the second derivative has the value N for all frequencies, where

$$N = \widetilde{a^2}2\sigma. \tag{130}$$

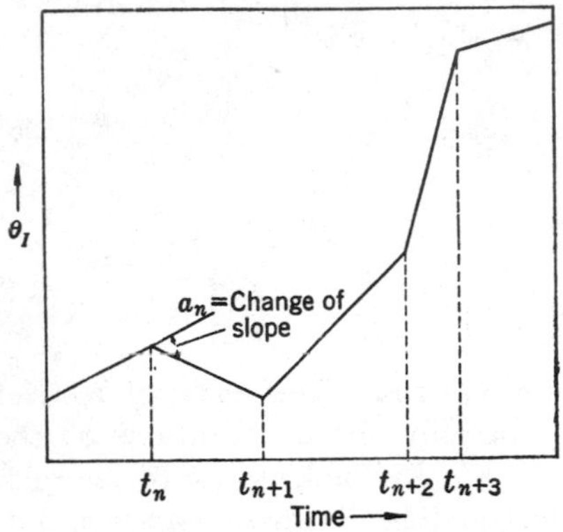

FIG. 8·15.—Graph of θ_I.

Since the transfer function contains a factor of p^2, no difficulty results from working with the improper spectral density

$$G_I(f) = \frac{N}{(2\pi f)^4}. \tag{131}$$

The mean-square error obtained by using the above input is precisely the same as the integrated-square error for an input $\sqrt{N/2}\,x(t)$. Hence the answer also gives a measure of the transient response to a ramp-function input.

As in Sec. 7·2, the error spectrum is simply

$$G_\epsilon(f) = |Y(2\pi jf)|^2 G_I(f), \tag{132}$$

where $Y(2\pi jf)$ is the transfer function,

$$Y(2\pi jf) = \frac{\left(\frac{2\pi jfL}{3} + 1\right)^3 (2\pi jf)^2}{\left(\frac{2\pi jfL}{3} + 1\right)^3 (2\pi jf)^2 + \nu_2(2\pi jf)^2 + \left(\nu_1 + \frac{\nu_2}{T_a}\right)2\pi jf + \frac{\nu_1}{T_a}}. \tag{133}$$

The mean-square error is

$$\overline{\epsilon^2} = \lim_{T\to\infty} \frac{1}{2T}\int_{-T}^{T} dt\, \epsilon^2(t) = \int_0^\infty df\, G_\epsilon(f). \tag{134}$$

This can be evaluated by the table of integrals in the appendix. One obtains

$$\overline{\epsilon^2} = \frac{L^2N}{4\beta} \times \frac{8 + 7\gamma - \gamma^2 - 3\alpha + 3\beta - 3^{-1}\beta\gamma + 10 \times 3^{-3}\alpha\beta - 2 \times 3^{-3}\beta^2 + 3^{-3}\alpha\beta\gamma}{8\alpha - 8\beta + 2 \times 3^{-1}\alpha\beta + 7\alpha\gamma + \gamma\beta - 3\alpha^2 - 3^{-3}\beta^2 - \alpha\gamma^2}, \tag{135}$$

where

$$\alpha = \nu_1 L + \nu_2 \frac{L}{T_a}, \qquad \beta = \nu_1 L \frac{L}{T_a}, \qquad \gamma = \nu_2. \tag{136}$$

The system is stable for the set of all those control parameters (ν_1, ν_2, T_a) which lie in the region of stability. This region is bounded by the surface over which the denominator of Eq. (135) vanishes. It is clear that the plane $L/T_a = 0$ and the plane $\nu_1 L = 0$ bound the region of stability. Figure 8·16 is a three-dimensional sketch of this region.

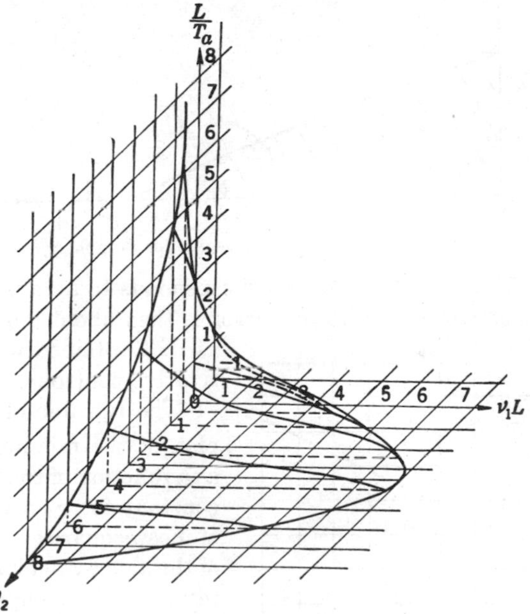

FIG. 8·16.—Stability region.

The mean-square error, $\overline{\epsilon^2}$ attains its minimum value 0.0825 NL^2, at the point $L/T_a = 0.55$, $\nu_1 L = 2.25$, $\nu_2 = 4$. This means that the best tracking can be done with an aided-tracking constant $T_a = 1.8L$ and with $\nu_2/\nu_1 = L/0.56$. For a time lag L of 0.5 sec this gives $T_a = 0.9$ sec and $\nu_2/\nu_1 = 0.9$ sec; the operator should thus use about as much derivative control as proportional control. However, in the experiments[1] performed the operator was not able to introduce very much derivative control. We therefore set ν_2 equal to zero.

When $\nu_2 = 0$, Eq. (135) becomes

$$\overline{\epsilon^2} = \frac{L^2 N}{4\beta} \frac{8 - 3\alpha + 3\beta + 10 \times 3^{-3}\alpha\beta - 2 \times 3^{-3}\beta^2}{8\alpha - 8\beta + 2 \times 3^{-1}\alpha\beta - 3\alpha^2 - 3^{-3}\beta^2}, \tag{137}$$

[1] A. Sobczyk, "Aided Tracking," RL Report No. 430, Sept. 17, 1943.

where

$$\alpha = \nu_1 L \qquad \text{and} \qquad \beta = \nu_1 L \frac{L}{T_a}. \tag{138}$$

The region of stability becomes the area shown in Fig. 8·17. The mean-square error attains its minimum value $1.1NL^2$ for $L/T_a = 0.2$ and

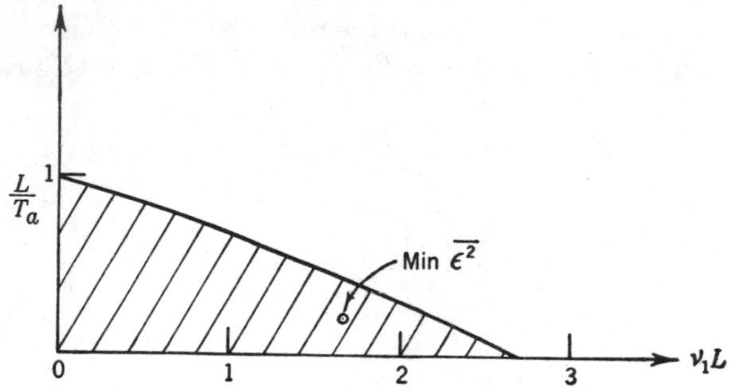

FIG. 8·17.—Stability region for $\nu_2 = 0$.

$\nu_1 L = 1.7$. With $L = 0.5$ sec, this corresponds to a value of 2.5 sec for the aiding constant T_a. The rms error is then about 3.6 times as large as that obtained with optimal derivative control.

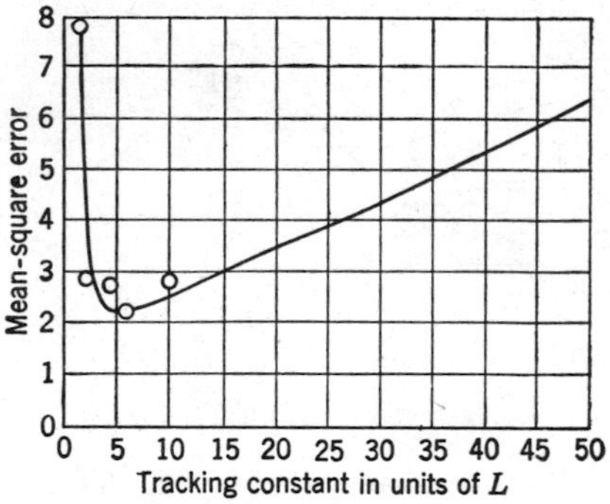

FIG. 8·18.—Aided-tracking error for a random-velocity input. $\nu_2 = 0$.

The full line of Fig. 8·18 is a plot of the minimum value of $\overline{\epsilon^2}$ as a function of the aided-tracking constant for $\nu_2 = 0$. This curve of mean-square error as a function of the aided-tracking constant corresponds very closely to what is obtained experimentally. The circled dots on this graph are experimental average mean-square errors for the corresponding aided-tracking time constants. These data were obtained with a handwheel tracking unit.[1] The ordinate scale for the experimental points has been so adjusted that the two minima coincide. The theoretical optimal value for T_a with $\nu_2 = 0$ is $5L \approx 2.5$ sec; the optimal value as found experimentally was between 2 and 3 sec.

[1] Sobczyk, *op. cit.*, p. 21.

APPENDIX

TABLE OF INTEGRALS

The following is a table of integrals of the type

$$I_n = \frac{1}{2\pi j}\int_{-\infty}^{\infty} dx \, \frac{g_n(x)}{h_n(x)h_n(-x)},$$

where

$$\begin{aligned} h_n(x) &= a_0x^n + a_1x^{n-1} + \cdots + a_n, \\ g_n(x) &= b_0x^{2n-2} + b_1x^{2n-4} + \cdots + b_{n-1}, \end{aligned}$$

and the *roots of $h_n(x)$ all lie in the upper half plane.* The table lists the integrals I_n for values of n from 1 to 7 inclusive.[1]

$$I_1 = \frac{b_0}{2a_0a_1}$$

$$I_2 = \frac{-b_0 + \dfrac{a_0b_1}{a_2}}{2a_0a_1}$$

$$I_3 = \frac{-a_2b_0 + a_0b_1 - \dfrac{a_0a_1b_2}{a_3}}{2a_0(a_0a_3 - a_1a_2)}$$

$$I_4 = \frac{b_0(-a_1a_4 + a_2a_3) - a_0a_3b_1 + a_0a_1b_2 + \dfrac{a_0b_3}{a_4}(a_0a_3 - a_1a_2)}{2a_0(a_0a_3^2 + a_1^2a_4 - a_1a_2a_3)}$$

$$I_5 = \frac{M_5}{2a_0\Delta_5}$$

$$\begin{aligned} M_5 = {} & b_0(-a_0a_4a_5 + a_1a_4^2 + a_2^2a_5 - a_2a_3a_4) + a_0b_1(-a_2a_5 + a_3a_4) \\ & + a_0b_2(a_0a_5 - a_1a_4) + a_0b_3(-a_0a_3 + a_1a_2) \\ & + \frac{a_0b_4}{a_5}(-a_0a_1a_5 + a_0a_3^2 + a_1^2a_4 - a_1a_2a_3) \end{aligned}$$

$$\begin{aligned} \Delta_5 = {} & a_0^2a_5^2 - 2a_0a_1a_4a_5 - a_0a_2a_3a_5 + a_0a_3^2a_4 + a_1^2a_4^2 + a_1a_2^2a_5 \\ & - a_1a_2a_3a_4 \end{aligned}$$

$$I_6 = \frac{M_6}{2a_0\Delta_6}$$

$$\begin{aligned} M_6 = {} & b_0(-a_0a_3a_5a_6 + a_0a_4a_5^2 - a_1^2a_6^2 + 2a_1a_2a_5a_6 + a_1a_3a_4a_6 \\ & - a_1a_4^2a_5 - a_2^2a_5^2 - a_2a_3^2a_6 + a_2a_3a_4a_5) \\ & + a_0b_1(-a_1a_5a_6 + a_2a_5^2 + a_3^2a_6 - a_3a_4a_5) \end{aligned}$$

[1] This table was computed by G. R. MacLane, following the method developed in Sec. 7·9.

$$+ a_0b_2(-a_0a_5^2 - a_1a_3a_6 + a_1a_4a_5)$$
$$+ a_0b_3(a_0a_3a_5 + a_1^2a_6 - a_1a_2a_5)$$
$$+ a_0b_4(a_0a_1a_5 - a_0a_3^2 - a_1^2a_4 + a_1a_2a_3)$$
$$+ \frac{a_0b_5}{a_6}(a_0^2a_5^2 + a_0a_1a_3a_6 - 2a_0a_1a_4a_5 - a_0a_2a_3a_5 + a_0a_3^2a_4$$
$$-a_1^2a_2a_6 + a_1^2a_4^2 + a_1a_2^2a_5 - a_1a_2a_3a_4)$$

$$\Delta_6 = a_0^2a_5^3 + 3a_0a_1a_2a_5a_6 - 2a_0a_1a_4a_5^2 - a_0a_2a_3a_5^2 - a_0a_3^3a_6 + a_0a_3^2a_4a_5$$
$$+ a_1^3a_6^2 - 2a_1^2a_2a_5a_6 - a_1^2a_3a_4a_6 + a_1^2a_4^2a_5 + a_1a_2^2a_5^2$$
$$+ a_1a_2a_3^2a_6 - a_1a_2a_3a_4a_5$$

$$I_7 = \frac{M_7}{2a_0\Delta_7}, \qquad \text{where } M_7 = b_0m_0 + a_0b_1m_1 + a_0b_2m_2 + \cdots + a_0b_6m_6.$$

$$m_0 = a_0^2a_6a_7^2 - 2a_0a_1a_6^2a_7 - 2a_0a_2a_4a_7^2 + a_0a_2a_5a_6a_7 + a_0a_3a_5a_6^2$$
$$+ a_0a_4^2a_5a_7 - a_0a_4a_5^2a_6 + a_1^2a_6^3 + 3a_1a_2a_4a_6a_7 - 2a_1a_2a_5a_6^2$$
$$- a_1a_3a_4a_6^2 - a_1a_4^3a_7 + a_1a_4^2a_5a_6 + a_2^3a_7^2 - 2a_2^2a_3a_6a_7$$
$$- a_2^2a_4a_5a_7 + a_2^2a_5^2a_6 + a_2a_3a_4^2a_7 - a_2a_3a_4a_5a_6 + a_2a_3^2a_6^2$$

$$m_1 = a_0a_4a_7^2 - a_0a_5a_6a_7 - a_1a_4a_6a_7 + a_1a_5a_6^2 - a_2^2a_7^2 + 2a_2a_3a_6a_7$$
$$+ a_2a_4a_5a_7 - a_2a_5^2a_6 - a_3^2a_6^2 - a_3a_4^2a_7 + a_3a_4a_5a_6$$

$$m_2 = a_0a_2a_7^2 - a_0a_3a_6a_7 - a_0a_4a_5a_7 + a_0a_5^2a_6 - a_1a_2a_6a_7$$
$$+ a_1a_3a_6^2 + a_1a_4^2a_7 - a_1a_4a_5a_6$$

$$m_3 = -a_0^2a_7^2 + 2a_0a_1a_6a_7 + a_0a_3a_4a_7 - a_0a_3a_5a_6 - a_1^2a_6^2 - a_1a_2a_4a_7$$
$$+ a_1a_2a_5a_6$$

$$m_4 = a_0^2a_5a_7 - a_0a_1a_4a_7 - a_0a_1a_5a_6 - a_0a_2a_3a_7 + a_0a_3^2a_6$$
$$+ a_1^2a_4a_6 + a_1a_2^2a_7 - a_1a_2a_3a_6$$

$$m_5 = a_0^2a_3a_7 - a_0^2a_5^2 - a_0a_1a_2a_7 - a_0a_1a_3a_6 + 2a_0a_1a_4a_5$$
$$+ a_0a_2a_3a_5 - a_0a_3^2a_4 + a_1^2a_2a_6 - a_1^2a_4^2 - a_1a_2^2a_5 + a_1a_2a_3a_4$$

$$m_6 = \frac{1}{a_7}(a_0^2a_1a_7^2 - 2a_0^2a_3a_5a_7 + a_0^2a_5^3 - 2a_0a_1^2a_6a_7 + a_0a_1a_2a_5a_7$$
$$+ 3a_0a_1a_3a_5a_6 - 2a_0a_1a_4a_5^2 + a_0a_2a_3^2a_7 - a_0a_2a_3a_5^2 - a_0a_3^3a_6$$
$$+ a_0a_3^2a_4a_5 + a_1^3a_6^2 + a_1^2a_2a_4a_7 - 2a_1^2a_2a_5a_6 - a_1^2a_3a_4a_6$$
$$+ a_1^2a_4^2a_5 - a_1a_2^2a_3a_7 + a_1a_2^2a_5^2 + a_1a_2a_3^2a_6 - a_1a_2a_3a_4a_5)$$

$$\Delta_7 = -a_0^3a_7^3 + 3a_0^2a_1a_6a_7^2 + a_0^2a_2a_5a_7^2 + 2a_0^2a_3a_4a_7^2$$
$$- 3a_0^2a_3a_5a_6a_7 - a_0^2a_4a_5^2a_7 + a_0^2a_5^3a_6 - 3a_0a_1^2a_6^2a_7$$
$$- 3a_0a_1a_2a_4a_7^2 + a_0a_1a_2a_5a_6a_7 + 3a_0a_1a_3a_5a_6^2 - a_0a_1a_3a_4a_6a_7$$
$$+ 2a_0a_1a_4^2a_5a_7 - 2a_0a_1a_4a_5^2a_6 - a_0a_2^2a_3a_7^2 + 2a_0a_2a_3^2a_6a_7$$
$$+ a_0a_2a_3a_4a_5a_7 - a_0a_2a_3a_5^2a_6 - a_0a_3^3a_6^2 - a_0a_3^2a_4^2a_7$$
$$+ a_0a_3^2a_4a_5a_6 + a_1^3a_6^3 + 3a_1^2a_2a_4a_6a_7 - 2a_1^2a_2a_5a_6^2$$
$$- a_1^2a_3a_4a_6^2 - a_1^2a_4^3a_7 + a_1^2a_4^2a_5a_6 + a_1a_2^3a_7^2 - 2a_1a_2^2a_3a_6a_7$$
$$- a_1a_2^2a_4a_5a_7 + a_1a_2^2a_5^2a_6 + a_1a_2a_3^2a_6^2 + a_1a_2a_3a_4^2a_7 - a_1a_2a_3a_4a_5a_6$$

Index

CATALOGUE OF DOVER BOOKS

BOOKS EXPLAINING SCIENCE AND MATHEMATICS

General

WHAT IS SCIENCE?, Norman Campbell. This excellent introduction explains scientific method, role of mathematics, types of scientific laws. Contents: 2 aspects of science, science & nature, laws of science, discovery of laws, explanation of laws, measurement & numerical laws, applications of science. 192pp. 5⅜ x 8. S43 Paperbound **$1.25**

THE COMMON SENSE OF THE EXACT SCIENCES, W. K. Clifford. Introduction by James Newman, edited by Karl Pearson. For 70 years this has been a guide to classical scientific and mathematical thought. Explains with unusual clarity basic concepts, such as extension of meaning of symbols, characteristics of surface boundaries, properties of plane figures, vectors, Cartesian method of determining position, etc. Long preface by Bertrand Russell. Bibliography of Clifford. Corrected, 130 diagrams redrawn. 249pp. 5⅜ x 8. T61 Paperbound **$1.60**

SCIENCE THEORY AND MAN, Erwin Schrödinger. This is a complete and unabridged reissue of SCIENCE AND THE HUMAN TEMPERAMENT plus an additional essay: "What is an Elementary Particle?" Nobel laureate Schrödinger discusses such topics as nature of scientific method, the nature of science, chance and determinism, science and society, conceptual models for physical entities, elementary particles and wave mechanics. Presentation is popular and may be followed by most people with little or no scientific training. "Fine practical preparation for a time when laws of nature, human institutions . . . are undergoing a critical examination without parallel," Waldemar Kaempffert, N. Y. TIMES. 192pp. 5⅜ x 8. T428 Paperbound **$1.35**

FADS AND FALLACIES IN THE NAME OF SCIENCE, Martin Gardner. Examines various cults, quack systems, frauds, delusions which at various times have masqueraded as science. Accounts of hollow-earth fanatics like Symmes; Velikovsky and wandering planets; Hoerbiger; Bellamy and the theory of multiple moons; Charles Fort; dowsing, pseudoscientific methods for finding water, ores, oil. Sections on naturopathy, iridiagnosis, zone therapy, food fads, etc. Analytical accounts of Wilhelm Reich and orgone sex energy; L. Ron Hubbard and Dianetics; A. Korzybski and General Semantics; many others. Brought up to date to include Bridey Murphy, others. Not just a collection of anecdotes, but a fair, reasoned appraisal of eccentric theory. Formerly titled IN THE NAME OF SCIENCE. Preface. Index. x + 384pp. 5⅜ x 8. T394 Paperbound **$1.50**

A DOVER SCIENCE SAMPLER, edited by George Barkin. 64-page book, sturdily bound, containing excerpts from over 20 Dover books, explaining science. Edwin Hubble, George Sarton, Ernst Mach, A. d'Abro, Galileo, Newton, others, discussing island universes, scientific truth, biological phenomena, stability in bridges, etc. Copies limited; no more than 1 to a customer, FREE

POPULAR SCIENTIFIC LECTURES, Hermann von Helmholtz. Helmholtz was a superb expositor as well as a scientist of genius in many areas. The seven essays in this volume are models of clarity, and even today they rank among the best general descriptions of their subjects ever written. "The Physiological Causes of Harmony in Music" was the first significant physiological explanation of musical consonance and dissonance. Two essays, "On the Interaction of Natural Forces" and "On the Conservation of Force," were of great importance in the history of science, for they firmly established the principle of the conservation of energy. Other lectures include "On the Relation of Optics to Painting," "On Recent Progress in the Theory of Vision," "On Goethe's Scientific Researches," and "On the Origin and Significance of Geometrical Axioms." Selected and edited with an introduction by Professor Morris Kline. xii + 286pp. 5⅜ x 8½. T799 Paperbound **$1.45**

BOOKS EXPLAINING SCIENCE AND MATHEMATICS

Physics

CONCERNING THE NATURE OF THINGS, Sir William Bragg. Christmas lectures delivered at the Royal Society by Nobel laureate. Why a spinning ball travels in a curved track; how uranium is transmuted to lead, etc. Partial contents: atoms, gases, liquids, crystals, metals, etc. No scientific background needed; wonderful for intelligent child. 32pp. of photos, 57 figures. xii + 232pp. 5⅜ x 8. T31 Paperbound **$1.50**

THE RESTLESS UNIVERSE, Max Born. New enlarged version of this remarkably readable account by a Nobel laureate. Moving from sub-atomic particles to universe, the author explains in very simple terms the latest theories of wave mechanics. Partial contents: air and its relatives, electrons & ions, waves & particles, electronic structure of the atom, nuclear physics. Nearly 1000 illustrations, including 7 animated sequences. 325pp. 6 x 9. T412 Paperbound **$2.00**

FROM EUCLID TO EDDINGTON: A STUDY OF THE CONCEPTIONS OF THE EXTERNAL WORLD, Sir Edmund Whittaker. A foremost British scientist traces the development of theories of natural philosophy from the western rediscovery of Euclid to Eddington, Einstein, Dirac, etc. The inadequacy of classical physics is contrasted with present day attempts to understand the physical world through relativity, non-Euclidean geometry, space curvature, wave mechanics, etc. 5 major divisions of examination: Space; Time and Movement; the Concepts of Classical Physics; the Concepts of Quantum Mechanics; the Eddington Universe. 212pp. 5⅜ x 8. T491 Paperbound **$1.35**

PHYSICS, THE PIONEER SCIENCE, L. W. Taylor. First thorough text to place all important physical phenomena in cultural-historical framework; remains best work of its kind. Exposition of physical laws, theories developed chronologically, with great historical, illustrative experiments diagrammed, described, worked out mathematically. Excellent physics text for self-study as well as class work. Vol. 1: Heat, Sound: motion, acceleration, gravitation, conservation of energy, heat engines, rotation, heat, mechanical energy, etc. 211 illus. 407pp. 5⅜ x 8. Vol. 2: Light, Electricity: images, lenses, prisms, magnetism, Ohm's law, dynamos, telegraph, quantum theory, decline of mechanical view of nature, etc. Bibliography. 13 table appendix. Index. 551 illus. 2 color plates. 508pp. 5⅜ x 8.
Vol. 1 S565 Paperbound **$2.00**
Vol. 2 S566 Paperbound **$2.00**
The set **$4.00**

A SURVEY OF PHYSICAL THEORY, Max Planck. One of the greatest scientists of all time, creator of the quantum revolution in physics, writes in non-technical terms of his own discoveries and those of other outstanding creators of modern physics. Planck wrote this book when science had just crossed the threshold of the new physics, and he communicates the excitement felt then as he discusses electromagnetic theories, statistical methods, evolution of the concept of light, a step-by-step description of how he developed his own momentous theory, and many more of the basic ideas behind modern physics. Formerly "A Survey of Physics." Bibliography. Index. 128pp. 5⅜ x 8. S650 Paperbound **$1.15**

THE ATOMIC NUCLEUS, M. Korsunsky. The only non-technical comprehensive account of the atomic nucleus in English. For college physics students, etc. Chapters cover: Radioactivity, the Nuclear Model of the Atom, the Mass of Atomic Nuclei, the Disintegration of Atomic Nuclei, the Discovery of the Positron, the Artificial Transformation of Atomic Nuclei, Artificial Radioactivity, Mesons, the Neutrino, the Structure of Atomic Nuclei and Forces Acting Between Nuclear Particles, Nuclear Fission, Chain Reaction, Peaceful Uses, Thermoculear Reactions. Slightly abridged edition. Translated by G. Yankovsky. 65 figures. Appendix includes 45 photographic illustrations. 413 pp. 5⅜ x 8. S1052 Paperbound **$2.00**

PRINCIPLES OF MECHANICS SIMPLY EXPLAINED, Morton Mott-Smith. Excellent, highly readable introduction to the theories and discoveries of classical physics. Ideal for the layman who desires a foundation which will enable him to understand and appreciate contemporary developments in the physical sciences. Discusses: Density, The Law of Gravitation, Mass and Weight, Action and Reaction, Kinetic and Potential Energy, The Law of Inertia, Effects of Acceleration, The Independence of Motions, Galileo and the New Science of Dynamics, Newton and the New Cosmos, The Conservation of Momentum, and other topics. Revised edition of "This Mechanical World." Illustrated by E. Kosa, Jr. Bibliography and Chronology. Index. xiv + 171pp. 5⅜ x 8½. T1067 Paperbound **$1.00**

THE CONCEPT OF ENERGY SIMPLY EXPLAINED, Morton Mott-Smith. Elementary, non-technical exposition which traces the story of man's conquest of energy, with particular emphasis on the developments during the nineteenth century and the first three decades of our own century. Discusses man's earlier efforts to harness energy, more recent experiments and discoveries relating to the steam engine, the engine indicator, the motive power of heat, the principle of excluded perpetual motion, the bases of the conservation of energy, the concept of entropy, the internal combustion engine, mechanical refrigeration, and many other related topics. Also much biographical material. Index. Bibliography. 33 illustrations. ix + 215pp. 5⅜ x 8½. T1071 Paperbound **$1.25**

HEAT AND ITS WORKINGS, Morton Mott-Smith. One of the best elementary introductions to the theory and attributes of heat, covering such matters as the laws governing the effect of heat on solids, liquids and gases, the methods by which heat is measured, the conversion of a substance from one form to another through heating and cooling, evaporation, the effects of pressure on boiling and freezing points, and the three ways in which heat is transmitted (conduction, convection, radiation). Also brief notes on major experiments and discoveries. Concise, but complete, it presents all the essential facts about the subject in readable style. Will give the layman and beginning student a first-rate background in this major topic in physics. Index. Bibliography. 50 illustrations. x + 165pp. 5⅜ x 8½. T978 Paperbound **$1.00**

THE STORY OF ATOMIC THEORY AND ATOMIC ENERGY, J. G. Feinberg. Wider range of facts on physical theory, cultural implications, than any other similar source. Completely non-technical. Begins with first atomic theory, 600 B.C., goes through A-bomb, developments to 1959. Avogadro, Rutherford, Bohr, Einstein, radioactive decay, binding energy, radiation danger, future benefits of nuclear power, dozens of other topics, told in lively, related, informal manner. Particular stress on European atomic research. "Deserves special mention . . . authoritative," Saturday Review. Formerly "The Atom Story." New chapter to 1959. Index. 34 illustrations. 251pp. 5⅜ x 8. T625 Paperbound **$1.60**

THE STRANGE STORY OF THE QUANTUM, AN ACCOUNT FOR THE GENERAL READER OF THE GROWTH OF IDEAS UNDERLYING OUR PRESENT ATOMIC KNOWLEDGE, B. Hoffmann. Presents lucidly and expertly, with barest amount of mathematics, the problems and theories which led to modern quantum physics. Dr. Hoffmann begins with the closing years of the 19th century, when certain trifling discrepancies were noticed, and with illuminating analogies and examples takes you through the brilliant concepts of Planck, Einstein, Pauli, de Broglie, Bohr, Schroedinger, Heisenberg, Dirac, Sommerfeld, Feynman, etc. This edition includes a new, long postscript carrying the story through 1958. "Of the books attempting an account of the history and contents of our modern atomic physics which have come to my attention, this is the best," H. Margenau, Yale University, in "American Journal of Physics." 32 tables and line illustrations. Index. 275pp. 5⅜ x 8. T518 Paperbound **$1.50**

THE EVOLUTION OF SCIENTIFIC THOUGHT FROM NEWTON TO EINSTEIN, A. d'Abro. Einstein's special and general theories of relativity, with their historical implications, are analyzed in non-technical terms. Excellent accounts of the contributions of Newton, Riemann, Weyl, Planck, Eddington, Maxwell, Lorentz and others are treated in terms of space and time, equations of electromagnetics, finiteness of the universe, methodology of science. 21 diagrams. 482pp. 5⅜ x 8. T2 Paperound **$2.25**

THE RISE OF THE NEW PHYSICS, A. d'Abro. A half-million word exposition, formerly titled THE DECLINE OF MECHANISM, for readers not versed in higher mathematics. The only thorough explanation, in everyday language, of the central core of modern mathematical physical theory, treating both classical and modern theoretical physics, and presenting in terms almost anyone can understand the equivalent of 5 years of study of mathematical physics. Scientifically impeccable coverage of mathematical-physical thought from the Newtonian system up through the electronic theories of Dirac and Heisenberg and Fermi's statistics. Combines both history and exposition; provides a broad yet unified and detailed view, with constant comparison of classical and modern views on phenomena and theories. "A must for anyone doing serious study in the physical sciences," JOURNAL OF THE FRANKLIN INSTITUTE. "Extraordinary faculty . . . to explain ideas and theories of theoretical physics in the language of daily life," ISIS. First part of set covers philosophy of science, drawing upon the practice of Newton, Maxwell, Poincaré, Einstein, others, discussing modes of thought, experiment, interpretations of causality, etc. In the second part, 100 pages explain grammar and vocabulary of mathematics, with discussions of functions, groups, series, Fourier series, etc. The remainder is devoted to concrete, detailed coverage of both classical and quantum physics, explaining such topics as analytic mechanics, Hamilton's principle, wave theory of light, electromagnetic waves, groups of transformations, thermodynamics, phase rule, Brownian movement, kinetics, special relativity, Planck's original quantum theory, Bohr's atom, Zeeman effect, Broglie's wave mechanics, Heisenberg's uncertainty, Eigen-values, matrices, scores of other important topics. Discoveries and theories are covered for such men as Alembert, Born, Cantor, Debye, Euler, Foucault, Galois, Gauss, Hadamard, Kelvin, Kepler, Laplace, Maxwell, Pauli, Rayleigh, Volterra, Weyl, Young, more than 180 others. Indexed. 97 illustrations. ix + 982pp. 5⅜ x 8.
T3 Volume 1, Paperbound **$2.00**
T4 Volume 2, Paperbound **$2.00**

SPINNING TOPS AND GYROSCOPIC MOTION, John Perry. Well-known classic of science still unsurpassed for lucid, accurate, delightful exposition. How quasi-rigidity is induced in flexible and fluid bodies by rapid motions; why gyrostat falls, top rises; nature and effect on climatic conditions of earth's precessional movement; effect of internal fluidity on rotating bodies, etc. Appendixes describe practical uses to which gyroscopes have been put in ships, compasses, monorail transportation. 62 figures. 128pp. 5⅜ x 8. T416 Paperbound **$1.00**

THE UNIVERSE OF LIGHT, Sir William Bragg. No scientific training needed to read Nobel Prize winner's expansion of his Royal Institute Christmas Lectures. Insight into nature of light, methods and philosophy of science. Explains lenses, reflection, color, resonance, polarization, x-rays, the spectrum, Newton's work with prisms, Huygens' with polarization, Crookes' with cathode ray, etc. Leads into clear statement of 2 major historical theories of light, corpuscle and wave. Dozens of experiments you can do. 199 illus., including 2 full-page color plates. 293pp. 5⅜ x 8. S538 Paperbound **$1.85**

THE STORY OF X-RAYS FROM RÖNTGEN TO ISOTOPES, A. R. Bleich. Non-technical history of x-rays, their scientific explanation, their applications in medicine, industry, research, and art, and their effect on the individual and his descendants. Includes amusing early reactions to Röntgen's discovery, cancer therapy, detections of art and stamp forgeries, potential risks to patient and operator, etc. Illustrations show x-rays of flower structure, the gall bladder, gears with hidden defects, etc. Original Dover publication. Glossary. Bibliography. Index. 55 photos and figures. xiv + 186pp. 5⅜ x 8. T662 Paperbound **$1.35**

ELECTRONS, ATOMS, METALS AND ALLOYS, Wm. Hume-Rothery. An introductory-level explanation of the application of the electronic theory to the structure and properties of metals and alloys, taking into account the new theoretical work done by mathematical physicists. Material presented in dialogue-form between an "Old Metallurgist" and a "Young Scientist." Their discussion falls into 4 main parts: the nature of an atom, the nature of a metal, the nature of an alloy, and the structure of the nucleus. They cover such topics as the hydrogen atom, electron waves, wave mechanics, Brillouin zones, co-valent bonds, radioactivity and natural disintegration, fundamental particles, structure and fission of the nucleus,etc. Revised, enlarged edition. 177 illustrations. Subject and name indexes. 407pp. 5⅜ x 8½. S1046 Paperbound **$2.25**

TEACH YOURSELF MECHANICS, P. Abbott. The lever, centre of gravity, parallelogram of force, friction, acceleration, Newton's laws of motion, machines, specific gravity, gas, liquid pressure, much more. 280 problems, solutions. Tables. 163 illus. 271pp. 6⅞ x 4¼.
Clothbound **$2.00**

MATTER & MOTION, James Clerk Maxwell, This excellent exposition begins with simple particles and proceeds gradually to physical systems beyond complete analysis: motion, force, properties of centre of mass of material system, work, energy, gravitation, etc. Written with all Maxwell's original insights and clarity. Notes by E. Larmor. 17 diagrams. 178pp. 5⅜ x 8.
S188 Paperbound **$1.35**

SOAP BUBBLES, THEIR COLOURS AND THE FORCES WHICH MOULD THEM, C. V. Boys. Only complete edition, half again as much material as any other. Includes Boys' hints on performing his experiments, sources of supply. Dozens of lucid experiments show complexities of liquid films, surface tension, etc. Best treatment ever written. Introduction. 83 illustrations. Color plate. 202pp. 5⅜ x 8. T542 Paperbound **95¢**

MATTER & LIGHT, THE NEW PHYSICS, L. de Broglie. Non-technical papers by a Nobel laureate explain electromagnetic theory, relativity, matter, light and radiation, wave mechanics, quantum physics, philosophy of science. Einstein, Planck, Bohr, others explained so easily that no mathematical training is needed for all but 2 of the 21 chapters. Unabridged. Index. 300pp. 5⅜ x 8. T35 Paperbound **$1.75**

SPACE AND TIME, Emile Borel. An entirely non-technical introduction to relativity, by world-renowned mathematician, Sorbonne professor. (Notes on basic mathematics are included separately.) This book has never been surpassed for insight, and extraordinary clarity of thought, as it presents scores of examples, analogies, arguments, illustrations, which explain such topics as: difficulties due to motion; gravitation a force of inertia; geodesic lines; wave-length and difference of phase; x-rays and crystal structure; the special theory of relativity; and much more. Indexes. 4 appendixes. 15 figures. xvi + 243pp. 5⅜ x 8.
T592 Paperbound **$1.45**

BOOKS EXPLAINING SCIENCE AND MATHEMATICS

Astronomy

THE FRIENDLY STARS, Martha Evans Martin. This engaging survey of stellar lore and science is a well-known classic, which has introduced thousands to the fascinating world of stars and other celestial bodies. Descriptions of Capella, Sirius, Arcturus, Vega, Polaris, etc.—all the important stars, with informative discussions of rising and setting of stars, their number, names, brightness, distances, etc. in a non-technical, highly readable style. Also: double stars, constellations, clusters—concentrating on stars and formations visible to the naked eye. New edition, revised (1963) by D. H. Menzel, Director Harvard Observatory. 23 diagrams by Prof. Ching-Sung Yu. Foreword by D. H. Menzel and W. W. Morgan. 2 Star Charts. Index. xii + 147pp. 5⅜ x 8½. T1099 Paperbound **$1.00**

AN ELEMENTARY SURVEY OF CELESTIAL MECHANICS, Y. Ryabov. Elementary exposition of gravitational theory and celestial mechanics. Historical introduction and coverage of basic principles, including: the elliptic, the orbital plane, the 2- and 3-body problems, the discovery of Neptune, planetary rotation, the length of the day, the shapes of galaxies, satellites (detailed treatment of Sputnik I), etc. First American reprinting of successful Russian popular exposition. Elementary algebra and trigonometry helpful, but not necessary; presentation chiefly verbal. Appendix of theorem proofs. 58 figures. 165pp. 5⅜ x 8.
T756 Paperbound **$1.25**

THE SKY AND ITS MYSTERIES, E. A. Beet. One of most lucid books on mysteries of universe; deals with astronomy from earliest observations to latest theories of expansion of universe, source of stellar energy, birth of planets, origin of moon craters, possibility of life on other planets. Discusses effects of sunspots on weather; distances, ages of several stars; master plan of universe; methods and tools of astronomers; much more. "Eminently readable book," London Times. Extensive bibliography. Over 50 diagrams. 12 full-page plates, fold-out star map. Introduction. Index. 5¼ x 7½. T627 Clothbound **$3.50**

THE REALM OF THE NEBULAE, E. Hubble. One of the great astronomers of our time records his formulation of the concept of "island universes," and its impact on astronomy. Such topics are covered as the velocity-distance relation; classification, nature, distances, general field of nebulae; cosmological theories; nebulae in the neighborhood of the Milky Way. 39 photos of nebulae, nebulae clusters, spectra of nebulae, and velocity distance relations shown by spectrum comparison. "One of the most progressive lines of astronomical research," The Times (London). New introduction by A. Sandage. 55 illustrations. Index. iv + 201pp. 5⅜ x 8. S455 Paperbound **$1.50**

OUT OF THE SKY, H. H. Nininger. A non-technical but comprehensive introduction to "meteoritics", the young science concerned with all aspects of the arrival of matter from outer space. Written by one of the world's experts on meteorites, this work shows how, despite difficulties of observation and sparseness of data, a considerable body of knowledge has arisen. It defines meteors and meteorites; studies fireball clusters and processions, meteorite composition, size, distribution, showers, explosions, origins, craters, and much more. A true connecting link between astronomy and geology. More than 175 photos, 22 other illustrations. References. Bibliography of author's publications on meteorites. Index. viii + 336pp. 5⅜ x 8. T519 Paperbound **$1.85**

SATELLITES AND SCIENTIFIC RESEARCH, D. King-Hele. Non-technical account of the manmade satellites and the discoveries they have yielded up to the autumn of 1961. Brings together information hitherto published only in hard-to-get scientific journals. Includes the life history of a typical satellite, methods of tracking, new information on the shape of the earth, zones of radiation, etc. Over 60 diagrams and 6 photographs. Mathematical appendix. Bibliography of over 100 items. Index. xii + 180pp. 5⅜ x 8½. T703 Paperbound **$2.00**

BOOKS EXPLAINING SCIENCE AND MATHEMATICS

Mathematics

CHANCE, LUCK AND STATISTICS: THE SCIENCE OF CHANCE, Horace C. Levinson. Theory of probability and science of statistics in simple, non-technical language. Part I deals with theory of probability, covering odd superstitions in regard to "luck," the meaning of betting odds, the law of mathematical expectation, gambling, and applications in poker, roulette, lotteries, dice, bridge, and other games of chance. Part II discusses the misuse of statistics, the concept of statistical probabilities, normal and skew frequency distributions, and statistics applied to various fields—birth rates, stock speculation, insurance rates, advertising, etc. "Presented in an easy humorous style which I consider the best kind of expository writing," Prof. A. C. Cohen, Industry Quality Control. Enlarged revised edition. Formerly titled "The Science of Chance." Preface and two new appendices by the author. Index. xiv + 365pp. 5⅜ x 8. T1007 Paperbound **$1.85**

PROBABILITIES AND LIFE, Emile Borel. Translated by M. Baudin. Non-technical, highly readable introduction to the results of probability as applied to everyday situations. Partial contents: Fallacies About Probabilities Concerning Life After Death; Negligible Probabilities and the Probabilities of Everyday Life; Events of Small Probability; Application of Probabilities to Certain Problems of Heredity; Probabilities of Deaths, Diseases, and Accidents; On Poisson's Formula. Index. 3 Appendices of statistical studies and tables. vi + 87pp. 5⅜ x 8½. T121 Paperbound **$1.00**

GREAT IDEAS OF MODERN MATHEMATICS: THEIR NATURE AND USE, Jagjit Singh. Reader with only high school math will understand main mathematical ideas of modern physics, astronomy, genetics, psychology, evolution, etc., better than many who use them as tools, but comprehend little of their basic structure. Author uses his wide knowledge of non-mathematical fields in brilliant exposition of differential equations, matrices, group theory, logic, statistics, problems of mathematical foundations, imaginary numbers, vectors, etc. Original publication. 2 appendices. 2 indexes. 65 illustr. 322pp. 5⅜ x 8. S587 Paperbound **$1.75**

MATHEMATICS IN ACTION, O. G. Sutton. Everyone with a command of high school algebra will find this book one of the finest possible introductions to the application of mathematics to physical theory. Ballistics, numerical analysis, waves and wavelike phenomena, Fourier series, group concepts, fluid flow and aerodynamics, statistical measures, and meteorology are discussed with unusual clarity. Some calculus and differential equations theory is developed by the author for the reader's help in the more difficult sections. 88 figures. Index. viii + 236pp. 5⅜ x 8. T440 Clothbound **$3.50**

THE FOURTH DIMENSION SIMPLY EXPLAINED, edited by H. P. Manning. 22 essays, originally Scientific American contest entries, that use a minimum of mathematics to explain aspects of 4-dimensional geometry: analogues to 3-dimensional space, 4-dimensional absurdities and curiosities (such as removing the contents of an egg without puncturing its shell), possible measurements and forms, etc. Introduction by the editor. Only book of its sort on a truly elementary level, excellent introduction to advanced works. 82 figures. 251pp. 5⅜ x 8. T711 Paperbound **$1.35**

BOOKS EXPLAINING SCIENCE AND MATHEMATICS

Engineering, technology, applied science etc.

TEACH YOURSELF ELECTRICITY, C. W. Wilman. Electrical resistance, inductance, capacitance, magnets, chemical effects of current, alternating currents, generators and motors, transformers, rectifiers, much more. 230 questions, answers, worked examples. List of units. 115 illus. 194pp. 6⅞ x 4¼. Clothbound **$2.00**

ELEMENTARY METALLURGY AND METALLOGRAPHY, A. M. Shrager. Basic theory and descriptions of most of the fundamental manufacturing processes involved in metallurgy. Partial contents: the structure of metals; slip, plastic deformation, and recrystalization; iron ore and production of pig iron; chemistry involved in the metallurgy of iron and steel; basic processes such as the Bessemer treatment, open-hearth process, the electric arc furnace—with advantages and disadvantages of each; annealing, hardening, and tempering steel; copper, aluminum, magnesium, and their alloys. For freshman engineers, advanced students in technical high schools, etc. Index. Bibliography. 177 diagrams. 17 tables. 284 questions and problems. 27-page glossary. ix + 389pp. 5⅜ x 8. S138 Paperbound **$2.25**

BASIC ELECTRICITY, Prepared by the Bureau of Naval Personnel. Originally a training course text for U.S. Navy personnel, this book provides thorough coverage of the basic theory of electricity and its applications. Best book of its kind for either broad or more limited studies of electrical fundamentals . . . for classroom use or home study. Part 1 provides a more limited coverage of theory: fundamental concepts, batteries, the simple circuit, D.C. series and parallel circuits, conductors and wiring techniques, A.C. electricity, inductance and capacitance, etc. Part 2 applies theory to the structure of electrical machines—generators, motors, transformers, magnetic amplifiers. Also deals with more complicated instruments, synchros, servo-mechanisms. The concluding chapters cover electrical drawings and blueprints, wiring diagrams, technical manuals, and safety education. The book contains numerous questions for the student, with answers. Index and six appendices. 345 illustrations. x + 448pp. 6½ x 9¼. S973 Paperbound **$2.95**

BASIC ELECTRONICS, prepared by the U.S. Navy Training Publications Center. A thorough and comprehensive manual on the fundamentals of electronics. Written clearly, it is equally useful for self-study or course work for those with a knowledge of the principles of basic electricity. Partial contents: Operating Principles of the Electron Tube; Introduction to Transistors; Power Supplies for Electronic Equipment; Tuned Circuits; Electron-Tube Amplifiers; Audio Power Amplifiers; Oscillators; Transmitters; Transmission Lines; Antennas and Propagation; Introduction to Computers; and related topics. Appendix. Index. Hundreds of illustrations and diagrams. vi + 471pp. 6½ x 9¼. S1076 Paperbound **$2.75**

BASIC THEORY AND APPLICATION OF TRANSISTORS, Prepared by the U.S. Department of the Army. An introductory manual prepared for an army training program. One of the finest available surveys of theory and application of transistor design and operation. Minimal knowledge of physics and theory of electron tubes required. Suitable for textbook use, course supplement, or home study. Chapters: Introduction; fundamental theory of transistors; transistor amplifier fundamentals; parameters, equivalent circuits, and characteristic curves; bias stabilization; transistor analysis and comparison using characteristic curves and charts; audio amplifiers; tuned amplifiers; wide-band amplifiers; oscillators; pulse and switching circuits; modulation, mixing, and demodulation; and additional semiconductor devices. Unabridged, corrected edition. 240 schematic drawings, photographs, wiring diagrams, etc. 2 Appendices. Glossary. Index. 263pp. 6½ x 9¼. S380 Paperbound **$1.25**

TEACH YOURSELF HEAT ENGINES, E. De Ville. Measurement of heat, development of steam and internal combustion engines, efficiency of an engine, compression-ignition engines, production of steam, the ideal engine, much more. 318 exercises, answers, worked examples. Tables. 76 illus. 220pp. 6⅞ x 4¼. Clothbound **$2.00**

BOOKS EXPLAINING SCIENCE AND MATHEMATICS

Miscellaneous

ON THE SENSATIONS OF TONE, Hermann Helmholtz. This is an unmatched coordination of such fields as acoustical physics, physiology, experiment, history of music. It covers the entire gamut of musical tone. Partial contents: relation of musical science to acoustics, physical vs. physiological acoustics, composition of vibration, resonance, analysis of tones by sympathetic resonance, beats, chords, tonality, consonant chords, discords, progression of parts, etc. 33 appendixes discuss various aspects of sound, physics, acoustics, music, etc. Translated by A. J. Ellis. New introduction by Prof. Henry Margenau of Yale. 68 figures. 43 musical passages analyzed. Over 100 tables. Index. xix + 576pp. 6⅛ x 9¼. S114 Paperbound **$3.00**

THE NATURE OF LIGHT AND COLOUR IN THE OPEN AIR, M. Minnaert. Why is falling snow sometimes black? What causes mirages, the fata morgana, multiple suns and moons in the sky? How are shadows formed? Prof. Minnaert of the University of Utrecht answers these and similar questions in optics, light, colour, for non-specialists. Particularly valuable to nature, science students, painters, photographers. Translated by H. M. Kremer-Priest, K. Jay. 202 illustrations, including 42 photos. xvi + 362pp. 5⅜ x 8. T196 Paperbound **$2.00**

THE PHYSICS OF MUSIC, Alexander Wood. Introduction for musicians to the physical aspect of sound. No scientific training necessary to understand concepts, etc. Wealth of material on origin and development of instruments, physical principles involved in the production of their sounds, pitch, intensity and loudness, mechanism of the ear, dissonance and consonance, sound reproduction and recordings, concert halls, etc. Extensively revised by Dr. J. M. Bowsher. Indices. Bibliography. 16 plates. 114 illustrations. 270pp. 5⅛ x 8⅛. T322 Paperbound **$2.25**

GREAT IDEAS AND THEORIES OF MODERN COSMOLOGY, Jagjit Singh. The theories of Jeans, Eddington, Milne, Kant, Bondi, Gold, Newton, Einstein, Gamow, Hoyle, Dirac, Kuiper, Hubble, Weizsäcker and many others on such cosmological questions as the origin of the universe, space and time, planet formation, "continuous creation," the birth, life, and death of the stars, the origin of the galaxies, etc. By the author of the popular "Great Ideas of Modern Mathematics." A gifted popularizer of science, he makes the most difficult abstractions crystal-clear even to the most non-mathematical reader. Index. xii + 276 pp. 5⅜ x 8½. T925 Paperbound **$1.85**

PIONEERS OF SCIENCE, O. Lodge. Eminent scientist-expositor's authoritative, yet elementary survey of great scientific theories. Concentrating on individuals—Copernicus, Brahe, Kepler, Galileo, Descartes, Newton, Laplace, Herschel, Lord Kelvin, and other scientists—the author presents their discoveries in historical order adding biographical material on each man and full, specific explanations of their achievements. The clear and complete treatment of the post-Newtonian astronomers is a feature seldom found in other books on the subject. Index. 120 illustrations. xv + 404pp. 5⅜ x 8. T716 Paperbound **$1.65**

BIOGRAPHY OF SCIENTISTS

ISAAC NEWTON: A BIOGRAPHY, Louis Trenchard More. The definitive biography of Newton, his life and work. Presents Newton as a living man, with a critical, objective analysis of his character as well as a careful survey of his manifold accomplishments, scientific, theological, etc. The author, himself a professor of physics, has made full use of all of Newton's published works and all material in the Portsmouth Collection of Newton's personal and unpublished papers. The text includes numerous letters by Newton and his acquaintances, and many other of his papers—some translated from Latin to English by the author. A universally-esteemed work. Unabridged republication. 1 full-page plate. Index. xiii + 675pp. 5⅜ x 8½. T579 Paperbound **$2.50**

PIERRE CURIE, Marie Curie. Mme. Curie, Nobel Prize winner, creates a memorable portrait of her equally famous husband and his lifelong scientific researches. She brings to life the determined personality of a great scientist at work. Her own autobiographical notes, included in this volume, reconstruct her own work on radiation which resulted in the isolation of radium. "A delightful book. It marks one of the few instances in which the proverbially humdrum life of the student of physical science, together with the austere ideals, has been made intelligible," New York Times. Unabridged reprint. Translated by Charlotte and Vernon Kellogg. Introduction by Mrs. Wm. Brown Meloney. 8 halftones. viii + 120pp. 5⅜ x 8½. T199 Paperbound **$1.00**

THE BOOK OF MY LIFE (DE VITA PROPRIA LIBER), Jerome Cardan. The remarkable autobiography of an important Renaissance mathematician, physician, and scientist, who at the same time was a paranoid, morbid, superstitious man, consumed with ambition and self-love (and self-pity). These chronicles of his fortunes and misfortunes make absorbing reading, giving us an extremely insightful view of a man's reactions and sensations—the first psychological autobiography. Through his eyes we can also see the superstitions and beliefs of an age, Renaissance medical practices, and the problems that concerned a trained mind in the 16th century. Unabridged republication of original English edition, translated by Jean Stoner. Introduction. Notes. Bibliography. xviii + 331pp. 5⅜ x 8½. T345 Paperbound **$1.60**

THE AUTOBIOGRAPHY OF CHARLES DARWIN, AND SELECTED LETTERS, edited by **Francis Darwin.** Darwin's own record of his early life; the historic voyage aboard the "Beagle"; the furor surrounding evolution, and his replies; reminiscences of his son. Letters to Henslow, Lyell, Hooker, Huxley, Wallace, Kingsley, etc., and thoughts on religion and vivisection. We see how he revolutionized geology with his concept of ocean subsidence; how his great books on variation of plants and animals, primitive man, the expression of emotion among primates, plant fertilization, carnivorous plants, protective coloration, etc., came into being. Appendix. Index. 365pp. 5⅜ x 8. T479 Paperbound **$1.65**

PHILOSOPHY OF SCIENCE AND MATHEMATICS

FOUNDATIONS OF SCIENCE: THE PHILOSOPHY OF THEORY AND EXPERIMENT, N. R. Campbell. A critique of the most fundamental concepts of science in general and physics in particular. Examines why certain propositions are accepted without question, demarcates science from philosophy, clarifies the understanding of the tools of science. Part One analyzes the presuppositions of scientific thought: existence of the material world, nature of scientific laws, multiplication of probabilities, etc.: Part Two covers the nature of experiment and the application of mathematics: conditions for measurement, relations between numerical laws and theories, laws of error, etc. An appendix covers problems arising from relativity, force, motion, space, and time. A classic in its field. Index. xiii + 565pp. 5⅝ x 8⅜.
S372 Paperbound **$2.95**

THE NATURE OF PHYSICAL THEORY, P. W. Bridgman. Here is how modern physics looks to a highly unorthodox physicist—a Nobel laureate. Pointing out many absurdities of science, and demonstrating the inadequacies of various physical theories, Dr. Bridgman weighs and analyzes the contributions of Einstein, Bohr, Newton, Heisenberg, and many others. This is a non-technical consideration of the correlation of science and reality. Index. xi + 138pp. 5⅜ x 8.
S33 Paperbound **$1.25**

THE VALUE OF SCIENCE, Henri Poincaré. Many of the most mature ideas of the "last scientific universalist" covered with charm and vigor for both the beginning student and the advanced worker. Discusses the nature of scientific truth, whether order is innate in the universe or imposed upon it by man, logical thought versus intuition (relating to math, through the works of Weierstrass, Lie, Klein, Riemann), time and space (relativity, psychological time, simultaneity), Hertz's concept of force, interrelationship of mathematical physics to pure math, values within disciplines of Maxwell, Carnot, Mayer, Newton, Lorentz, etc. Index. iii + 147pp. 5⅜ x 8.
S469 Paperbound **$1.35**

SCIENCE AND HYPOTHESIS, Henri Poincaré. Creative psychology in science. How such concepts as number, magnitude, space, force, classical mechanics were developed, and how the modern scientist uses them in his thought. Hypothesis in physics, theories of modern physics. Introduction by Sir James Larmor. "Few mathematicians have had the breadth of vision of Poincaré, and none is his superior in the gift of clear exposition," E. T. Bell. Index. 272pp. 5⅜ x 8.
S221 Paperbound **$1.35**

PHILOSOPHY AND THE PHYSICISTS, L. S. Stebbing. The philosophical aspects of modern science examined in terms of a lively critical attack on the ideas of Jeans and Eddington. Discusses the task of science, causality, determinism, probability, consciousness, the relation of the world of physics to that of everyday experience. Probes the philosophical significance of the Planck-Bohr concept of discontinuous energy levels, the inferences to be drawn from Heisenberg's Uncertainty Principle, the implications of "becoming" involved in the 2nd law of thermodynamics, and other problems posed by the discarding of Laplacean determinism. 285pp. 5⅜ x 8.
T480 Paperbound **$1.65**

THE PHILOSOPHICAL WRITINGS OF PEIRCE, edited by Justus Buchler. (Formerly published as THE PHILOSOPHY OF PEIRCE.) This is a carefully balanced exposition of Peirce's complete system, written by Peirce himself. It covers such matters as scientific method, pure chance vs. law, symbolic logic, theory of signs, pragmatism, experiment, and other topics. Introduction by Justus Buchler, Columbia University. xvi + 368pp. 5⅜ x 8.
T217 Paperbound **$2.00**

LANGUAGE, TRUTH AND LOGIC, A. Ayer. A clear introduction to the Vienna and Cambridge schools of Logical Positivism. It sets up specific tests by which you can evaluate validity of ideas, etc. Contents: Function of philosophy, elimination of metaphysics, nature of analysis, a priori, truth and probability, etc. 10th printing. "I should like to have written it myself," Bertrand Russell. Index. 160pp. 5⅜ x 8.
T10 Paperbound **$1.25**

MATHEMATICS AND SCIENCE: LAST ESSAYS (DERNIÈRES PENSÉES), Henri Poincaré. Translated by J. W. Bolduc. A posthumous volume of articles and lectures by the great French mathematician, philosopher, scientist. Here are nine pieces, never before translated into English, on such subjects as The Evolution of Laws, Space and Time, Space and 3 Dimensions, The Logic of infinity in Mathematics (discussing Russell's theory of types), Mathematics and Logic, The Quantum Theory and its Modern Applications, Relationship Between Matter and Ether, Ethics and Science and The Moral Alliance. First English translation of Dernières Pensées. New index. viii + 128pp. 5⅜ x 8½.
S1101 Paperbound **$1.25**

THE PSYCHOLOGY OF INVENTION IN THE MATHEMATICAL FIELD, J. Hadamard. Where do ideas come from? What role does the unconscious play? Are ideas best developed by mathematical reasoning, word reasoning, visualization? What are the methods used by Einstein, Poincaré, Galton, Riemann? How can these techniques be applied by others? Hadamard, one of the world's leading mathematicians, discusses these and other questions. xiii + 145pp. 5⅜ x 8.
T107 Paperbound **$1.25**

EXPERIMENT AND THEORY IN PHYSICS, Max Born. A Nobel laureate examines the nature and value of the counterclaims of experiment and theory in physics. Synthetic versus analytical scientific advances are analyzed in the work of Einstein, Bohr, Heisenberg, Planck, Eddington, Milne, and others by a fellow participant. 44pp. 5⅜ x 8. S308 Paperbound **75¢**

THE PHILOSOPHY OF SPACE AND TIME, H. Reichenbach. An important landmark in the development of the empiricist conception of geometry, covering the problem of the foundations of geometry, the theory of time, the consequences of Einstein's relativity, including: relations between theory and observations; coordinate and metrical properties of space; the psychological problem of visual intuition of non-Euclidean structures; and many other important topics in modern science and philosophy. The majority of ideas require only a knowledge of intermediate math. Introduction by R. Carnap. 49 figures. Index. xviii + 296pp. 5⅜ x 8.
S443 Paperbound **$2.00**

OBSERVATION AND INTERPRETATION IN THE PHILOSOPHY OF PHYSICS: WITH SPECIAL REFERENCE TO QUANTUM MECHANICS, Edited by S. Körner. A collection of papers by philosophers and physicists arising out of a symposium held at Bristol, England in 1957 under the auspices of the Colston Research Society. One of the most important contributions to the philosophy of science in recent years. The discussions center around the adequacy or inadequacy of quantum mechanics in its orthodox formulations. Among the contributors are A. J. Ayer, D. Bohm, K. Popper, F. Bopp, S. Körner, J. P. Vigier, M. Polanyi, P. K. Feyerabend, W. C. Kneale. W. B. Gallie, G. Ryle, Sir Charles Darwin, and R. B. Braithwaite. xiv + 218pp. 5⅜ x 8½. S131 Paperbound **$1.60**

SPACE AND TIME IN CONTEMPORARY PHYSICS: AN INTRODUCTION TO THE THEORY OF RELATIVITY AND GRAVITATION, Moritz Schlick. Exposition of the theory of relativity by the leader of the famed "Vienna Circle." Its essential purpose is to describe the physical doctrines of special and general relativity with particular reference to their philosophical significance. Explanations of such topics as the geometrical relativity of space, the connection with inertia and gravitation, the measure-determination of the space-time continuum, the finite universe, etc., with their philosophical ramifications. Index. xii + 89pp. 5⅜ x 8½.
T1008 Paperbound **$1.00**

SUBSTANCE AND FUNCTION, & EINSTEIN'S THEORY OF RELATIVITY, Ernst Cassirer. Two books bound as one. Cassirer establishes a philosophy of the exact sciences that takes into consideration newer developments in mathematics, and also shows historical connections. Partial contents: Aristotelian logic, Mill's analysis, Helmholtz & Kronecker, Russell & cardinal numbers, Euclidean vs. non-Euclidean geometry, Einstein's relativity. Bibliography. Index. xxi + 465pp. 5⅜ x 8. T50 Paperbound **$2.25**

PRINCIPLES OF MECHANICS, Heinrich Hertz. This last work by the great 19th century physicist is not only a classic, but of great interest in the logic of science. Creating a new system of mechanics based upon space, time, and mass, it returns to axiomatic analysis, to understanding of the formal or structural aspects of science, taking into account logic, observation, and a priori elements. Of great historical importance to Poincaré, Carnap, Einstein, Milne. A 20-page introduction by R. S. Cohen, Wesleyan University, analyzes the implications of Hertz's thought and the logic of science. Bibliography. 13-page introduction by Helmholtz. xlii + 274pp. 5⅜ x 8. S316 Clothbound **$3.50**
S317 Paperbound **$1.85**

THE ANALYSIS OF MATTER, Bertrand Russell. How do our senses concord with the new physics? This volume covers such topics as logical analysis of physics, prerelativity physics, causality, scientific inference, physics and perception, special and general relativity, Weyl's theory, tensors, invariants and their physical interpretation, periodicity and qualitative series. "The most thorough treatment of the subject that has yet been published," THE NATION. Introduction by L. E. Denonn. 422pp. 5⅜ x 8. T231 Paperbound **$1.95**

FOUNDATIONS OF GEOMETRY, Bertrand Russell. Analyzing basic problems in the overlap area between mathematics and philosophy, Nobel laureate Russell examines the nature of geometrical knowledge, the nature of geometry, and the application of geometry to space. It covers the history of non-Euclidean geometry, philosophic interpretations of geometry—especially Kant—projective and metrical geometry. This is most interesting as the solution offered in 1897 by a great mind to a problem still current. New introduction by Prof. Morris Kline of N. Y. University. xii + 201pp. 5⅜ x 8. S232 Clothbound **$3.25**
S233 Paperbound **$1.75**

IDENTITY AND REALITY, Emile Meyerson. Called by Einstein a "brilliant study in the theory of knowledge," this book by the renowned Franco-German thinker is a major treatise in the philosophy of science and epistemology. Thorough, critical inquiries into causality, scientific laws, conservation of matter and energy, the unity of matter, Carnot's principle, the irrational, the elimination of time. Searches out the solutions of epistemological questions that form the bases of the scientific method. Authorized translation by Kate Loewenberg. Author's prefaces. Editor's preface. Appendices. Index. 495pp. 5⅜ x 8½.
T65 Paperbound **$2.25**

ESSAYS IN EXPERIMENTAL LOGIC, John Dewey. This stimulating series of essays touches upon the relationship between inquiry and experience, dependence of knowledge upon thought, character of logic; judgments of practice, data and meanings, stimuli of thought, etc. Index. viii + 444pp. 5⅜ x 8. T73 Paperbound **$1.95**

PHYSICS

General physics

FOUNDATIONS OF PHYSICS, R. B. Lindsay & H. Margenau. Excellent bridge between semi-popular works & technical treatises. A discussion of methods of physical description, construction of theory; valuable for physicist with elementary calculus who is interested in ideas that give meaning to data, tools of modern physics. Contents include symbolism, mathematical equations; space & time foundations of mechanics; probability; physics & continua; electron theory; special & general relativity; quantum mechanics; causality. "Thorough and yet not overdetailed. Unreservedly recommended," NATURE (London). Unabridged, corrected edition. List of recommended readings. 35 illustrations. xi + 537pp. 5⅜ x 8.
S377 Paperbound **$2.75**

FUNDAMENTAL FORMULAS OF PHYSICS, ed. by D. H. Menzel. Highly useful, fully inexpensive reference and study text, ranging from simple to highly sophisticated operations. Mathematics integrated into text—each chapter stands as short textbook of field represented. Vol. 1: Statistics, Physical Constants, Special Theory of Relativity, Hydrodynamics, Aerodynamics, Boundary Value Problems in Math. Physics; Viscosity, Electromagnetic Theory, etc. Vol. 2: Sound, Acoustics, Geometrical Optics, Electron Optics, High-Energy Phenomena, Magnetism, Biophysics, much more. Index. Total of 800pp. 5⅜ x 8. Vol. 1 S595 Paperbound **$2.00**
Vol. 2 S596 Paperbound **$2.00**

MATHEMATICAL PHYSICS, D. H. Menzel. Thorough one-volume treatment of the mathematical techniques vital for classic mechanics, electromagnetic theory, quantum theory, and relativity. Written by the Harvard Professor of Astrophysics for junior, senior, and graduate courses, it gives clear explanations of all those aspects of function theory, vectors, matrices, dyadics, tensors, partial differential equations, etc., necessary for the understanding of the various physical theories. Electron theory, relativity, and other topics seldom presented appear here in considerable detail. Scores of definitions, conversion factors, dimensional constants, etc. "More detailed than normal for an advanced text . . . excellent set of sections on Dyadics, Matrices, and Tensors," JOURNAL OF THE FRANKLIN INSTITUTE. Index. 193 problems, with answers. x + 412pp. 5⅜ x 8. S56 Paperbound **$2.00**

THE SCIENTIFIC PAPERS OF J. WILLARD GIBBS. All the published papers of America's outstanding theoretical scientist (except for "Statistical Mechanics" and "Vector Analysis"). Vol I (thermodynamics) contains one of the most brilliant of all 19th-century scientific papers—the 300-page "On the Equilibrium of Heterogeneous Substances," which founded the science of physical chemistry, and clearly stated a number of highly important natural laws for the first time; 8 other papers complete the first volume. Vol II includes 2 papers on dynamics, 8 on vector analysis and multiple algebra, 5 on the electromagnetic theory of light, and 6 miscellaneous papers. Biographical sketch by H. A. Bumstead. Total of xxxvi + 718pp. 5⅝ x 8⅜.
S721 Vol I Paperbound **$2.50**
S722 Vol II Paperbound **$2.00**
The set **$4.50**

BASIC THEORIES OF PHYSICS, Peter Gabriel Bergmann. Two-volume set which presents a critical examination of important topics in the major subdivisions of classical and modern physics. The first volume is concerned with classical mechanics and electrodynamics: mechanics of mass points, analytical mechanics, matter in bulk, electrostatics and magnetostatics, electromagnetic interaction, the field waves, special relativity, and waves. The second volume (Heat and Quanta) contains discussions of the kinetic hypothesis, physics and statistics, stationary ensembles, laws of thermodynamics, early quantum theories, atomic spectra, probability waves, quantization in wave mechanics, approximation methods, and abstract quantum theory. A valuable supplement to any thorough course or text.
Heat and Quanta: Index. 8 figures. x + 300pp. 5⅜ x 8½. S968 Paperbound **$1.75**
Mechanics and Electrodynamics: Index. 14 figures. vii + 280pp. 5⅜ x 8½.
S969 Paperbound **$1.75**

THEORETICAL PHYSICS, A. S. Kompaneyets. One of the very few thorough studies of the subject in this price range. Provides advanced students with a comprehensive theoretical background. Especially strong on recent experimentation and developments in quantum theory. Contents: Mechanics (Generalized Coordinates, Lagrange's Equation, Collision of Particles, etc.), Electrodynamics (Vector Analysis, Maxwell's equations, Transmission of Signals, Theory of Relativity, etc.), Quantum Mechanics (the Inadequacy of Classical Mechanics, the Wave Equation, Motion in a Central Field, Quantum Theory of Radiation, Quantum Theories of Dispersion and Scattering, etc.), and Statistical Physics (Equilibrium Distribution of Molecules in an Ideal Gas, Boltzmann statistics, Bose and Fermi Distribution, Thermodynamic Quantities, etc.). Revised to 1961. Translated by George Yankovsky, authorized by Kompaneyets. 137 exercises. 56 figures. 529pp. 5⅜ x 8½. S972 Paperbound **$2.50**

ANALYTICAL AND CANONICAL FORMALISM IN PHYSICS, André Mercier. A survey, in one volume, of the variational principles (the key principles—in mathematical form—from which the basic laws of any one branch of physics can be derived) of the several branches of physical theory, together with an examination of the relationships among them. Contents: the Lagrangian Formalism, Lagrangian Densities, Canonical Formalism, Canonical Form of Electrodynamics, Hamiltonian Densities, Transformations, and Canonical Form with Vanishing Jacobian Determinant. Numerous examples and exercises. For advanced students, teachers, etc. 6 figures. Index. viii + 222pp. 5⅜ x 8½. S1077 Paperbound **$1.75**

Acoustics, optics, electricity and magnetism, electromagnetics, magneto-hydrodynamics

THE THEORY OF SOUND, Lord Rayleigh. Most vibrating systems likely to be encountered in practice can be tackled successfully by the methods set forth by the great Nobel laureate, Lord Rayleigh. Complete coverage of experimental, mathematical aspects of sound theory. Partial contents: Harmonic motions, vibrating systems in general, lateral vibrations of bars, curved plates or shells, applications of Laplace's functions to acoustical problems, fluid friction, plane vortex-sheet, vibrations of solid bodies, etc. This is the first inexpensive edition of this great reference and study work. Bibliography. Historical introduction by R. B. Lindsay. Total of 1040pp. 97 figures. 5⅜ x 8.
S292, S293, Two volume set, paperbound, **$4.70**

THE DYNAMICAL THEORY OF SOUND, H. Lamb. Comprehensive mathematical treatment of the physical aspects of sound, covering the theory of vibrations, the general theory of sound, and the equations of motion of strings, bars, membranes, pipes, and resonators. Includes chapters on plane, spherical, and simple harmonic waves, and the Helmholtz Theory of Audition. Complete and self-contained development for student and specialist; all fundamental differential equations solved completely. Specific mathematical details for such important phenomena as harmonics, normal modes, forced vibrations of strings, theory of reed pipes, etc. Index. Bibliography. 86 diagrams. viii + 307pp. 5⅜ x 8. S655 Paperbound **$1.50**

WAVE PROPAGATION IN PERIODIC STRUCTURES, L. Brillouin. A general method and application to different problems: pure physics, such as scattering of X-rays of crystals, thermal vibration in crystal lattices, electronic motion in metals; and also problems of electrical engineering. Partial contents: elastic waves in 1-dimensional lattices of point masses. Propagation of waves along 1-dimensional lattices. Energy flow. 2 dimensional, 3 dimensional lattices. Mathieu's equation. Matrices and propagation of waves along an electric line. Continuous electric lines. 131 illustrations. Bibliography. Index. xii + 253pp. 5⅜ x 8.
S34 Paperbound **$2.00**

THEORY OF VIBRATIONS, N. W. McLachlan. Based on an exceptionally successful graduate course given at Brown University, this discusses linear systems having 1 degree of freedom, forced vibrations of simple linear systems, vibration of flexible strings, transverse vibrations of bars and tubes, transverse vibration of circular plate, sound waves of finite amplitude, etc. Index. 99 diagrams. 160pp. 5⅜ x 8. S190 Paperbound **$1.35**

LIGHT: PRINCIPLES AND EXPERIMENTS, George S. Monk. Covers theory, experimentation, and research. Intended for students with some background in general physics and elementary calculus. Three main divisions: 1) Eight chapters on geometrical optics—fundamental concepts (the ray and its optical length, Fermat's principle, etc.), laws of image formation, apertures in optical systems, photometry, optical instruments etc.; 2) 9 chapters on physical optics—interference, diffraction, polarization, spectra, the Rayleigh refractometer, the wave theory of light, etc.; 3) 23 instructive experiments based directly on the theoretical text. "Probably the best intermediate textbook on light in the English language. Certainly, it is the best book which includes both geometrical and physical optics," J. Rud Nielson, PHYSICS FORUM. Revised edition. 102 problems and answers. 12 appendices. 6 tables. Index. 270 illustrations. xi +489pp. 5⅜ x 8½. S341 Paperbound **$2.50**

PHOTOMETRY, John W. T. Walsh. The best treatment of both "bench" and "illumination" photometry in English by one of Britain's foremost experts in the field (President of the International Commission on Illumination). Limited to those matters, theoretical and practical, which affect the measurement of light flux, candlepower, illumination, etc., and excludes treatment of the use to which such measurements may be put after they have been made. Chapters on Radiation, The Eye and Vision, Photo-Electric Cells, The Principles of Photometry, The Measurement of Luminous Intensity, Colorimetry, Spectrophotometry, Stellar Photometry, The Photometric Laboratory, etc. Third revised (1958) edition. 281 illustrations. 10 appendices. xxiv + 544pp. 5½ x 9¼. S319 Clothbound **$10.00**

EXPERIMENTAL SPECTROSCOPY, R. A. Sawyer. Clear discussion of prism and grating spectrographs and the techniques of their use in research, with emphasis on those principles and techniques that are fundamental to practically all uses of spectroscopic equipment. Beginning with a brief history of spectroscopy, the author covers such topics as light sources, spectroscopic apparatus, prism spectroscopes and graphs, diffraction grating, the photographic process, determination of wave length, spectral intensity, infrared spectroscopy, spectrochemical analysis, etc. This revised edition contains new material on the production of replica gratings, solar spectroscopy from rockets, new standard of wave length, etc. Index. Bibliography. 111 illustrations. x + 358pp. 5⅜ x 8½. S1045 Paperbound **$2.25**

FUNDAMENTALS OF ELECTRICITY AND MAGNETISM, L. B. Loeb. For students of physics, chemistry, or engineering who want an introduction to electricity and magnetism on a higher level and in more detail than general elementary physics texts provide. Only elementary differential and integral calculus is assumed. Physical laws developed logically, from magnetism to electric currents, Ohm's law, electrolysis, and on to static electricity, induction, etc. Covers an unusual amount of material; one third of book on modern material: solution of wave equation, photoelectric and thermionic effects, etc. Complete statement of the various electrical systems of units and interrelations. 2 Indexes. 75 pages of problems with answers stated. Over 300 figures and diagrams. xix +669pp. 5⅜ x 8. S745 Paperbound **$2.75**

MATHEMATICAL ANALYSIS OF ELECTRICAL AND OPTICAL WAVE-MOTION, Harry Bateman. Written by one of this century's most distinguished mathematical physicists, this is a practical introduction to those developments of Maxwell's electromagnetic theory which are directly connected with the solution of the partial differential equation of wave motion. Methods of solving wave-equation, polar-cylindrical coordinates, diffraction, transformation of coordinates, homogeneous solutions, electromagnetic fields with moving singularities, etc. Index. 168pp. 5⅜ x 8. S14 Paperbound **$1.75**

PRINCIPLES OF PHYSICAL OPTICS, Ernst Mach. This classical examination of the propagation of light, color, polarization, etc. offers an historical and philosophical treatment that has never been surpassed for breadth and easy readability. Contents: Rectilinear propagation of light. Reflection, refraction. Early knowledge of vision. Dioptrics. Composition of light. Theory of color and dispersion. Periodicity. Theory of interference. Polarization. Mathematical representation of properties of light. Propagation of waves, etc. 279 illustrations, 10 portraits. Appendix. Indexes. 324pp. 5⅜ x 8. S178 Paperbound **$2.00**

THE THEORY OF OPTICS, Paul Drude. One of finest fundamental texts in physical optics, classic offers thorough coverage, complete mathematical treatment of basic ideas. Includes fullest treatment of application of thermodynamics to optics; sine law in formation of images, transparent crystals, magnetically active substances, velocity of light, apertures, effects depending upon them, polarization, optical instruments, etc. Introduction by A. A. Michelson. Index. 110 illus. 567pp. 5⅜ x 8. S532 Paperbound **$2.45**

ELECTRICAL THEORY ON THE GIORGI SYSTEM, P. Cornelius. A new clarification of the fundamental concepts of electricity and magnetism, advocating the convenient m.k.s. system of units that is steadily gaining followers in the sciences. Illustrating the use and effectiveness of his terminology with numerous applications to concrete technical problems, the author here expounds the famous Giorgi system of electrical physics. His lucid presentation and well-reasoned, cogent argument for the universal adoption of this system form one of the finest pieces of scientific exposition in recent years. 28 figures. Index. Conversion tables for translating earlier data into modern units. Translated from 3rd Dutch edition by L. J. Jolley. x + 187pp. 5½ x 8¾. S909 Clothbound **$6.00**

ELECTRIC WAVES: BEING RESEARCHES ON THE PROPAGATION OF ELECTRIC ACTION WITH FINITE VELOCITY THROUGH SPACE, Heinrich Hertz. This classic work brings together the original papers in which Hertz—Helmholtz's protegé and one of the most brilliant figures in 19th-century research—probed the existence of electromagnetic waves and showed experimentally that their velocity equalled that of light, research that helped lay the groundwork for the development of radio, television, telephone, telegraph, and other modern technological marvels. Unabridged republication of original edition. Authorized translation by D. E. Jones. Preface by Lord Kelvin. Index of names. 40 illustrations. xvii + 278pp. 5⅜ x 8½. S57 Paperbound **$1.75**

PIEZOELECTRICITY: AN INTRODUCTION TO THE THEORY AND APPLICATIONS OF ELECTROMECHANICAL PHENOMENA IN CRYSTALS, Walter G. Cady. This is the most complete and systematic coverage of this important field in print—now regarded as something of scientific classic. This republication, revised and corrected by Prof. Cady—one of the foremost contributors in this area—contains a sketch of recent progress and new material on Ferroelectrics. Time Standards, etc. The first 7 chapters deal with fundamental theory of crystal electricity. 5 important chapters cover basic concepts of piezoelectricity, including comparisons of various competing theories in the field. Also discussed: piezoelectric resonators (theory, methods of manufacture, influences of air-gaps, etc.); the piezo oscillator; the properties, history, and observations relating to Rochelle salt; ferroelectric crystals; miscellaneous applications of piezoelectricity; pyroelectricity; etc. "A great work," W. A. Wooster, NATURE. Revised (1963) and corrected edition. New preface by Prof. Cady. 2 Appendices. Indices. Illustrations. 62 tables. Bibliography. Problems. Total of 1 + 822pp. 5⅜ x 8½.
S1094 Vol. I Paperbound **$2.50**
S1095 Vol. II Paperbound **$2.50**
Two volume set Paperbound **$5.00**

MAGNETISM AND VERY LOW TEMPERATURES, H. B. G. Casimir. A basic work in the literature of low temperature physics. Presents a concise survey of fundamental theoretical principles, and also points out promising lines of investigation. Contents: Classical Theory and Experimental Methods, Quantum Theory of Paramagnetism, Experiments on Adiabatic Demagnetization. Theoretical Discussion of Paramagnetism at Very Low Temperatures, Some Experimental Results, Relaxation Phenomena. Index. 89-item bibliography. ix + 95pp. 5⅜ x 8. S943 Paperbound **$1.25**

SELECTED PAPERS ON NEW TECHNIQUES FOR ENERGY CONVERSION: THERMOELECTRIC METHODS; THERMIONIC; PHOTOVOLTAIC AND ELECTRICAL EFFECTS; FUSION, Edited by Sumner N. Levine. Brings together in one volume the most important papers (1954-1961) in modern energy technology. Included among the 37 papers are general and qualitative descriptions of the field as a whole, indicating promising lines of research. Also: 15 papers on thermoelectric methods, 7 on thermionic, 5 on photovoltaic, 4 on electrochemical effect, and 2 on controlled fusion research. Among the contributors are: Joffe, Maria Telkes, Herold, Herring, Douglas, Jaumot, Post, Austin, Wilson, Pfann, Rappaport, Morehouse, Domenicali, Moss, Bowers, Harman, Von Doenhoef. Preface and introduction by the editor. Bibliographies. xxviii + 451pp. 6⅛ x 9¼. S37 Paperbound **$3.00**

SUPERFLUIDS: MACROSCOPIC THEORY OF SUPERCONDUCTIVITY, Vol. I, Fritz London. The major work by one of the founders and great theoreticians of modern quantum physics. Consolidates the researches that led to the present understanding of the nature of superconductivity. Prof. London here reveals that quantum mechanics is operative on the macroscopic plane as well as the submolecular level. Contents: Properties of Superconductors and Their Thermodynamical Correlation; Electrodynamics of the Pure Superconducting State; Relation between Current and Field; Measurements of the Penetration Depth; Non-Viscous Flow vs. Superconductivity; Micro-waves in Superconductors; Reality of the Domain Structure; and many other related topics. A new epilogue by M. J. Buckingham discusses developments in the field up to 1960. Corrected and expanded edition. An appreciation of the author's life and work by L. W. Nordheim. Biography by Edith London. Bibliography of his publications. 45 figures. 2 Indices. xviii + 173pp. 5⅝ x 8⅜. S44 Paperbound **$1.45**

SELECTED PAPERS ON PHYSICAL PROCESSES IN IONIZED PLASMAS, Edited by Donald H. Menzel, Director, Harvard College Observatory. 30 important papers relating to the study of highly ionized gases or plasmas selected by a foremost contributor in the field, with the assistance of Dr. L. H. Aller. The essays include 18 on the physical processes in gaseous nebulae, covering problems of radiation and radiative transfer, the Balmer decrement, electron temperatives, spectrophotometry, etc. 10 papers deal with the interpretation of nebular spectra, by Bohm, Van Vleck, Aller, Minkowski, etc. There is also a discussion of the intensities of "forbidden" spectral lines by George Shortley and a paper concerning the theory of hydrogenic spectra by Menzel and Pekeris. Other contributors: Goldberg, Hebb, Baker, Bowen, Ufford, Liller, etc. viii + 374pp. 6⅛ x 9¼. S60 Paperbound **$2.95**

THE ELECTROMAGNETIC FIELD, Max Mason & Warren Weaver. Used constantly by graduate engineers. Vector methods exclusively: detailed treatment of electrostatics, expansion methods, with tables converting any quantity into absolute electromagnetic, absolute electrostatic, practical units. Discrete charges, ponderable bodies, Maxwell field equations, etc. Introduction. Indexes. 416pp. 5⅜ x 8. S185 Paperbound **$2.00**

THEORY OF ELECTRONS AND ITS APPLICATION TO THE PHENOMENA OF LIGHT AND RADIANT HEAT, H. Lorentz. Lectures delivered at Columbia University by Nobel laureate Lorentz. Unabridged, they form a historical coverage of the theory of free electrons, motion, absorption of heat, Zeeman effect, propagation of light in molecular bodies, inverse Zeeman effect, optical phenomena in moving bodies, etc. 109 pages of notes explain the more advanced sections. Index. 9 figures. 352pp. 5⅜ x 8. S173 Paperbound **$1.85**

FUNDAMENTAL ELECTROMAGNETIC THEORY, Ronold P. King, Professor Applied Physics, Harvard University. Original and valuable introduction to electromagnetic theory and to circuit theory from the standpoint of electromagnetic theory. Contents: Mathematical Description of Matter—stationary and nonstationary states; Mathematical Description of Space and of Simple Media—Field Equations, Integral Forms of Field Equations, Electromagnetic Force, etc.; Transformation of Field and Force Equations; Electromagnetic Waves in Unbounded Regions; Skin Effect and Internal Impedance—in a solid cylindrical conductor, etc.; and Electrical Circuits—Analytical Foundations, Near-zone and quasi-near zone circuits, Balanced two-wire and four-wire transmission lines. Revised and enlarged version. New preface by the author. 5 appendices (Differential operators: Vector Formulas and Identities, etc.). Problems. Indexes. Bibliography. xvi + 580pp. 5⅜ x 8½. S1023 Paperbound **$2.75**

Hydrodynamics

A TREATISE ON HYDRODYNAMICS, A. B. Basset. Favorite text on hydrodynamics for 2 generations of physicists, hydrodynamical engineers, oceanographers, ship designers, etc. Clear enough for the beginning student, and thorough source for graduate students and engineers on the work of d'Alembert, Euler, Laplace, Lagrange, Poisson, Green, Clebsch, Stokes, Cauchy, Helmholtz, J. J. Thomson, Love, Hicks, Greenhill, Besant, Lamb, etc. Great amount of documentation on entire theory of classical hydrodynamics. Vol I: theory of motion of frictionless liquids, vortex, and cyclic irrotational motion, etc. 132 exercises. Bibliography. 3 Appendixes. xii + 264pp. Vol II: motion in viscous liquids, harmonic analysis, theory of tides, etc. 112 exercises, Bibliography. 4 Appendixes. xv + 328pp. Two volume set. 5⅜ x 8.

S724 Vol I Paperbound **$1.75**
S725 Vol II Paperbound **$1.75**
The set **$3.50**

HYDRODYNAMICS, Horace Lamb. Internationally famous complete coverage of standard reference work on dynamics of liquids & gases. Fundamental theorems, equations, methods, solutions, background, for classical hydrodynamics. Chapters include Equations of Motion, Integration of Equations in Special Gases, Irrotational Motion, Motion of Liquid in 2 Dimensions, Motion of Solids through Liquid-Dynamical Theory, Vortex Motion, Tidal Waves, Surface Waves, Waves of Expansion, Viscosity, Rotating Masses of liquids. Excellently planned, arranged; clear, lucid presentation. 6th enlarged, revised edition. Index. Over 900 footnotes, mostly bibliographical. 119 figures. xv + 738pp. 6⅛ x 9¼. S256 Paperbound **$3.75**

PHYSICS, HISTORIES AND CLASSICS

A HISTORY OF PHYSICS: IN ITS ELEMENTARY BRANCHES (THROUGH 1925), INCLUDING THE EVOLUTION OF PHYSICAL LABORATORIES, Florian Cajori. Revised and enlarged edition. The only first-rate brief history of physics. Still the best entry for a student or teacher into the antecedents of modern theories of physics. A clear, non-mathematical, handy reference work which traces in critical fashion the developments of ideas, theories, techniques, and apparatus from the Greeks to the 1920's. Within each period he analyzes the basic topics of mechanics, light, electricity and magnetism, sound, atomic theory and structure of matter, radioactivity, etc. A chapter on modern research: Curie, Kelvin, Planck's quantum theory, thermodynamics, Fitzgerald and Lorentz, special and general relativity, J. J. Thomson's model of an atom, Bohr's discoveries and later results, wave mechanics, and many other matters. Much bibliographic detail in footnotes. Index. 16 figures. xv + 424pp. 5⅜ x 8. T970 Paperbound **$2.00**

A HISTORY OF THE MATHEMATICAL THEORIES OF ATTRACTION AND THE FIGURE OF THE EARTH: FROM THE TIME OF NEWTON TO THAT OF LAPLACE, I. Todhunter. A technical and detailed review of the theories concerning the shape of the earth and its gravitational pull, from the earliest investigations in the seventeenth century up to the middle of the nineteenth. Some of the greatest mathematicians and scientists in history applied themselves to these questions: Newton ("Principia Mathematica"), Huygens, Maupertuis, Simpson, d'Alembert, etc. Others discussed are Poisson, Gauss, Plana, Lagrange, Boit, and many more. Particular emphasis is placed on the theories of Laplace and Legendre, several chapters being devoted to Laplace's "Mécanique Céleste" and his memoirs, and several others to the memoirs of Legendre. Important to historians of science and mathematics and to the specialist who desires background information in the field. 2 volumes bound as 1. Index. xxxvi + 984pp. 5⅜ x 8.
S148 Clothbound **$7.50**

OPTICKS, Sir Isaac Newton. In its discussions of light, reflection, color, refraction, theories of wave and corpuscular theories of light, this work is packed with scores of insights and discoveries. In its precise and practical discussion of construction of optical apparatus, contemporary understandings of phenomena it is truly fascinating to modern physicists, astronomers, mathematicians. Foreword by Albert Einstein. Preface by I. B. Cohen of Harvard University. 7 pages of portraits, facsimile pages, letters, etc. cxvi + 414pp. 5⅜ x 8.
S205 Paperbound **$2.25**

TREATISE ON LIGHT, Christiaan Huygens. The famous original formulation of the wave theory of light, this readable book is one of the two decisive and definitive works in the field of light (Newton's "Optics" is the other). A scientific giant whose researches ranged over mathematics, astronomy, and physics, Huygens, in this historic work, covers such topics as rays propagated in straight lines, reflection and refraction, the spreading and velocity of light, the nature of opaque bodies, the non-spherical nature of light in the atmosphere, properties of Iceland Crystal, and other related matters. Unabridged republication of original (1912) English edition. Translated and introduced by Silvanus P. Thompson. 52 illustrations. xii + 129pp. 5⅜ x 8. S179 Paperbound **$1.35**

FARADAY'S EXPERIMENTAL RESEARCHES IN ELECTRICITY. Faraday's historic series of papers containing the fruits of years of original experimentation in electrical theory and electrochemistry. Covers his findings in a variety of areas: Induction of electric currents, Evolution of electricity from magnetism, New electrical state or condition of matter, Explication of Arago's magnetic phenomena, New law of electric conduction, Electro-chemical decomposition, Electricity of the Voltaic Pile, Static Induction, Nature of the electric force or forces, Nature of electric current, The character and direction of the electric force of the Gymnotus, Magneto-electric spark, The magnetization of light and the illumination of magnetic lines of force, The possible relation of gravity to electricity, Sub-terraneous electro-telegraph wires, Some points of magnetic philosophy, The diamagnetic conditions of flame and gases, and many other matters. Complete and unabridged republication. 3 vols. bound as 2. Originally reprinted from the Philosophical Transactions of 1831-8. Indices. Illustrations. Total of 1463pp. 5⅜ x 8. S783-4, Clothbound **$17.50** (tentative)

REFLECTIONS ON THE MOTIVE POWER OF FIRE, Sadi Carnot, and other papers on the 2nd law of thermodynamics by E. Clapeyron and R. Clausius. Carnot's "Reflections" laid the groundwork of modern thermodynamics. Its non-technical, mostly verbal statements examine the relations between heat and the work done by heat in engines, establishing conditions for the economical working of these engines. The papers by Clapeyron and Clausius here reprinted added further refinements to Carnot's work, and led to its final acceptance by physicists. Selections from posthumous manuscripts of Carnot are also included. All papers in English. New introduction by E. Mendoza. 12 illustrations. xxii + 152pp. 5⅜ x 8.
S661 Paperbound **$1.50**

DIALOGUES CONCERNING TWO NEW SCIENCES, Galileo Galilei. This classic of experimental science, mechanics, engineering, is as enjoyable as it is important. A great historical document giving insights into one of the world's most original thinkers, it is based on 30 years' experimentation. It offers a lively exposition of dynamics, elasticity, sound, ballistics, strength of materials, the scientific method. "Superior to everything else of mine," Galileo. Trans. by H. Crew, A. Salvio. 126 diagrams. Index. xxi + 288pp. 5⅜ x 8.
S99 Paperbound **$1.75**

ENGINEERING AND TECHNOLOGY

General and mathematical

ENGINEERING MATHEMATICS, Kenneth S. Miller. A text for graduate students of engineering to strengthen their mathematical background in differential equations, etc. Mathematical steps very explicitly indicated. Contents: Determinants and Matrices, Integrals, Linear Differential Equations, Fourier Series and Integrals, Laplace Transform, Network Theory, Random Function . . . all vital requisites for advanced modern engineering studies. Unabridged republication. Appendices: Borel Sets; Riemann-Stieltjes Integral; Fourier Series and Integrals. Index. References at Chapter Ends. xii + 417pp. 6 x 8½. S1121 Paperbound **$2.00**

MATHEMATICAL ENGINEERING ANALYSIS, Rufus Oldenburger. A book designed to assist the research engineer and scientist in making the transition from physical engineering situations to the corresponding mathematics. Scores of common practical situations found in all major fields of physics are supplied with their correct mathematical formulations—applications to automobile springs and shock absorbers, clocks, throttle torque of diesel engines, resistance networks, capacitors, transmission lines, microphones, neon tubes, gasoline engines, refrigeration cycles, etc. Each section reviews basic principles of underlying various fields: mechanics of rigid bodies, electricity and magnetism, heat, elasticity, fluid mechanics, and aerodynamics. Comprehensive and eminently useful. Index. 169 problems, answers. 200 photos and diagrams. xiv + 426pp. 5⅜ x 8½. S919 Paperbound **$2.00**

MATHEMATICS OF MODERN ENGINEERING, E. G. Keller and R. E. Doherty. Written for the Advanced Course in Engineering of the General Electric Corporation, deals with the engineering use of determinants, tensors, the Heaviside operational calculus, dyadics, the calculus of variations, etc. Presents underlying principles fully, but purpose is to teach engineers to deal with modern engineering problems, and emphasis is on the perennial engineering attack of set-up and solve. Indexes. Over 185 figures and tables. Hundreds of exercises, problems, and worked-out examples. References. Two volume set. Total of xxxiii + 623pp. 5⅜ x 8.
S734 Vol I Paperbound **$1.85**
S735 Vol II Paperbound **$1.85**
The set **$3.70**

MATHEMATICAL METHODS FOR SCIENTISTS AND ENGINEERS, L. P. Smith. For scientists and engineers, as well as advanced math students. Full investigation of methods and practical description of conditions under which each should be used. Elements of real functions, differential and integral calculus, space geometry, theory of residues, vector and tensor analysis, series of Bessel functions, etc. Each method illustrated by completely-worked-out examples, mostly from scientific literature. 368 graded unsolved problems. 100 diagrams. x + 453pp. 5⅝ x 8⅜. S220 Paperbound **$2.00**

THEORY OF FUNCTIONS AS APPLIED TO ENGINEERING PROBLEMS, edited by R. Rothe, F. Ollendorff, and K. Pohlhausen. A series of lectures given at the Berlin Institute of Technology that shows the specific applications of function theory in electrical and allied fields of engineering. Six lectures provide the elements of function theory in a simple and practical form, covering complex quantities and variables, integration in the complex plane, residue theorems, etc. Then 5 lectures show the exact uses of this powerful mathematical tool, with full discussions of problem methods. Index. Bibliography. 108 figures. x + 189pp. 5⅜ x 8.
S733 Paperbound **$1.35**

Aerodynamics and hydrodynamics

AIRPLANE STRUCTURAL ANALYSIS AND DESIGN, E. E. Sechler and L. G. Dunn. Systematic authoritative book which summarizes a large amount of theoretical and experimental work on structural analysis and design. Strong on classical subsonic material still basic to much aeronautic design . . . remains a highly useful source of information. Covers such areas as layout of the airplane, applied and design loads, stress-strain relationships for stable structures, truss and frame analysis, the problem of instability, the ultimate strength of stiffened flat sheet, analysis of cylindrical structures, wings and control surfaces, fuselage analysis, engine mounts, landing gears, etc. Originally published as part of the CALCIT Aeronautical Series. 256 Illustrations. 47 study problems. Indexes. xi + 420pp. 5⅜ x 8½.
S1043 Paperbound **$2.25**

FUNDAMENTALS OF HYDRO- AND AEROMECHANICS, L. Prandtl and O. G. Tietjens. The well-known standard work based upon Prandtl's lectures at Goettingen. Wherever possible hydrodynamics theory is referred to practical considerations in hydraulics, with the view of unifying theory and experience. Presentation is extremely clear and though primarily physical, mathematical proofs are rigorous and use vector analysis to a considerable extent. An Engineering Society Monograph, 1934. 186 figures. Index. xvi + 270pp. 5⅜ x 8.
S374 Paperbound **$1.85**

FLUID MECHANICS FOR HYDRAULIC ENGINEERS, H. Rouse. Standard work that gives a coherent picture of fluid mechanics from the point of view of the hydraulic engineer. Based on courses given to civil and mechanical engineering students at Columbia and the California Institute of Technology, this work covers every basic principle, method, equation, or theory of interest to the hydraulic engineer. Much of the material, diagrams, charts, etc., in this self-contained text are not duplicated elsewhere. Covers irrotational motion, conformal mapping, problems in laminar motion, fluid turbulence, flow around immersed bodies, transportation of sediment, general charcteristics of wave phenomena, gravity waves in open channels, etc. Index. Appendix of physical properties of common fluids. Frontispiece + 245 figures and photographs. xvi + 422pp. 5⅜ x 8. S729 Paperbound **$2.25**

WATERHAMMER ANALYSIS, John Parmakian. Valuable exposition of the graphical method of solving waterhammer problems by Assistant Chief Designing Engineer, U.S. Bureau of Reclamation. Discussions of rigid and elastic water column theory, velocity of waterhammer waves, theory of graphical waterhammer analysis for gate operation, closings, openings, rapid and slow movements, etc., waterhammer in pump discharge caused by power failure, waterhammer analysis for compound pipes, and numerous related problems. "With a concise and lucid style, clear printing, adequate bibliography and graphs for approximate solutions at the project stage, it fills a vacant place in waterhammer literature," WATER POWER. 43 problems. Bibliography. Index. 113 illustrations. xiv + 161pp. 5⅜ x 8½.
S1061 Paperbound **$1.65**

AERODYNAMIC THEORY: A GENERAL REVIEW OF PROGRESS, William F. Durand, editor-in-chief. A monumental joint effort by the world's leading authorities prepared under a grant of the Guggenheim Fund for the Promotion of Aeronautics. Intended to provide the student and aeronautic designer with the theoretical and experimental background of aeronautics. Never equalled for breadth, depth, reliability. Contains discussions of special mathematical topics not usually taught in the engineering or technical courses. Also: an extended two-part treatise on Fluid Mechanics, discussions of aerodynamics of perfect fluids, analyses of experiments with wind tunnels, applied airfoil theory, the non-lifting system of the airplane, the air propeller, hydrodynamics of boats and floats, the aerodynamics of cooling, etc. Contributing experts include Munk, Giacomelli, Prandtl, Toussaint, Von Karman, Klemperer, among others. Unabridged republication. 6 volumes bound as 3. Total of 1,012 figures, 12 plates. Total of 2,186pp. Bibliographies. Notes. Indices. 5⅜ x 8.
S328-S330 Clothbound, The Set **$17.50**

APPLIED HYDRO- AND AEROMECHANICS, L. Prandtl and O. G. Tietjens. Presents, for the most part, methods which will be valuable to engineers. Covers flow in pipes, boundary layers, airfoil theory, entry conditions, turbulent flow in pipes, and the boundary layer, determining drag from measurements of pressure and velocity, etc. "Will be welcomed by all students of aerodynamics," NATURE. Unabridged, unaltered. An Engineering Society Monograph, 1934. Index. 226 figures, 28 photographic plates illustrating flow patterns. xvi + 311pp. 5⅜ x 8.
S375 Paperbound **$1.85**

SUPERSONIC AERODYNAMICS, E. R. C. Miles. Valuable theoretical introduction to the supersonic domain, with emphasis on mathematical tools and principles, for practicing aerodynamicists and advanced students in aeronautical engineering. Covers fundamental theory, divergence theorem and principles of circulation, compressible flow and Helmholtz laws, the Prandtl-Busemann graphic method for 2-dimensional flow, oblique shock waves, the Taylor-Maccoll method for cones in supersonic flow, the Chaplygin method for 2-dimensional flow, etc. Problems range from practical engineering problems to development of theoretical results. "Rendered outstanding by the unprecedented scope of its contents . . . has undoubtedly filled a vital gap," AERONAUTICAL ENGINEERING REVIEW. Index. 173 problems, answers. 106 diagrams. 7 tables. xii + 255pp. 5⅜ x 8. S214 Paperbound **$1.45**

HYDRAULIC TRANSIENTS, G. R. Rich. The best text in hydraulics ever printed in English . . . by one of America's foremost engineers (former Chief Design Engineer for T.V.A.). Provides a transition from the basic differential equations of hydraulic transient theory to the arithmetic intergration computation required by practicing engineers. Sections cover Water Hammer, Turbine Speed Regulation, Stability of Governing, Water-Hammer Pressures in Pump Discharge Lines, The Differential and Restricted Orifice Surge Tanks, The Normalized Surge Tank Charts of Calame and Gaden, Navigation Locks, Surges in Power Canals—Tidal Harmonics, etc. Revised and enlarged. Author's prefaces. Index. xiv + 409pp. 5⅜ x 8½.
S116 Paperbound **$2.50**

HYDRAULICS AND ITS APPLICATIONS, A. H. Gibson. Excellent comprehensive textbook for the student and thorough practical manual for the professional worker, a work of great stature in its area. Half the book is devoted to theory and half to applications and practical problems met in the field. Covers modes of motion of a fluid, critical velocity, viscous flow, eddy formation, Bernoulli's theorem, flow in converging passages, vortex motion, form of effluent streams, notches and weirs, skin friction, losses at valves and elbows, siphons, erosion of channels, jet propulsion, waves of oscillation, and over 100 similar topics. Final chapters (nearly 400 pages) cover more than 100 kinds of hydraulic machinery: Pelton wheel, speed regulators, the hydraulic ram, surge tanks, the scoop wheel, the Venturi meter, etc. A special chapter treats methods of testing theoretical hypotheses: scale models of rivers, tidal estuaries, siphon spillways, etc. 5th revised and enlarged (1952) edition. Index. Appendix. 427 photographs and diagrams. 95 examples, answers. xv + 813pp. 6 x 9.
S791 Clothbound **$8.00**

FLUID MECHANICS THROUGH WORKED EXAMPLES, D. R. L. Smith and J. Houghton. Advanced text covering principles and applications to practical situations. Each chapter begins with concise summaries of fundamental ideas. 163 fully worked out examples applying principles outlined in the text. 275 other problems, with answers. Contents; The Pressure of Liquids on Surfaces; Floating Bodies; Flow Under Constant Head in Pipes; Circulation; Vorticity; The Potential Function; Laminar Flow and Lubrication; Impact of Jets; Hydraulic Turbines; Centrifugal and Reciprocating Pumps; Compressible Fluids; and many other items. Total of 438 examples. 250 line illustrations. 340pp. Index. 6 x 8⅞. S981 Clothbound **$6.00**

THEORY OF SHIP MOTIONS, S. N. Blagoveshchensky. The only detailed text in English in a rapidly developing branch of engineering and physics, it is the work of one of the world's foremost authorities—Blagoveshchensky of Leningrad Shipbuilding Institute. A senior-level treatment written primarily for engineering students, but also of great importance to naval architects, designers, contractors, researchers in hydrodynamics, and other students. No mathematics beyond ordinary differential equations is required for understanding the text. Translated by T. & L. Strelkoff, under editorship of Louis Landweber, Iowa Institute of Hydraulic Research, under auspices of Office of Naval Research. Bibliography. Index. 231 diagrams and illustrations. Total of 649pp. 5⅜ x 8½. Vol. I: S234 Paperbound **$2.00**
Vol. II: S235 Paperbound **$2.00**

THEORY OF FLIGHT, Richard von Mises. Remains almost unsurpassed as balanced, well-written account of fundamental fluid dynamics, and situations in which air compressibility effects are unimportant. Stressing equally theory and practice, avoiding formidable mathematical structure, it conveys a full understanding of physical phenomena and mathematical concepts. Contains perhaps the best introduction to general theory of stability. "Outstanding," Scientific, Medical, and Technical Books. New introduction by K. H. Hohenemser. Bibliographical, historical notes. Index. 408 illustrations. xvi + 620pp. 5⅜ x 8⅜. S541 Paperbound **$2.95**

THEORY OF WING SECTIONS, I. H. Abbott, A. E. von Doenhoff. Concise compilation of subsonic aerodynamic characteristics of modern NASA wing sections, with description of their geometry, associated theory. Primarily reference work for engineers, students, it gives methods, data for using wing-section data to predict characteristics. Particularly valuable: chapters on thin wings, airfoils; complete summary of NACA's experimental observations, system of construction families of airfoils. 350pp. of tables on Basic Thickness Forms, Mean Lines, Airfoil Ordinates, Aerodynamic Characteristics of Wing Sections. Index. Bibliography. 191 illustrations. Appendix. 705pp. 5⅜ x 8. S558 Paperbound **$3.25**

WEIGHT-STRENGTH ANALYSIS OF AIRCRAFT STRUCTURES, F. R. Shanley. Scientifically sound methods of analyzing and predicting the structural weight of aircraft and missiles. Deals directly with forces and the distances over which they must be transmitted, making it possible to develop methods by which the minimum structural weight can be determined for any material and conditions of loading. Weight equations for wing and fuselage structures. Includes author's original papers on inelastic buckling and creep buckling. "Particularly successful in presenting his analytical methods for investigating various optimum design principles," AERONAUTICAL ENGINEERING REVIEW. Enlarged bibliography. Index. 199 figures. xiv + 404pp. 5⅝ x 8⅜. S660 Paperbound **$2.45**

Electricity

TWO-DIMENSIONAL FIELDS IN ELECTRICAL ENGINEERING, L. V. Bewley. A useful selection of typical engineering problems of interest to practicing electrical engineers. Introduces senior students to the methods and procedures of mathematical physics. Discusses theory of functions of a complex variable, two-dimensional fields of flow, general theorems of mathematical physics and their applications, conformal mapping or transformation, method of images, freehand flux plotting, etc. New preface by the author. Appendix by W. F. Kiltner. Index. Bibliography at chapter ends. xiv + 204pp. 5⅜ x 8½. S1118 Paperbound **$1.50**

FLUX LINKAGES AND ELECTROMAGNETIC INDUCTION, L. V. Bewley. A brief, clear book which shows proper uses and corrects misconceptions of Faraday's law of electromagnetic induction in specific problems. Contents: Circuits, Turns, and Flux Linkages; Substitution of Circuits; Electromagnetic Induction; General Criteria for Electromagnetic Induction; Applications and Paradoxes; Theorem of Constant Flux Linkages. New Section: Rectangular Coil in a Varying Uniform Medium. Valuable supplement to class texts for engineering students. Corrected, enlarged edition. New preface. Bibliography in notes. 49 figures. xi + 106pp. 5⅜ x 8. S1103 Paperbound **$1.25**

INDUCTANCE CALCULATIONS: WORKING FORMULAS AND TABLES, Frederick W. Grover. An invaluable book to everyone in electrical engineering. Provides simple single formulas to cover all the more important cases of inductance. The approach involves only those parameters that naturally enter into each situation, while extensive tables are given to permit easy interpolations. Will save the engineer and student countless hours and enable them to obtain accurate answers with minimal effort. Corrected republication of 1946 edition. 58 tables. 97 completely worked out examples. 66 figures. xiv + 286pp. 5⅜ x 8½.
S974 Paperbound **$1.85**

GASEOUS CONDUCTORS: THEORY AND ENGINEERING APPLICATIONS, J. D. Cobine. An indispensable text and reference to gaseous conduction phenomena, with the engineering viewpoint prevailing throughout. Studies the kinetic theory of gases, ionization, emission phenomena; gas breakdown, spark characteristics, glow, and discharges; engineering applications in circuit interrupters, rectifiers, light sources, etc. Separate detailed treatment of high pressure arcs (Suits); low pressure arcs (Langmuir and Tonks). Much more. "Well organized, clear, straightforward," Tonks, Review of Scientific Instruments. Index. Bibliography. 83 practice problems. 7 appendices. Over 600 figures. 58 tables. xx + 606pp. 5⅜ x 8. S442 Paperbound **$2.95**

INTRODUCTION TO THE STATISTICAL DYNAMICS OF AUTOMATIC CONTROL SYSTEMS, V. V. Solodovnikov. First English publication of text-reference covering important branch of automatic control systems—random signals; in its original edition, this was the first comprehensive treatment. Examines frequency characteristics, transfer functions, stationary random processes, determination of minimum mean-squared error, of transfer function for a finite period of observation, much more. Translation edited by J. B. Thomas, L. A. Zadeh. Index. Bibliography. Appendix. xxii + 308pp. 5⅜ x 8. S420 Paperbound **$2.25**

TENSORS FOR CIRCUITS, Gabriel Kron. A boldly original method of analyzing engineering problems, at center of sharp discussion since first introduced, now definitely proved useful in such areas as electrical and structural networks on automatic computers. Encompasses a great variety of specific problems by means of a relatively few symbolic equations. "Power and flexibility . . . becoming more widely recognized," Nature. Formerly "A Short Course in Tensor Analysis." New introduction by B. Hoffmann. Index. Over 800 diagrams. xix + 250pp. 5⅜ x 8. S534 Paperbound **$2.00**

SELECTED PAPERS ON SEMICONDUCTOR MICROWAVE ELECTRONICS, edited by Sumner N. Levine and Richard R. Kurzrok. An invaluable collection of important papers dealing with one of the most remarkable devolopments in solid-state electronics—the use of the **p-n** junction to achieve amplification and frequency conversion of microwave frequencies. Contents: General Survey (3 introductory papers by W. E. Danielson, R. N. Hall, and M. Tenzer); General Theory of Nonlinear Elements (3 articles by A. van der Ziel, H. E. Rowe, and Manley and Rowe); Device Fabrication and Characterization (3 pieces by Bakanowski, Cranna, and Uhlir, by McCotter, Walker and Fortini, and by S. T. Eng); Parametric Amplifiers and Frequency Multipliers (13 articles by Uhlir, Heffner and Wade, Matthaei, P. K. Tien, van der Ziel, Engelbrecht, Currie and Gould, Uenohara, Leeson and Weinreb, and others); and Tunnel Diodes (4 papers by L. Esaki, H. S. Sommers, Jr., M. E. Hines, and Yariv and Cook). Introduction. 295 Figures. xiii + 286pp. 6½ x 9¼. S1126 Paperbound **$2.25**

THE PRINCIPLES OF ELECTROMAGNETISM APPLIED TO ELECTRICAL MACHINES, B. Hague. A concise, but complete, summary of the basic principles of the magnetic field and its applications, with particular reference to the kind of phenomena which occur in electrical machines. Part I: General Theory—magnetic field of a current, electromagnetic field passing from air to iron, mechanical forces on linear conductors, etc. Part II: Application of theory to the solution of electromechanical problems—the magnetic field and mechanical forces in non-salient pole machinery, the field within slots and between salient poles, and the work of Rogowski, Roth, and Strutt. Formery titled "Electromagnetic Problems in Electrical Engineering." 2 appendices. Index. Bibliography in notes. 115 figures. xiv + 359pp. 5⅜ x 8½. S246 Paperbound **$2.25**

Mechanical engineering

DESIGN AND USE OF INSTRUMENTS AND ACCURATE MECHANISM, T. N. Whitehead. For the instrument designer, engineer; how to combine necessary mathematical abstractions with independent observation of actual facts. Partial contents: instruments & their parts, theory of errors, systematic errors, probability, short period errors, erratic errors, design precision, kinematic, semikinematic design, stiffness, planning of an instrument, human factor, etc. Index. 85 photos, diagrams. xii + 288pp. 5⅜ x 8. S270 Paperbound **$2.00**

A TREATISE ON GYROSTATICS AND ROTATIONAL MOTION: THEORY AND APPLICATIONS, Andrew Gray. Most detailed, thorough book in English, generally considered definitive study. Many problems of all sorts in full detail, or step-by-step summary. Classical problems of Bour, Lottner, etc.; later ones of great physical interest. Vibrating systems of gyrostats, earth as a top, calculation of path of axis of a top by elliptic integrals, motion of unsymmetrical top, much more. Index. 160 illus. 550pp. 5⅜ x 8. S589 Paperbound **$2.75**

MECHANICS OF THE GYROSCOPE, THE DYNAMICS OF ROTATION, R. F. Deimel, Professor of Mechanical Engineering at Stevens Institute of Technology. Elementary general treatment of dynamics of rotation, with special application of gyroscopic phenomena. No knowledge of vectors needed. Velocity of a moving curve, acceleration to a point, general equations of motion, gyroscopic horizon, free gyro, motion of discs, the damped gyro, 103 similar topics. Exercises. 75 figures. 208pp. 5⅜ x 8. S66 Paperbound **$1.65**

STRENGTH OF MATERIALS, J. P. Den Hartog. Distinguished text prepared for M.I.T. course, ideal as introduction, refresher, reference, or self-study text. Full clear treatment of elementary material (tension, torsion, bending, compound stresses, deflection of beams, etc.), plus much advanced material on engineering methods of great practical value: full treatment of the Mohr circle, lucid elementary discussions of the theory of the center of shear and the "Myosotis" method of calculating beam deflections, reinforced concrete, plastic deformations, photoelasticity, etc. In all sections, both general principles and concrete applications are given. Index. 186 figures (160 others in problem section). 350 problems, all with answers. List of formulas. viii + 323pp. 5⅜ x 8. S755 Paperbound **$2.00**

PHOTOELASTICITY: PRINCIPLES AND METHODS, H. T. Jessop, F. C. Harris. For the engineer, for specific problems of stress analysis. Latest time-saving methods of checking calculations in 2-dimensional design problems, new techniques for stresses in 3 dimensions, and lucid description of optical systems used in practical photoelasticity. Useful suggestions and hints based on on-the-job experience included. Partial contents: strained and stress-strain relations, circular disc under thrust along diameter, rectangular block with square hole under vertical thrust, simply supported rectangular beam under central concentrated load, etc. Theory held to minimum, no advanced mathematical training needed. Index. 164 illustrations. viii + 184pp. 6⅛ x 9¼. S720 Paperbound **$2.00**

APPLIED ELASTICITY, J. Prescott. Provides the engineer with the theory of elasticity usually lacking in books on strength of materials, yet concentrates on those portions useful for immediate application. Develops every important type of elasticity problem from theoretical principles. Covers analysis of stress, relations between stress and strain, the empirical basis of elasticity, thin rods under tension or thrust, Saint Venant's theory, transverse oscillations of thin rods, stability of thin plates, cylinders with thin walls, vibrations of rotating disks, elastic bodies in contact, etc. "Excellent and important contribution to the subject, not merely in the old matter which he has presented in new and refreshing form, but also in the many original investigations here published for the first time," NATURE. Index. 3 Appendixes. vi + 672pp. 5⅜ x 8. S726 Paperbound **$2.95**

APPLIED MECHANICS FOR ENGINEERS, Sir Charles Inglis, F.R.S. A representative survey of the many and varied engineering questions which can be answered by statics and dynamics. The author, one of first and foremost adherents of "structural dynamics," presents distinctive illustrative examples and clear, concise statement of principles—directing the discussion at methodology and specific problems. Covers fundamental principles of rigid-body statics, graphic solutions of static problems, theory of taut wires, stresses in frameworks, particle dynamics, kinematics, simple harmonic motion and harmonic analysis, two-dimensional rigid dynamics, etc. 437 illustrations. xii + 404pp. 5⅜ x 8½. S1119 Paperbound **$2.00**

THEORY OF MACHINES THROUGH WORKED EXAMPLES, G. H. Ryder. Practical mechanical engineering textbook for graduates and advanced undergraduates, as well as a good reference work for practicing engineers. Partial contents: Mechanisms, Velocity and Acceleration (including discussion of Klein's Construction for Piston Acceleration), Cams, Geometry of Gears, Clutches and Bearings, Belt and Rope Drives, Brakes, Inertia Forces and Couples, General Dynamical Problems, Gyroscopes, Linear and Angular Vibrations, Torsional Vibrations, Transverse Vibrations and Whirling Speeds (Chapters on vibrations considerably enlarged from previous editions). Over 300 problems, many fully worked out. Index. 195 line illustrations. Revised and enlarged edition. viii + 280pp. 5⅝ x 8¾. S980 Clothbound **$5.00**

THE KINEMATICS OF MACHINERY: OUTLINES OF A THEORY OF MACHINES, Franz Reuleaux. The classic work in the kinematics of machinery. The present thinking about the subject has all been shaped in great measure by the fundamental principles stated here by Reuleaux almost 90 years ago. While some details have naturally been superseded, his basic viewpoint has endured; hence, the book is still an excellent text for basic courses in kinematics and a standard reference work for active workers in the field. Covers such topics as: the nature of the machine problem, phoronomic propositions, pairs of elements, incomplete kinematic chains, kinematic notation and analysis, analyses of chamber-crank trains, chamber-wheel trains, constructive elements of machinery, complete machines, etc., with main focus on controlled movement in mechanisms. Unabridged republication of original edition, translated by Alexander B. Kennedy. New introduction for this edition by E. S. Ferguson. Index. 451 illustrations. xxiv + 622pp. 5⅜ x 8½. S1124 Paperbound **$3.00**

ANALYTICAL MECHANICS OF GEARS, Earle Buckingham. Provides a solid foundation upon which logical design practices and design data can be constructed. Originally arising out of investigations of the ASME Special Research Committee on Worm Gears and the Strength of Gears, the book covers conjugate gear-tooth action, the nature of the contact, and resulting gear-tooth profiles of: spur, internal, helical, spiral, worm, bevel, and hypoid or skew bevel gears. Also: frictional heat of operation and its dissipation, friction losses, etc., dynamic loads in operation, and related matters. Familiarity with this book is still regarded as a necessary prerequisite to work in modern gear manufacturing. 263 figures. 103 tables. Index. x + 546pp. 5⅜ x 8½. S1073 Paperbound **$2.75**

Optical design, lighting

THE SCIENTIFIC BASIS OF ILLUMINATING ENGINEERING, Parry Moon, Professor of Electrical Engineering, M.I.T. Basic, comprehensive study. Complete coverage of the fundamental theoretical principles together with the elements of design, vision, and color with which the lighting engineer must be familiar. Valuable as a text as well as a reference source to the practicing engineer. Partial contents: Spectroradiometric Curve, Luminous Flux, Radiation from Gaseous-Conduction Sources, Radiation from Incandescent Sources, Incandescent Lamps, Measurement of Light, Illumination from Point Sources and Surface Sources, Elements of Lighting Design. 7 Appendices. Unabridged and corrected republication, with additions. New preface containing conversion tables of radiometric and photometric concepts. Index. 707-item bibliography. 92-item bibliography of author's articles. 183 problems. xxiii + 608pp. 5⅜ x 8½. S242 Paperbound **$2.85**

OPTICS AND OPTICAL INSTRUMENTS: AN INTRODUCTION WITH SPECIAL REFERENCE TO PRACTICAL APPLICATIONS, B. K. Johnson. An invaluable guide to basic practical applications of optical principles, which shows how to set up inexpensive working models of each of the four main types of optical instruments—telescopes, microscopes, photographic lenses, optical projecting systems. Explains in detail the most important experiments for determining their accuracy, resolving power, angular field of view, amounts of aberration, all other necessary facts about the instruments. Formerly "Practical Optics." Index. 234 diagrams. Appendix. 224pp. 5⅜ x 8. S642 Paperbound **$1.65**

APPLIED OPTICS AND OPTICAL DESIGN, A. E. Conrady. With publication of vol. 2, standard work for designers in optics is now complete for first time. Only work of its kind in English; only detailed work for practical designer and self-taught. Requires, for bulk of work, no math above trig. Step-by-step exposition, from fundamental concepts of geometrical, physical optics, to systematic study, design, of almost all types of optical systems. Vol. 1: all ordinary ray-tracing methods; primary aberrations; necessary higher aberration for design of telescopes, low-power microscopes, photographic equipment. Vol. 2: (Completed from author's notes by R. Kingslake, Dir. Optical Design, Eastman Kodak.) Special attention to high-power microscope, anastigmatic photographic objectives. "An indispensable work," J., Optical Soc. of Amer. "As a practical guide this book has no rival," Transactions, Optical Soc. Index. Bibliography. 193 diagrams. 852pp. 6⅛ x 9¼. Vol. 1 S366 Paperbound **$2.95**
Vol. 2 S612 Paperbound **$2.95**

Miscellaneous

THE MEASUREMENT OF POWER SPECTRA FROM THE POINT OF VIEW OF COMMUNICATIONS ENGINEERING, R. B. Blackman, J. W. Tukey. This pathfinding work, reprinted from the "Bell System Technical Journal," explains various ways of getting practically useful answers in the measurement of power spectra, using results from both transmission theory and the theory of statistical estimation. Treats: Autocovariance Functions and Power Spectra; Direct Analog Computation; Distortion, Noise, Heterodyne Filtering and Pre-whitening; Aliasing; Rejection Filtering and Separation; Smoothing and Decimation Procedures; Very Low Frequencies; Transversal Filtering; much more. An appendix reviews fundamental Fourier techniques. Index of notation. Glossary of terms. 24 figures. XII tables. Bibliography. General index. 192pp. 5⅜ x 8. S507 Paperbound **$1.85**

CALCULUS REFRESHER FOR TECHNICAL MEN, A. Albert Klaf. This book is unique in English as a refresher for engineers, technicians, students who either wish to brush up their calculus or to clear up uncertainties. It is not an ordinary text, but an examination of most important aspects of integral and differential calculus in terms of the 756 questions most likely to occur to the technical reader. The first part of this book covers simple differential calculus, with constants, variables, functions, increments, derivatives, differentiation, logarithms, curvature of curves, and similar topics. The second part covers fundamental ideas of integration, inspection, substitution, transformation, reduction, areas and volumes, mean value, successive and partial integration, double and triple integration. Practical aspects are stressed rather than theoretical. A 50-page section illustrates the application of calculus to specific problems of civil and nautical engineering, electricity, stress and strain, elasticity, industrial engineering, and similar fields.—756 questions answered. 566 problems, mostly answered. 36 pages of useful constants, formulae for ready reference. Index. v + 431pp. 5⅜ x 8. T370 Paperbound **$2.00**

METHODS IN EXTERIOR BALLISTICS, Forest Ray Moulton. Probably the best introduction to the mathematics of projectile motion. The ballistics theories propounded were coordinated with extensive proving ground and wind tunnel experiments conducted by the author and others for the U.S. Army. Broad in scope and clear in exposition, it gives the beginnings of the theory used for modern-day projectile, long-range missile, and satellite motion. Six main divisions: Differential Equations of Translatory Motion of a projectile; Gravity and the Resistance Function; Numerical Solution of Differential Equations; Theory of Differential Variations; Validity of Method of Numerical Integration; and Motion of a Rotating Projectile. Formerly titled: "New Methods in Exterior Ballistics." Index. 38 diagrams. viii + 259pp. 5⅜ x 8½. S232 Paperbound **$1.75**

LOUD SPEAKERS: THEORY, PERFORMANCE, TESTING AND DESIGN, N. W. McLachlan. Most comprehensive coverage of theory, practice of loud speaker design, testing; classic reference, study manual in field. First 12 chapters deal with theory, for readers mainly concerned with math. aspects; last 7 chapters will interest reader concerned with testing, design. Partial contents: principles of sound propagation, fluid pressure on vibrators, theory of moving-coil principle, transients, driving mechanisms, response curves, design of horn type moving coil speakers, electrostatic speakers, much more. Appendix. Bibliography. Index. 165 illustrations, charts. 411pp. 5⅜ x 8. S588 Paperbound **$2.25**

MICROWAVE TRANSMISSION, J. C. Slater. First text dealing exclusively with microwaves, brings together points of view of field, circuit theory, for graduate student in physics, electrical engineering, microwave technician. Offers valuable point of view not in most later studies. Uses Maxwell's equations to study electromagnetic field, important in this area. Partial contents: infinite line with distributed parameters, impedance of terminated line, plane waves, reflections, wave guides, coaxial line, composite transmission lines, impedance matching, etc. Introduction. Index. 76 illus. 319pp. 5⅜ x 8. S564 Paperbound **$1.50**

MICROWAVE TRANSMISSION DESIGN DATA, T. Moreno. Originally classified, now rewritten and enlarged (14 new chapters) for public release under auspices of Sperry Corp. Material of immediate value or reference use to radio engineers, systems designers, applied physicists, etc. Ordinary transmission line theory; attenuation; capacity; parameters of coaxial lines; higher modes; flexible cables; obstacles, discontinuities, and injunctions; tunable wave guide impedance transformers; effects of temperature and humidity; much more. "Enough theoretical discussion is included to allow use of data without previous background," Electronics. 324 circuit diagrams, figures, etc. Tables of dielectrics, flexible cable, etc., data. Index. ix + 248pp. 5⅜ x 8. S459 Paperbound **$1.65**

RAYLEIGH'S PRINCIPLE AND ITS APPLICATIONS TO ENGINEERING, G. Temple & W. Bickley. Rayleigh's principle developed to provide upper and lower estimates of true value of fundamental period of a vibrating system, or condition of stability of elastic systems. Illustrative examples; rigorous proofs in special chapters. Partial contents: Energy method of discussing vibrations, stability. Perturbation theory, whirling of uniform shafts. Criteria of elastic stability. Application of energy method. Vibrating systems. Proof, accuracy, successive approximations, application of Rayleigh's principle. Synthetic theorems. Numerical, graphical methods. Equilibrium configurations, Ritz's method. Bibliography. Index. 22 figures. ix + 156pp. 5⅜ x 8. S307 Paperbound **$1.50**

ELASTICITY, PLASTICITY AND STRUCTURE OF MATTER, R. Houwink. Standard treatise on rheological aspects of different technically important solids such as crystals, resins, textiles, rubber, clay, many others. Investigates general laws for deformations; determines divergences from these laws for certain substances. Covers general physical and mathematical aspects of plasticity, elasticity, viscosity. Detailed examination of deformations, internal structure of matter in relation to elastic and plastic behavior, formation of solid matter from a fluid, conditions for elastic and plastic behavior of matter. Treats glass, asphalt, gutta percha, balata, proteins, baker's dough, lacquers, sulphur, others. 2nd revised, enlarged edition. Extensive revised bibliography in over 500 footnotes. Index. Table of symbols. 214 figures. xviii + 368pp. 6 x 9¼. S385 Paperbound **$2.45**

THE SCHWARZ-CHRISTOFFEL TRANSFORMATION AND ITS APPLICATIONS: A SIMPLE EXPOSITION, Miles Walker. An important book for engineers showing how this valuable tool can be employed in practical situations. Very careful, clear presentation covering numerous concrete engineering problems. Includes a thorough account of conjugate functions for engineers—useful for the beginner and for review. Applications to such problems as: Stream-lines round a corner, electric conductor in air-gap, dynamo slots, magnetized poles, much more. Formerly "Conjugate Functions for Engineers." Preface. 92 figures, several tables. Index. ix + 116pp. 5⅜ x 8½. S1149 Paperbound **$1.25**

THE LAWS OF THOUGHT, George Boole. This book founded symbolic logic some hundred years ago. It is the 1st significant attempt to apply logic to all aspects of human endeavour. Partial contents: derivation of laws, signs & laws, interpretations, eliminations, conditions of a perfect method, analysis, Aristotelian logic, probability, and similar topics. xviii + 424pp. 5⅜ x 8. S28 Paperbound **$2.00**

SCIENCE AND METHOD, Henri Poincaré. Procedure of scientific discovery, methodology, experiment, idea-germination—the intellectual processes by which discoveries come into being. Most significant and most interesting aspects of development, application of ideas. Chapters cover selection of facts, chance, mathematical reasoning, mathematics, and logic; Whitehead, Russell, Cantor; the new mechanics, etc. 288pp. 5⅜ x 8. S222 Paperbound **$1.35**

FAMOUS BRIDGES OF THE WORLD, D. B. Steinman. An up-to-the-minute revised edition of a book that explains the fascinating drama of how the world's great bridges came to be built. The author, designer of the famed Mackinac bridge, discusses bridges from all periods and all parts of the world, explaining their various types of construction, and describing the problems their builders faced. Although primarily for youngsters, this cannot fail to interest readers of all ages. 48 illustrations in the text. 23 photographs. 99pp. 6⅛ x 9¼. T161 Paperbound **$1.00**

Technological, historical

A DIDEROT PICTORIAL ENCYCLOPEDIA OF TRADES AND INDUSTRY, Manufacturing and the Technical Arts in Plates Selected from "L'Encyclopédie ou Dictionnaire Raisonné des Sciences, des Arts, et des Métiers" of Denis Diderot. Edited with text by C. Gillispie. This first modern selection of plates from the high point of 18th century French engraving is a storehouse of valuable technological information to the historian of arts and science. Over 2000 illustrations on 485 full-page plates, most of them original size, show the trades and industries of a fascinating era in such great detail that the processes and shops might very well be reconstructed from them. The plates teem with life, with men, women, and children performing all of the thousands of operations necessary to the trades before and during the early stages of the industrial revolution. Plates are in sequence, and show general operations, closeups of difficult operations, and details of complex machinery. Such important and interesting trades and industries are illustrated as sowing, harvesting, bee-keeping, cheesemaking, operating windmills, milling flour, charcoal burning, tobacco processing, indigo, fishing, arts of war, salt extraction, mining, smelting, casting iron, steel, extracting mercury, zinc, sulphur, copper, etc., slating, tinning, silverplating, gilding, making gunpowder, cannons, bells, shoeing horses, tanning, papermaking, printing, dyeing, and more than 40 other categories. Professor Gillispie, of Princeton, supplies a full commentary on all the plates, identifying operations, tools, processes, etc. This material, presented in a lively and lucid fashion, is of great interest to the reader interested in history of science and technology. Heavy library cloth. 920pp. 9 x 12. T421 Two volume set **$18.50**

CHARLES BABBAGE AND HIS CALCULATING ENGINES, edited by P. Morrison and E. Morrison. Babbage, leading 19th century pioneer in mathematical machines and herald of modern operational research, was the true father of Harvard's relay computer Mark I. His Difference Engine and Analytical Engine were the first machines in the field. This volume contains a valuable introduction on his life and work; major excerpts from his autobiography, revealing his eccentric and unusual personality; and extensive selections from "Babbage's Calculating Engines," a compilation of hard-to-find journal articles by Babbage, the Countess of Lovelace, L. F. Menabrea, and Dionysius Lardner. 8 illustrations, Appendix of miscellaneous papers. Index. Bibliography. xxxviii + 400pp. 5⅜ x 8. T12 Paperbound **$2.00**

HISTORY OF HYDRAULICS, Hunter Rouse and Simon Ince. First history of hydraulics and hydrodynamics available in English. Presented in readable, non-mathematical form, the text is made especially easy to follow by the many supplementary photographs, diagrams, drawings, etc. Covers the great discoveries and developments from Archimedes and Galileo to modern giants—von Mises, Prandtl, von Karman, etc. Interesting browsing for the specialist; excellent introduction for teachers and students. Discusses such milestones as the two-piston pump of Ctesibius, the aqueducts of Frontius, the anticipations of da Vinci, Stevin and the first book on hydrodynamics, experimental hydraulics of the 18th century, the 19th-century expansion of practical hydraulics and classical and applied hydrodynamics, the rise of fluid mechanics in our time, etc. 200 illustrations. Bibliographies. Index. xii + 270pp. 5¾ x 8. S1131 Paperbound **$2.00**

BRIDGES AND THEIR BUILDERS, David Steinman and Sara Ruth Watson. Engineers, historians, everyone who has ever been fascinated by great spans will find this book an endless source of information and interest. Dr. Steinman, recipient of the Louis Levy medal, was one of the great bridge architects and engineers of all time, and his analysis of the great bridges of history is both authoritative and easily followed. Greek and Roman bridges, medieval bridges, Oriental bridges, modern works such as the Brooklyn Bridge and the Golden Gate Bridge, and many others are described in terms of history, constructional principles, artistry, and function. All in all this book is the most comprehensive and accurate semipopular history of bridges in print in English. New, greatly revised, enlarged edition. 23 photographs, 26 line drawings. Index. xvii + 401pp. 5⅜ x 8. T431 Paperbound **$2.00**

Prices subject to change without notice.

Dover publishes books on art, music, philosophy, literature, languages, history, social sciences, psychology, handcrafts, orientalia, puzzles and entertainments, chess, pets and gardens, books explaining science, intermediate and higher mathematics, mathematical physics, engineering, biological sciences, earth sciences, classics of science, etc. Write to:

Dept. catrr.
Dover Publications, Inc.
180 Varick Street, N.Y. 14, N.Y.